TEACHER'S GUIDE

Volume B

IMPACT MATHEMATICS

Algebra and More

Course 3

Developed by
Education Development Center, Inc.

Principal Investigator: Faye Nisonoff Ruopp

Senior Project Director: Cynthia J. Orrell

Senior Curriculum Developers: Michelle Manes, Susan Janssen, Sydney Foster, Daniel Lynn Watt, Nina Arshavsky, Ricky Carter, Joan Lukas

Curriculum Developers: Larry Davidson, Haim Eshach, Phil Lewis, Debbie Winkler, Peter Braunfeld

McGraw Hill Glencoe

New York, New York   Columbus, Ohio   Chicago, Illinois   Peoria, Illinois   Woodland Hills, California

 **Glencoe**

The **McGraw·Hill** Companies

The algebra content for *Impact Mathematics* was adapted from the series, *Access to Algebra*, by Neville Grace, Jayne Johnston, Barry Kissane, Ian Lowe, and Sue Willis. Permission to adapt this material was obtained from the publisher, Curriculum Corporation of Level 5, 2 Lonsdale Street, Melbourne, Australia.

Send all inquiries to:
Glencoe/McGraw-Hill
8787 Orion Place
Columbus, OH 43240-4027

ISBN 0-07-860931-3

2 3 4 5 6 7 8 9 10   058/055   14 13 12 11 10 09 08 07 06 05

Impact Mathematics Project Reviewers

Education Development Center appreciates all the feedback from the curriculum specialists and teachers who participated in review and testing.

Special thanks to:

Peter Braunfeld
Professor of Mathematics Emeritus
University of Illinois

Sherry L. Meier
Assistant Professor of Mathematics
Illinois State University

Judith Roitman
Professor of Mathematics
University of Kansas

Marcie Abramson
Thurston Middle School
Boston, Massachusetts

Sandi Curtiss
Gateway Middle School
Everett, Washington

Kathleen Forgac
Waring School
Beverly, Massachusetts

Denise Airola
Fayetteville Public Schools
Fayetteville, Arizona

Alan Dallman
Amherst Middle School
Amherst, Massachusetts

Steven J. Fox
Bendle Middle School
Burton, Michigan

Chadley Anderson
Syracuse Junior High School
Syracuse, Utah

Sharon DeCarlo
Sudbury Public Schools
Sudbury, Massachusetts

Kenneth L. Goodwin Jr.
Middletown Middle School
Middletown, Delaware

Jeanne A. Arnold
Mead Junior High
Elk Grove Village, Illinois

David P. DeLeon
Preston Area School
Lakewood, Pennsylvania

Fred E. Gross
Sudbury Public Schools
Sudbury, Massachusetts

Joanne J. Astin
Lincoln Middle School
Forrest City, Arkansas

Jacob J. Dick
Cedar Grove School
Cedar Grove, Wisconsin

Penny Hauben
Murray Avenue School
Huntingdon, Pennsylvania

Jack Beard
Urbana Junior High
Urbana, Ohio

Sharon Ann Dudek
Holabird Middle School
Baltimore, Maryland

Jean Hawkins
James River Day School
Lynchburg, Virginia

Cynthia Bergan
Day Middle School
Newton, Massachusetts

Cheryl Elisara
Centennial Middle School
Spokane, Washington

Robert Kalac
Butler Junior High
Frombell, Pennsylvania

Chad Cluver
Maroa-Forsyth Junior High
Maroa, Illinois

Patricia Elsroth
Wayne Highlands Middle School
Honesdale, Pennsylvania

Robin S. Kalder
Somers High School
Somers, New York

Robert C. Bieringer
Patchogue-Medford School Dist.
Center Moriches, New York

Dianne Fink
Bell Junior High
San Diego, California

Darrin Kamps
Lucille Umbarge Elementary
Burlington, Washington

Susan Coppleman
Nathaniel H. Wixon Middle School
South Dennis, Massachusetts

Terry Fleenore
E.B. Stanley Middle School
Abingdon, Virginia

Sandra Keller
Middletown Middle School
Middletown, Delaware

CONTENTS

v

► Program Philosophy

In developing *Impact Mathematics: Algebra and More,* we, the authors at Education Development Center, Inc., have relied on our collective experiences as teachers, parents, and former students. Our main goal is to offer a curriculum that respects the background and knowledge of middle school teachers, recognizes the competence and energy of middle school students, and addresses the need for intellectually challenging and inclusive mathematics materials. With *Impact Mathematics,* we have combined the best of what is known as "reform" curricula with the best of "traditional" curricula, incorporating more active involvement on the part of students in making sense of important mathematical ideas.

With middle grades teachers and students in mind, we have created a comprehensive curriculum for Grades 6 through 8 that completes a full year of algebra by the end of Grade 8. While the number and operations, geometry, and data and probability strands were created especially for this program, the algebra strand is based on the highly successful Australian program, *Access to Algebra,* developed by Curriculum Corporation.

The rewarding and interesting introduction to algebra offered by this program can help develop and maintain students' ongoing interest in all areas of mathematics. The materials created for *Impact Mathematics* follow the *Access to Algebra* material in style: use of narrative and realistic contexts, personalization in the form of cartoons in which middle grades students explain how they approach problems, and opportunities for students to choose or create their own problems.

Conceptual Understanding and Basic Skills

Discussions regarding mathematics learning in both professional circles and the popular media might lead you to believe that teaching for conceptual understanding and teaching basic skills are mutually exclusive. But, in fact, the opposite is true. Conceptual understanding and basic skills are not opposing interests; they go hand in hand and support each other.

Impact Mathematics makes the big ideas as well as the important skills of mathematics accessible to middle school students. It presents mathematical ideas intact, not broken down into bite-sized bits that lack the big idea. *Impact Mathematics* helps students both build new mathematical ideas and see how these new ideas relate to ideas they have already developed. In this way, *Impact Mathematics* takes a conceptual approach.

At the same time, *Impact Mathematics* recognizes that for students to be able to use the new ideas and procedures effectively, they need practice. Practice need not be the enemy of learning; the enemy of learning is mindless drill. Instead, practice can encourage students to stay interested in the mathematical concepts. *Impact Mathematics* provides plenty of opportunity for practice, but with variety and contrast to keep students' attention focused.

Algebraic Focus in a Comprehensive Program

Impact Mathematics is a comprehensive program including number and operations, proportional reasoning, geometry, probability, and data, with a focus on the development of algebraic thinking. The program takes a developmental approach to algebra. Student understanding of the algebra strand—interwoven with and related to the other mathematical strands—evolves over a three-year period, allowing the ideas and skills to develop and become familiar over time.

Most students develop strong algebraic ideas in the early years of elementary school, but they don't acquire ways of expressing and manipulating them in algebraic terms until later, when algebra is formally taught. For example, young children know how to share $36 among three people by first distributing the ten dollar bills and then distributing the ones. Later, if children learn a standard method for dividing $3\overline{)36}$ they may see again that the process is like dividing $3\overline{)30}$, then dividing $3\overline{)6}$, and finally adding the results. If this process is written out as $\frac{36}{3} = \frac{30}{3} + \frac{6}{3}$, that concise statement contains an important idea about adding fractions and an even more general algebraic idea. Students who understand *why* $\frac{36}{3} = \frac{30}{3} + \frac{6}{3}$ know that the sum of $\frac{30}{3}$ and $\frac{6}{3}$ must be $\frac{36}{3}$, and not $\frac{36}{6}$. The idea, expressed more generally, is $\frac{a}{3} + \frac{b}{3} = \frac{a+b}{3}$, and even more generally, is $\frac{a}{c} + \frac{b}{c} = \frac{a+b}{c}$, and so leads to the distributive law of division over addition.

Our approach in *Impact Mathematics* is to start with algebra as a notation for "generic" arithmetic, a description of processes that students understand. Later, algebra also becomes a handy language for "unlocking secrets" (equation solving) and building mathematical models. By the end of Course 3, students will have learned both to express functions using variables and to graph these functions. They will have also learned how to use variables to set up and solve equations, as well as how to factor some familiar polynomials, and to understand the origin and use of the quadratic formula.

Use of Manipulatives and Calculators

Manipulatives and calculators can be powerful tools for teaching and learning mathematics. There is, however, much discussion and controversy about the appropriateness of their use. As the authors of *Impact Mathematics,* we believe that when manipulatives and calculators are used, they must be used to support the content learning. More specifically, we consider the important mathematical ideas first and then determine whether manipulatives or calculators can be used in learning those ideas more completely.

We believe it's critical that students develop good number sense and calculation skills before they work extensively with calculators. For example, we incorporate graphing calculators in Course 3 to explore families of functions, but only *after* students have a firm idea of how to graph "parent" functions by hand. Graphing technology can then be used to allow students to graph more complex functions, analyze their behavior, and compare representations. Similar to our philosophy of integrating skills with understanding, we believe that students need experiences with pencil and paper along with graphing technology.

Organization by Content

Impact Mathematics often uses applications to help develop a particular mathematical concept or place it in context. However, *Impact Mathematics* remains organized by mathematical content, not by contexts. This organization helps both teacher and student keep the mathematical ideas at the fore, easily recognizable and never buried or lost in the settings. While the mathematical focus shifts with each chapter, the *Impact Mathematics* approach offers opportunities to connect topics to one another so that earlier learning is not abandoned as new ideas are introduced.

Developing Concepts in Varied Contexts

The contexts used for developing concepts and practicing skills include real-world applications, as well as mathematical settings such as number puzzles, and the world of the imagination such as a factory that uniformly resizes objects using stretching machines. Sometimes, *Impact Mathematics* provides exercises that are *not* set in contexts or integrated into word problems precisely so that students can focus on the mathematical ideas, undistracted by surrounding material.

A Final Note

The unique power of mathematics stems from the world of the imagination in which one envisions triangles with perfectly straight sides, or two-dimensional objects embedded in perfectly smooth planes. In the real world, all objects are three dimensional (even a line drawn on paper has thickness, or it wouldn't be visible!), all lines are irregular, and all surfaces are pitted. Likewise, all measurements are only approximations, and no physical object can have an irrational length. Our minds reason well precisely because we can ignore irregularities and focus instead on the essential features. We can reason about quantities that no physical ruler can measure but that we can "measure" with our mental rulers. In sum, we reason well because we can abstract reality.

We, the authors of *Impact Mathematics,* recognize that all people, from early childhood on, do reason abstractly, and that what grows over time is both their ability to recognize the abstractions, and the formality with which they are able to express abstractions. We also recognize that mathematics, while not simply common sense, is rooted in common sense. Mathematics is a human product that has developed as an extension and a codification of ways of thinking that are natural to us all. Students must not think of mathematics as a departure from natural, logical thinking. To that aim *Impact Mathematics* is written to help students use and sharpen their own logical thinking, learn to be comfortable with the abstractions that give mathematics its power, develop their ideas and mathematical imagination, and acquire the skills that support all that good thinking and the ability to express it clearly to others.

We hope you will enjoy teaching and learning with these materials.

▶ Scope and Sequence

Number and Operations

Topics	Course 1 1	2	3	4	5	6	7	8	9	10	Course 2 1	2	3	4	5	6	7	8	9	10	Course 3 1	2	3	4	5	6	7	8	9	10
Numbers and Number Sense	Develop										Develop										Review & Extend									
Whole Numbers	C	F	C				C	C			C	C	C	C		C	C							C				C	C	
Signed Numbers	C	F						C						F	C						C		C							
Exponents and Roots							F					F	F	F	C				F			F	F				F			
Rationals and Irrationals	Develop										Review & Extend										Review & Extend									
Fractions and Decimal Concepts		F	F	C		C											C									C				
Percents			F									C		C		C	F						C			C				
Ratios and Rates	Expose										Develop										Review & Extend									
Meaning and Representations		C		C					C		C			F	F	C	F				F			C						
Proportions				C					C	C	C			F	F	C	F							C						
Algorithms and Operations	Review & Extend										Review & Extend										Review & Extend									
Fractions	C	F	F	F			C				C					C										C				
Decimals		F	F	F			C				C																			
Signed Numbers													F																	

Algebra

Topics	Course 1 1	2	3	4	5	6	7	8	9	10	Course 2 1	2	3	4	5	6	7	8	9	10	Course 3 1	2	3	4	5	6	7	8	9	10
Algebraic Representations	Develop										Develop										Develop									
Coordinate Graphs		C			F	F		C	F		C		C	F	F	F	C	C	F	C	F	F	F	F	F				F	F
Tables and Graphs	C	C			F	F		F	F	C	C		C	F	F	F		F	F		F	F	F	F	F		C	C	F	F
Algebraic Reasoning	Develop										Develop										Develop									
Patterns and Numeric Forms	F	F		C	C	C		F	F		F	F	F	F	F	F	C	C	F	F	F	F	F	C		F	F	F		F
Properties and Rules	F	C	C				F	F	C		F			F	F	C	F					C	C	F	C		F	F	C	
Functions and Relations	Expose										Develop										Develop									
Linear Expressions/Equations					C	C			F		F			C	F	F	C	F	F		F			F					F	F
Quadratic Expressions/Equations										C	C	C	C		C				F				F	F	F			F	F	C
Exponential Expressions/Equations					C	C		C	C					F	C				F					F	F		F		F	C
Rational Expressions/Equations																C	C								F		F		C	C

F = This topic is a Focus of Instruction in this chapter.

C = This topic is Connected to the content of the chapter and is either reviewed in this chapter or informally introduced.

Expose: Ideas are introduced at an informal concrete level and will be fully developed later in the program.

Develop: Ideas are formalized and fully developed.

Review & Extend: Ideas are reviewed and used to extend understanding of related ideas.

Geometry

Topics	Course 1 1	2	3	4	5	6	7	8	9	10	Course 2 1	2	3	4	5	6	7	8	9	10	Course 3 1	2	3	4	5	6	7	8	9	10
Two-Dimensional Shapes	Develop										Review & Extend										Review & Extend									
Polygons	F	C	C					F				C					C	C							C					
Quadrilaterals	F							F				C					C	C							C					
Triangles	F							F				C		C			F	F							C					
Angles	C							F									C	C							C					
Geometric Relationships	Expose										Develop										Review & Extend									
Congruence																	F	C							C					
Similarity						C			C		C			C	C		F	F			C				C					
Three-Dimensional Figures	Expose										Develop										Review & Extend									
Spatial Visualization												F					C													
3-D Solids												F					C													
Measurement	Develop										Develop										Review & Extend									
Perimeter and Area		C	C					F			F		C				F	C							C					
Surface Area and Volume								C			F						F	C							C					
Coordinate Geometry	Develop										Develop										Develop									
Coordinate Representations					F	F		C	C		C			F	F	F	F	C	C	F	C	F	F	F	F	C		F		F
Transformations												C		C			F								F		C			

Data and Probability

Topics	Course 1 1	2	3	4	5	6	7	8	9	10	Course 2 1	2	3	4	5	6	7	8	9	10	Course 3 1	2	3	4	5	6	7	8	9	10
Data Analysis	Develop										Develop										Review & Extend									
Graphs and Displays	C	C		C	F	F				F								C	F		C									
Modeling and Analysis	C	C			F	F				F		C			C				F		C									F
Statistical Measures						F				C									F											C
Surveys and Sampling										F							C		F											C
Probability	Develop										Develop										Develop									
Basic Concepts and Rules										F									F										F	
Counting Methods																			F										F	
Experiments and Simulations										F									F										F	

Expectations

Entrance Expectations for
Course 3

What students should know as they begin Course 3

Algebra

- Write algebraic expressions to represent situations and patterns
- Apply the distributive property to expand expressions and to factor out a common monomial factor (includes combining like terms)
- Solve single-variable linear equations in which the variable appears on both sides (by doing the same thing to both sides)
- Recognize a linear relationship from a written description, a table, a graph, or an equation
- Have a thorough understanding of slope (rise/run, rate of change, constant change, and so on)

Geometry

- Understand volume and surface and have important formulas committed to memory
- Understand and apply ideas about similarity and scale factor
- Understand and apply the relationship between scale factor, area, and volume
- Plot points in all four quadrants
- Apply the distance formulas

Number and Operation

- Are proficient with operations with signed numbers
- Are proficient in working with positive and negative integer exponents
- Are proficient with percent operations, including calculating percent increase and percent decrease
- Understand ratios, rates, and proportions and solve problems that require comparing ratio or solving proportions

Data and Probability

- Calculate probabilities in situations involving multipart outcomes (tossing four coins, spinning two spinners, and so on)
- Conduct simple simulations to find probabilities
- Interpret box plots
- Understand the purpose of sampling and the importance of selecting a random sample

Exit Expectations for
Course 3

What students should know as they finish Course 3

Algebra

- Solve linear inequalities
- Solve linear systems
- Write a linear equation given two points or a point and a slope
- Understand how the graph of $y = x^2$ is changed if a constant is added to x^2 or if x^2 is multiplied by a constant
- Recognize a quadratic relationship from a table, a graph, or an equation
- Multiply binomials
- Solve quadratic equations graphically, by using the quadratic formula and (in fairly simple cases) by factoring
- Understand the exponential growth pattern and recognize this pattern from a table, graph, or equation
- Understand inverse variation and recognize inverse variation from a table, graph, or equation
- Solve simple equations involving rational expressions and radical expressions
- Understand the meaning of function
- Use technology to graph functions and identify solutions to equations, maximum and minimum points, intercepts, and lines of symmetry

Geometry

- Recognize and describe reflectional and rotational symmetry (including identifying lines of symmetry and specifying angles of rotation)
- Write and recognize algebraic rules for similarity transformations, translations, simple reflections (over the x-axis, over the y-axis, over the line $y = x$), and simple rotations (90°, 180°, 270°)

Number and Operation

- Understand square roots and manipulate expressions involving square roots
- Understand the distinction between rational and irrational numbers

Data and Probability

- Perform computations involving combinations or permutations
- Solve probability problems that require using combinatorics to count outcomes
- Fit a line to a set of linear data (by eyeballing) and then use the graph or equation of the line to make predictions

▶ The Instructional Cycle

Impact Mathematics is designed to actively engage students in their own learning. To facilitate the learning and teaching process, *Impact Mathematics* is designed around a three-step instructional cycle.

Introduce

Each multiday lesson begins with a class discussion, activity, or problem designed to introduce the mathematics and help set a context for learning. To help guide the introduction, **Explore** activities and **Think & Discuss** questions are provided in the student materials.

Develop

Each lesson in *Impact Mathematics* is composed of in-class **Investigations** that provide a mix of worked-out examples, direct modeling through cartoons, and interactive problem sets. During Investigations, the mathematics, not an artificial format, determines the approach and the day's activity. Each Investigation is designed to last about 45 minutes or one class period. Positioned at logical breaking points, Investigations help teachers determine pacing and help make multiday lessons manageable.

The **Share & Summarize** questions signal the end of each Investigation. These questions offer students an opportunity to share what they did and what was learned. They also provide a summary of major points. For teachers they offer an important assessment opportunity. When used as part of class discussion, Share & Summarize questions serve as a checkpoint to make sure that appropriate learning has taken place and that students can move forward in the lesson successfully.

Assign & Assess

Independent assignments and opportunities to assess what students have learned are a regular part of the curriculum. The **On Your Own Exercises** at the end of each lesson are an integral part of program instruction and are intended for individual work done primarily outside of class. You will find three types of problems in each set of On Your Own Exercises.

- *Practice & Apply* problems provide opportunities for students to reinforce and directly apply the skills and concepts they have learned in each of the Investigations.

- *Connect & Extend* problems relate student learning in the lesson to other mathematical topics and strands, and sometimes require students to stretch their thinking. Connections may reach back to ideas previously developed in the program or might offer a preview of how current topics are related to what's to come.

- *Mixed Review* problems are an important part of the instructional and assignment structure. Frequent review of previously learned skills helps students maintain mastery and replaces the need to reteach topics.

Assignment guides for each Investigation are provided in the Teacher's Guide.

Assessment in Impact Mathematics

The assessment tools in *Impact Mathematics* are broader than those in traditional mathematics programs. They encompass the processes of problem solving, reasoning, communication, connections, concepts, applications, representational strategies, and procedures.

The flexibility and variety of assessment in *Impact Mathematics* addresses the various ability levels and learning styles of students, as well as the instructional needs of teachers.

In the Student Edition

- **Share & Summarize** questions provide a forum for students to summarize and share their learning with the class.
- **On Your Own Exercises,** an integral part of daily instruction, are independent assignments intended for individual work outside of class.
- **Review & Self-Assessment** provides students with an opportunity to reflect on the important topics within the chapter and to prepare for formal assessment.

In the Teacher's Guide

- **Problem Set Wrap-Ups** ensure students are making appropriate progress through an Investigation.
- **Troubleshooting** notes provide remedial work students might need in order to move on to the next Investigation successfully.
- **Additional Examples** can be used as on-the-run assessment tools.
- **Quick Checks** provide checklists of what students should be able to do at the end of each lesson.
- **Quick Quizzes** provide brief end-of-lesson assessment opportunities.

In the Assessment Resources Book

- A **Pretest** determines whether students have the prerequisite skills for the course.
- **Refresher Worksheets** help students review prerequisite skills.
- **Chapter Tests** provide a comprehensive evaluation of chapter content.
- **Performance Assessments** provide open-ended opportunities to measure student achievement. They can be used to supplement or replace items on chapter and semester tests, as take-home assignments, as group assessments, or as challenge or extra-credit problems.
- **Semester Tests** provide cumulative mid-year and end-of-year evaluations.

▶ Pacing

Impact Mathematics and the accompanying support materials allow you to create a mathematics course that meets the needs of your students. The chart shown on these two pages offers general suggestions for pacing your students through the book.

Chapter	Lesson (Investigation)	Day(s)
1	Lesson 1.1(1)	1–2
	Lesson 1.1(2)	3–4
	Lesson 1.1(3)	5–6
	Lesson 1.2(1)	7–8
	Lesson 1.2(2)	9
	Lesson 1.2(3)	10–11
	Lab (optional); Quiz, Lessons 1.1–1.2	12
	Lesson 1.3(1)	13–14
	Lesson 1.3(2)	15
	Lesson 1.3(3)	16–17
	Chapter 1 Review	18
	Chapter 1 Test	19
2	Lesson 2.1(1)	20–21
	Lesson 2.1(2)	22
	Lesson 2.2(1)	23–24
	Lesson 2.2(2)	25
	Lesson 2.2(3)	26
	Lesson 2.2(4)	27
	Lab (optional); Quiz, Lessons 2.1–2.2	28
	Lesson 2.3(1)	29–30
	Lesson 2.3(2)	31
	Lesson 2.3(3)	32
	Quiz, Lesson 2.3	33
	Lesson 2.4(1)	34–35
	Lesson 2.4(2)	36
	Chapter 2 Review	37
	Chapter 2 Test	38
3	Lesson 3.1(1)	39–40
	Lesson 3.1(2)	41
	Lesson 3.1(3)	42
	Lesson 3.1(4)	43
	Lab (optional); Quiz, Lesson 3.1	44

Chapter	Lesson (Investigation)	Day(s)
3	Lesson 3.2(1)	45–46
	Lesson 3.2(2)	47
	Lesson 3.2(3)	48
	Lesson 3.2(4)	49
	Lesson 3.3(1)	50–51
	Lesson 3.3(2)	52–53
	Lesson 3.3(3)	54
	Lesson 3.3(4)	55
	Quiz, Lessons 3.2–3.4	56
	Chapter 3 Review	57
	Chapter 3 Test	58
4	Lesson 4.1(1); Lab (optional)	59–60
	Lesson 4.2(1)	61–62
	Lesson 4.2(2)	63
	Lesson 4.2(3)	64–65
	Quiz, Lessons 4.1–4.2	66
	Lesson 4.3(1)	67–68
	Lesson 4.3(2)	69
	Lesson 4.4(1)	70–71
	Lesson 4.4(2)	72
	Lesson 4.4(3)	73
	Lesson 4.4(4) Lab (optional); Quiz,	74
	Lessons 4.3–4.4	75
	Chapter 4 Review	76
	Chapter 4 Test	77
5	Lesson 5.1(1)	78–79
	Lesson 5.1(2)	80
	Lesson 5.1(3)	81
	Quiz, Lesson 5.1	82
	Lesson 5.2(1)	83–84
	Lesson 5.2(2)	85
	Lesson 5.2(3)	86
	Lesson 5.3(1)	87–88

Chapter	Lesson (Investigation)	Day(s)
5	Lesson 5.3(2)	89
	Lab (optional); Quiz,	90
	Lessons 5.2–5.3	91–92
	Lesson 5.4(1)	93–94
	Lesson 5.5(1)	95
	Lesson 5.5(2)	96
	Chapter 5 Review	97
	Chapter 5 Test	98–99
6	Lesson 6.1(1)	100–101
	Lesson 6.1(2); Lab (optional)	102–103
	Lesson 6.2(1)	104
	Lesson 6.2(2)	105
	Lesson 6.2(3)	106
	Lesson 6.2(4)	107
	Quiz, Lessons 6.1–6.2	108–109
	Lesson 6.3(1)	110
	Lesson 6.3(2)	111–112
	Lesson 6.4(1)	113
	Lesson 6.4(2)	114
	Quiz, Lessons 6.3–6.4	115–116
	Lesson 6.5(1)	117
	Lesson 6.5(2)	118
	Lesson 6.5(3)	119
	Chapter 6 Review	120
	Chapter 6 Test	121–122
7	Lesson 7.1(1)	123
	Lesson 7.1(2)	124–125
	Lesson 7.2(1)	126
	Lesson 7.2(2)	127
	Lesson 7.2(3)	128
	Quiz, Lessons 7.1–7.2	129–130
	Lesson 7.3(1)	131
	Lesson 7.3(2)	132–133
	Lesson 7.4(1)	134
	Lesson 7.4(2)	135
	Lesson 7.4(3)	136
	Quiz, Lessons 7.3–7.4	137
	Chapter 7 Review	138
	Chapter 7 Test	139–140

Chapter	Lesson (Investigation)	Day(s)
8	Lesson 8.1(1)	141
	Lesson 8.1(2)	142
	Lesson 8.1(3)	143
	Lesson 8.1(4)	144
	Lab (optional); Quiz, Lesson 8.1	145–146
	Lesson 8.2(1)	147
	Lesson 8.2(2)	148
	Lesson 8.2(3)	
	Lesson 8.2(4)	149
	Quiz, Lesson 8.2	150
	Chapter 8 Review	151
	Chapter 8 Test	152
9	Lab (optional); Lesson 9.1(1)	153–154
	Lesson 9.1(2)	155
	Lesson 9.1(3)	156
	Lesson 9.2(1)	157–158
	Lesson 9.2(2)	159
	Lesson 9.2(3)	160
	Quiz, Lessons 9.1–9.2	161
	Lesson 9.3(1)	162–163
	Lesson 9.3(2)	164
	Chapter 9 Review	165
	Chapter 9 Test	166
10	Lesson 10.1(1)	167–168
	Lesson 10.1(2)	169
	Lesson 10.1(3)	170
	Lesson 10.1(4)	171
	Quiz, Lesson 10.1	172
	Lesson 10.2(1)	173–174
	Lesson 10.2(2)	175
	Lesson 10.2(3)	176
	Lesson 10.2(4)	177
	Quiz, Lesson 10.2	178
	Chapter 10 Review	179
	Chapter 10 Test	180

Problem-Solving Strategies and Estimation

Problem Solving

Problem solving occurs when students are engaged in activities for which the method of solving the problem is not immediately known. Problem solving is an integral part of *Impact Mathematics*. Students have frequent opportunities to formulate problems, solve them, and reflect upon the process.

The following problem-solving strategies are embedded throughout *Impact Mathematics*. The lesson notes in the Teacher's Guide indicate places where these problem-solving strategies are used.

Problem-Solving Strategies

- Act it out
- Choose the method of computation
- Determine reasonable answers
- Draw a picture or diagram
- Eliminate possibilities
- Guess-check-and-improve
- Identify irrelevant or missing information
- Look for a pattern
- Make a model
- Make a table or chart
- Make an organized list
- Make and test a conjecture
- Solve a simpler problem
- State problem in own words
- Use a graph
- Use a Venn diagram
- Use benchmarks
- Use logical reasoning
- Work backward
- Write an equation or rule

Estimation

Students in the middle grades are learning to compute fluently with rational numbers—fractions, decimals, percents, and integers. One important part of the computation process involves estimation. In *Impact Mathematics,* students develop and use strategies to estimate the results of rational number computations and use the results to judge whether the result is reasonable.

The lesson notes in the Teacher's Guide indicate places where the students estimate with rational numbers. The notes also indicate where estimation is used in other aspects of mathematics, such as geometry, graph interpretation, and statistics.

Course 3
CONTENTS

Volume A

Chapter Three

Exponents and Exponential Variation 143a

Chapter Four

Solving Equations 211a

Volume B

Chapter Six

Chapter Seven

Chapter Eight

Chapter Nine

Probability 541a

Chapter Ten

Modeling with Data 599a

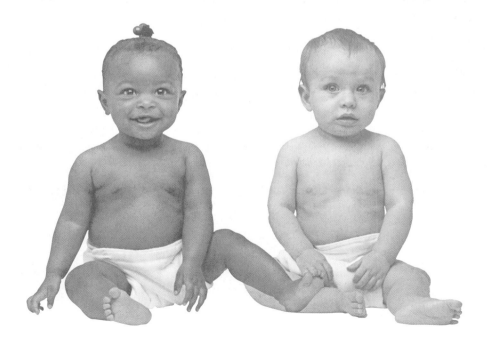

CHAPTER 6

Working with Expressions

Chapter Overview

In this chapter, students learn how to work with algebraic expressions, in particular, polynomials, binomial products, and algebraic fractions. They learn how to expand products of two binomials, including square binomials and differences of squares. They also learn how to combine like terms. Finally, students consider how to simplify and combine expressions involving algebraic fractions, as well as how to solve equations using them.

the Big Picture

Chapter 6 Highlights	Links to the Past	Links to the Future
Using geometric models to expand expressions (6.1, 6.2)	**Course 2:** Using the distributive property	**Chapter 7:** Solving quadratic equations by factoring
Using the distributive property to expand expressions (6.1, 6.2, 6.3)	**Course 2:** Using the distributive property	**Chapter 7:** Solving quadratic equations by factoring and by completing the square
Expanding expressions of the forms $(ax + b)^2$, $(ax - b)^2$, and $(ax + b)(ax - b)$ (6.3)	**Course 2:** Using the distributive property	**Chapter 7:** Solving quadratic equations by factoring
Simplifying expressions involving algebraic fractions (6.4, 6.5)	**Course 1:** Simplifying and operating with numeric fractions **Course 2:** Comparing and scaling ratios and rates **Chapter 2:** Working with inverse relationships	**Chapter 8:** Describing the domain and range of a function **High School and College:** Using the definition of derivatives
Solving equations involving algebraic fractions (6.5)	**Course 2:** Solving equations using various methods **Course 2:** Writing and solving proportions	**High School:** Working with rational functions

Lesson Objectives	Pacing	Materials	NCTM Standards	Hot Topics
6.1 Rearranging Algebraic Expressions page 375b • To use geometric models in illustrating the distributive property to expand expressions of the form $a(b + c)$ • To represent algebraic expressions using rectangle models • To simplify expressions by combining like terms	6 class periods	★ • Algebra tiles (optional) • Graphing calculators • Master 45 • 1-cm graph paper • Scissors • Master 46 • Rulers (optional)	2, 3, 6, 7, 8, 9, 10	pp. 284–290
6.2 Expanding Products of Binomials page 372a • To use geometric models to multiply binomials • To multiply binomials using the distributive property • To understand patterns for shortcuts in multiplying binomials	5 class periods	★ • Algebra tiles (optional)	2, 3, 6, 7, 8, 9, 10	
6.3 Patterns in Products of Binomials page 389b • To understand the pattern and apply a shortcut to square binomials of the forms $(a + b)^2$ and $(a - b)^2$ • To understand the pattern and apply a shortcut to expand binomials of the form $(x + a)(x - a)$	3 class periods	★ • Algebra tiles (optional)	1, 2, 6, 7, 8, 9, 10	
6.4 Working with Algebraic Fractions page 399b • To understand when the denominator of an algebraic fraction is undefined • To understand how the graph and the table of an equation with an algebraic fraction show values for which the equation is undefined • To simplify algebraic fractions • To multiply and divide algebraic fractions	3 class periods	• Graphing calculators	1, 2, 6, 7, 8, 9, 10	
6.5 Adding and Subtracting Algebraic Fractions page 410a • To add and subtract algebraic fractions using common denominators • To use the graphs of equations containing algebraic fractions to estimate solutions • To solve equations containing algebraic fractions	4 class periods	• Master 47 • Graphing calculators ★ • Transparency of Master 48 (optional)	2, 6, 7, 8, 9, 10	

★ Included in Impact Mathematics Manipulative Kit

Key to NCTM Curriculum and Evaluation Standards: 1=Number and Operations, 2=Algebra, 3=Geometry, 4=Measurement, 5=Data Analysis and Probability, 6=Problem Solving, 7=Reasoning and Proof, 8=Communication, 9=Connections, 10=Representation

Assessment Opportunities

Standard Assessment

Impact Mathematics offers three types of formal assessment. The Chapter 6 Review and Self-Assessment in the Student Edition serves as a self-assessment tool for students. In the Teacher's Guide, a Quick Quiz at the end of each lesson allows you to check students' understanding before moving to the next lesson. The Assessment Resources include blackline masters for chapter and quarterly tests.

- **Student Edition** Chapter 6 Review and Self-Assessment, pages 426–429

- **Teacher's Guide** Quick Quizzes, pages 371, 388, 399, A660, 425

- **Assessment Resources** Chapter 6 Test Form A, pages 174–177; Chapter 6 Test Form B, pages 178–181

Ongoing Assessment

Impact Mathematics provides numerous opportunities for you to assess your students informally as they work through the investigations. Share & Summarize questions help you determine whether students understand the important ideas of an investigation. If students are struggling, Troubleshooting tips provide suggestions for helping them. On the Spot Assessment notes appear throughout the teaching notes. They give you suggestions for preventing or remedying common student errors. Assessment Forms in the Assessment Resources provide convenient ways to record student progress.

- **Student Edition** Share & Summarize, pages 361, 365, 375, 378, 380, 383, 392, 395, 403, 406, 413, 417, 420

- **Teacher's Guide** On the Spot Assessment, pages T360, T361, T363, T378, T379, T390, T391, T393, T405, T412
  Troubleshooting, pages T361, T365, T375, T378, T380, T383, T392, T395, T403, T406, T413, T417, T420

- **Assessment Resources** Chapter 6 Assessment Checklists, pages 292–293

Alternative Assessment, Portfolios, and Journal Ideas

The alternative assessment items in *Impact Mathematics* are perfect for inclusion in student portfolios and journals. The In Your Own Words feature in the Student Edition gives students a chance to write about mathematical ideas. The Performance Assessment items in the Assessment Resources provide rich, open-ended problems, ideal for take-home or group assessment.

- **Student Edition** In Your Own Words, pages 369, 387, 398, 409

- **Assessment Resources** Chapter 6 Performance Assessments, pages 182–183

Assessment Resources

The Assessment Resources provide a chapter test in two equivalent forms, along with additional performance items. The performance items can be used in a variety of ways. They are ideal for take-home assessment or in-class group assessment.

- Chapter 6 Test Form A, pages 174–177
- Chapter 6 Test Form B, pages 178–181
- Chapter 6 Performance Assessment, pages 182–183
- Chapter 6 Assessment Solutions, pages 184–186

Ch. 6 Test Form A

Ch. 6 Test Form B
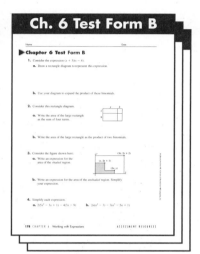

Ch. 6 Perf. Assess

Additional Resources

- **Math Skills Maintenance Workbook,** 4, 5, 6, 15, 16, 17, 18, 19, 20, 21, 22, 23, 24, 25, 26, 30, 33
- **Investigations for the Special Education Student in the Mathematics Classroom,** 10
- **StudentWorks™ CD-ROM**
- **Reading and Writing in the Mathematics Classroom**
- **Using the Internet in the Mathematics Classroom**

ExamView® Pro

Use ExamView® Pro Testmaker CD-ROM to:

- Create Multiple versions of tests.
- Create Modified tests for Inclusion students with one mouse click.
- Edit existing questions and Add your own questions.
- Build tests aligned with state standards using built-in State Curriculum Correlations.
- Change English tests to Spanish with one mouse click and vice versa.

CHAPTER 6

Working with Expressions

Introduce

Many real-life situations can be represented mathematically with the use of algebraic expressions. Some expressions will involve fractions that contain variables. Ask students to point out an algebraic fraction they see on this page.

You can also present the following example as another situation that can be represented by an algebraic fraction.

Example

For an overnight nature-studies field trip, an eighth grade class charters a few buses for $3,000. The students and chaperones stay in dormitories, which costs another $1,500. Food and other supplies cost $8 per person. If there are x people on the trip, the cost per person is
$C = \frac{3,000}{x} + \frac{1,500}{x} + 8x$.

Think About It

40,000 represents the product of the elephant's distance from the fulcrum and the force applied by the elephant, or $10,000 \times 4$.

Real-Life Math

Heavy Lifting Do you think you could lift a 10,000-pound elephant? If you could find a lever long and strong enough, you could! Using a lever allows you to apply more force to an object than you could with your bare hands.

Suppose the elephant is 4 feet from the fulcrum of the lever. Then, the amount of force F you would need to apply is $F = \frac{40,000}{d}$, where d is the distance from the fulcrum to where you apply the force.

If your lever was as long as the world's tallest tree (about 368 feet), you would need to apply only about 110 pounds of force to the end of the lever to lift the elephant!

Think About It In the equation $F = \frac{40,000}{d}$, what do you think the number 40,000 represents?

Family Letter

Dear Student and Family Members,

Our class is about to begin a new topic of study in mathematics, one in which students create, work with, and simplify *algebraic expressions*. Much of the work of this chapter may feel familiar to you if you recall your own study of algebra.

Algebra is one of the most powerful tools of mathematics. Part of its usefulness—and even beauty—is the way algebra allows you to state and solve many problems with little effort. Here is an example:

> The cost of a movie is $4.50 for each adult plus half of the adult price for each of four children, less your $3 coupon. How much will you pay? The answer is $[4.50x + 2.25(4) − 3]$, where x is the number of adults.

In this chapter, we will begin by learning to multiply expressions like $x(x + 5)$ and $(x + 1)(x + 5)$ by referring to a *geometric model*. For example, to find the area of the large rectangle below, you can multiply the length by the width, or $x(x + 3)$. However, we can also find the area of the square, $x \cdot x$ or x^2, and add the area of the small rectangle, $x \cdot 3$ or $3x$, to get $x^2 + 3x$. This shows that $x(x + 3) = x^2 + 3x$.

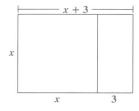

Vocabulary

Along the way, we'll be learning about these new vocabulary terms:

binomial   **expanding**   **like terms**

What can you do at home?

Throughout this chapter, students will work with concrete situations and geometric models so that they can develop a sense of *why* their calculations with symbols work the way that they do. You can encourage a deeper understanding by asking your student to explain his or her work to you, using both geometric models and symbols.

Another version of the Family Letter, available in English and Spanish, is found in the Teaching Resources. You may want to send a copy of this letter home with your students.

Mathematical Background

Chapter 6 is largely about *algebra*—one of the most powerful tools in the tool kit of mathematics. In particular, one of the glories of algebra is its wonderful *notation,* which makes it possible to state and solve problems quickly and easily. Without that symbolism, many elementary problems become quite difficult. Consider, for example, the following:

> Two less than 3 times a certain quantity is the same as 14 more than half that quantity. What is the quantity?

> versus

$3x - 2 = \frac{1}{2}x + 14$. What does x represent?

Note how much more efficient the algebraic version of the problem is compared to the verbal version. To solve the algebraic problem, we might begin by subtracting $\frac{1}{2}x$ from both sides and adding 2 to both sides: $\frac{5}{2}x = 16$. In the English version, it's far from clear that the statement "Half of 5 times a quantity is the same as 16" is equivalent to the original statement.

Multiplying and Factoring Polynomials Multiplying and factoring polynomials, mainly expressions of the form $(a + b)(c + d)$ or the equivalent $ac + bc + ad + bd,$ rests on the distributive property of multiplication over addition, which says:

> For any numbers a, b, and c, $a(b + c) = ab + ac.$

Notice first that this can be read in two directions. Reading from left to right, it tells us something about *multiplying*; reading from right to left, it tells us something about *factoring*.

The chapter provides a concrete model of multiplying and factoring polynomials by interpreting multiplication as area and drawing the corresponding diagram. Note that the area of the large rectangle can be seen as $a(b + c)$ and as $ab + ac.$

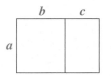

Other distributive properties exist, including

- the distributive property of multiplication over subtraction: $a(b - c) = ab - ac$
- the distributive property of division over addition: $\frac{a + b}{c} = \frac{a}{c} + \frac{b}{c}$
- the distributive property of division over subtraction: $\frac{a - b}{c} = \frac{a}{c} - \frac{b}{c}$

Much to the dismay of their teachers, many students often find the distributive principle irresistible, and they will apply it in all kinds of cases where it does not apply. For example, there is no distributive property of squaring over addition, nor of finding absolute value over addition. In general,
$(a + b)^2 \neq a^2 + b^2$ and $|a + b| \neq |a| + |b|.$

- ***Teaching notes continued on page A681***

6.1

Rearranging Algebraic Expressions

Objectives

▶ To use geometric models in illustrating the distributive property to expand expressions of the form $a(b + c)$

▶ To represent algebraic expressions using rectangle models

▶ To simplify expressions by combining like terms

Overview (pacing: about 6 class periods)

In this lesson, students revisit the distributive property in the context of geometric models. They use areas of rectangles to demonstrate how the distributive property works. (This is a prelude to expanding products of binomials, which they'll explore in Lesson 6.2.) Students also work with simplifying expressions by combining like terms.

Advance Preparation

Algebra tiles can be helpful for students to model the situations in this lesson. You may want to give copies of Master 45 to students for use in the Explore that introduces Investigation 2. The lab investigation requires that each student has a sheet of 1-centimeter graph paper and scissors. Rulers would be helpful, but are not mandatory. You may also want to give copies of Master 46 to students.

	Summary	Materials	On Your Own Exercises	Assessment Opportunities
Investigation 1 page T359	This lesson introduces a geometric model—areas of rectangles—as a way to think about the distributive property.	*• Algebra tiles (optional)	Practice & Apply: 1–8, pp. 368–369 Connect & Extend: 22–32, p. 370 Mixed Review: 36–45, p. 372	On the Spot Assessment, pages T360, T361 Share & Summarize, pages T361, 361 Troubleshooting, page T361
Investigation 2 page T362	Students learn to simplify expressions by combining like terms.	*• Algebra tiles (optional) • Graphing calculators • Master 45	Practice & Apply: 9–21, pp. 369–370 Connect & Extend: 33–35, pp. 370–371 Mixed Review: 36–45, p. 372	On the Spot Assessment, page T363 Share & Summarize, pages T365, 365 Troubleshooting, page T365
Lab Investigation page T366	Students practice combining like terms and solving simple equations by comparing areas and perimeters of various shapes.	• 1-cm graph paper • Scissors • Master 46 (optional) • Rulers (optional)		Informal Assessment, page 371 Quick Quiz, page 371

* Included in Impact Mathematics Manipulative Kit

Introduce

The overall purpose of this lesson is to introduce a geometric model—areas of rectangles—as a way to think about the distributive property. Students will continue to make use of this model when they multiply two binomials such as $(a + b)(c + d)$, and therefore it is important they feel comfortable with it from the start.

1 Students who remember the distributive property may resist returning to the concept once again. Explain to them that the focus here is on the area model, a model that will come up again later. You may also want to mention in introducing this lesson that often ideas from geometry are useful in explaining algebraic concepts, and in this lesson, they will explore such a connection.

2 Although it is tempting, do not begin the lesson by reviewing the distributive property. Begin by introducing the Think & Discuss on page 358, since it motivates the workings of the distributive property in finding the areas of rectangles.

Think & Discuss

3 To demonstrate the idea of breaking a large rectangle into two smaller parts to find its area, it may be helpful to have the rectangle on page 358 drawn on a piece of construction paper, with the dimensions labeled as given. Hold up the rectangle, and use scissors to cut the rectangle into a square and a smaller rectangle. Ask students what the dimensions of each of these pieces are. You might tape the pieces on the board. Alternatively, you can draw on the board or use algebra tiles on an overhead projector as a way of demonstrating the two rectangles.

4 Ask students the questions in the Think & Discuss. In the last question, they are asked to confirm the equivalence of $h(h + 1)$ and $h^2 + h$. Some students may simply state that they know this from the distributive property, which in fact they do. Encourage them, however, to make use of the geometric model to show this: the area of the large rectangle, $h(h + 1)$, is also the sum of the areas of the two smaller pieces, or $h^2 + h$.

5

Rearranging Algebraic Expressions

Ideas from geometry can sometimes shed light on certain concepts in algebra. In this investigation, you will look at a geometric model involving rectangles to help you work with and simplify algebraic expressions.

Think & Discuss

This rectangle can be thought of as a square with a strip added to one side. The large rectangle's width is 1 unit longer than its height.

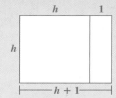

If you cut the large rectangle apart, you get a square and a small rectangle with the dimensions shown below.

- What is the area of the square? h^2

- What is the area of the small rectangle? h

- Using the expressions you wrote above, write an expression for the area of the large rectangle. $h^2 + h$

- What does this tell you about $h(h + 1)$ and $h^2 + h$? Why?   See ①.

① The expressions are equivalent, because a second way to find the area of the large rectangle is to multiply the vertical dimension h by the horizontal dimension $h + 1$, giving $h(h + 1)$.

Rectangle diagrams, like those above, are geometric models that can help you think about how the distributive property works. That is, they can help you understand why $a(b + c) = ab + ac$.

Problem-Solving Strategies

- Make a model
- Draw a diagram

2 Begin the lesson by working through the Think & Discuss with the class.

3 You might demonstrate cutting a rectangle as shown.

4 Discuss the questions.

5 Encourage students to explain using the model instead of the distributive property.

1 Explain to students that looking at the areas of rectangles can help them think about how the distributive property works, or why $a(b + c) = ab + ac$. Tell them that using the distributive property in this way is often referred to as *expanding* the expression. Ask for other examples of expanding expressions, such as $2(x + 3) = 2x + 6$ or $^-6(g - 2k) = ^-6g + 12k$.

Investigation 1

In this investigation, students use a rectangle model to formulate an algebraic expression that represents the rectangle's area. They also take this in the other direction, creating a geometric model to represent a given algebraic expression for area. In each case, students are breaking a large rectangle into two smaller rectangles, comparing the areas of the two parts and the whole, and relating the expressions to the results of the distributive property.

You may want to have algebra tiles on hand to help students model the situations in this investigation, especially students who are having difficulty visualizing how to separate the large rectangle into two smaller rectangles.

2 **Problem Set A** **Suggested Grouping: Pairs**
The use of diagrams in this problem set can be enhanced by using algebra tiles or cutting out squares and strips of unit width. Some students will find it advantageous to have the freedom to move and arrange the shapes, especially when overlaying the strip on the square to model $a - 1$, for example. This strategy also allows for various students to use squares of different side lengths to help reinforce that a is a variable that can take on different values.

One issue that may arise in this problem set is that students may resist drawing diagrams to illustrate that $a(b + c) = ab + ac$ if they feel they already understand the distributive property. It would not be a good idea to tell them to assume they "don't know" the distributive property; asking students to deny what they already know may make them distrust the logical nature of mathematics in the process. Instead, explain that the geometric area model gives added meaning to the distributive property, and will be useful later in expanding more complicated expressions.

Problem 1 is similar to the problem in the Think & Discuss and should be relatively easy for students to complete.

VOCABULARY
expanding

Using the distributive property to multiply the factors *a* and $(b + c)$ is called **expanding** the expression. For example, to expand the expression $2(x + 1)$, multiply 2 and $(x + 1)$ to get $2x + 2$. The expanded version of $h(h + 1)$ is $h^2 + h$.

1 Introduce the new vocabulary.

Investigation ▶1▶ Using Geometric Models

In this investigation, you will use rectangle models to represent algebraic expressions.

Problem Set A

1. One of the rectangles in this diagram has an area of $x(x + 3)$.

2 You may have students work in pairs.

1a. The entire rectangle has area $x(x + 3)$.

1b. $x^2 + 3x$; Possible explanation: The sum of the areas of the small rectangles, $x^2 + 3x$, is equal to the area of the large rectangle, $x(x + 3)$.

a. Copy the diagram, and indicate the rectangle that has area $x(x + 3)$.

b. Use your diagram to expand the expression $x(x + 3)$. Explain what you did.

2. Dante and Héctor are making another rectangle diagram.

3 If necessary, explain that the area model gives added meaning to the distributive property and will be very useful with more complicated expressions.

2a. $x(x - 3)$ or $x^2 - 3x$

a. Answer Dante's question by writing an expression.

b. Is Héctor right? Explain your thinking.
Yes; you can express the area as $x(x - 3)$ or $x^2 - 3x$.

In **Problem 3,** students consider the case of removing a rectangle from a square to write an expression for the remaining rectangle.

Students can simply use the labels of the sides in the diagram to represent the area of the unshaded rectangle: $a(a - 1)$. Alternatively, they can think of the unshaded rectangle as the difference in areas of the square and the smaller rectangle, $a^2 - a(1) = a^2 - a$.

Problem 4 gives students the opportunity to construct their own rectangle drawings given specific algebraic expressions. This is a good problem to go over with the entire class since it extends students' thinking about the use of area models in demonstrating the distributive property. When students label their diagrams, make sure they are clear about what lengths the variables represent. They may need to use brackets or arrows to make their labels clear.

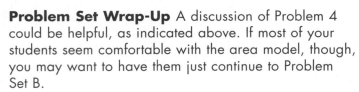 **Problem Set Wrap-Up** A discussion of Problem 4 could be helpful, as indicated above. If most of your students seem comfortable with the area model, though, you may want to have them just continue to Problem Set B.

 Problem Set B Suggested Grouping: Pairs or Individuals

This problem set makes use of more complicated geometric models, rectangle diagrams containing more than two smaller rectangles.

In **Problem 1,** students start with a square, add on another square and a rectangle, and then write an expression for the area of the resulting large rectangle.

On the Spot Assessment

Be on the lookout for students who compute $x^2 + x^2 = x^4$; this is a common mistake that plagues students even beyond their first year of algebra. There are at least two ways to clarify this using Problem 1.

- First of all, students can look at $x^2 + x^2$ and think about taking out a common factor of x^2: $x^2(1 + 1) = 2x^2$.

- Or, using the geometric model, they can see that the area of the large rectangle is $x(2x + 1)$, which is equivalent to the sum of the areas of the smaller pieces: $x^2 + x^2 + x$. The first expression, using the distributive property, expands to $2x^2 + x$, so $x^2 + x^2$ must be equivalent to $2x^2$.

Note that no units of measurement are used in these problems. If this causes concern for you or students, you can tell them to think of these rectangles as having length x units, 1 unit, and so on, or have them consider a specific unit of length. However, since x is an unknown, the diagrams cannot be considered accurate in displaying the relative lengths of x units and 1 unit.

3. Multiply the length and width of the square, to get a^2, and subtract the area of the shaded rectangle, which is $a \cdot 1$, to get $a^2 - a$. Or, multiply a by $a - 1$ to get $a(a - 1)$.

4a. $b^2 + 4b$

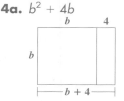

4b. $m^2 - 6m$

3. In this diagram, the rectangle that is shaded has been removed from the square.

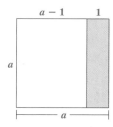

Explain two ways you could use the diagram to find an expression for the area of the unshaded rectangle. Give your expressions.

4. Use the distributive property to rewrite each expression. Then draw a rectangle diagram that shows why the two expressions are equivalent. Use shading to indicate when a region's area is being removed.

  a. $b(b + 4)$

  b. $m(m - 6)$

You will now explore more complex combinations of rectangles and the algebraic expressions they represent.

Problem Set B

1. Start with a square that has side length x. Create a large rectangle by adding another square of the same size and a 1-unit strip.

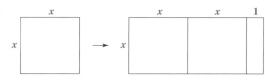

  a. What is the height of the large rectangle? x

  b. Write a simplified expression for the width of the large rectangle.

1b. $2x + 1$

  c. Use the dimensions from Parts a and b to write an expression for the area of the large rectangle. $x(2x + 1)$

1d. area of each square $= x^2$, area of small rectangle $= x$; total area $= 2x^2 + x$

  d. The large rectangle is composed of two squares and a smaller rectangle. Write an expression for the area of each of these parts. Then use the areas to write an expression for the area of the large rectangle, simplifying it if necessary.

  e. Your two expressions for the area of the large rectangle, from Parts c and d, are equivalent. Write an equation that states this, and then use the distributive property to verify your equation.

$x(2x + 1) = 2x^2 + x$; $x(2x + 1) = x(2x) + x(1)$
$$= 2x^2 + x$$

1 **Problem 4** may be challenging for students; creating the rectangle diagrams to match the expressions is a more difficult task than being given the geometric model and supplying the expression. If students need help starting, suggest that they begin with a square of side length *a* (or *b* or *c* as the case may be) and build on it to fit the given expression.

2 ## On the **Spot Assessment**

In **Problem 5,** watch for students who incorrectly multiply $3a(a)$ in Part a, $2m(3m)$ in Part b, or $4x(2x)$ in Part c by forgetting the exponent and thus getting an answer such as $3a(a + 4) = 3a + 12$ or $3a + 12a$.

If students write, for example, $6m$ rather than $6m^2$ in Part b, you may want to have them write each step: $2m(3m - 2) = 2m(3m) - 2m(2) = 2 \cdot 3 \cdot m \cdot m - 2 \cdot 2 \cdot m$. Then ask them what the $m \cdot m$ portion of the first term will be.

3 ## Share & Summarize

This is a good problem for students to do in pairs and then compare explanations with their partners. Because this model involves three variables, some students may need to redraw the rectangle as two separate smaller rectangles and label each side of the resulting rectangles. You may want to ask students how their explanations are the same as their partners' or how they are different. Ask: Which explanation would you use if you were teaching someone else about expanding expressions?

Troubleshooting

If students are having difficulty with the distributive property and expanding expressions, ask them to make up their own problems (or give them additional examples) and create rectangle drawings that go with them. Since adding strips is easier than subtracting them, begin with some simple cases similar to the type in the Think & Discuss on page 358. Although the next investigation does not use the area model, it will be important for students to understand in Lesson 6.2 when they multiply binomials.

Additional Examples Draw a rectangle diagram to model each expression, and then give the expanded form.

$x(2x + 3)$

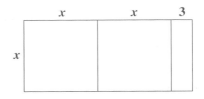

$$x(2x + 3) = 2x^2 + 3x$$

$3x(x + 1)$

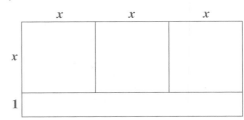

$$3x(x + 1) = 3x^2 + 3x$$

$2x(x - 2)$

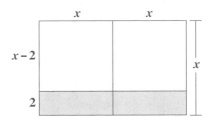

$$2x(x - 2) = 2x^2 - 4x$$

On Your Own Exercises

Practice & Apply: 1–8, pp. 368–369
Connect & Extend: 22–32, p. 370
Mixed Review: 35–45, pp. 371–372

2. Possible explanation: The area of the large rectangle is the height, x, times the width, $2x - 1$, or $x(2x - 1)$. This is the same as the area of the two squares, $2x^2$, minus the area of the strip, x, or $2x^2 - x$.

3b. Possible explanation: $2x(x + 1)$ is the area of the large rectangle found by multiplying the two dimensions ($2x$ and $x + 1$), and $2x^2 + 2x$ is the area of the large rectangle found by adding the areas of its components (x^2, x^2, and $2x$).

4b. $b(b - 3)$

4c. $c(c + 2)$

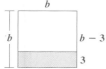

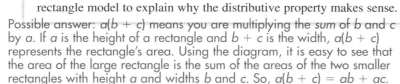
---

2. Start with a square with side length x, add another square of the same size, and *remove* a strip with width 1.

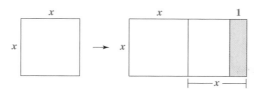

Use the diagram to help explain why $x(2x - 1) = 2x^2 - x$.

3. Now start with a square with side length x and make a rectangle with sides $2x$ and $x + 1$.

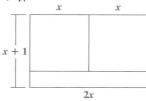

a. Use the distributive property to expand $2x(x + 1)$. $2x^2 + 2x$

b. Use the diagram to explain why your expansion is equivalent to the original expression.

4. Draw a rectangle diagram that models each expression. Use your diagram to help you write the expression in a different form.

a. $2a(a - 1)$ **4a.** Possible expression: $2a^2 - 2a$

b. $b^2 - 3b$

c. $c^2 + 2c$

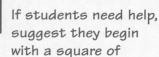

5. Expand each expression.

a. $3a(a + 4)$ $3a^2 + 12a$

b. $2m(3m - 2)$ $6m^2 - 4m$

c. $4x(3 + 2x)$ $12x + 8x^2$

Share & Summarize

According to the distributive property, $a(b + c) = ab + ac$. Use a rectangle model to explain why the distributive property makes sense.

Possible answer: $a(b + c)$ means you are multiplying the *sum* of b and c by a. If a is the height of a rectangle and $b + c$ is the width, $a(b + c)$ represents the rectangle's area. Using the diagram, it is easy to see that the area of the large rectangle is the sum of the areas of the two smaller rectangles with height a and widths b and c. So, $a(b + c) = ab + ac$.

LESSON 6.1 Rearranging Algebraic Expressions **361**

Investigation 2

In this investigation, students visit a common topic in algebra: simplifying expressions by combining like terms. Undoubtedly, this is an area that causes difficulties for students. In fact, students may wonder why simplifying expressions is important at all. One reason is that expressions are often easier to use if they are in simplified form, especially when they need to be evaluated for specific values of the variables. Another reason is that in order to recognize and prove that expressions are equivalent, they often must be simplified first.

If students need more concrete models for understanding how to combine like terms, you may want to provide algebra tiles.

Think & Discuss

1 Begin this investigation by having students work in small groups or pairs on the floor-area problem. Master 45 reproduces this floor layout so that students can do their computations right on the diagram. Then ask the class for

2 as many different expressions as they were able to find.

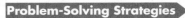
Problem-Solving Strategies

- Students may divide the floor into rectangular or square sections for which they can then find the area; some may divide it as given in the answer.

- Students may imagine removing the middle section that is 5 feet wide and pushing together the two sections that are m feet wide. The expression for that portion is $2m(m + 4)$. Adding the other sections, including the one they removed, gives

$$2m(m + 4) + 0.5m(m + 7) + 5m$$

Teaching Resources

▶ **Master 45**

Lesson 6.1 Investigation 2 Explore

TEACHING RESOURCES   CHAPTER 6   Working with Expressions   **63**

Investigation 2 ▶ Simplifying Expressions

In Investigation 1, you learned about expanding expressions by removing parentheses. To make expanded expressions easier to use, you will sometimes want to shorten, or simplify, them.

Think & Discuss

This floor plan is for a living room. Imagine that you want to buy new carpeting for the room. All dimensions are in feet.

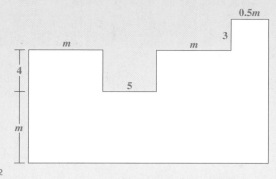

① Possible expressions: $m(m + 4) + 5m + m(m + 4) + 0.5m(7 + m)$ or, after expanding, $m^2 + 4m + 5m + m^2 + 4m + 3.5m + 0.5m^2$

• Write an expression for the area of the floor.   See ①.

• Tamika wrote this expression for the area of the floor:

$$m^2 + 4m + 5m + m^2 + 4m + 3.5m + 0.5m^2$$

Is her expression correct?   yes

• Evaluate Tamika's expression for $m = 6$.
  $6^2 + 4(6) + 5(6) + 6^2 + 4(6) + 3.5(6) + 0.5(6)^2 = 189$

1 Have students work in pairs or small groups.

2 Ask the class for as many different expressions as they can give.

1 To introduce the vocabulary *like terms,* have students look at the expression on page 363:

$$k + 4k^2 + 3 - 2k^3 + 2k - 16 - 6k^4 + 3k^2 + 7k^3 + 19k^8$$

Explain that the parts k and $2k$ are called *like terms:* they have the same variable raised to the same power. You might ask what they think $k + 2k$ is equivalent to. Students can think about this in a variety of ways: they can think about the distributive property and rewrite $k + 2k$ as $k(1 + 2)$, or $3k$. Or they can think about a rectangle with dimensions k by 1 to represent the first term; then consider adding two more identical rectangles to represent the second term ($2k$). Combining these gives a rectangle of dimensions $3k$ by 1. Explain that like terms can also be subtracted, such as $7k^3 - 2k^3$, or $5k^3$.

Ask students to look at the expression in the text once again and group the terms that are like. You may need to prompt them to consider the constant terms. Finally, ask them to combine each group of like terms and to rewrite the expression as simply as possible:

$$19k^8 - 6k^4 + 5k^3 + 7k^2 + 3k - 13$$

You may want to extend the discussion by asking students the following:

> Are $3sr$ and $4rs$ like terms? Are $6xrt$ and $7trx$ like terms? **yes, yes**

> Explain why $x + x$ is not x^2, using either a geometric or an algebraic argument.

Geometric:

The area is the sum of the two smaller rectangles or $x + x$. The area is also the area of the larger rectangle or $x \cdot 2$ or $2x$. Therefore $x + x = 2x$, not x^2.

Algebraic:
Using the distributive property, $x + x$ can be rewritten as $x(1 + 1)$ which simplifies to $x(2)$ or $2x$.

2 **Problem Set C** Suggested Grouping: Pairs
This problem set gives students some practice combining like terms, focusing on common mistakes students make and how to verify results.

The first two problems are straightforward simplification problems. You may want to give students a minute to try **Problem 1,** and then have a couple of students describe to the class how they found their answers.

On the Spot Assessment

Watch for students who incorrectly simplify $2p - p$ as 2 in Problem 1. This mistake is more common than one might think and needs attention from the start. The rectangle model that students used in Investigation 1 could be useful here: draw a rectangle and label it with dimensions 2 and p. Ask the student how you might remove a rectangle of area p from this one. You may want to remind him or her that $p = 1p$.

3 **Problems 3–6** address some additional misconceptions and are worth going over with the class. Whenever possible, have students try to prove their answers, using the techniques in the previous investigation.

On the Spot Assessment

In Problem 3, watch for students who state that $x + x = x^2$. Again, you might have them create a rectangle diagram and find the total area:

Tamika's area expression has several terms, but you can write an equivalent expression that is easier to work with.

For example, consider this expression:

$$k + 4k^2 + 3 - 2k^3 + 2k - 16 - 6k^4 + 3k^2 + 7k^3 + 19k^8$$

Two of the terms are k and $2k$. You can reason that their sum is $3k$ even though you don't know what k stands for. A number plus twice that number is three times that number, no matter what the number is.

The parts k and $2k$ are called *like terms*. **Like terms** have the same variable raised to the same power; they can be added or subtracted and then written as a single term. For example, in the expression above,

$$4k^2 + 3k^2 = 7k^2 \qquad \text{and} \qquad {}^-2k^3 + 7k^3 = 5k^3$$

Similarly, 3 and $^-16$ are like terms because they are both constants (terms with no variable) and can be combined to give $^-13$. Since the terms $^-6k^4$ and $19k^8$ are unlike each other and unlike the other terms, they stand alone.

You can rewrite the expression more simply as

$$19k^8 - 6k^4 + 5k^3 + 7k^2 + 3k - 13$$

Notice that, in the above expression, the terms are ordered by the exponent on the variable k.

Problem Set C

1. Which of these expressions are equivalent to the expression $p + 2p - p + 6 - 3 + 2p$? $4p + 3$ and $2p + 3 + 2p$

$$3p \qquad 7p \qquad 4p + 3 \qquad 6p + 3 \qquad 2p + 3 + 2p \qquad 4p - 3$$

2. Which of these expressions are equivalent to the expression $y(2y + 3) - 5 + 2y - 2 + 3y^2 + 7$?

$$10 \qquad 2y^2 + 3y^2 + 5y \qquad 10y^2 \qquad 12y + 14 \qquad 5y^2 + 5y$$

Evan tried to simplify the expressions below but made some errors. For each, tell whether the simpler expression is correct. If it's not, identify Evan's mistake and write the correct expression.

3. $x + x + 7 = 2x + 7$ correct

4. $m^2 + m^2 - 4 = m^4 - 4$

5. $2 + b + b^2 = 2 + b^3$

6. $3 - b^2 + b(b + 2b) = 2b^2 + 3$ correct

2. $2y^2 + 3y^2 + 5y$ and $5y^2 + 5y$

4. He added the exponents instead of the terms; $2m^2 - 4$.

5. He added the exponents on b^1 and b^2; $2 + b + b^2$ can't be simplified further.

LESSON 6.1 Rearranging Algebraic Expressions **363**

1 In **Problem 7a,** it is important to note that the terminology "as simply as you can" is somewhat relative. The commonly used term *simplest form* implies that there is only one simplest form for any expression. However, it is not clear that, for example, $(x + 1)^2$ is any simpler than $x^2 + 2x + 1$. In fact, the "simplicity" of the form really depends upon what you want to do with the expression. This point may not be relevant enough to mention to students, but it is worth considering when assessing students' understanding of simplified forms.

The same issue arises with fractional forms. For example, $\frac{2}{6}$ might be considered a "simpler" form than $\frac{1}{3}$ when expressing the chances of rolling 3 or 5 on a die, since the denominator, 6, represents the total number of outcomes.

Problem 8 brings up an interesting method for checking whether two expressions are equivalent. The point is that substituting one value is not a good test for determining whether expressions are equivalent. However, only one counterexample is needed to prove expressions are *not* equivalent.

2 **Problem Set Wrap-Up** You may want to review student responses to Problems 3–6. You may also want to discuss the method in Problem 8. Certainly, one value for which the expressions disagree is enough to show that the expressions are not equivalent, but students may enjoy thinking about how many values are necessary to determine conclusively whether two expressions *are* equivalent. They should agree that the more values you test, the more confident you can be that two expressions are equivalent. You may want to give them a linear example. Display the equation $3x - 2(x - 1) = 5x - 2$, and ask:

> What about this equation? If $x = 1$, the expression on the left is $3 - 0$, or 3, and the expression on the right is $5 - 2$, also 3. Is that enough to show they're equivalent? *no*

> Try another value for x. What do you get? *Any other value for x gives two different values for the two sides.*

Now change the expression on the right to $x + 2$.

> Now, $x = 1$ still gives 3 on the left and 3 on the right. Let's try another value, say, $x = -2$. The left sides gives $-6 - 2(-3)$, or 0. The right side gives $-2 + 2$, also 0. Is that enough?

Students have seen that specific examples are not enough to prove conjectures; however, with the additional information that two points determine a line, it is enough to show that two linear expressions share the same outputs for two input values. If no students think of this, ask what kind of expression is on each side of the equals sign. Then tell them to imagine plotting the two (input, output) pairs for the left side: (1, 3) and (-2, 0). (You may want to plot them yourself.) Ask if there is more than one line that can go through those two points. Once students realize the answer is no, ask whether the two tests are enough to say conclusively that these two lines are the same.

Be sure to point out that students can be sure of the results using two points *only* because they recognized that the two sides of the equation are both linear expressions.

About the Mathematics

Actually, for single-variable polynomials of degree n (that is, the highest exponent on any term is n), only $n + 1$ values are needed. This is because $n + 1$ points uniquely determine an nth-degree relationship. Using $n + 1$ points (x, y), you can create a system of $n + 1$ equations with $n + 1$ unknowns by substituting each x in $a_n x^n + a_{n-1} x^{n-1} + \ldots + a_1 x + a_0$, and setting the result equal to the corresponding y. The $n + 1$ unknowns are then $a_n, \ldots, a_0$. For example, the three points $(-2, 1)$, $(1, 4)$, and $(3, 7)$ determine a quadratic relationship (degree 2):

$a_2(-2)^2 + a_1(-2) + a_0 = 1$ or $4a_2 - 2a_1 + a_0 = 1$

$a_2(1)^2 + a_1(1) + a_0 = 4$ or $a_2 + a_1 + a_0 = 4$

$a_2(3)^2 + a_1(3) + a_0 = 7$ or $9a_2 + 3a_1 + a_0 = 7$

Solving the system gives $a_2 = 0.1$, $a_1 = 1.1$, and $a_0 = 2.8$, so the quadratic is $y = 0.1x^2 + 1.1x + 2.8$.

---

3 **Problem Set D** **Suggested Grouping: Individuals** This problem set combines using the distributive property and combining like terms.

In **Problems 1, 3, and 4,** students have to think about subtraction in relation to the distributive property. This is an area that often causes difficulty for students, and it would be worthwhile going over their solutions.

• ***Teaching notes continued on page A681***

8a. no; Possible explanations: Combining
the a^2 terms gives
$4a^2$. Or, if the
expressions were
equivalent, Keenan
would have found
the same result for
$a = 2$.

8b. Possible answer:
Just because one
value works
doesn't mean two
expressions are
equivalent. It's
better to substitute
two or three values
so that you have
more evidence to
help you decide
whether they are
equivalent.

▶ **MATERIALS**

graphing calculator

Remember

Subtracting a number
is equivalent to adding
its opposite; for exam-
ple, $3 - 5 = 3 + {}^-5$.

7. Copy the expression you wrote for the area of the floor in the
Think & Discuss on page 362.

   a. Write the expression as simply as you can. $2.5m^2 + 16.5m$

   b. How many square feet of carpet do you need if m is 6 ft? 189 ft^2

   c. In the Think & Discuss, you evaluated Tamika's expression for
$m = 6$. Which was easier, evaluating Tamika's expression or your
expression from Part a? the expression from Part a

8. Lana and Keenan simplified $5a^2 + 10 - 4a^2 - 5 + 3a^2$ to $3a^2 + 5$.
Lana checked the answer by substituting 0 for a. She found that
both expressions equal 5 when a is 0, and she concluded that they
are equivalent.

Keenan asked, "But what happens when we substitute 2?" Using
$a = 2$, he found that the first expression equals 21 and that the
simplified expression equals 17.

   a. Did Lana and Keenan simplify correctly? Explain.

   b. Lana and Keenan tested the equivalence of the expressions by
substituting the same value into each expression to see whether
the results were equal. Do you think this test should work? What
did you learn from the results of their tests?

Problem Set D

Write each expression as simply as you can.

   1. $3(x + 1) + 7(2 - x) - 10(2x - 0.5)$ ${}^-24x + 22$

   2. $3a + 2(a - 6) + \frac{1}{2}(8 - 4a)$ $3a - 8$

   3. $3y + 9 - (2y - 9) - y$ 18

   4. $(x^2 - 7) - 2(1 - x + x^2)$ ${}^-x^2 + 2x - 9$

In this addition chart, the expression in each white cell is the sum of the
first expressions in that row and column. For example, the sum of a^2 and
$a(a - 1)$ is $a^2 + a(a - 1) = a^2 + a^2 - a = 2a^2 - a$.

+	a	$a(a - 1)$
$a - 1$	$2a - 1$	$a^2 - 1$
a^2	$a^2 + a$	$2a^2 - a$

1 Consider students'
understanding of sim-
plified forms as you
assess their answers.

2 You may want to discuss Problems 3–6
and 8.

3 You may have students
work on their own.

Problem 5 may take some time to complete. Students must apply the distributive property in some of the expressions and then perform the addition of rows and columns.

Problem 6 is open-ended and may be a good discussion item. Many students will work backward to solve this problem. For example, to "remove" the $3x^2$ that the given part supplies, $\frac{-3}{2}x^2$ must be in the remaining portion; to get $^-3$, 3 must be added to the $^-6$ supplied by the given part, so $+\frac{3}{2}$ is needed in the blank. This technique clearly has value and is worth mentioning to the class.

In **Problem 7,** some students may simplify the right side of the equation before they graph it. This illustrates one of the advantages of simplifying expressions when performing certain tasks. They should get $y = 2x + 2$, a line with y-intercept 2 and slope 2.

It is worth discussing that graphs alone are not definitive when determining the kind of relationship between two variables. Graphs can provide hints about the nature of the relationship, but in fact, students are seeing only a portion of the graph, so they should consider the possibility that, if they graphed more of the relationship, they would get a nonlinear part of the graph. Also, it is possible to take sections of any graph and, by adjusting the scale, make it look linear.

Share & Summarize

Students should enjoy creating their own expressions to be simplified; of course, they can also get carried away trying to make them as difficult as possible! It would be helpful to set time limits (perhaps 3 minutes to create an expression and 3 minutes to analyze their partner's creation). If you have time, post particularly interesting or challenging expressions on the board and perhaps assign them for extra credit.

Troubleshooting There are several ways students may have trouble with simplifying expressions. If subtraction of quantities inside parentheses is causing difficulties, suggest the students write subtraction as equivalent addition problems, using $^-1$ where appropriate. Rewriting the expression with like terms grouped together (maybe crossing out the terms from the expression as they are included in the new one) may help many students. Some students may need help just knowing where to begin; you may want to suggest a plan of attack, such as using the distributive property to remove all parentheses, then finding the terms with the highest exponent and combining them, then the terms with the next highest exponent, and so on.

Some additional examples are given below, which you may want to assign or use to determine where the difficulties lie. Students will get more exposure to simplifying in the next lesson.

Additional Examples Simplify each expression.

$^-a^2 - 3a + 8a + a^2 - 3 \quad 5a - 3$

$8b + 3b^3 - 2 - 14b + 3b^2$
$3b^3 + 3b^2 - 6b - 2$

$3(c - 2) + c(c - 3) - 3c^2 \quad ^-2c^2 - 6$

$d^2 + 3 - 2d + 7(d^2 + d) - d(5 + d) \quad 7d^2 + 3$

$e^2 + 2(e - 3e^2) - 9e + 10 \quad ^-5e^2 - 7e + 10$

$13 - f + 3f(f + 1) - 6f^2 \quad ^-3f^2 + 2f + 13$

On Your Own Exercises

Practice & Apply: 9–21, pp. 369–370
Connect & Extend: 33–35, pp. 370–371
Mixed Review: 36–45, p. 372

5. Copy and complete this chart by finding the missing expressions.

+	$a + 3$	$2a(a - 5)$	$a(2a + 1)$
a	$2a + 3$	$2a^2 - 9a$	$2a^2 + 2a$
$a(a + 1)$	$a^2 + 2a + 3$	$3a^2 - 9a$	$3a^2 + 2a$
$a^2 + 4a$ or $a(a + 4)$	$a^2 + 5a + 3$	$3a^2 - 6a$	$3a^2 + 5a$

6. By completing the expression below, create an expression that simplifies to $4x - 3$. See below.

$$3(x^2 + x - 2) + 2(\underline{\hspace{3cm}})$$

7. Lucita and Mikayla are discussing this equation.

$$y = 2x^2 + 5x + 4 - 2(x^2 + 1) - 3x$$

Mikayla says it is a quadratic equation because it has x^2 terms. Lucita graphed the equation and thinks it is not quadratic.

7a. See Additional Answers.

a. Graph the equation. Based on the graph, what kind of relationship does this equation appear to represent: linear, quadratic, cubic, reciprocal, exponential, or something else? linear

b. How can you tell for certain what type of relationship this equation represents? Expand the right side and then combine like terms. The equation is equivalent to $y = 2x + 2$, a linear equation.

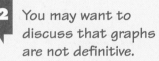
1 **Problem-Solving Strategy**

Work backward

2 You may want to discuss that graphs are not definitive.

3 It may be helpful to set time limits, such as 3 min to write expressions and 3 min to analyze them.

Share & Summarize Answers will vary.

Try to stump your partner! Write an expression that simplifies to one of these three expressions.

$$3x - 1 \qquad 5x + 2 \qquad 3x^3 - 7x - 2$$

Include at least five terms in your expression, let no more than two terms be single numbers, and include some terms with variables raised to a power. When you are done, swap with your partner, and figure out which expression above is equivalent to your partner's.

6. Possible answer: $3(x^2 + x - 2) + 2\left(\frac{-3}{2}x^2 + \frac{1}{2}x + \frac{3}{2}\right)$

Additional Answers

7a.

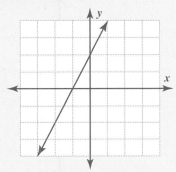

Lab Investigation

1 **Grouping: Pairs**

In this lab, students transform a specific shape into another shape and analyze the effects on perimeter and area. The sides of the shape are given as variables, so students can simultaneously practice combining like terms and solving simple equations to compare area and perimeter. Students should discover that if there is no overlap of the pieces, rearranging the given shape always preserves area but may not preserve perimeter.

Materials and Preparation

Each student will need a sheet of 1-centimeter graph paper and scissors. Rulers and a copy of Master 46 would be helpful but are not mandatory.

Introduce

2 To introduce this lab, explain to students that they will be using their knowledge of combining like terms to compare the perimeter and area of shapes they will be creating. They will also be looking at what determines *how* area and perimeter change when shapes are transformed.

Analyze the H-Shape

Even if students work in pairs on this lab, each individual student should copy the shape and find the perimeter and area. Master 46 reproduces this shape, but at this point in the lab, students should copy the H onto graph paper and then cut it out so that they have a concrete, hands-on sense of the shape, its perimeter, and its area. Later, when students are asked to make a rectangle from the H-shape, it may be more convenient to use the master.

3 In **Question 3,** students may be puzzled that they are being asked for an algebraic expression when they have previously been given specific values for *a* and *b*. However, students should be used to generalizing results, and you can tell them that this is what the question is asking them to do. Ask them to think of *a* and *b* as variables now, and ask whether they can envision how the shape might change when *a* and *b* have different values, such as $a = 4$ cm and $b = 1$ cm. By working with the variables, they can arrive at more powerful conclusions that will work for all values of *a* and *b*.

Students should notice that in **Questions 5 and 6,** now that they have general expressions for perimeter and area regardless of the values of *a* and *b*, they can

use the expressions to calculate perimeter and area for any given values. In fact, this is a much easier way to determine area and perimeter of multiple shapes.

Transform the H-Shape

4 In answering **Question 7,** students may need the added instruction that their shapes should maintain right angles to make computation of area and perimeter easier. Using acute or obtuse angles is acceptable but would require computations with triangles. If a student uses curved sides, point out that the calculations would be very complicated, and suggest trying an easier shape to begin. (Students can always try to work with other shapes later, if they have time.) You might also mention that their new shape doesn't have to be a rectangle or a square, or any other common polygon.

It will be helpful to have students cut out the H-shape so they can rearrange the pieces easily. (They may want to enlarge it so that the pieces are easier to manipulate.)

In **Question 7b,** students should notice that regardless of the new figure they created, the area expression is equivalent to the area expression of the original H-shape. If students have cut out the original H and rearranged the pieces, the fact that the areas are equivalent will make sense and will help them understand why the expressions are equivalent.

Problem-Solving Strategies There are different ways to answer **Question 7d.**

- The least efficient (but valid) way is to use a guess-check-and-improve strategy. Students choose values for *a* and *b*, and depending on what they get, adjust the two values. For example, using the possible answer for Question 7a, values of $a = 1$ and $b = 1$ give 13 for the H-shape's perimeter and 11 for the new shape's perimeter. A student might then try increasing *a* to 2, giving 19 for the H-shape and 13 for the new shape. Since these numbers are farther apart than the first guess, reducing *a* to, say, $\frac{1}{2}$ or leaving $a = 1$ and changing *b* might work better.

- Students can set the expression for the perimeter of their new shape equal to the perimeter of the H-shape, which is $6a + 7b$. For the possible answer given for Question 7a, this would give $6a + 7b = 9b + 2a$. Students can then choose a value for one of the variables and solve for the other. Or, they might solve for one variable in terms of the other (for example, $a = 0.5b$) and then choose a value for the unsolved variable and calculate the solved one (for example, if $b = 2$, then $a = 1$).

Lab Investigation ▶ Making the Cut

MATERIALS
- 1-cm graph paper
- scissors

In this H-shape, a and b are positive numbers and the angles are all right angles.

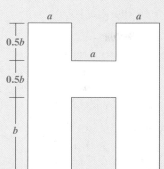

Analyze the H-Shape

1. 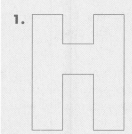 On graph paper, draw an H-shape in which $a = 1$ cm and $b = 2$ cm.

2. Find the perimeter and the area of your H-shape. 20 cm, 9 cm^2

3. Write an algebraic expression for the perimeter of your H-shape in terms of a and b. $6a + 7b$

4. *4.5ab* Write an expression for the area of your H-shape in terms of a and b.

5. Use your expression from Question 3 to calculate the perimeter of your H-shape when $a = 1$ cm and $b = 2$ cm. Does it agree with your answer to Question 2? 20 cm, yes

6. Now use your expression from Question 4 to calculate the area of your H-shape when $a = 1$ cm and $b = 2$ cm. Does it agree with your answer to Question 2? 9 cm^2, yes

Transform the H-Shape

7. Create a new figure—different from the H-shape—with an area the same as the H-shape shown above but a different perimeter.

a. Draw your figure. See below.

b. Write an algebraic expression for your figure's area. Is it equivalent to the expression for the area of the H-shape from Question 4?

c. Write an expression for your figure's perimeter.

d. The expression for the perimeter of the figure you drew probably looks very different from the perimeter expression for the H-shape. Try to find values of a and b for which the perimeters of the two figures are the same. If you find such values, does that mean the perimeters of the general shapes are equivalent? Explain.

7b. 4.5ab, yes

7c. for the figure in the answer to Part a: $9b + 2a$

7d. Possible answer: For the figure in the answer to Part a, the perimeters will be the same when $a = 1$ and $b = 2$. This doesn't mean the perimeters are equivalent; just because they're equal for one set of values doesn't mean they're always equal.

7a. Possible figure:

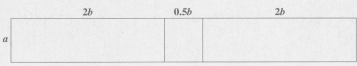

1 Have students work in pairs after Questions 1 and 2.

2 Let students know they will combine like terms to find perimeters and areas.

3 If necessary, rephrase to have students generalize the perimeter.

4 Suggest that students keep their figures fairly simple (using only right angles), but not necessarily rectangles.

Problem-Solving Strategies
- Guess-check-and-improve
- Write an equation

Problem-Solving Strategies In **Question 8,** students may have different approaches to creating a shape with the same perimeter.

- Some may work strictly from the algebraic expression, $6a + 7b$. If they choose a rectangle as a shape, they can take half of this expression, $3a + 3.5b$, and label two of the sides, one with $3a$ and one with $3.5b$.

- They might think about part of $6a + 7b$ (such as $2a + 3b$) and use that for each of two opposite sides, leaving the remainder (in this case, $2a + b$) to be divided between the other two sides.

1 ▶ For **Question 8d,** students might try setting the two areas equal, which would give a single equation with two variables, a and b. You may need to suggest students consider one variable to be a constant and solve for the other, or tell them to assume one variable has a particular value (such as $a = 1$) just to see what happens. They should realize that the only possible solution is $a = 0$ or $b = 0$, which doesn't make sense in the context since both a and b describe lengths.

Make a Rectangle

If students already formed a rectangle for their answer in Question 7a, tell them they need to create a different one for this question. This will pose an interesting challenge for them. You may want to distribute Master 46, which reproduces two copies of the H-shape for students to work with.

Make a Prediction

2 ▶ In **Question 11,** most students will realize that since they rearranged all the pieces of one shape to create another, the areas of the two shapes are equal. You may want to collect some of the different shapes students have created and tape them to the board or display them on the overhead so students can analyze which shapes preserve perimeter as well.

Check Your Prediction

3 ▶ Students may need some help in **Question 12** in figuring out when the two expressions are equal. In the answer given, they would set $6a + 3b = 6a + 7b$. It is clear that the only time these two expressions will be equal is when $b = 0$, and therefore the rectangle doesn't exist. This problem provides good practice in solving and analyzing equations as well.

What Did You Learn?

4 ▶ Encourage students to come up with several counter-examples to disprove Jenny's assertion.

Problem-Solving Strategies Students will have various ways of approaching this.

- Some students will simply try guessing to create rectangles like those described in the answer for **Question 14.**

- Another strategy is to cut and arrange, as students have done earlier in the lab. For example, take a 4×4 square and cut it in half, placing the two halves next to each other so that the sides of length 2 coincide. The resulting rectangle has dimensions 8×2, with perimeter 20. The original square has perimeter 16.

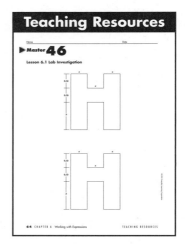

8a. Possible figure:

8c. for the figure in the answer to Part a: 10.5ab

9. Possible rectangle:

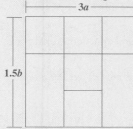

12. For the rectangle in the answer to Question 9: 6a + 3b. In this case the perimeters are different for all nonzero values of a and b.

14. Jenny is incorrect. Students may cite examples in which the area stays the same when the perimeter increases, such as going from a 6-by-6 to a 3-by-12 rectangle; the area in each case is 36 but the perimeter increases from 24 to 30. Or they might find figures whose area actually decreases, such as going from a 6-by-6 to a 8.5-by-4 rectangle, in which the perimeter increases from 24 to 25 but the area decreases from 36 to 34.

8. Now consider a figure that has the same perimeter as the H-shape but a different area.

   a. Draw such a figure.

   b. Write an expression for your figure's perimeter. Is it equivalent to the expression for the perimeter of the H-shape? $6a + 7b$, yes

   c. Write an expression for your figure's area.

   d. Are there any values of a and b for which the areas of the two figures are the same? (To answer this question, you might want to write and try to solve an equation.) no

Make a Rectangle

Copy the H-shape from page 366, cut it into pieces, and rearrange the pieces to form a rectangle. Keep track of the lengths of the sides of your pieces in terms of a and b. You will need this information later.

  9. Draw the rectangle you formed from the H-shape, and label the lengths of the sides.

Make a Prediction

  10. Without doing any calculations, think about how the perimeter of the original H-shape compares to the perimeter of your rectangle. Are they the same or different? Answers will vary.

  11. Without doing any calculations, think about how the area of the original H-shape compares to the area of your rectangle. Are they the same or different? the same

Check Your Prediction

  12. Write an expression for the perimeter of your rectangle in terms of a and b. Check your prediction from Question 10. Are there specific values of a and b that would make the perimeters the same? Different?

  13. Write an expression for the area of your rectangle in terms of a and b. Check your prediction from Question 11. Are there specific values of a and b that would make the areas the same? Different?

$4.5ab$; the areas are the same regardless of the values of a and b.

What Did You Learn?

  14. Jenny thinks that if you increase the perimeter of a figure, the area must also increase. Write a letter to her explaining whether she is correct and why. You may want to include examples or illustrations.

1 Suggest students consider one variable to be a constant and solve for the other, or choose a value for one and think about changing values for the other.

2 You may want to display the various shapes students create.

3 Help students decide when two expressions are equal, as needed.

4 Problem-Solving Strategies

- Guess-check-and-improve
- Make a model

On Your Own Exercises

Investigation 1,
pp. 359–361
Practice & Apply: 1–8
Connect & Extend: 22–32

Investigation 2,
pp. 362–365
Practice & Apply: 9–21
Connect & Extend: 33–35

Assign Anytime
Mixed Review: 36–45

Exercise 1:

In this exercise, it might be useful to point out to students that the context restricts the value of x to numbers less than 7.

Exercises 6 and 7:

Some students may start these exercises by applying the distributive property (in reverse) and using the resulting factors as indicators of length and width. Others may build the rectangle from the original expression. For example, in Exercise 6, they may think of $2x^2$ as two squares with side length x, placed side by side, and then add a rectangle of area x, with dimensions x by 1.

Quick Review
Math Handbook

Hot Topics
pp. 284–290

On Your Own Exercises

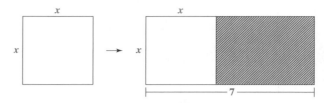

Practice & Apply

1. Start with a square with side length x cm. Imagine extending the length of one side to 7 cm.

a. What is the area of the original square? What is the area of the new, large rectangle? x^2, $7x$

b. Use the areas you found to write an expression for the area of the striped rectangle. $7x - x^2$

c. Now write expressions for the length and width of the striped rectangle. $7 - x$, x

d. Use the dimensions from Part c to write an expression for the area of the striped rectangle. $x(7 - x)$

e. What do your answers to Parts b and d suggest about the expansion of $x(7 - x)$?

2. Use the distributive property to expand $3x(x - 2)$. Then draw a rectangle diagram and use it to help explain why the two expressions are equivalent.

Use the distributive property to expand each expression.

3. $3z(z + 1)$ $3z^2 + 3z$

4. $\frac{1}{2}x(x - 2)$ $\frac{1}{2}x^2 - x$

5. $t(2 - t)$ $2t - t^2$

Draw a rectangle diagram to match each expression, and use it to write the expression in factored form.

6. $2x^2 + x$

7. $2x^2 - x$ $x(2x - 1)$

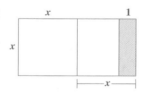

1e. $x(7 - x) = 7x - x^2$

2. $3x^2 - 6x$; The dimensions of the entire unshaded region are $3x$ and $x - 2$, so its area is $3x(x - 2)$. The area of the unshaded region is also the sum of the areas of the three squares, $3x^2$, minus the sum of the areas of the three shaded rectangles, $3(2x) = 6x$. So $3x(x - 2) = 3x^2 - 6x$.

6. $x(2x + 1)$

 impactmath.com/self_check_quiz

8. This diagram shows the grassy area between two buildings and the rectangular walkway through the middle of the area. The length of the grassy area is four times its width. The edges of the walkway are 2.5 meters from the sides of the rectangle.

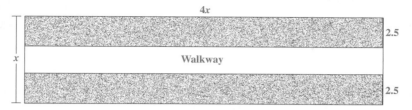

4x

2.5

x

Walkway

2.5

Write two expressions for the area of the walkway, one in factored form and one in expanded form. $4x(x - 5)$, $4x^2 - 20x$

Write each expression as simply as you can.

In your
own words

Describe some of the steps you take when you simplify an algebraic expression, and explain how you know when an expression is simplified as much as possible.

9. $2a^2 + 3$

11. $3x - 8$

12. $3p^2 + 6p - 6$

13. $n^3 + n^2 - 2n$

14. $4q^2 - 6q$

15. $c^2 - 6$

16. $^-c^2 + 4c + 6$

9. $2a(a + 2) - 4a + 3$

10. $n(n + 1) - n$ n^2

11. $x(3 - 2x) + 2(x^2 - 4)$

12. $p(3p - 4) - 2(3 - 5p)$

13. $n(n^2 - 1) - n(1 - n)$

14. $q - 3q - 4q(1 - q)$

15. $2(c - 3) + c(c - 2)$

16. $2(c + 3) - c(c - 2)$

Simplify each expression and then tell whether it is linear, quadratic, cubic, or none of these.

17. $p(p + 1) - \frac{2}{p} + 2 + p^2 - \left(1 - \frac{2}{p}\right) - 1$ $2p^2 + p$, quadratic

18. $w(1 - w) + 2w\left(\frac{1}{w}\right) - 2w - (1 - w^2)$ $1 - w$, linear

19. $6x - 2(1 + x) + 2\left(\frac{1}{x} - 1\right) - (4x - 1)$ $\frac{2}{x} - 3$, none of these

20. Complete this expression to create an expression that simplifies to $x + 2$.

Possible answer:

$^-4(x + x^2 - 1) + \underline{\quad 4x^2 + 5x - 2 \quad}$

21. See Additional Answers.

22.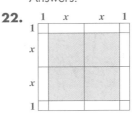

Connect & Extend

23. Possible answer:
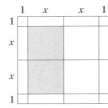

24–27. See Additional Answers.

31. $16w^2 - 8wx - 4w$

21. Sort these expressions into groups of equivalent expressions.

a. $5(x^4 - 1) - 10 - 2x^4 + 5 - 5x^2 + 2x^4 + 2x^2 + 7$

b. $3x^5 + 2x^4 + 3x^2$

c. $5x^5 + 2(x^4 - x^5) - 10 - 2x + 3x^2 + 2x + 3 + 7$

d. $^-3x^2 - 3 + 5x^4$

e. $x + 4 + 5(x + x^2) - 8 + 2x - 10x + 5 - 2x - 5x^2$

f. $3(x^5 + x^2) + 2(x^4 + 3x) - 6x$

For each expression, copy the diagram and shade an area that matches the expression.

22. $(2x)^2$

23. $2x^2$

24. $x(2x + 1)$

25. $2x + 2$

26. $(2x + 2)^2$

27. $x(2x + 2)$

Expand each expression.

28. $x(a - b + c)$ $ax - bx + cx$ **29.** $\frac{k}{7}(21a - 0.7)$ $3ak - 0.1k$

30. $\frac{x}{3}\left(\frac{a}{2} - \frac{b}{3} + \frac{c}{4}\right)$ $\frac{ax}{6} - \frac{bx}{9} + \frac{cx}{12}$ **31.** $4w(4w - 2x - 1)$

32. This diagram shows a drawer and the surrounding cabinet. The drawer is 2 inches wider than it is tall, and there is a 1-inch gap between the drawer and the outside of the cabinet on all sides. The length of both the drawer and the cabinet is y.

Write two equivalent expressions for the volume of the drawer, one in factored form and one in expanded form. $x(x + 2)y,$ $x^2y + 2xy$

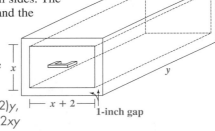

24. Possible answer:
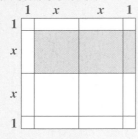

25. Possible answer:

26. Possible answer:
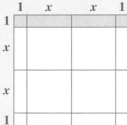

27. Possible answer:
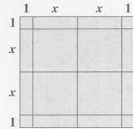

33. Ben and Lucita are discussing algebraic expressions.

33a. Folding along the side of length x: $\frac{x}{2}(x - 1)$; folding along the side of length $x - 1$: $x\left(\frac{x-1}{2}\right)$. The expressions are equivalent. Possible explanations: Both expressions represent half of the same quantity, so they must be equal. *Or*, both are equivalent to $\frac{x^2 - x}{2}$.

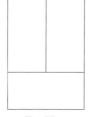

★ **a.** After the 1-cm strip is removed, there are two ways to fold the remaining piece of paper. For each possibility, write an expression for the area of the final piece (after the paper is folded and then cut in half). Are the expressions equivalent? Explain.

★ **b.** Ben posed a new problem: *Imagine a square with side length x. Fold the square in half, cut it, and throw away one half. Now remove a 1-cm strip from the remaining half. Write an expression for the area of the remaining piece.*

Lucita said there are two ways to interpret Ben's instructions. Find both ways, and write an expression for each. Are the two expressions equivalent? Explain. See Additional Answers.

34. A construction worker made a stack of bricks 16 layers high. Each layer consists of three bricks arranged in the pattern shown at left below. Each brick is twice as long as it is wide and has a thickness $1\frac{1}{2}$ inches less than its width.

Top View **Side View**

Layer 4
Layer 3
Layer 2
Layer 1

a. How many bricks are in the 16-layer stack? 48

★ **b.** Write an expression for volume of the stack, using w for the width of each brick.
$16(2w)(3w)(w - 1.5)$, $48(2w)(w)(w - 1.5)$, or $96w^3 - 144w^2$

LESSON 6.1 Rearranging Algebraic Expressions **371**

Additional Answers

33b. In both cases, the x-by-x square is cut in half to form an x-by-$\frac{x}{2}$ rectangle. The 1-cm strip can be cut from the x side or the $\frac{x}{2}$ side. One way gives the expression $\frac{x}{2}(x - 1)$; the other gives $x\left(\frac{x}{2} - 1\right)$. These expressions are not equivalent: expanding the first gives $\frac{x^2}{2} - \frac{x}{2}$; expanding the second gives $\frac{x^2}{2} - x$.

• continued on next page

Quick Check

Informal Assessment
Students should be able to:

✔ use geometric models in illustrating the distributive property to expand expressions of the form $a(b + c)$

✔ represent algebraic expressions using rectangle models

✔ simplify expressions by combining like terms

Quick Quiz

1. Copy this diagram.

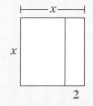

a. Shade the rectangle with area $x(x - 2)$.

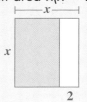

b. Use the diagram to expand the expression $x(x - 2)$. Explain how you used the diagram.
$x^2 - 2x$; The area of the shaded rectangle is the area of the square, x^2, minus the area of the unshaded rectangle, $2x$.

2. Consider the expression $x(2x + 3)$.

   a. Use the distributive property to rewrite the expression. $2x^2 + 3x$

   b. Draw a rectangle diagram that shows why the two expressions are equivalent.

3. Write each expression as simply as you can.

   a. $x^2 - 3x - 2(2 - 4x + 5x^2)$
   $-9x^2 + 5x - 4$

   b. $-2y(5y - 7) + \frac{y}{2}(6y^2 - 10y + 12)$
   $3y^3 - 15y^2 + 20y$

4. Is the following equation quadratic, linear, or neither? linear

   $y = 3x^2 - 7x + 5 - (-x^2 + 4x) - (4x^2 - 10x)$

Mixed Review

35. Possible answer: $y = -\frac{7}{5}x + \frac{31}{5}$

36.

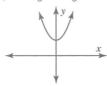

37.

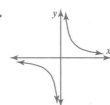

38.

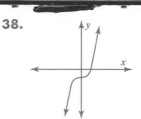

39. already simplified

---

35. Find an equation for the line through the points (3, 2) and (8, $^-$5).

Make a rough sketch showing the general shape and location of the graph of each equation.

36. $y = x^2 + 3$ **37.** $y = \frac{2}{x}$ **38.** $y = x^3 - 1$

Simplify each expression as much as possible.

39. $\sqrt{34}$ **40.** $\sqrt{99x^4}$ $3x^2\sqrt{11}$ **41.** $^-\sqrt{60b}$ $^-2\sqrt{15b}$

Use the distributive property to rewrite each expression without parentheses.   **42.** $^-3n + 4$ **43.** $12p - 3p^2$

42. $^-(3n - 4)$ **43.** $3p(4 - p)$ **44.** $^-k(^-k - k)$ $2k^2$

45. Probability The game of backgammon involves two players, one with black markers and one with white. Players can remove one of their opponent's markers from the board by landing on a space occupied by a single opposing marker. The opponent can return the marker to the board on one of six spaces, if any of the six holds no more than 1 of the first player's markers.

For example, on the board below, the white marker can enter if a 5 or a 3 is rolled. If a 3 is rolled, the black marker in that space is removed.

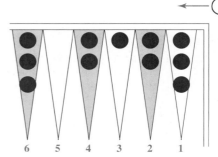

On each turn, a player rolls two standard dice.

   a. What is the probability that the white marker can enter the board on this turn? That is, what is the probability of rolling either a 5 or a 3 on either of two dice? $\frac{20}{36}$, or $\frac{5}{9}$

   b. What is the probability that the white marker will send out a black marker when it enters? That is, what is the probability of rolling a 3 on either die? $\frac{11}{36}$

   c. What is the probability that the white marker *cannot* enter the board on this turn? $\frac{16}{36}$, or $\frac{4}{9}$

6.2

Expanding Products of Binomials

Objectives

▸ To use geometric models to multiply binomials

▸ To multiply binomials using the distributive property

▸ To understand patterns for shortcuts in multiplying binomials

Overview (pacing: about 5 class periods)

In this lesson, students learn how to multiply two binomials using an area model similar to the one used in the Lesson 6.1. They use the model and the distributive property to multiply binomials involving addition and then subtraction. The lesson ends with an investigation on shortcut methods for multiplying binomials.

Advance Preparation

Although they are not required, you may want to use algebra tiles to illustrate the rectangle models for students.

Lesson Planner

	Summary	Materials	On Your Own Exercises	Assessment Opportunities
Investigation 1 page T374	Students use a geometric model to multiply binomials involving addition, $(a + b)(c + d)$.	*● Algebra tiles (optional)	Practice & Apply: 1–6, p. 384 Connect & Extend: 34, 35, p. 386 Mixed Review: 51–63, pp. 388–389	Share & Summarize, pages T375, 375 Troubleshooting, page T375
Investigation 2 page T376	Students connect the distributive property to the rectangle model for multiplying binomials involving addition.	*● Algebra tiles (optional)	Practice & Apply: 7–10, pp. 384–385 Connect & Extend: 36–41, pp. 386–387 Mixed Review: 51–63, pp. 388–389	On the Spot Assessment, page T378 Share & Summarize, pages T378, 378 Troubleshooting, page T378
Investigation 3 page T378	Students expand binomial products in which one or both binomials involve subtraction.		Practice & Apply: 11–23, p. 385 Connect & Extend: 42–46, p. 387 Mixed Review: 51–63, pp. 388–389	On the Spot Assessment, page T379 Share & Summarize, pages T380, 380 Troubleshooting, page T380
Investigation 4 page T381	Students consider shortcut methods for expanding binomial products.	*● Algebra tiles (optional)	Practice & Apply: 24–33, p. 386 Connect & Extend: 47–50, p. 388 Mixed Review: 51–63, pp. 388–389	Share & Summarize, pages T383, 383 Troubleshooting, page T383 Informal Assessment, page 388 Quick Quiz, page 388

* Included in Impact Mathematics Manipulative Kit

Introduce

1 In this lesson, students expand on the area model they used in Lesson 6.1. Use a simple example to review with them how they used the model: they drew a diagram with two or more rectangles using the factors of a product to determine the dimensions, and then wrote an algebraic expression that represented the area using the areas of the individual rectangles. Then work through the Think & Discuss as a class.

Think & Discuss

In this Think & Discuss, students explore the kinds of algebraic expressions that result when two rectangular strips are added to a square, one on the bottom and one on the right.

> ### Tips
> from **Teachers**
>
> "I use transparent algebra tiles on the overhead projector. It's particularly useful in demonstrating this area model for multiplying binomials."

2 It is important that students see the variety of strategies that can be used to find the area of the large rectangle. You may want to make this more of an Explore activity, letting them work for about 10 minutes in small groups to find at least three strategies for finding the area. If you think it might be helpful, have students draw the rectangle and cut out the pieces or use algebra tiles to represent the different areas. Demonstrate each strategy they find on the overhead projector or the board.

Problem-Solving Strategies Here are a few strategies students may discover.

- Divide the rectangle into two smaller rectangles along the vertical line, so that one rectangle has sides $m + 1$ and m and the other has sides $m + 1$ and 3.

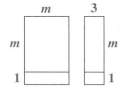

  The areas of the two smaller rectangles are $m(m + 1)$ and $3(m + 1)$, so the total area is $m^2 + m + 3m + 3$, or $m^2 + 4m + 3$.

- Divide the rectangle into two smaller rectangles along the horizontal line. One will have sides $m + 3$ and m, and the other will have sides $m + 3$ and 1. The areas of the two smaller rectangles are $m(m + 3)$ and $1(m + 3)$, so the total area is $m^2 + 3m + m + 3$, or $m^2 + 4m + 3$.

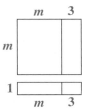

- Divide the rectangle into four smaller rectangles with dimensions $m \times m$, $3 \times m$, $1 \times m$, and 1×3. The total area is $m^2 + 3m + m + 3$, or $m^2 + 4m + 3$.

 3 After students have found as many different ways of computing the area as possible, explain that a *binomial* is the sum or difference of two unlike terms and give them examples, such as $m + 3$, $x^2 - 3$, and $2y + x$. You may want to mention that the prefix "bi" means "two," and ask what they think a *trinomial* is.

 4 Point out that the area of the large rectangle in the Think & Discuss is the product of two binomials, $m + 3$ and $m + 1$, and show where these expressions appear as the length and width in the diagram. From their work above, it appears that $(m + 3)(m + 1) = m^2 + 4m + 3$. Tell students that in this lesson, they will be learning how to multiply two binomials using a variety of methods, and eventually will learn a shortcut they will encounter frequently in their study of algebra.

> ### Tips
> from **Teachers**
>
> "I like to take extra time in introducing students to multiplying binomials, since many find it abstract. I usually slow my pacing in the beginning until I'm sure they understand what they are doing. You may want to spend two days on the first investigation for this reason."

6.2 Expanding Products of Binomials

In Lesson 6.1, you examined rectangle diagrams consisting of a square with a rectangular strip added to or taken away from one side. What if you were to add or remove *two* rectangular strips?

1 Review the area model for the distributive property from Lesson 6.1.

Think & Discuss

Start with a square with side length m cm. Add a 3-cm strip to one side.

Now add a 1-cm strip to an adjacent side of the new rectangle.

What is the area of the final large rectangle? Describe how you found it. Are there other ways to find this area? See ①.

① $(m + 1)(m + 3)$, or $m^2 + 3m + 1m + 3$, or $m^2 + 4m + 3$; See the teaching notes for possible strategies.

2 You may want to let small groups find multiple strategies for finding the area.

3 Introduce the new vocabulary.

VOCABULARY
binomial

In Lesson 6.1, you used the distributive property to multiply expressions in the forms $m(m + a)$ and $m(m - a)$. That is, you found the product of a number or variable and a binomial. A **binomial** is the sum or difference of two unlike terms.

The expression $x + 5$ is a binomial because it is the sum of two unlike terms. Similarly, $x^2 - 7$ is a binomial; it is the difference of two terms that can't be combined into one term.

Expressions such as $x^2 + x - 1$ and x^2 have more than or fewer than two terms, so they are not binomials. The expression $x + 2x$ is not a binomial either: its terms are like terms, and the expression is equivalent to $3x$.

The area of the final large rectangle in the Think & Discuss is the product of *two* binomials: $m + 3$ and $m + 1$. In this lesson, you will learn how to multiply two binomials.

4 • Point out that area of the rectangle above is a product of two binomials

• Show where the binomials came from in the model (the dimensions).

LESSON 6.2 Expanding Products of Binomials **373**

Investigation 1

Here students adapt the geometric model they encountered in the previous lesson to multiplying two binomials. The visual and concrete image of the algebraic expressions will likely help them *understand* how to expand the product of two binomials, an often poorly understood process.

Problem Set A Suggested Grouping: Pairs
Because multiplying binomials is abstract and often difficult, it is helpful to have students work together.

In **Problem 1,** encourage students to use any of the strategies they developed in the Think & Discuss (as described in the sample strategies). It is important that they correctly write the expression for the area of the large rectangle as $(a + 2)(a + 3)$ and that they understand that it is customary to omit a multiplication symbol between the two binomials.

Problem 2 requires that students use the method of breaking the large rectangle into four smaller parts to write the expression for the area. After students complete the problem, it might be helpful to write on the board the equation that states the result of multiplying the two binomials:

$$(x + 4)(x + 3) = x^2 + 7x + 12$$

Doing so gives students a chance to check their answer before completing the problem set, and also gives them another example they can refer to if necessary.

Investigation Using Geometric Models to Multiply Binomials

The geometric model you used to think about multiplying a term and a binomial can be adapted for multiplying two binomials.

Problem Set A

1. Look at this rectangle.

   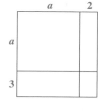

   a. Write two expressions, one for the length of the large rectangle and one for the width. $a + 3, a + 2$

   b. Use your expressions to write an expression for the area of the large rectangle. $(a + 2)(a + 3)$

   c. Use the diagram to expand your expression for the area of the large rectangle. That is, write the area of the large rectangle without using parentheses. $a^2 + 5a + 6$

2. Arturo wanted to expand $(x + 4)(x + 3)$. He drew a rectangle $x + 4$ units wide and $x + 3$ units high.

   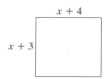

   He then drew lines to break the rectangle into four parts.

   Arturo then wrote: Area of large rectangle $= (x + 4)(x + 3)$.

   He then found the area of each of the four smaller parts and used them to write another expression for the area of the large rectangle. Finally, he simplified his expression by combining like terms. What was his final expression? $x^2 + 7x + 12$

1 You may have students work in pairs.

2 Encourage students to use their strategies from the Think & Discuss.

3 It might be helpful to write the problem and result on the board.

Problem 3 stresses the same concept as the previous problems, but students have to draw a rectangle diagram that matches a given expression.

Problem-Solving Strategies ▶ **Part c** is more difficult because the term $(2n + 3)$ includes a coefficient on the variable. Students may find different ways to work with this.

- Some students may construct six smaller rectangles rather than four, labeling the length $n + n + 3$ and the width $n + 1$, as shown in the given answer.

- Other students may label the length with two segments, $2n$ and 3, rather than three segments, two of length n and one of length 3. In this case, they will get four rectangles, of areas $2n^2$, $2n$, $3n$, and 3.

Problem 4 gives some hints to students about how to approach Problem 5, which is more challenging. In Problem 4, students are given $6y + 3y$, unsimplified, to provide some clues about how to construct the rectangle. The 6 and the 3 are indicators that the side lengths will be $y + 3$ and $y + 6$. It might be helpful to point this out to students.

In **Problem 5,** then, students need to think about what numbers add to $5y$. If they guess 4 and 1 first, don't tell them that this is incorrect. At some point in the process, they will discover that the product of the two numbers has to be 6, and 2 and 3 are the only pair that work. This is a lovely preview into the work they will do in factoring quadratic expressions later on.

Share & Summarize

This question highlights one of the most common mistakes students make when multiplying binomials: neglecting the "middle" terms. In future lessons, students will have many more opportunities to explore this misconception, but it helps to point this out now as well. You might also want to refer students to Problem 3b, for which even more students tend to forget to find the middle term.

As an extension, ask students if they can think of any pair of binomials that multiply to produce $n^2 + 15$. There are none (using only real numbers, that is). They will probably experiment with different rectangle diagrams to try this. You may want to press them to reason why it's not possible: in each expanded form of $(an + b)(cn + d)$, there is a linear, or middle, term. They may think about using subtraction with one of the binomials; if so, let them know that they will work with subtraction in the next investigation.

Troubleshooting Students will get lots more practice doing these types of problems in the next investigation. It is fine to go on from here even if they haven't mastered the rectangle model.

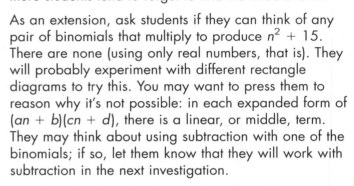

On Your Own Exercises

Practice & Apply: 1–6, p. 384
Connect & Extend: 34, 35, p. 386
Mixed Review: 51–63, pp. 388–389

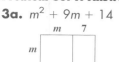

3. For Parts a–c, do the following:

- Draw a rectangle diagram to model the product.
- Use your diagram to help expand the expression.

  a. $(m + 7)(m + 2)$

  b. $(w + 2)^2$

  c. $(2n + 3)(n + 1)$

4. A certain rectangle has area $y^2 + 6y + 3y + 18$.

  a. Draw a rectangle diagram that models this expression.

  b. Use your diagram to help you rewrite the area expression as a product of two binomials. $(y + 6)(y + 3)$

5. Challenge Another rectangle has area $y^2 + 5y + 6$.

  a. Draw a rectangle diagram that models this expression.

  b. Use your diagram to help you rewrite the area expression as a product of two binomials. $(y + 2)(y + 3)$

Share & Summarize

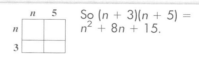

So $(n + 3)(n + 5) = n^2 + 8n + 15$.

Ben thinks that $(n + 3)(n + 5) = n^2 + 15$. Show him why he is incorrect. Include a rectangle diagram that models the correct expansion of $(n + 3)(n + 5)$.

Just the facts

At right is a geometric model of carbon-60. This molecule is composed of 60 interlinked carbon atoms arranged in 12 pentagons and 20 hexagons. Because of its structural similarity to the geodesic dome, designed by U.S. architect R. Buckminster Fuller, it was named buckminsterfullerene.

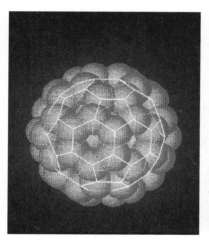

1 It may be helpful to point out that the 6 and 3 give clues to the rectangle's dimensions.

2 Let students struggle a little with Problem 5.

3 Refer students to Problem 3b as well.

LESSON 6.2 Expanding Products of Binomials **375**

Investigation 2

In this investigation, students look at the multiplication of two binomials using the distributive property. In explaining how the distributive property applies, it is important that students see the geometric connection at each step.

 Introduce the investigation by reviewing the steps given in the text for how the expression $m(m + 3)$ can be expanded using both the distributive property and a rectangle diagram.

 Continue with expanding $(m + 2)(m + 3)$ by explaining that students can think about multiplying $m + 2$ by each term in the expression $m + 3$:

$$(m + 2)(m + 3) = m(m + 2) + 3(m + 2)$$

Again, the text illustrates this step.

 Ask students to complete the problem by using the distributive property to simplify each term.

Investigation 2 Multiplying Binomials That Involve Addition

Rectangle models can help you understand how the distributive property works. For example, the expression $m(m + 3)$ is expanded below with the distributive property and a rectangle diagram.

$$m(m + 3) = m \cdot m + m \cdot 3$$
$$= m^2 + 3m$$

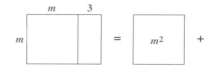

1 Review expanding $m(m + 3)$ using both methods.

You can also use the distributive property and rectangle diagrams to expand such expressions as $(m + 2)(m + 3)$. Just think of $m + 2$ in the same way you thought about the first variable m in the expression $m(m + 3)$ above. That is, multiply $m + 2$ by each term in $m + 3$:

$$(m + 2)(m + 3) = (m + 2) \cdot m + (m + 2) \cdot 3$$
$$= m(m + 2) + 3(m + 2)$$

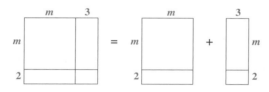

2 Demonstrate using the distributive property once with binomials, and show how the model illustrates this also.

The distributive property can then be used to simplify each term. Start by simplifying the first term, $m(m + 2)$:

$$m(m + 2) = m \cdot m + m \cdot 2$$
$$= m^2 + 2m$$

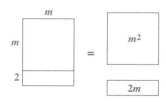

3 Ask students to complete the rest using the distributive property on each term.

After students have completed the expansion, you can show them how each term is connected to a rectangle drawing, as illustrated on page 377.

You might want to ask students what happens if you multiply $m + 3$ by each term in $m + 2$, that is, $m(m + 3) + 2(m + 3)$. Ask them to draw the rectangle diagrams that go with each step. The class can discuss why the answers are the same in both cases.

 Problem Set B Suggested Grouping: Individuals
In this problem set, students are asked to expand an expression using the distributive property and then to draw a rectangle diagram to model the expression. You may want to explain to students that it is helpful to label each part of their diagrams with its area, as was done in the diagram just before the problem set, so that they can see how the separate pieces correspond to the terms in the algebraic expansion.

Problem Set Wrap-Up Problem 2 is a good example to review with the class since it represents squaring a binomial, a process that often causes difficulty for students. In fact, a common error made by students when expanding the product of any two binomials is to forget that there are middle terms. The rectangle diagrams, while they may be cumbersome for students to do, are useful in reinforcing the existence of these terms.

And then simplify the second term, $3(m + 2)$:

$$3(m + 2) = 3 \cdot m + 3 \cdot 2$$
$$= 3m + 6$$

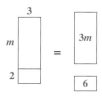

Finally, put everything together and combine like terms:

$$(m + 2)(m + 3) = m(m + 2) + 3(m + 2)$$
$$= m^2 + 2m + 3m + 6$$
$$= m^2 + 5m + 6$$

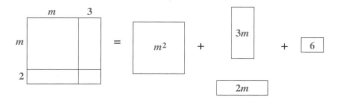

Problem Set B

For each problem, do the following:

- Expand the expression using the distributive property.
- Draw a rectangle diagram to model the expression, and check your expansion.

1. $(x + 3)(x + 4)$

2. $(k + 5)^2$

3. $(x + a)(x + b)$ $x^2 + ax + bx + ab$ or $x^2 + (a + b)x + ab$

	x	b
x	x^2	bx
a	ax	ab

1 Show students how each term is connected to the rectangle drawing.

2 You may have students work on their own.

3 Suggest that students label the parts of the drawings with their areas.

4 Problem 2 makes a good wrap-up example.

1. $x^2 + 7x + 12$

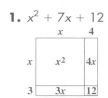

	x	4
x	x^2	$4x$
3	$3x$	12

2. $k^2 + 10k + 25$

	k	5
k	k^2	$5k$
5	$5k$	25

1 **Problem Set C** **Suggested Grouping: Pairs**
In this problem set, students gain some practice in multiplying binomials through a different context, one of completing a table given a complicated equation of y in terms of x. Students may be surprised to see that the y value is always 0 regardless of what they choose for x. Their surprise should motivate them to want to figure out why this is happening, as requested in Problem 3.

2 In **Problem 3,** students will have to multiply not just two binomials, but two binomials and a constant: $-3(x + 1)(x + 2)$. You may want to make sure the students in each pair are watching and helping each other in doing this problem.

On the Spot Assessment

In Problem 3, watch for students who are still having difficulty with subtraction in applying the distributive property. You may want to have students rewrite $x(x + 1) - 3(x + 1)(x + 2) \ldots$ as $x(x + 1) + -3(x + 1)(x + 2) \ldots$ so that they can think about distributing -3. This kind of problem is worth spending time on, since this issue arises often.

Share & Summarize

3 This question allows students to generalize the work they have done previously by expanding $(a + b)(c + d)$. Again, when students draw their rectangle diagrams, have them label the areas of each of the smaller rectangles so that they can match the terms $ac, bc, ad,$ and bd with the individual pieces.

Troubleshooting If students are having difficulty applying the distributive property in expanding the product of two binomials, you may want to use algebra tiles (if you haven't already), or have students create rectangles and cut them into smaller ones, to give them an even more concrete model to work with. If students are having trouble creating diagrams with the proper dimensions, you may need to point out that each term, such as d or 3 in $d + 3$, needs to be represented separately. When students do use diagrams, be sure they label each rectangle with its area. You may want to offer them the following examples for extra practice.

Additional Examples Expand each expression.

1. $(m + 6)(m + 3)$ $m^2 + 9m + 18$
2. $(z + 10)^2$ $z^2 + 20z + 100$
3. $(3x + 2)(4x + 1)$ $12x^2 + 11x + 2$
4. $(n + 5)(4n + 2)$ $4n^2 + 22n + 10$
5. $(2s + 7)^2$ $4s^2 + 28s + 49$

On Your Own Exercises

Practice & Apply: 7–10, pp. 384–385
Connect & Extend: 36–41, pp. 386–387
Mixed Review: 51–63, pp. 388–389

Investigation 3

Students continue their work with the distributive property and rectangle diagrams in this investigation, but here they see cases in which the multiplication of binomials involves subtraction. The rectangle diagrams are a bit more difficult to use in this context, and students will have to be careful to shade areas that are taken away, or subtracted. The last problem set involves number patterns in binomials that express consecutive integers. For students who moved quickly through Investigation 2, you may want to spend less time on Problem Set D and more on Problem Sets E and F.

Example

4 It is a good idea to ask students how they might represent $(d - 1)(d + 3)$ as a diagram before you have them consider the one in the text. Then go through the Example with the class.

Problem Set C

Problem Set C Answer

2. y is always 0.

Share & Summarize Answer

$ac + ad + bc + bd$;
Possible explanation:
The dimensions are
$a + b$ and $c + d$.
The areas of the
four rectangles are
ac, bc, ad, and bd.
Adding these gives
$ac + ad + bc + bd$.

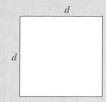

1. Complete the table by substituting values for x into this equation.

$$y = x(x + 1) - 3(x + 1)(x + 2) + 3(x + 2)(x + 3) - (x + 3)(x + 4)$$

x	0	1	2	3	4	5
y	0	0	0	0	0	0

2. Make a conjecture about the value of y for other values of x. Test your conjecture by trying more numbers, including some decimals and negative numbers. Revise your conjecture if necessary.

3. Prove It! Use your knowledge of expanding binomial products to show that your conjecture is true.
Expand the right-hand side of the equation:
$x^2 + x - 3x^2 - 9x - 6 + 3x^2 + 15x + 18 - x^2 - 7x - 12$;
simplifying by combining like terms gives 0.

Share & Summarize

Use the distributive property to expand $(a + b)(c + d)$. Draw a rectangle diagram, and explain how it shows your expansion is correct.

Investigation 3 ▶ Multiplying Binomials That Involve Subtraction

You have used rectangle models to think about multiplying binomials involving addition—expressions of the form $(a + b)(c + d)$. Now you will learn to expand products of binomials that involve subtraction.

EXAMPLE

Here's one way to create a rectangle diagram to represent $(d - 1)(d + 3)$.

First draw a square with side length d.

Then subtract a 1-cm strip from one side, and add a 3-cm strip to the adjacent side.

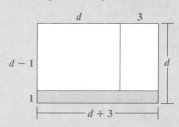

The unshaded rectangle that remains has an area of $(d - 1)(d + 3)$.

Develop

Think & Discuss

Make sure students can expand the expression $(d-1)(d+3)$ using both the distributive property and the rectangle diagram. Using the diagram, they should see that the left piece has area $d(d-1)$, or $d^2 - d$; and the right piece has area $3(d-1)$, or $3d - 3$; so the total area is $d^2 - d + 3d - 3$, or $d^2 + 2d - 3$.

Problem Set D Suggested Grouping: Pairs

In this problem set, students are asked to expand binomial products, first using the distributive property and then by drawing the rectangle diagram that represents the expression.

Problems 1 and 2 are very similar to the Example on page 378 and should not be difficult for students.

Problem 3 has a slight twist: the variable is the second term in each binomial. You may need to help students draw their diagrams.

Problem Set Wrap-Up Problem 4 is a good one to go over with the class, since the unsimplified form of the expression gives clues about what the diagram should look like: $+ 5y - 2y$ indicates that a strip of 5 should be added onto the square and a strip of 2 should be subtracted.

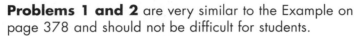

Problem Set E Suggested Grouping: Pairs

Here students use the distributive property to multiply two binomials, both involving subtraction. Rectangle models are more complicated than helpful in such situations. In fact, this is a good example of when to drop the use of a manipulative or concrete model: when the model loses its ability to enhance the concept being taught, or when the model itself takes on a life of its own due to its complexity.

For students who enjoy challenges, however, you might ask them how a rectangle diagram can be drawn to illustrate this kind of product. They will have to recognize that they will be removing one area (typically the lower-right corner) twice, so they have to add it back in once.

On the Spot Assessment

In **Problem 2,** watch for students who answer $R^2 - 4$ or $R^2 + 4$. Some may need to rewrite the problem as $(R - 2)(R - 2)$ to see what is happening. In all of these problems, students will have to rely on their knowledge of multiplication of signed numbers, and you may need to review the rules with them.

Think & Discuss See Additional Answers.

Expand the expression $(d - 1)(d + 3)$ using either the distributive property or the diagram in the Example on page 378. Describe how you found the answer.

Problem Set D Answers

1. $b^2 + b - 6$

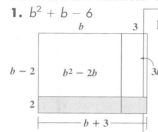

2. $a^2 - 3a - 4$

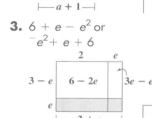

3. $6 + e - e^2$ or $^-e^2 + e + 6$

4a.

```
        y      5
 y - 2 ┌──────┬───┐
       │      │   │
     2 ├──────┴───┤
       └─ y + 5 ──┘
```

4b. $(y + 5)(y - 2)$

Problem Set D

For each expression below, do the following:

- Expand the expression using the distributive property.
- Draw a rectangle diagram that represents the expression. Use shading to indicate areas that are being removed.
- Use your diagram to check that your expansion is correct.

1. $(b - 2)(b + 3)$

2. $(a + 1)(a - 4)$

3. $(2 + e)(3 - e)$

4. A certain rectangle has area $y^2 + 5y - 2y - 10$.

   a. Draw a rectangle diagram to represent this expression.

   b. Write the area of this rectangle as a product of two binomials.

You will now use the distributive property to expand products of two binomials that both involve subtraction.

Problem Set E

Expand each expression using the distributive property, and then combine like terms. Your final answer should have no parentheses and no like terms.

1. $(x - 4)(x - 5)$ $x^2 - 9x + 20$

2. $(R - 2)^2$ $R^2 - 4R + 4$

3. $(2 - f)(3 - f)$ $6 - 5f + f^2$ or $f^2 - 5f + 6$

4. $(a - 2b)(3a - b)$ $3a^2 - 7ab + 2b^2$

1 Make sure students can expand using both methods.

2 You may have students work in pairs.

3 You may need to help students in Problem 3.

4 Discuss Problem 4 with the class.

5 You may have students work in pairs.

6 Watch for students who answer $R^2 + 4$ or $R^2 - 4$ for Problem 2.

Additional Answers
Think & Discuss

$d^2 + 2d - 3$; Possible explanations: Distribute $d - 1$ to the d and then to the 3, giving $d(d - 1) + 3(d - 1)$; then use the distributive property twice more to get $d^2 - d + 3d - 3$, or $d^2 + 2d - 3$. Or, using the diagram, the left part of the remaining rectangle has area $d^2 - d$, and the right side has area $3d - 3$, giving a total area of $d^2 - d + 3d - 3$, or $d^2 + 2d - 3$.

Problem Set F Suggested Grouping: Pairs

In this problem set, students will use their newly formed skills for multiplying binomials to prove some conjectures about number patterns involving consecutive numbers. You may need to review the meaning of *counterexample*, as well as how to prove that a statement is true—in particular, that it isn't enough to show the statement is true for several specific examples.

It is important that students be able to represent algebraically any group of consecutive integers (x, $x + 1$, $x + 2$, and so on), as well as consecutive even ($2x$, $2x + 2$) and odd ($2x + 1$, $2x + 3$) integers. There is a hint about this in Problem 1, but you may want to go over these representations before students begin the problem set.

The wording in **Problem 1** may be confusing for students, since it requires several steps and algebraic representations. Remind students to refer to the numerical example in the problem if they are having difficulty getting started. Make sure they have represented the four consecutive numbers as x, $x + 1$, $x + 2$, and $x + 3$ before they begin to multiply them.

In **Problem 3c,** students have to construct a rectangle diagram that represents $4x^2 + 4x + 1$. You might suggest that if the conjecture is true, they have to find a square with appropriate dimensions: a square with area $4x^2$ must have side length $2x$. They can figure out the remaining part of the expression from there.

Share & Summarize

The question posed here illustrates the general form of multiplying two binomials, one involving subtraction and one involving addition. You may want to have students label the parts of the diagram with their areas.

Troubleshooting If students are having difficulty, provide other examples for them. If necessary, give them paper and scissors to cut out the pieces of the rectangles to form the different diagrams. In the next investigation, they will learn some shortcuts for expanding binomials and try to explain why the shortcuts work, so they will have another opportunity to practice these skills.

Additional Examples Expand each expression.

1. $(x + 4)(x + 4)$ $x^2 + 8x + 16$
2. $(1 - 2f)(3 - 3f)$ $3 - 9f + 6f^2$
3. $(2x + 1)(x - 1)$ $2x^2 - x - 1$

On Your Own Exercises

Practice & Apply: 11–23, p. 385
Connect & Extend: 42–46, p. 387
Mixed Review: 51–63, pp. 388–389

★ indicates multi-step problem

2. The trick doesn't work. Possible counterexample: 1, 2 and 3, with a product of 6

Remember

A *counterexample* is an example for which a conjecture does not work.

3b. $2x(2x + 2) + 1 = 4x^2 + 4x + 1$

3c.

You will now apply what you have learned about expanding products of binomials to analyze some number tricks.

Problem Set F

Lydia thinks she's found some number tricks.

Prove It! In Problems 1 and 2, determine whether Lydia's trick really works. If it does, prove it. If not, give a counterexample.

★ **1.** Lydia said, "Take any four consecutive integers. Multiply the least number and the greatest number, and then multiply the remaining two numbers. If you subtract the first product from the second, you will always get 2.   **1.** See Additional Answers.

For example, for the integers 3, 4, 5, and 6, the product of the least and greatest numbers, 3 and 6, is 18. The product of the remaining two numbers, 4 and 5, is 20. The difference between these products is 2." (Hint: If the least integer is x, what are the other three?)

★ **2.** Lydia said, "Take any three consecutive integers and multiply them. Their product is divisible by 4. For example, the product of 4, 5, and 6 is 120, which is divisible by 4."

3. Here's another number trick Lydia proposed: "Take any two consecutive even integers, multiply them, and add 1. The result is always a perfect square. For example, 4 and 6 multiply to give 24; add 1 to get 25, which is a perfect square."

   a. Since the numbers are both even, they have 2 as a factor. Suppose the lesser number is $2x$. What is the greater number? $2x + 2$

   b. Using $2x$ and the expression you wrote for Part a, find the resulting expression, which Lydia claims is always a perfect square.

   c. Assume the result in Part b is a perfect square. Try to draw a rectangle diagram showing the binomial that can be squared to get that product.

   d. What binomial is being squared in Part c? $2x + 1$

   e. Have you proved that Lydia's trick always works? Explain.
   Yes; since $(2x + 1)^2$ is equivalent to $2x(2x + 2) + 1$, which represents Lydia's number trick and is a perfect square, the trick works.

Share & Summarize

Use the distributive property to expand $(a - b)(c + d)$. Then draw a rectangle diagram to show why your expansion is correct.

$$ac + ad - bc - bd$$

1 You may have students work in pairs.

2 Problem-Solving Strategy

Use logical reasoning

3 You might suggest that a square with area $4x^2$ would require side length $2x$.

4 You may have students label the diagram's parts with their areas.

Additional Answers
Problem Set F

1. The trick works. Let the integers be x, $x + 1$, $x + 2$, $x + 3$. Product of least and greatest: $x(x + 3) = x^2 + 3x$. Product of other numbers: $(x + 1)(x + 2) = x^2 + 3x + 2$. Difference: $(x^2 + 3x + 2) - (x^2 + 3x) = 2$.

Investigation 4

In this investigation, students look at patterns in the computation of binomial products. The goal here is to have students compute these products efficiently and accurately and develop quick ways of combining like middle terms. Although the FOIL (First-Outer-Inner-Last) method is not named, you may want to refer to this mnemonic device as students begin to develop some facility with the process.

1 Begin the investigation by having students read the cartoon. Students should notice that Mikayla's method is the same as the method they used in the previous investigation, where they used the distributive property to expand binomial products.

2 **Problem Set G** Suggested Grouping:
Pairs or Individuals

In this problem set, students are asked to use Mikayla's method to expand binomial products. These should not take students long to do, since they are using essentially the same method they have used previously.

3 You may want to draw attention to **Problem 5,** in which the n terms drop out. This will be an important observation later when students begin to look at factoring the difference of two squares.

4 **Think & Discuss**

Students should be able to see the connection between Mikayla's method and the use of the distributive property: multiplying the first term of the first binomial by each of the terms in the second binomial, and then doing the same with the second term of the first binomial.

Investigation ▶4 Shortcuts for Multiplying Binomials

You have been using the distributive property and rectangle diagrams to think about how to multiply two binomials. Have you noticed any patterns in your computations? In this investigation, you will look at patterns that can help you multiply binomials quickly and efficiently.

Here's how Mikayla multiplied $(2x + 7)(x - 3)$.

1 Have students read the cartoon.

Problem Set G

2 You may have students work in pairs or on their own.

Use Mikayla's method to multiply each pair of binomials.

1. $(y + 6)(y - 3)$ $y^2 - 3y + 6y - 18 = y^2 + 3y - 18$

2. $(p + 4)(p + 3)$ $p^2 + 3p + 4p + 12 = p^2 + 7p + 12$

3. $(t - 11)(t - 3)$ $t^2 - 3t - 11t + 33 = t^2 - 14t + 33$

4. $(2x + 1)(3x + 2)$ $6x^2 + 4x + 3x + 2 = 6x^2 + 7x + 2$

5. $(2n + 3)(2n - 3)$ $4n^2 - 6n + 6n - 9 = 4n^2 - 9$

3 Draw attention to Problem 5.

Think & Discuss

Why does Mikayla's method work?
Possible answer: When you use the distributive property, you can distribute the first binomial to both terms of the second binomial. But then you have to distribute the single terms to the two terms of the first binomial, so each term in one binomial multiplies each term in the other. Mikayla's doing just that: multiplying the first term of the first binomial by each term in the second binomial and then doing the same with the second term of the first binomial.

4 Discuss Mikayla's method with the class.

LESSON 6.2 Expanding Products of Binomials **381**

1 After students answer the Think & Discuss on page 381, let them read the second cartoon, which introduces Tamika's method. Tamika's method is most like FOIL, in that she multiplies the *first* terms, then the *last* terms, and then looks at the *inner* and *outer* products as a duo so that she can combine them as like terms. In FOIL, this combination takes place in the middle rather than at the end.

2 **Problem Set H** **Suggested Grouping: Pairs**
This problem set is an opportunity for students to use Tamika's method to find binomial products. You might want to ask students if they think Tamika's method is quicker than previous methods they have used. It is important for students to understand that in these problems, the outer and inner products are the ones that can be combined as like terms.

While students should try combining like terms in their heads for this problem set, this may be more than some students can handle. If so, suggest they continue to write the two products, perhaps to the side or on scrap paper, and then combine them.

Tips from Teachers

"There is an additional method that works well for students who have difficulty with all the arrows in the cartoon and also extends to more difficult expressions. Set up the problem like two-digit multiplication, lining up terms that are alike:

$$
\begin{array}{r}
2x + 3 \\
\times\ 3x - 2 \\
\hline
-4x - 6 \\
6x^2 + 9x \\
\hline
6x^2 + 5x - 6
\end{array}
$$

Students are familiar with this model. Stress lining up like terms before adding."

---

3 **Think & Discuss**
Students should have little difficulty seeing that Tamika's method is basically the same as Mikayla's method. The only difference is that Tamika is doing the individual products in a different order and combining like terms in her head.

Here's how Tamika approaches these problems.

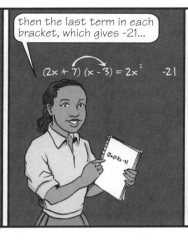

1 Have students read the cartoon.

Problem Set H

Use Tamika's method to multiply each pair of binomials.

1. $(y + 7)(y - 4)$ $y^2 + 3y - 28$

2. $(p + 1)(p - 5)$ $p^2 - 4p - 5$

3. $(t - 4)(t - 4)$ $t^2 - 8t + 16$

4. $(2x - 1)(x - 2)$ $2x^2 - 5x + 2$

5. $(3n + 2)(2n - 3)$ $6n^2 - 5n - 6$

2 • You may have students work in pairs.

• If necessary, suggest some students write the x-terms, or linear terms, on scrap paper or to the side before combining them.

Think & Discuss

Why does Tamika's method work?

Possible answer: Tamika is doing the same thing Mikayla did, just in a different order so she can add the like terms in her head.

3 Discuss Tamika's method with the class.

In the next problem set, you will apply what you have learned about expanding binomials.

Problem Set 1 Suggested Grouping: Pairs or Small Groups

In the first five problems of this problem set, students look at a version of "always, sometimes, never" questions. This kind of thinking is sophisticated, and it may be a good idea to go over **Problem 1** as a class so that students understand what is being asked. Note that just because the two expressions on either side of the equal sign are not equivalent does *not* mean the equation can't be true for *some* value of x.

Problems 2 and 3 are examples of *identities*, equations that are true for all values of the variable. Although it is not used in the text, you may want to introduce this term.

Problem 5 may be difficult for some students. Expanding the left side gives $x^2 - 9 = x^2 - 6x - 9$.

Problem-Solving Strategies ▷ Students may think about this in different ways.

- Some students may reason that the two sides of the equation are equal except for the $6x$ term on the right. Therefore, $6x$ must be 0, and thus x must be 0.

- Some students may first subtract x^2 from both sides and then add 9 to both sides. This leaves the equation $0 = {}^-6x$, and therefore $x = 0$.

Problem 6 should spark students' curiosity. Calendar patterns are fun to discover, and the examples here are just the beginning. In each problem, it is important that students find general ways of representing the different "cells" of the calendar. For example, if x is the number in any cell, the number below it is $x + 7$, and the number above it is $x - 7$. The numbers immediately to the right and left are $x + 1$ and $x - 1$, respectively. The number diagonally below to the right is $x + 8$, and that diagonally below to the left is $x + 6$.

In **Problem 6b,** students need only to find a counterexample.

In **Problem 6c,** you may want to review with students how to prove a number is always even by showing that 2 must be a factor. An alternate strategy students might use is to consider that each row contains an even and an odd number, so the product is always even for each row. The difference of two even numbers is always even.

Access for all Learners

Extra Challenge There are problems like the following in the Connect & Extend exercises for this investigation, but you may want to give advanced students this one in class:

What do you think the product of this binomial and trinomial is?

$$(x + 4)(x^2 - 5x + 1)$$

$$x^3 - x^2 - 19x + 4$$

Share & Summarize

This question reviews students' approaches to expanding binomial products. Don't expect all students to choose one method over any other. Some students prefer doing work in their heads while others prefer writing out every step. The important thing is that they understand at least one method, and that they take the time to consider the advantages their method has over others.

Troubleshooting If students are having difficulty expanding binomial products using shortcut methods, you may want to go back to the rectangle diagrams or use algebra tiles to explain the steps of the process.

On Your Own Exercises

Practice & Apply: 24–33, p. 386
Connect & Extend: 47–50, p. 388
Mixed Review: 51–63, p. 388–389

	JULY					
			1	2	3	
4	5	6	7	8	9	10
11	12	13	14	15	16	17
18	19	20	21	22	23	24
25	26	27	28	29	30	31

Problem Set I

For each equation, do Parts a and b.

a. Decide whether the equation is true for all values of x, for some but not all values of x, or for no values of x.

b. Explain how you know your answer is correct. If the equation is true for some but not all values of x, indicate which values make it true.

1. $(x - 2)(x - 3) = 0$

2. $(x + 3)(x + 2) = x^2 + 5x + 6$

3. $(x - b)^2 = x^2 - 2xb + b^2$

4. $(x + 3)(x - 1) = x^2 + 2x + 3$

5. $(x - 3)(x + 3) = x^2 - 6x - 9$

6. Brian thinks he has found some number patterns on a calendar. He says his patterns work for any 2-by-2 square on a calendar, such as the three shown here. Decide whether each of his patterns works, and justify your answers. See Additional Answers.

a. Find the product of each diagonal. Their positive difference is always 7. For example, for the square containing 2, 3, 9, and 10, the products of the diagonals are $2 \cdot 10 = 20$ and $3 \cdot 19 = 27$. Their difference is $27 - 20 = 7$.

b. Find the product of each column. Their positive difference is always 12. For example, for the square containing 2, 3, 9, and 10, the products of the columns are $2 \cdot 9 = 18$ and $3 \cdot 10 = 30$. Their difference is $30 - 18 = 12$.

c. Find the product of each row. Their difference is always even. For example, for the square containing 2, 3, 9, and 10, the products of the rows are $2 \cdot 3 = 6$ and $9 \cdot 10 = 90$. Their difference is $90 - 6 = 84$, which is even.

> **1** You may have students work in pairs or small groups.
>
> **2** You may want to go over Problem 1 as a class.
>
> **3** You may want to review how to prove an expression is even.
>
> **4** Don't expect all students to agree on one method over the others.

Share & Summarize

You have seen several methods for expanding the product of two binomials.

1. Choose the method you like best, and explain how to use it to expand $(2x + 3)(x - 1)$.

2. Why do you like your chosen method?   Possible answer: I don't have to write as much.

Additional Answers
Problem Set I

6a. This pattern works. Possible explanation: If x is the first number in the square, $x + 1$ is the second and $x + 7$ and $x + 8$ are the others. The products of the diagonals are $x(x + 8) = x^2 + 8x$ and $(x + 1)(x + 7) = x^2 + 8x + 7$. Their positive difference is 7.

6b. This pattern does not always work. Possible explanation: The square with 11, 12, 18, and 19 has products 198 and 228; their positive difference is 30.

6c. This pattern works. Possible explanation: The product of the top row is $x(x + 1) = x^2 + x$, and the product of the bottom row is $(x + 7)(x + 8) = x^2 + 15x + 56$. Their difference is $14x + 56$, or $2(7x + 28)$, which is always even since it has a factor of 2.

On Your Own Exercises

**On Your
Own
Exercises**

Investigation 1,
pp. 374–375
Practice & Apply: 1–6
Connect & Extend: 34, 35

Investigation 2
pp. 376–378
Practice & Apply: 7–10
Connect & Extend: 36–41

Investigation 3
pp. 378–380
Practice & Apply: 11–23
Connect & Extend: 42–46

Investigation 4
pp. 381–383
Practice & Apply: 24–33
Connect & Extend: 47–50

Assign Anytime
Mixed Review: 51–63

Exercise 6:
Students may find this exercise harder than the previous ones, since the $6y$ and y terms do not give straightforward clues about the lengths of the sides. Encourage them to experiment with different possibilities, especially those that focus on the $2y^2$ term, which may lead them to lengths of $2y$ and y.

Practice 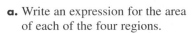 **Apply**

1a. a^2, $2a$, $10a$, 20

1b. $a^2 + 12a + 20$

2a. y^2, $9y$, $8y$, 72

2b. $y^2 + 17y + 72$

3. $6k^2 + 17k + 12$

5a.

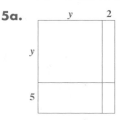

6a.

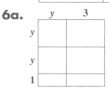

7a. $p^2 + 8p + 15$

7b.

1. This diagram shows a rectangle with area $(a + 10)(a + 2)$.

  a. Write an expression for the area of each of the four regions.

  b. Use your answer from Part a to expand the expression for the area of the large rectangle. That is, express the area without using parentheses. Simplify your answer by combining like terms.

2. This diagram shows a rectangle with area $(y + 9)(y + 8)$.

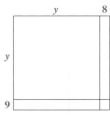

  a. Write an expression for the area of each of the four regions.

  b. Use your answer from Part a to expand the expression for the area of the large rectangle. That is, express the area without using parentheses. Simplify your answer by combining like terms.

Draw a rectangle diagram to model each product, and then use your diagram to expand the product. Simplify your answer by combining like terms.

3. $(3 + 2k)(4 + 3k)$

4. $(1 + 4x)(x + 2)$

4. $4x^2 + 9x + 2$

5. A certain rectangle has area $y^2 + 5y + 2y + 10$.

  a. Draw a rectangle diagram that models this expression.

  b. Use your diagram to help you rewrite the area expression as a product of two binomials. $(y + 2)(y + 5)$

6. A certain rectangle has area $2y^2 + 6y + y + 3$.

  a. Draw a rectangle diagram that models this expression.

  b. Use your diagram to help you rewrite the area expression as a product of two binomials. $(2y + 1)(y + 3)$

7. Consider the expression $(p + 3)(p + 5)$.

  a. Use the distributive property to expand the expression.

  b. Draw a rectangle diagram to model the expression, and check your expansion.

 impactmath.com/self_check_quiz

★ indicates multi-step problem

11. $(x + 3)(x - 3)$
$= x^2 - 3x + 3x - 9$
$= x^2 - 9$

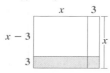

13a. $h^2 - 4$

13b.

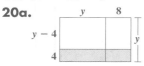

14. $x^2 - 9x + 14$

15. $g^2 - 7g + 12$

16. $2p^2 - 12p + 16$

17. $2w^2 - 11w - 6$

18. $-10q^2 - 8q + 2$

19. $3v^2 - 2v - 5$

20a.

21a.

Use the distributive property to expand each expression.

8. $(1 + 3a)(5 + 10a)$ $5 + 25a + 30a^2$ or $30a^2 + 25a + 5$

9. $3\left(2x + \frac{1}{3}\right)(x + 2) - (x + 3)(1 + x)$ $5x^2 + 9x - 1$

10. $\left(s + \frac{1}{4}\right)(3s + 1) - \left(\frac{1}{4} + s\right)(1 + s)$ $2s^2 + \frac{1}{2}s$

Draw a rectangle diagram to model each product. Then expand the product using your diagram. Simplify your answer by combining like terms.

11. $(x + 3)(x - 3)$ **12.** $(p - 4)(3p + 2)$ See Additional Answers.

13. Consider the expression $(h - 2)(h + 2)$.

   a. Use the distributive property to expand the expression.

   b. Draw a rectangle diagram to represent the expression. Shade areas that are being removed. Use your diagram to check that your expansion is correct.

Expand each expression using the distributive property.

14. $(x - 7)(x - 2)$ **15.** $(3 - g)(4 - g)$

16. $(4 - 2p)(4 - p)$ **17.** $(2w + 1)(w - 6)$

18. $(1 - 5q)(2 + 2q)$ **19.** $(3v - 5)(v + 1)$

20. A certain rectangle has area $y^2 - 4y + 8y - 32$.

   a. Draw a rectangle diagram to represent this expression.

   b. Use your diagram to help you rewrite the area expression as a product of two binomials. $(y + 8)(y - 4)$

21. Challenge A certain rectangle has area $2y^2 + 4y - 3y - 6$.

   a. Draw a rectangle diagram to represent this expression.

   b. Use your diagram to help you rewrite the area expression as a product of two binomials. $(2y - 3)(y + 2)$

Prove It! Determine whether each number trick below works. If it does, prove it. If not, give a counterexample.

★ **22.** Take any three consecutive integers. Multiply the least and the greatest. That product is equal to the square of the middle integer minus 1.   See Additional Answers.

★ **23.** Think of any two consecutive odd integers. Square both integers, and subtract the lesser result from the greater. The result is always evenly divisible by 6.
Doesn't work. Possible counterexample: 3 and 5 square to give 9 and 25, and $25 - 9 = 16$, which isn't divisible by 6.

LESSON 6.2 Expanding Products of Binomials   **385**

Exercise 9:
Encourage students to examine this exercise before they begin expanding the binomials. It is easier to distribute 3 through the first binomial, so that $\frac{1}{3}$ becomes 1 after multiplying by 3. This kind of "pre-analysis" is a great tool for students to learn in order to simplify their calculations.

Exercise 21:
This exercise is a preview of certain kinds of factoring problems in which the coefficient of the squared term is not 1. Here, the coefficient of y^2, which is 2, plays a role in the construction of the $4y$ term. This may be an important exercise to go over in class. Ask students to present their strategies; they may not have done this in the same way.

Exercise 23:
If the numbers are $2x + 1$ and $2x + 3$, the difference of their squares is $(2x + 3)^2 - (2x + 1)^2$, which expands to $4x^2 + 12x + 9 - 4x^2 - 4x - 1$, which simplifies to $8x + 8$. That means the result is divisible by 2, 4, and 8, but not necessarily by 6.

Additional Answers

12. $(p - 4)(3p + 2) = 3p^2 - 12p + 2p - 8 = 3p^2 - 10p - 8$

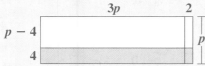

22. It works; $x(x + 2) = x^2 + 2x$ and $(x + 1)^2 - 1 = x^2 + 2x + 1 - 1$, and $x^2 + 2x + 1 - 1 = x^2 + 2x$.

Exercises 34 and 35:
Some students may need
some help thinking about
how the coordinates given
in the graph are indicators
of the length and width of
the two rectangles.

Exercises 36 and 37:
Although most students
should be able to complete
these exercises, they may
feel intimidated by having
two variables. Encourage
them to concentrate on
each step. When expand-
ing the binomials, they
may even find it helpful to
write each step in the
multiplication down before
trying to find the product,
for example,
$(1 + x^2)(x + y) = 1 \cdot x +$
$x^2 \cdot x + 1 \cdot y + x^2 \cdot y.$

---

25. $r^2 - 24r + 144$
26. $2x^2 - 2x - 4$
28. $25M^2 + 50M + 25$

JULY

				1	2	3
4	5	6	7	8	9	10
11	12	13	14	15	16	17
18	19	20	21	22	23	24
25	26	27	28	29	30	31

Connect &
Extend

33. Yes; if the first date
is x, the others are
x + 7 and x + 14.
$(x + 7)^2 - x(x + 14)$
$= x^2 + 14x + 49 -$
$x^2 - 14x = 49.$

34b. $(x + 2)(y + 2) - xy,$
$2x + 2y + 4$

37. $8x + 2y + 3x^2 +$
$x^2y + 2xy$

Expand each expression. Simplify your expansion if possible.

24. $(4x + 1)(4x - 1)$ $16x^2 - 1$ **25.** $(r - 12)(r - 12)$

26. $(2x + 2)(x - 2)$ **27.** $(4x + 1)^2$ $16x^2 + 8x + 1$

28. $(5M + 5)^2$ **29.** $(n + 1)^2 + (n - 1)^2$ $2n^2 + 2$

Decide whether each equation is true for all values of x, for some but not
all values of x, or for no values of x.

30. $(x + 3)(x - 4) = x^2 + 7x - 12$ for one value only $(x = 0)$

31. $(2x + 1)(x - 1) = 2x^2 - x - 1$ for all x

32. $(3x + 1)(3x - 1)x = 9x^3 - x - 1$ for no values of x

33. After working with the calendar problems in Problem Set I, Chapa
wrote one: "Choose a block of three dates in a column (so they're
all the same day of the week). Square the middle date, and subtract
the product of the first and the last dates. The result is always 49."

Does Chapa's number trick always work? If so, show why. If not,
give a counterexample.

34. Consider this graph.
   a. Write an expression for
   the area of the unshaded
   region. xy

   b. Write two expressions,
   one with and one
   without parentheses,
   for the area of the
   shaded region.

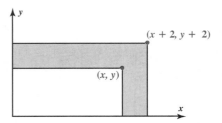

35. Write an expression for
the area of the shaded
region in this graph.
$(x + 5)(y + 4) - 8 =$
$xy + 4x + 5y + 12$

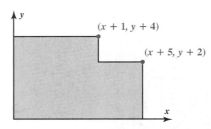

Expand each expression. Simplify your results by combining like terms.

36. $(1 + x^2)(x + y) + (1 + y)(x + y) - x^2(x + y) - xy$ $2x + 2y + y^2$

37. $2(x + y) + x(3 + y)(x + 2)$

386 CHAPTER 6 Working with Expressions

A *trinomial* is an expression with three unlike terms. Expand the follow-ing products of a trinomial and a binomial. You may find it helpful to use a rectangle diagram.

38. $(x + y + 1)(x + 1)$ $x^2 + 2x + xy + y + 1$

39. $(a + b + 1)(a + 2)$ $a^2 + 3a + ab + 2b + 2$

40. $(x + y + 2)(x + 1)$ $x^2 + 3x + xy + y + 2$

41. Consider the product $(2x + y)(x + 2y)$.

   a. Expand the expression using the distributive property.

   b. Draw a rectangle diagram that represents the expression. Use your diagram to check that your expansion is correct.

41a. $2x^2 + 5xy + 2y^2$

41b.
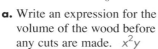

42. This block of wood has length y and a square base with sides of length x. A woodworker will cut the block of wood twice, taking off two strips from adjacent sides. Each cut removes $1\frac{1}{8}$ inches.

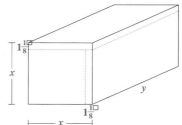

   a. Write an expression for the volume of the wood before any cuts are made. x^2y

   b. Write an expression without parentheses for the volume of the wood after the cuts are made.
$(x - 1\frac{1}{8})(x - 1\frac{1}{8}) \cdot y = x^2y - \frac{9}{4}xy + \frac{81}{64}y$

43b.

43. Consider the product $(2a + 3)(3a - 4)$.

   a. Expand and then simplify the expression. $6a^2 + a - 12$

   b. Draw a rectangle diagram to represent the expression. Use your diagram to check that your expansion is correct.

Expand the following products of a trinomial and a binomial.

44. $(x + y + 1)(x - 1)$ $x^2 + xy - y - 1$

45. $(x - y - 1)(x + 1)$ $x^2 - xy - y - 1$

46. $(x + y - 2)(x - 1)$ $x^2 - 3x + xy - y + 2$

Exercises 38–40:
You may want to tell students that it might be helpful to think about the distributive property in approaching these prob-lems. They can distribute each term of the binomial through each term of the trinomial and then combine like terms.

Exercises 44–46:
See the note above for Exercises 38–40.

Quick Quiz

1. The diagram below shows a rectangle with area $(r + 2)(r + 5)$.

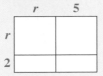

      r 5

r

2

a. Write an expression for the area of each of the four regions.
r^2, $5r$, $2r$, 10

b. Use your answer to Part a to expand the expression for the area of the large rectangle without using parentheses. Simplify your answer by combining like terms.
$r^2 + 5r + 2r + 10 = r^2 + 7r + 10$

47e. Possible answer: Square the first term, add the square of the second term, and subtract twice the product of the two terms.

48b.

54.

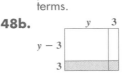

Mixed Review

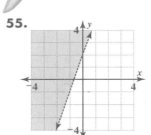

55.

---

47. Preview Expand and simplify the expressions in Parts a–d.

  a. $(x - 3)^2$ $x^2 - 6x + 9$ **b.** $(x - 4)^2$ $x^2 - 8x + 16$

  c. $(x - 5)^2$ $x^2 - 10x + 25$ **d.** $(x - a)^2$ $x^2 - 2ax + a^2$

  e. Look for a pattern relating the factored and expanded forms of the expressions in Parts a–c. Describe a shortcut for expanding the square of a binomial difference.

48. Consider the expression $y^2 - 9$. $(y + 3)(y - 3)$

  a. Write the expression as the product of two binomials.

  b. Create a diagram to illustrate $y^2 - 9$ as a rectangular area.

Expand and then simplify each expression.

49. $(n + 2)^2 - n(n + 4)$ $n^2 + 4n + 4 - n^2 - 4n = 4$

50. $(n + p)^2 - n(n + 2p)$ $n^2 + 2pn + p^2 - n^2 - 2pn = p^2$

Solve each equation.

                                                                                      1.05

51. $\frac{2x}{3} - 7 = 3$ 15 **52.** $3K + \frac{4}{5} = \frac{1}{5}$ $-\frac{1}{5}$ **53.** $3.2 - 2b = 1.1$

54. Copy this figure and vector. Translate the figure using the vector.

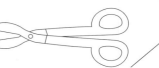

55. Graph the inequality $y > 3x + 2$.

56. Suppose r is a number between $^-1$ and 0. Order these numbers from least to greatest. r^{-3}, r, r^3, r^2

           r r^{-3} r^2 r^3

Tell whether the pattern in each table can best be described by a *linear*, *quadratic*, *exponential*, or *reciprocal* relationship.

57.

x	y
$^-2$	6
$^-1$	1
0	$^-2$
1	$^-3$
2	$^-2$

quadratic

58.

a	b
$^-3$	$^-4$
$^-1$	$^-12$
1	12
3	4
5	2.4

reciprocal

59.

s	n
$^-2$	$0.\bar{1}$
$^-1$	$0.\bar{3}$
0	1
1	3
2	9

exponential

388 CHAPTER 6   Working with Expressions

• **continued on next page**

Solve each proportion.

60. $\frac{8}{3} = \frac{x}{9}$ 24   **61.** $\frac{18}{y} = \frac{4}{10}$ 45   **62.** $\frac{9.2}{3.6} = \frac{2.3}{w}$ 0.9

63. Economics When students first begin attending a college or university, they often receive applications for credit cards. Some students use credit cards to furnish or decorate their dormitory rooms or apartments, and quickly go into debt. Unfortunately, credit cards often have very high interest rates.

Suppose Jay charges $2,000 for electronic equipment and books using a credit card that has an interest rate of 18% per year, which is 1.5% per month.

a. If Jay doesn't pay any of the $2,000, how much interest will be added at the end of the month? $30

★ **b.** Jay figures he can afford to pay $100 per month on his bill. Assume he follows through with this plan and makes no more charges. (That may be a big assumption!) Copy and complete the table to show how much he still owes after 6 months. The interest added each month is based on the unpaid portion of the previous month's bill.

Month	Balance	Interest Added	Amount Paid	New Balance
1	$2,000.00	—	$100.00	$1,900.00
2	1,900.00	$28.50	100.00	1,828.50
3	1,828.50	27.43	100.00	1,755.93
4	1,755.93	26.34	100.00	1,682.27
5	1,682.27	25.23	100.00	1,607.50
6	1,607.50	24.11	100.00	1,531.61

c. How much money has Jay paid to his credit card company? $600

d. By how much has Jay's original $2,000 debt decreased? $468.39

e. How much money has Jay paid in interest? $131.61

---

2. Consider the expression $(x - 2)(x + 7)$.

   a. Draw a rectangle diagram to model this product.

   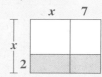

   b. Expand the product using your diagram or the distributive property.
   $x^2 + 5x - 14$

3. A certain rectangle has area $a^2 - 6a + 3a - 18$.

   a. Draw a rectangle diagram to represent this expression.

   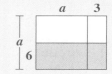

   b. Use your diagram to rewrite the area as a product of two binomials.
   $(a + 3)(a - 6)$

4. For what values of x is the following equation true? *none*

$(x - 6)^2 = x^2 - 12x - 36$

Teacher Notes

6.3

Patterns in Products of Binomials

Objectives

▶ To understand the pattern and apply a shortcut to square binomials of the forms $(a + b)^2$ and $(a - b)^2$

▶ To understand the pattern and apply a shortcut to expand binomials of the form $(x + a)(x - a)$

Overview (pacing: about 3 class periods)

This lesson introduces students to two common forms of binomials that deserve special attention: squaring binomials and the difference of two squares, which can be rewritten as a product of two binomials. The purpose of this lesson is to make dealing with these forms nearly automatic, since they arise often in the study of algebra. These patterns will also be helpful in Chapter 7, when students learn to factor quadratic expressions.

Students explore several examples and look for patterns; in doing so they gain practice in manipulating these forms. Whenever possible, applications using these forms are presented so that students can practice working with binomials in interesting and challenging contexts.

Advance Preparation

You may want to have algebra tiles on hand for modeling binomials squares of the form $(x - a)^2$.

Lesson Planner

	Summary	Materials	On Your Own Exercises	Assessment Opportunities
Investigation 1 page T390	Students find a shortcut for squaring binomials.	⋆● Algebra tiles (optional)	Practice & Apply: 1–13, p. 396 Connect & Extend: 27–32, p. 397 Mixed Review: 42–49, p. 399	On the Spot Assessment, pages T390, T391 Share & Summarize, pages T392, 392 Troubleshooting, page T392
Investigation 2 page T393	Students explore patterns in rewriting differences of squares as products of binomials.		Practice & Apply: 14–26, p. 396 Connect & Extend: 33–41, pp. 397–398 Mixed Review: 42–49, p. 399	On the Spot Assessment, page T393 Share & Summarize, pages T395, 395 Troubleshooting, page T395 Informal Assessment, page 399 Quick Quiz, page 399

* Included in Impact Mathematics Manipulative Kit

1 Remind the class that they have looked at several methods for expanding the products of binomials. Explain that certain forms of binomials, however, have special importance in algebra, because they occur often.

Access for all **Learners**

Language Diversity There are many mathematical terms in this lesson, like those below, that students should be familiar with. Take a minute when the words come up, either in your teaching or in the text, to explain them informally if necessary. Students will tell you quickly enough when they no longer need such support! You might also post the words and students' explanations or an example.

- binomial
- expanding a binomial
- product
- square, perfect square
- term

Explore

2 Have students work in pairs on the questions in this Explore. After they have completed all of the expansions, ask them to verbalize their patterns. They will likely say something like the following:

> The result of expanding $(x + a)^2$ is x^2, plus twice ax, plus the square of the a term.

You will find that students develop great speed in computing binomial squares and feel empowered when they can square binomials quickly. Problem Set A asks students to apply the shortcut they developed here, so if students are struggling to find a pattern, work through some additional examples with the class.

3 **Additional Examples** Expand and simplify each product.

$(a + 7)^2$ $a^2 + 14a + 49$

$(m + 12)^2$ $m^2 + 24m + 144$

$\left(x + \frac{1}{2}\right)^2$ $x^2 + x + \frac{1}{4}$

Investigation 1

In this investigation, students first look at some additional examples of squaring binomials of the form $(x + a)^2$ and then move into those of the form $(x - a)^2$. They also look at the general form of squaring binomials and use these forms to prove some conjectures about squares of consecutive numbers.

4 **Problem Set A** Suggested Grouping: Individuals
In **Problems 1 and 2,** students apply the pattern they noticed in the Explore to expand squares of binomials. These should not take students long to complete.

5 ### On the **Spot** **Assessment**

In Problem 2, make sure students are comfortable adding the terms $ax + ax$ to get $2ax$. If necessary, use the distributive property to explain the result by rewriting $ax + ax$ as $ax(1 + 1)$ and simplifying.

Patterns in Products of Binomials

1 Explain that students will look at special forms of binomials.

You have learned several methods for expanding products of binomials. Some binomials have products with identifiable patterns. Recognizing these patterns will make your work easier.

Explore

Expand and simplify each product.

$(x + 1)^2 = (x + 1)(x + 1) = x^2 + 2x + 1$

$(x + 2)^2 = x^2 + 4x + 4$

$(x + 3)^2 = x^2 + 6x + 9$

$(x + 4)^2 = x^2 + 8x + 16$

① The expansion is the first term in the binomial squared, plus twice the second term times the first term, plus the second term squared; $x^2 + 20x + 100$.

Describe the pattern you see in your work. Use the pattern to predict the expansion of $(x + 10)^2$. See ①.

Check your prediction by expanding and simplifying $(x + 10)^2$.

$x^2 + 20x + 100$

2 Have students work in pairs.

3 If students are having trouble, work through a few more examples with the class.

Investigation 1 ▶ Squaring Binomials

In this investigation, you will learn some shortcuts for expanding squares of binomials.

Problem Set A

2. $x^2 + 2ax + a^2$; Check: $(x + a)(x + a) = x^2 + ax + ax + a^2 = x^2 + 2ax + a^2$

1. Apply the pattern you discovered in the Explore to expand these squares of binomials.

1a. $m^2 + 18m + 81$

1b. $m^2 + 40m + 400$

1c. $m^2 + 0.2m + 0.01$

    a. $(m + 9)^2$ **b.** $(m + 20)^2$ **c.** $(m + 0.1)^2$

2. Apply the pattern to predict the expansion of $(x + a)^2$. Check your answer by using the distributive property.

4 You may have students work on their own.

5 Make sure students are comfortable combining $ax + ax$.

390 CHAPTER 6 Working with Expressions

Develop

 Problems 3 and 4 preview of later problems in which students will be using binomial expansions to perform specific calculations. Encourage them to think about 100 as the sum of $93 + 7$, and therefore $100^2 = (93 + 7)^2$.

 Problem Set Wrap-Up If you notice many students still having trouble with these problems, you may want to let students get into pairs to compare answers quickly, and then review the problem set as a class. If most students seem to understand the basic pattern, let them continue to Problem Set B.

 Problem Set B **Suggested Grouping: Pairs**
This problem set examines binomial squares of the form $(x - a)^2$. For some students, it is easier to think about expanding binomials of this form if they rewrite the binomial using addition: $(x + {}^-a)$. After students do enough of these, they will probably find that they don't need to take this extra step.

 For **Problem 2,** students may use the pattern from the Explore, rewriting the subtraction as adding the opposite; or they may use the distributive property. You may want to make sure students are getting the signs correct in their solutions before they continue.

 In **Problem 4,** students use a rectangle diagram to explain their answer to **Problem 3,** the generalized form of expanding a binomial square with subtraction. This rectangle diagram is not obvious, and the class may need some further explanation. In essence, since two strips are being subtracted, one from each of two sides, the square with area a^2 (probably in the lower-right corner) is in fact being subtracted twice, and therefore must be added back once, accounting for the final a^2 term. Algebra tiles may make it clearer that the tiles "double up" in that spot. If students still seem puzzled by this, there is no need to dwell on it. ■

 When students finish Problem Set B, you may want to take a minute to write the following generalizations on the board:

$$(a + b)^2 = a^2 + 2ab + b^2$$
$$(a - b)^2 = a^2 - 2ab + b^2$$

Explain to students that a and b can represent any expressions. Have them do the following expansion, using the generalized form: $(2x + 3y)^2$.

 Problem Set C **Suggested Grouping: Pairs**
In this problem set, students look at binomial squares that are more challenging, as well as applications of squaring binomials. This problem set will take longer than Problem Sets A and B, so leave enough time for students to work on this.

You may want to observe students' work in **Problem 3** to make sure they are multiplying $2m$ and $4n$ correctly.

On the **Spot** **Assessment**

In **Problem 4,** watch for students who multiply a^4 by a^4, or square a^4, incorrectly. Remind them of the rules for exponents, or return to the definition of a^4 ($a \times a \times a \times a$) as a way of explaining that the result is a^8.

3. Possible answer: Since $100^2 = (93 + 7)^2$, there must be a middle term (twice the product of 93 and 7) along with the squares of 93 and 7, so 100^2 must be greater.

4. If they were equal to each other, $2ax$ must be 0, which means either x or a would be 0.

**Problem Set B
Answers**

1b. $(x + {}^-1)(x + {}^-1)$
$= x^2 - x - x + 1$
$= x^2 - 2x + 1$

2a. $m^2 - 18m + 81$

2b. $m^2 - 40m + 400$

2c. $m^2 - 0.2m + 0.01$

4.

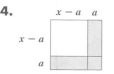

Possible explanations: If you start with an x-by-x square, you can subtract the rectangle with area ax along the right side and then subtract the rectangle with area ax along the bottom. However, both of those strips include the square in the lower-right corner, with area a^2, so you have to add that area back once, giving $x^2 - ax - ax + a^2$, or $x^2 - 2ax + a^2$. Or, the areas of the four rectangles are $(x - a)^2$, $a(x - a)$, $a(x - a)$, and a^2. So $(x - a)^2$ is the area of the big square, x^2, minus the area of the three others: $x^2 - a(x - a) - a(x - a) - a^2$, or $x^2 - ax + a^2 - ax + a^2 - a^2$, or $x^2 - 2ax + a^2$.

3. Use the pattern you discovered to explain, without calculating, why $100^2 \neq 93^2 + 7^2$. Is 100^2 greater than or less than $93^2 + 7^2$?

4. In Problem 3, you saw that $(93 + 7)^2 \neq 93^2 + 7^2$. Are there any values of x or a for which $(x + a)^2$ *does* equal $x^2 + a^2$? If so, what are they? How do you know?

You have just studied expressions of the form $(a + b)^2$. Now you will look at expressions of the form $(a - b)^2$.

Problem Set B

1. Recall that $(x - 1)^2$ can be thought of as $(x + {}^-1)^2$.

   a. Use this fact, along with your findings in Problem Set A, to expand $(x - 1)^2$. $x^2 + {}^-2x + 1$ or $x^2 - 2x + 1$

   b. Check your answer to Part a by using the distributive property to expand $(x - 1)^2$.

2. Expand each expression using any method you like

   a. $(m - 9)^2$ **b.** $(m - 20)^2$ **c.** $(m - 0.1)^2$

3. What is the expansion of $(x - a)^2$? $x^2 - 2a + a^2$

4. Use a rectangle diagram to help explain your answer to Problem 3.

You have seen by now that these two statements are true:

$$(a + b)^2 = a^2 + 2ab + b^2 \qquad (a - b)^2 = a^2 - 2ab + b^2$$

The variables a and b can represent any expressions. For example:

$$(2x + 3y)^2 = (2x)^2 + 2 \cdot 2x \cdot 3y + (3y)^2 = 4x^2 + 12xy + 9y^2$$

Problem Set C

Expand each expression.

1. $(3m + 2)^2$ $9m^2 + 12m + 4$

2. $(2x - y)^2$ $4x^2 - 4xy + y^2$

3. $(2m - 4n)^2$ $4m^2 - 16mn + 16n^2$

4. Challenge $(g^2 - a^4)^2$ $g^4 - 2g^2a^4 + a^8$

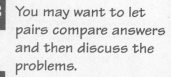

1 Encourage students to think about 100 as $93 + 7$.

2 You may want to let pairs compare answers and then discuss the problems.

3 You may have students work in pairs.

4 Make sure students are getting the signs right in their solutions.

5 You may need to explain the rectangle diagram to the class.

6 Write these generalizations on the board.

7 You may have students work in pairs.

Problem 5 supplies another visual way to stress the fact that $(n + a)^2$ is not $n^2 + a^2$, which is helpful if you still have students making this mistake.

Problem-Solving Strategies Students may have different ways of approaching **Part b.**

- Students may think of the number of tiles as the area of everything (their answer to Part a) minus the area of the garden, n^2.

- Students might use a counting strategy: n "inside" tiles on each side plus 4 corner pieces, or $4n + 4$.

For **Problem 6,** students may do some algebraic simplification, subtracting n^2 from $(n + 1)^2$. They should recognize that the result, $2n + 1$, must be an odd number.

Another approach is for students to realize that with two consecutive numbers, one must be odd and the other must be even. Squaring the odd number gives an odd result, and squaring the even number gives an even result. The difference between an even number and an odd number is always odd.

Access
for all Learners

Extra Challenge Ask students to take Evan's observation one step further and prove that any odd number can be written as a difference of squares.

Students who used the algebraic-manipulation solution to Problem 6 might reason that since every odd number can be written as $2n + 1$, every odd number can be expressed as the difference of the squares of two consecutive numbers, $(n + 1)^2 - n^2$. So if the odd number is 15, $n = 7$ (since $2n + 1 = 15$), and therefore the two consecutive numbers are 7 and 8: $64 - 49 = 15$.

Another way to see this is by considering the sequence of perfect squares—

$$1 \quad 4 \quad 9 \quad 16 \quad 25 \quad 36 \quad 49 \quad 64 \ldots$$

—and finding the difference of each pair of consecutive squares and observing the pattern they produce:

$$1 \quad 4 \quad 9 \quad 16 \quad 25 \quad 36 \quad 49 \quad 64 \ldots$$
$$3 \quad 5 \quad 7 \quad 9 \quad 11 \quad 13 \quad 15$$

The first differences form the sequence of odd numbers, so clearly every odd number is the difference of consecutive squares.

About the Mathematics

Interestingly, even integers divisible by 4 can be written as a difference of squares, but those not divisible by 4 cannot be expressed this way.

The difference between n^2 and $(n + 2)^2$ is $4n + 4$. Therefore, given a multiple of 4, all of which are of the form $4n + 4 = 4(n + 1)$ for some n, there are two squares whose difference is that number.

The proof that only even numbers divisible by 4 can be written as a difference of squares is more complicated.

Suppose x is an even number, and $x = (n + k)^2 - n^2$, where n and k are integers. The variable x can also be written as $2m$, where m is an integer. So

$$\begin{aligned} x = 2m &= (n + k)^2 - n^2 \\ &= n^2 + 2nk + k^2 - n^2 \\ &= 2nk + k^2 \\ m &= nk + \tfrac{k^2}{2} \end{aligned}$$

Since m is an integer and nk is an integer, $\frac{k^2}{2}$ must also be an integer. (If you add a non-integer to an integer, you can't get another integer.)

That means k^2 must be divisible by 2. For k^2 to be even, k has to be even.

So $k = 2a$, where a is an integer, producing:

$$m = 2an + \tfrac{4a^2}{2} = 2an + 2a^2$$

That means $x = 4an + 4a^2 = 4(an + a^2)$, so x is divisible by 4. Therefore, any even number that can be expressed as a difference of squares must be divisible by 4.

Share & Summarize

This question brings out a common misconception about squaring binomials. Even after students have done many problems squaring binomials, they still may resort to making these classic mistakes. You may want to have a couple of students read their letters, and allow the class to discuss the accuracy of the explanations.

Troubleshooting If students are having trouble with shortcuts in squaring binomials, return to rewriting the squared form as the product of two binomials, and have them use the distributive property to expand it. You can also provide more examples for students to work with if you feel they need more practice.

• *Teaching notes continued on page A682*

★ indicates multi-step problem

5. Imagine a square garden surrounded by a border of square tiles that are 1 unit by 1 unit. A variety of sizes are possible.

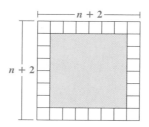

a. The garden has sides of length n, not including the tiles, where n is divisible by the length of a tile. Write an expression for the area of the ground covered by both the garden and the tiles.
$(n + 2)^2$ or $n^2 + 4n + 4$

6. Possible answer: If you take the difference of the squares of any two consecutive numbers, $(n + 1)^2 - n^2$, you get $n^2 + 2n + 1 - n^2$, or $2n + 1$, which is an odd number.

b. Write an expression for the number of tiles needed for the garden in Part a. $(n + 2)^2 - n^2$ or $4n + 4$

★ **6. Prove It!** Evan noticed that when he found the difference of 3^2 and 4^2, the result was odd: $16 - 9 = 7$. This is also true for the difference of 6^2 and 7^2: $49 - 36 = 13$. He conjectured that the difference of squares of consecutive numbers is always odd.

Prove Evan's conjecture, if possible. If not, give a counterexample.

Share & Summarize

Bharati is confused about squaring binomials. She thinks that for any numbers a and b,

$$(a + b)^2 = a^2 + b^2 \text{ and } (a - b)^2 = a^2 - b^2$$

Write her a letter explaining why she is incorrect. Include the correct expansions of $(a + b)^2$ and $(a - b)^2$ in your letter.

Possible letter: When you square a binomial, you have to multiply it by itself: $(a + b)^2 = (a + b)(a + b)$. Using the distributive property twice, this is $a^2 + 2ab + b^2$. And $(a - b)^2 = (a - b)(a - b) = a^2 - 2ab + b^2$.

1 You may want to have some students take this observation further.

2 You may have students read their letters for the class to discuss.

Investigation 2

In this investigation, students explore patterns related to the product of binomials of the form $(x + a)(x - a) = x^2 - a^2$. Because of the form of the result, this product is called the *difference of two squares*. Students use this form as a shortcut in performing certain calculations.

 Introduce the investigation by reminding students of their work with squared binomials. If you wish, make a connection by writing a squared binomial as a product of two binomials where students can see it. Then tell students they will look at another common product as you change one of the two operations from addition to subtraction (or vice versa).

 Problem Set D Suggested Grouping: Individuals
Students will undoubtedly see the pattern in **Problem 1** and find that they get through these quickly.

Problem 5 has several binomials containing decimals and fractions. Students should not use calculators on these problems, since the calculations should be easy to do in their heads.

 On the **Spot Assessment**

Some students may think that Problem 5h does not fit the pattern, since the variable is second in the binomial expression. You might ask those students if $(a - b)(a + b)$ fits the pattern. If they still don't believe this fits, ask them to try expanding the expression using the shortcuts from Lesson 6.2 or the distributive property. You may need to point out (here or in a Problem Set Wrap-Up) that the pattern should not dictate where the variable is located, only that the first terms in each binomial are identical, and that the last terms are identical, with addition in one and subtraction in the other.

Problem 6 is a preview of factoring, which students will look at later.

 Problem Set Wrap-Up You might want to take a moment to bring the class together and be sure everyone has the correct pattern in mind for differences of squares. The answers to Problem 5 would make a good review, especially Part h. (See the notes for Problem 5, above.) You can also use the Example on page 394.

Investigation Differences of Squares

2. Possible answers:
The second terms in
the factors of each
product are
opposites. *Or,* the
second terms are
the same, but one
is added and one
subtracted. *Or,* the
products look like
$(a + b)(a - b)$.

3. Possible answers:
They have no middle
term; they're all the
first term from one
of the binomials
squared minus the
second term from
one of the binomials
squared.

4. $x^2 - ax + ax - a^2$
$= x^2 - a^2$, which
is the square of the
first term minus the
square of the
second term.

In Investigation 1, you used a shortcut to expand squares of binomials such as $(a + b)^2$ and $(a - b)^2$. In this investigation, you will find a shortcut for a different kind of product of binomials.

Problem Set D

1. Expand each expression.

   a. $(x + 10)(x - 10)$ $x^2 - 100$ **b.** $(k + 3)(k - 3)$ $k^2 - 9$

   c. $(S + 1)(S - 1)$ $S^2 - 1$ **d.** $(x + 5)(x - 5)$ $x^2 - 25$

   e. $(2t + 5)(2t - 5)$ $4t^2 - 25$ **f.** $(3y - 7)(3y + 7)$ $9y^2 - 49$

2. How are the factors of the original products in Problem 1 similar?

3. How are the expansions of the products in Problem 1 similar?

4. Prove It! Expand $(x + a)(x - a)$, and show that the pattern you noticed in Problem 3 will always be true for this kind of product.

5. If the expression fits the pattern of the products in Problem 1, expand it using the pattern you described in Problem 3. If it doesn't fit the pattern, say so.

   a. $(x + 20)(x - 20)$ $x^2 - 400$

   b. $(b + 1)(b - 1)$ $b^2 - 1$

   c. $(n - 2.5)(n - 2.5)$ does not fit the pattern

   d. $\left(2m - \frac{1}{2}\right)\left(m + \frac{1}{2}\right)$ does not fit the pattern

   e. $(J + 0.2)(J - 0.2)$ $J^2 - 0.04$

   f. $(z + 25)(z - 100)$ does not fit the pattern

   g. $\left(2n - \frac{1}{3}\right)\left(2n + \frac{1}{3}\right)$ $4n^2 - \frac{1}{9}$

   h. $(3 - p)(3 + p)$ $9 - p^2$

6. Find two binomials with a product of $x^2 - 49$. $(x + 7)(x - 7)$

7. Some people call the expanded expressions you wrote in Problems 1 and 5 *differences of squares*. Explain why this name makes sense.
The expanded product is the difference between two squares.

1 Remind students of their work with binominals.

2 You may have students work on their own.

3 Help students who think Problem 5h does not follow the pattern.

4 Be sure everyone has the correct pattern in mind.

LESSON 6.3   Patterns in Products of Binomials   **393**

1 Example

Review the Example with the class. You may want to ask someone to articulate how Lydia used the pattern that students should have seen in Problem Set D. This discussion could be used as the wrap-up for Problem Set D, or part of the wrap-up.

2 Problem Set E Suggested Grouping: Individuals

This problem set extends differences of squares to an interesting computational context. In each of the problems, students have to think of a specific number with an amount added and subtracted from it. For example, in **Problem 1,** they need to think of 99 and 101 as 100 − 1 and 100 + 1, respectively. This set of problems provides excellent practice with mental arithmetic, and for those students who might enjoy the challenge, you might want to ask these orally.

Problem 7 is more challenging.

Problem-Solving Strategies ▸ Students may approach this in different ways.

- Some students may think about averaging the two numbers to find the middle: $^-14 + 16 = 2$ and $\frac{2}{2} = 1$. Therefore, they can express the numbers as $(1 − 15)$ and $(1 + 15)$.

- Other students may consider the entire problem first as a multiplication of a negative number and a positive number. Instead of dealing with the $^-14$ initially, they might look at $14 \cdot 16$ and write this as $(15 − 1)$ and $(15 + 1)$, do the multiplication, and then make the product negative at the end.

Problem 8 is a preview of Problem 13, in which students will actually find a quick way to multiply numbers that have a difference of 3.

The shortcut you found in Problem Set D can help you do some difficult-looking computations with stunning speed!

Problem Set E

1. Show how to use Lydia's method to calculate $99 \cdot 101$ without using a calculator.

Use a difference of squares to calculate each product. Check the first few until you are confident you're doing it correctly.

2. $49 \cdot 51$ **3.** $28 \cdot 32$

4. $43 \cdot 37$ **5.** $35 \cdot 25$

6. $4.1 \cdot 3.9$ **7.** $^-14 \cdot 16$

For which products below do you think using a difference of squares would be a reasonable method of calculation? If it seems reasonable, find the product.

8. $41 \cdot 38$ not reasonable   **9.** $99 \cdot ^-101$ $^-9,999$

10. $10\frac{1}{4} \cdot 9\frac{3}{4}$ $99\frac{15}{16}$ **11.** $1.2 \cdot ^-0.7$ not reasonable

12. Think about the kinds of products for which it is helpful to use differences of squares.

a. Make up a set of three multiplication problems for which you might want to use a difference of squares. Be adventurous! Do them yourself, and record the answers.

b. Give your problems to a partner to solve while you do your partner's set. Check that you agree on the answers and that the method works well for those problems.   See students' work.

1. $99 \cdot 101 = (100 - 1)(100 + 1) = 10,000 - 1 = 9,999$

2. $(50 - 1)(50 + 1) = 2,499$ **3.** $(30 - 2)(30 + 2) = 896$

4. $(40 + 3)(40 - 3) = 1,591$ **5.** $(30 + 5)(30 - 5) = 875$

6. $(4 + 0.1)(4 - 0.1) = 15.99$ **7.** $^-(15 - 1)(15 + 1) = ^-224$ or $(1 - 15)(1 + 15) = ^-224$

12a. Possible problems: $64 \cdot 56 = 3,584$; $83 \cdot 97 = 8,051$; $^-12.5 \cdot 13.5 = 168.5$

Students may need a hint to answer **Problem 13a,** Part i. If so, tell them the answer has something to do with the distributive property. To compute 32×29, they will be doing the following calculations:

$$31 \times 29 + 29 = (30 + 1)(30 - 1) + 29$$
$$= 900 - 1 + 29$$
$$= 928$$

Problem-Solving Strategies Students may use different strategies for **Problem 13b.**

- $21 = 22 - 1$, so $21 \cdot 18 = (22 - 1)18 =$
  $22 \cdot 18 - 18 = (20 + 2)(20 - 2) - 18 =$
  $400 - 4 - 18 = 378$

- $18 = 19 - 1$, so $21 \cdot 18 = 21(19 - 1) =$
  $21 \cdot 19 - 21 = (20 + 1)(20 - 1) - 21 =$
  $400 - 1 - 21 = 378$

- $21 = 20 + 1$, so $21 \cdot 18 = 18(20 + 1) =$
  $18 \cdot 20 + 18 = (19 - 1)(19 + 1) + 18 =$
  $381 - 1 + 18 = 378$

Note that in the third strategy above, the computation is a bit harder, since students need to know the square of 19. In the first two strategies, students have to square 20, which they are more likely to already know. You may want to mention that they should think about using numbers that are easy to work with when attempting problems of this type.

 After students tackle **Problem 13,** you might want to have them go back to Problem 8 with their newfound shortcut.

Share & Summarize
 This set of questions is a good review of the basis for understanding the difference of two squares. Students should be able to answer these on their own.

Troubleshooting If students are having difficulty recognizing patterns in the differences of two squares, you may want to review Problem 12 in Problem Set E with them. If they can make up their own problems, they will be well on their way to understanding the structure of the differences of two squares.

On Your Own Exercises

Practice & Apply: 14–26, p. 396
Connect & Extend: 33–41, pp. 397–398
Mixed Review: 42–49, p. 399

13. If you combine the difference-of-squares method of fast calculation with some other mathematical tricks, you can do even more astounding computations in your head.

    a. Consider the product $32 \cdot 29$.

        i. Explain why $32 \cdot 29 = 31 \cdot 29 + 29$.   See below.

        ii. Now use the difference-of-squares pattern to help compute the value of $31 \cdot 29$. $(30 + 1)(30 - 1) = 899$

        iii. Finally, use the product of 31 and 29 to compute $32 \cdot 29$.   928

    b. Compute $21 \cdot 18$ in your head.   378

    c. How did you find the answer to Part b?
Possible answers: $22 \cdot 18 - 18 = (20 + 2)(20 - 2) - 18 =$
$396 - 18$, or $21 \cdot 19 - 21 = (20 + 1)(20 - 1) - 21 = 399 - 21$

1 You may need to hint that students should use the distributive property.

2 After students finish, you may have them use the shortcut for Problem 8.

3 You may have students work on their own.

Share & Summarize

1. Suppose you want to expand an expression containing two binomials multiplied together.

    a. How do you know whether you can apply the shortcut you used to expand some of the products in Problem 5 of Problem Set D? Write two unexpanded products to help show what you mean.

    b. Describe the shortcut you use to write the expansion.

2. You may have noticed that when you multiply two binomials, you sometimes end up with another binomial and other times with an expression with three unlike terms, or a *trinomial*.

    a. Make up a product of two binomials that results in a binomial.

    b. Make up a product of two binomials that results in a trinomial.
        Possible answer: $(2x + 1)(x - 5)$

Problem Set E Answer

13a. i. 32 is $31 + 1$, so $(32)29 = (31 + 1)29$. Using the distributive property, $(31 + 1)29 = 31 \cdot 29 + 29$.

Share & Summarize Answers

1a. Possible answer: You can use it if the product is in the form $(a + b)(a - b)$. For example, $(x + 7)(x - 7)$.

1b. Square the first term and subtract the square of the second term.

2a. Possible answer: $(x - 4)(x + 4)$

On Your Own Exercises

Investigation 1,
  pp. 390–392
Practice & Apply: 1–13
Connect & Extend: 27–32

Investigation 2,
  pp. 393–395
Practice & Apply: 14–26
Connect & Extend: 33–41

Assign Anytime
Mixed Review: 42–49

Exercise 8:
Students may need some help in thinking about the middle term, $-2g^2$. Help them rewrite $g^2 - 1$ as $g^2 + -1$; then they will get $-g^2 + -g^2$. Although they have encountered this kind of combination before, it may still cause difficulty.

Exercise 9:
Squaring this binomial may cause the same kinds of issues for students as Exercise 8. The middle term, $-2s^2y^2$, may be problematic.

Exercise 13:
It may help students to draw a diagram showing the bottom of the pool and the border tiles.

Exercises 16 and 17:
You may want to tell students not to use calculators on these problems; the operations with decimals and fractions should be easy to do in their heads.

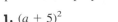

★ indicates multi-step problem

Practice & Apply

Expand and simplify each expression.

1. $(a + 5)^2$ **2.** $(m + 11)^2$ **3.** $(x + 2.5)^2$

4. $(t - 11)^2$ **5.** $(p - 2.5)^2$ **6.** $(2.5 - k)^2$

7. $\left(q - \frac{1}{4}\right)^2$ **8.** $(g^2 - 1)^2$ **9.** $(s^2 - y^2)^2$

10. $(3f + 2)^2$ **11.** $(3x + y)^2$ **12.** $(3m - 2n)^2$

1. $a^2 + 10a + 25$
2. $m^2 + 22m + 121$
3. $x^2 + 5x + 6.25$
4. $t^2 - 22t + 121$

5. $p^2 - 5p + 6.25$
6. $6.25 - 5k + k^2$
7. $q^2 - \frac{1}{2}q + \frac{1}{16}$
8. $g^4 - 2g^2 + 1$
9. $s^4 - 2s^2y^2 + y^4$
10. $9f^2 + 12f + 4$
11. $9x^2 + 6xy + y^2$
12. $9m^2 - 12mn + 4n^2$
16. $0.16 - 4x^2$
18. $(2x - 1)(2x + 1)$
19. $(4 - 5x)(4 + 5x)$
20. $(x - y)(x + y)$
22. $(30 - 3)(30 + 3) = 900 - 9 = 891$
23. $(200 + 7)(200 - 7) = 40,000 - 49 = 39,951$
24. $(100 + 11)(100 - 11) = 10,000 - 121 = 9,879$
25. $12 \cdot 9 = 11 \cdot 9 + 9 = (10 + 1)(10 - 1) + 9 = 100 - 1 + 9 = 108$
26. $37 \cdot 25 = 35 \cdot 25 + 25 + 25 = (30 + 5)(30 - 5) + 50 = 900 - 25 + 50 = 925$

13. Imagine a rectangular swimming pool in which the bottom is made of large square tiles. The pool is 25 tiles longer than it is wide. Around the edge of the pool, at the top, is a border made of the same square tiles. The border is one tile wide.

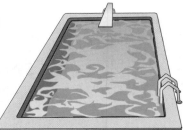

★ **a.** If n represents the number of tiles in the width of the bottom of the pool, write an expression for the total number of tiles in the bottom of the pool. $n(n + 25)$

★ **b.** Write an expression for the number of tiles in both the bottom of the pool and the border. $(n + 2)(n + 27)$

Expand and simplify each expression.

14. $(10 - k)(10 + k)$ $100 - k^2$ **15.** $(3h - 5)(3h + 5)$ $9h^2 - 25$

16. $(0.4 - 2x)(0.4 + 2x)$ **17.** $\left(\frac{1}{5} + k\right)\left(\frac{1}{5} - k\right)$ $\frac{1}{25} - k^2$

Write each expression as the product of binomials.

18. $4x^2 - 1$ **19.** $16 - 25x^2$ **20.** $x^2 - y^2$

Write each product as a difference of squares, and use this form to calculate the product. **21.** $(40 - 5)(40 + 5) = 1,600 - 25 = 1,575$

21. $35 \cdot 45$ **22.** $27 \cdot 33$

23. $207 \cdot 193$ **24.** $111 \cdot 89$

Look back at your work in Problem 13 of Problem Set E on page 395. Combine the difference-of-squares method with addition to calculate each product.

25. $12 \cdot 9$ **26.** $37 \cdot 25$

396 CHAPTER 6 Working with Expressions

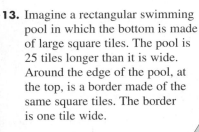 impactmath.com/self_check_quiz

---

Connect & Extend

27. $\frac{x^2}{4} + \frac{xy}{2} + \frac{y^2}{4}$

28. $9 - 6xy + x^2y^2$

29. $x^2y^2 - 2x^2y + x^2$

30. $8x^2y^2 - 4xy^2 + y^2 - 4xy + 1$

Expand and simplify each expression.

27. $\left(\frac{x}{2} + \frac{y}{2}\right)^2$

28. $(3 - xy)^2$

29. $(xy - x)^2$

30. $(2xy - 1)^2 + (2xy - y)^2$

31. Write an expression without parentheses for the area of the shaded triangle.
$\frac{1}{2}a^2 + 2a + 2$

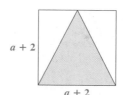

$a + 2$

$a + 2$

32. Challenge For what values of x and a is $(x + a)^2 > x^2 + a^2$? Justify your conclusion. (Hint: Expand the expression on the left side of the inequality.) $(x + a)^2 = x^2 + 2ax + a^2$, and $(x + a)^2 > x^2 + a^2$ when x and a are both positive or both negative, since the middle term ($2ax$) will be positive in both cases.

Expand and simplify each expression.

33. $(x^2 - y^2)(x^2 + y^2)$ $x^4 - y^4$

34. $(1 - y^3)(1 + y^3)$ $1 - y^6$

35. $(xy - x)(xy + x)$ $x^2y^2 - x^2$

Find the values of a and b that make each equation true.

36. $2x^2 + 7x + 3 = (a + bx)(3 + x)$ $a = 1, b = 2$

37. $20 - x - x^2 = (a + x)(b - x)$ $a = 5, b = 4$

38. $21 - 23x + 6x^2 = (3 - ax)(7 - bx)$ $a = 2, b = 3$

39. Physical Science An object is thrown straight upward from a height of 4 feet above the ground. The object's initial velocity is 30 feet per second. The equation relating the object's height in feet to the time t in seconds since it was released is $h = 30t - 16t^2 + 4$.

a. Find a and b to make this equation true: $a = 2, b = 16$

$$30t - 16t^2 + 4 = (2 - t)(a + bt)$$

b. The statement $xy = 0$ is true whenever one of the factors, x or y, is equal to 0. For example, the solutions to $(k - 1)(k + 2) = 0$ are 1 and $^-2$, because these values make the factors $k - 1$ and $k + 2$ equal to 0. Use this fact and your result from Part a to find two solutions to the equation $30t - 16t^2 + 4 = 0$. $2, -\frac{1}{8}$

c. One of your solutions tells you at what time the object hit the ground. Which solution is it, and how do you know?
2; The other solution is negative, indicating a time before the object was thrown.

LESSON 6.3   Patterns in Products of Binomials   **397**

Exercise 28:
Students may never have multiplied a term like xy by itself before. Watch for students who add xy to itself rather than multiply. They will have to perform a similar multiplication in **Exercise 30.**

Exercise 31 Extension:
You might want to ask students: Does it matter where the top vertex of the triangle meets the side of the square in terms of calculating the triangle's area? Explain. No; any triangle with a vertex on the top side of the square and base as the bottom of the square will have the same height and the same base, and therefore the same area.

Exercises 36–38:
Students may have a variety of ways of thinking about these problems, which can be challenging. Some may solve them just by inspection or trial and error. Others may actually expand the right side and solve for a and b.

Exercise 39:
This exercise makes a lovely connection to previous work students have done with quadratics. In finding the values of a and b, students may notice that if the constant term on the left side is 4, a must be 2 (since $2 \cdot 2 = 4$). From there, it is possible to find the value of b so that the linear terms add to 30, or to find b by noticing that $bt \cdot {}^-t = -16t^2$ and therefore $b = 16$.

Exercise 40:

The areas of a and b can be calculated as follows:

a. $\frac{1}{2}(x - 2)(1) = \frac{x}{2} - 1$

b. $\frac{1}{2}[(x + 2) - 1](x - 2) =$
$\frac{1}{2}(x + 1)(x - 2) =$
$\frac{1}{2}(x^2 - x - 2) =$
$\frac{x^2}{2} - \frac{x}{2} - 1$

There are various ways to find the area of Triangle c.

- Subtract areas a and b from the rectangle:

$(x + 2)(x - 2) -$
$\left(\frac{x}{2} - 1\right) - \left(\frac{x^2}{2} - \frac{x}{2} - 1\right) =$
$x^2 - 4 - \frac{x}{2} + 1 - \frac{x^2}{2} +$
$\frac{x}{2} + 1 = \frac{x^2}{2} - 2$

- Apply the formula for area of a triangle:

$\frac{1}{2}(x - 2)(x + 2) =$
$\frac{1}{2}(x^2 - 4) = \frac{x^2}{2} - 2$

If students use the second strategy, you may want to ask them to add the three areas and check that the sum is equal to the area of the rectangle, $x^2 - 4$.

Exercise 41:

It can be very difficult for students to see what Gilberto and especially Katie are thinking. Students may need to reproduce for themselves what is in the diagrams. Suggest that they copy and cut these up to see what is happening. However, understanding the rearrangement is only half the battle; they also have to understand how the rearrangement demonstrates that $(a + b)(a - b) = a^2 - b^2$. It may help if students explicitly identify each quantity ($a + b$, $a - b$, a^2, and b^2) in each case. For example, Katie started with area a^2 and then created a figure that could be cut into rectangles with dimensions $(a + b)(a - b)$ and b^2, showing that a^2 is b^2 more than $(a + b)(a - b)$. In Gilberto's case, the quantity b^2 is the *missing* piece from the square with area a^2.

In your **own** words

Write two multiplication problems that look difficult but that you can solve easily in your head using differences of squares. Explain how using differences of squares can help you find the products.

41a. Possible answer: The area of the original rectangle is the same as the area of the final rectangles. The original rectangle has area $(a - b)(a + b)$; the final shape is a square with area $a(a - b + b)$ or a^2 minus a piece with area $[a - (a - b)]b$ or b^2, so the area of the shape is $a^2 - b^2$.

41b. Possible answer: The area of the original square is the same as the area of the final rectangles. The area of the final rectangles is easier to see if you add a line:

The square at the bottom has dimensions b and b (since the left rectangle has a vertical length of $a - b$ and the right rectangle has a vertical length of a). The rest of the shape has dimensions $a - b$ and $a + b$. So $a^2 = (a - b)(a + b) + b^2$, or $a^2 - b^2 = (a - b)(a + b)$.

40. This rectangle is divided into three triangular regions. Find an expression without parentheses for each of the three areas.

40. Region a: $\frac{x}{2} - 1$

Region b: $\frac{x^2}{2} - \frac{x}{2} - 1$

Region c: $\frac{x^2}{2} - 2$

41. Challenge Katie and Gilberto used paper and scissors to convince themselves that $(a + b)(a - b)$ really is equal to $a^2 - b^2$.

a. Gilberto started with this paper rectangle. He wrote labels on the rectangle to represent lengths.

Gilberto then cut the rectangle and rearranged it.

Explain why this shows that $(a + b)(a - b)$ is equal to $a^2 - b^2$.

b. Katie started with this paper square.

Then she cut the square and rearranged it.

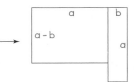

Explain why this shows that $(a + b)(a - b)$ is equal to $a^2 - b^2$. Hint: The areas of the two diagrams above must be the same, so expressions representing those areas must be equal.

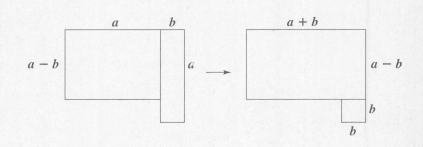

42. Challenge Prove that for a quadratic equation, $y = ax^2 + bx + c$, the second differences in a table with consecutive inputs must be constant. Hint: Suppose the inputs for the table are x, $x + 1$, $x + 2$, $x + 3$, and so on. What are the corresponding outputs?

See Additional Answers.

Mixed Review

Simplify each fraction.

43. $\dfrac{21}{99}$ $\dfrac{7}{33}$ **44.** $\dfrac{15}{75}$ $\dfrac{1}{5}$ **45.** $\dfrac{63}{210}$ $\dfrac{3}{10}$

Each table describes either a linear relationship, an exponential relationship, or an inverse variation. Write an equation describing each relationship.

46. $y = 80(0.4)^x$

47. $xy = 24$ or $y = \dfrac{24}{x}$

48. $y = {}^{-}7x - 18$

49.

46.

x	y
$^{-}2$	500
$^{-}1$	200
0	80
1	32
2	12.8

47.

x	y
$^{-}6$	$^{-}4$
$^{-}3$	$^{-}8$
$^{-}2$	$^{-}12$
2	12
3	8

48.

x	y
$^{-}4$	10
$^{-}3$	3
$^{-}1$	$^{-}11$
2	$^{-}32$
3	$^{-}39$

49. Sketch a graph of $y = \dfrac{1}{x}$.

50. Georgia brought a package containing 16 identical pieces of clay to school. She wanted to share the clay with some friends during recess.

    a. Georgia wants to divide the clay evenly among her friends. If she invites three friends to join her, how many pieces will each friend receive (including Georgia)?   4

    b. If Georgia invites five friends to join her, how many pieces will each friend receive (including Georgia)? $2\frac{2}{3}$

50c. $n = \dfrac{16}{f+1}$

    c. Write a formula giving the number of pieces n each friend will receive (including Georgia), if Georgia invites f friends.

    d. Use your expression in Part c to find n when f is 3 and when f is 5. If your answers do not agree with those for Parts a and b, find any mistakes you have made and correct them.   4, $2\frac{2}{3}$

Additional Answers

33. Possible answer: The outputs are $ax^2 + bx + c$, $a(x + 1)^2 + b(x + 1) + c$, $a(x + 2)^2 + b(x + 2) + c$, $a(x + 3)^2 + b(x + 3) + c$ and so on. Expanding gives $ax^2 + bx + c$, $ax^2 + 2ax + a + bx + b + c$, $ax^2 + 4ax + 4a + bx + 2b + c$, $ax^2 + 6ax + 9a + bx + 3b + c$, and so on. The first differences are $2ax + a + b$, $2ax + 3a + b$, $2ax + 5a + b$, and so on. The second differences are all $2a$, a constant.

Quick Check

Informal Assessment
Students should be able to:

✔ understand the pattern and apply a shortcut to square binomials of the forms $(a + b)^2$ and $(a - b)^2$

✔ understand the pattern and apply a shortcut to expand binomials of the form $(x + a)(x - a)$

Quick Quiz

1. Expand each expression.

   a. $(3x + 5)^2$
     $9x^2 + 30x + 25$

   b. $(2x - 3)^2$
     $4x^2 - 12x + 9$

   c. $(a^2 - b^3)^2$
     $a^4 - 2a^2b^3 + b^6$

2. Expand each expression.

   a. $(x - 7)(x + 7)$
     $x^2 - 49$

   b. $(3x + 4y)(3x - 4y)$
     $9x^2 - 16y^2$

   c. $(2r - 3s^2)(2r + 3s^2)$
     $4r^2 - 9s^4$

3. Use a difference of squares to calculate the product $52 \cdot 48$. Show your work.
   $(50 + 2)(50 - 2) =$
   $2{,}500 - 4 = 2{,}496$

Teacher Notes

Working with Algebraic Fractions

Objectives

▸ To understand when the denominator of an algebraic fraction is undefined

▸ To understand how the graph and the table of an equation with an algebraic fraction show values for which the equation is undefined

▸ To simplify algebraic fractions

◂ To multiply and divide algebraic fractions

Overview (pacing: about 3 class periods)

This lesson expands students' skills in working with algebraic expressions, focusing on algebraic fractions, which contain variables. This topic is briefly introduced here because it is often a difficult topic for students; teachers in future courses, specifically second-year algebra and precalculus, will be grateful that you paid attention to this topic early on. With some students, you may need to take some time to probe their understanding and uncover misconceptions. However, resist the temptation to spend more than the allotted time on this topic at this stage.

In this lesson, students look at issues of domain by considering what values of the variable will make the denominator 0. They also look at the graphs of equations with algebraic fractions as well as tables. Students simplify fractions with variables by removing common factors, and they work with the operations of multiplication and division of fractions with variables.

Advance Preparation

No advance preparation is required for this lesson.

Lesson Planner

	Summary	Materials	On Your Own Exercises	Assessment Opportunities
Investigation 1 page T401	Students consider domains of algebraic fractions in terms of what makes mathematical sense and what makes contextual sense.	• Graphing calculators	Practice & Apply: 1–3, p. 407 Connect & Extend: 20, 21, pp. 408–409 Mixed Review: 27–36, p. 410	Share & Summarize, pages T403, 403 Troubleshooting, page T403
Investigation 2 page T403	Students learn to simplify algebraic fractions, including products and quotients.		Practice & Apply: 4–19, pp. 407–408 Connect & Extend: 22–26, pp. 409–410 Mixed Review: 27–36, p. 410	On the Spot Assessment, page T405 Share & Summarize, pages T406, 406 Troubleshooting, page T406 Informal Assessment, page 410 Quick Quiz, page A660

Introduce

1 Begin this lesson by informing the class that they will extend their skills in working with algebraic expressions. You might want to ask them to give you an example of a fraction, and then explain that in this lesson, they will be looking at fractions like the example, but with variables in them. You might give them some examples: $\frac{5}{x}$, $\frac{3}{x-1}$, $\frac{r}{50}$. Let students know that these are called *algebraic fractions*, and ask them why they think these expressions have this name.

Think & Discuss

2 Read through the first paragraph with the class, and ask students for an algebraic fraction that will give the number of months needed to repay $100 at *d* dollars per month. This should be fairly straightforward.

Next, turn students' attention to the expressions at the bottom of the Think & Discuss box, and ask which give the number of months needed to repay $200 at *d* dollars per month.

Some students may be unconvinced that $\frac{100}{d} + \frac{100}{d}$ is the same as $\frac{200}{d}$. You may want to ask them for some specific values for *d* to test whether the expressions seem to be equivalent.

3 To transition into the first investigation, you might ask students what values make sense for *d*. Let them make suggestions, but don't comment on their accuracy. Explain that when an expression includes a variable in a denominator, the values of the variable for which the whole fraction makes sense are important to consider. Then tell them this is the question they will be considering in the next investigation.

Working with Algebraic Fractions

In earlier lessons, you discovered several tools for working with algebraic expressions more efficiently. Now you will expand your tool kit as you learn how to work with fractions that involve algebraic expressions. You saw fractions like these in Chapter 2, when you studied inverse variation.

Think & Discuss

Just before summer vacation, Adriana borrowed $100 from her favorite aunt to buy a pair of in-line skates for herself. She enjoyed them so much that she borrowed another $100 to buy a pair for her younger sister. She agreed to repay d dollars per month, and her aunt agreed not to charge interest.

Write an algebraic fraction to express how many months it will take Adriana to repay the first $100.

Which of these expressions show how many months it will take Adriana to repay the entire debt? See ①.

$$\frac{100}{d}$$

$$\frac{d}{200} \qquad \frac{d}{100} \qquad \frac{100}{2d} \qquad \frac{200}{2d}$$

$$\frac{100}{d} \qquad \frac{200}{d} \qquad \frac{100}{d} + \frac{100}{d}$$

① $\frac{200}{d}, \frac{100}{d} + \frac{100}{d}$

---

1. Tell the class they will extend their skills working with algebraic expressions.

2. Read the first paragraph with the class and ask the questions.

3. You might ask students what values make sense for d.

Investigation 1

In this investigation, students look at equations, tables, and graphs of algebraic fractions, and use them to determine which values make sense for the domain.

 Problem Set A Suggested Grouping: Pairs
In this problem set, students begin to determine the values that make sense for the denominators of algebraic fractions.

 You may want to encourage students to use calculators in **Problem 3** when they substitute values of x in the denominator. They will need to use parentheses when entering their expressions for binomials. If they enter the whole expression in one step, and when they enter the equation for graphing in **Problem 4,** they will need parentheses around the entire denominator. You may want to discuss this with the class. Use the following keystrokes:

$$24 \div ((x - 1)(x - 2)(x - 3)(x - 4))$$

The graph in **Problem 4** may seem unusual to students at first. In some cases, depending on the calculator and how the viewing window has been set, there will be a vertical (or nearly vertical) line connecting two sections of the graph; in other places, there may simply be a gap, with an abrupt change in y values from positive to negative, or vice versa.

 You may want to ask students if they have seen graphs similar to this one in the past. (Reciprocal graphs should come to mind.) It is important that students notice that the places where values of y get very large positively and negatively are the points at which the denominator takes on the value of 0: at $x = 1, 2, 3,$ and 4.

For **Problem 4b,** students may comment on the abrupt change in y values between positive and negative.

 Problem Set Wrap-Up After students finish Problem Set A, bring the class together to stress the point that algebraic fractions do not make mathematical sense for values of the variable that make the denominator 0. Be sure to explain that if the denominator is 0, the fraction is said to be *undefined* for these values.

Investigation ▶1 Making Sense of Algebraic Fractions

When you use expressions involving algebraic fractions, the expressions might not make sense for all values of the variables. In this investigation, you will explore some situations in which this is important.

Problem Set A

The denominator of the right-hand side of this equation has four factors.

$$y = \frac{24}{(x-1)(x-2)(x-3)(x-4)}$$

1. What is the value of y if you let $x = 5$? If you let $x = 6$? $1, \frac{1}{5}$

2. What happens to the value of y if $x = 1$? If $x = 2$? Are there other values of x for which this happens?

3. Choose a number less than 5 for which y does have a value. What is the value of y using your chosen value of x?

4. Look again at the equation above.

a. Use your calculator to make a table for the relationship, starting with $x = 0$ and using an increment of 0.25. Copy the results into a table on your paper. Use the calculator to help fill your table for x values up to $x = 5$.

How does your table show which values of x do not make sense?

b. Now use your calculator to graph the relationship, using x values from $^-1$ to 5 and y values from $^-100$ to 100. Make a rough sketch of the graph.

What happens to the graph at the x values that do not make sense?

Algebraic fractions don't make *mathematical* sense for values of the variables that make the denominator equal to 0—in other words, they are *undefined* for these values.

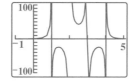

Develop

1 **Problem Set B** **Suggested Grouping: Pairs**
In this problem set, students explore the domain of *x* in
the context of buying comic books. Students are asked
to think about what values make sense, both *in context*
and *mathematically* (out of context). This exploration is
reminiscent of some of the work they did throughout
Course 2, in which they considered what inputs (usually
integer/non-integer) made sense for a situation.

2 In **Problem 1,** make sure students understand that
Carlota and Ling had set the same maximum price of
x dollars per comic book.

Problem 3 makes some fine distinctions in the difference
between what makes *mathematical sense* in an expression (where the context may not be the focus) and what
makes sense in terms of the *conditions inherent in the
context*. This distinction may be confusing to students at
3 first, and you may want to go over **Parts a and b** as
a class to be sure students understand what's being
asked and just what *mathematical sense* means.

The danger here is that students might believe that
mathematics is not "real world." Mathematics is, itself, a
context. Try not to dwell on this; the point is for students
to realize that if a mathematical expression is taken out
of a given context, certain restrictions on the domain (in
this case, for example, that *x* must be positive, as well
as others) may no longer be required.

Access for all **Learners**

Early Finishers Ask students who finish quickly to find
values of *x* in Problem 4 assuming that *x* can be *any* number that makes contextual sense (that is, not just whole
numbers, but any number that can be used to represent
money, including decimals to the hundredth place).

Students may try guessing values between 0 and 100 (or
95), or they may use a spreadsheet to calculate the number
of comic books for each price and then find the results that
are integers.

A more efficient method is to convert $100 into 10,000
cents and then find the values that divide evenly into
10,000. These values are how much Ling might have paid.
Carlota's cost will be $10 less, so any value less than
1,001 can be removed. For each remaining value *d*, consider whether *d* − 1,000 will divide evenly into 12,000.
This gives 1,250; 2,000; 2,500; and 5,000; so Ling paid
12.50, 20, 25, or 50 dollars. That means *x* must be 7.50,
15, 20, or 45—only one of which is not a whole number.

MATERIALS

graphing calculator

1. See Additional Answers.

3b. incorrect; Possible explanation: Just because the expression doesn't make sense for certain values doesn't mean it makes no sense at all.

3d. Incorrect; x can't be less than 5, or Carlota would have paid less than $0 per comic.

Problem Set B

Carlota and Ling attended a fundraising auction, hoping to bid for some collector's comic books. They both said they would bid no higher than x dollars per comic book.

Carlota bought some comic books she really wanted, each for $5 less than her set maximum price. She spent $120 in all. The comic books Ling wanted were worth more, and she ended up paying $5 more per comic book than she had intended. She spent $100 in all.

1. Explain what each expression means in terms of the auction story.

   a. x **b.** $x + 5$ **c.** $x - 5$

2. Write an expression to represent the number of comics Ling purchased. Then write an expression to represent the number Carlota bought.   Ling: $\frac{100}{x + 5}$; Carlota: $\frac{120}{x - 5}$

3. This algebraic expression represents the total number of comic books purchased by the friends.

$$\frac{100}{x + 5} + \frac{120}{x - 5}$$

   Read each comment about this expression, and decide whether the student is correct. If the student is incorrect, explain his or her mistake.

   a. Mikayla: "Even though you can't go to an auction intending to pay $^-$$10 per comic book, the expression is *mathematically* sensible when x has a value of $^-10$. The expression then has a value of $^-28$."   correct

   b. Ben: "The expression does not make sense at all because when $x = 5$, one of the denominators is 0, and you can't divide by 0."

   c. Héctor: "The expression makes *mathematical* sense for all values of the variable except 5 and $^-5$."   correct

   d. Tamika: "In the auction situation, we can only think about paying some positive number of dollars for a comic book. Therefore, for this story, the expression makes sense for positive values of x only, except 5 of course."

   e. Tala: "We can't use just *any* positive value of x in the expression. For example, if $x = 7$, Ling would have paid $x + 5 = 12 per comic book—which means she would have bought eight and a third comic books."   correct

   f. Kai: "The expression makes *mathematical* sense for any values of x except 5 and $^-5$. However, in the auction situation, there are only a small number of sensible answers."   correct

4. Consider Kai's statement. Find all the possible values for x given the auction situation. Assume x is a whole number.   15, 20, or 45

402 CHAPTER 6   Working with Expressions

Additional Answers

1a. the amount of money the friends intended to spend for each comic book

1b. the amount Ling spent on each comic book, or $5 more than her intended maximum

1c. the amount Carlota spent on each comic book, or $5 less than her intended maximum.

In **Problem 5,** students may note that the graph and the table show that values of y change abruptly from large negative values to large positive values when x changes from less than ⁻5 to more than ⁻5, and from less than 5 to more than 5. If so, you can acknowledge that this is an indicator of an x value for which the y value is undefined. However, you may want to point out that this won't happen with every value for which an expression is undefined. For example, $\frac{1}{x^2}$ does not change sign from one side of $x = 0$ to the other.

 Share & Summarize

This set of questions reinforces the distinction between what makes mathematical sense (not necessarily taking context into account) and what makes sense in the context of a specific situation. If students have trouble with **Question 1,** you might ask them to consider **Question 2** first and use their answers to help them articulate the distinction.

Troubleshooting If students are having difficulty with the ideas in this investigation, you may want to ask them to invent their own algebraic expressions or equations, put them in a context, and then describe the difference between what makes mathematical sense and sense in terms of the context.

 On Your Own Exercises

Practice & Apply: 1–3, p. 407
Connect & Extend: 20, 21, pp. 408–409
Mixed Review: 27–36, p. 410

Investigation 2

In this investigation, students work on simplifying algebraic fractions. This is not a topic that is likely to generate enormous enthusiasm. You will find, however, that the number tricks in Problem Set D will be appealing to most students.

It is important for students to understand that it is often helpful or easier to work with algebraic fractions in simplified form, just as it is with numeric fractions, such as $\frac{4}{24}$. One could argue that, in an age of advanced technology, the ability to put fractions in simplified form is no longer a necessary skill. Even if the topic is not a major focus, however, it is important for students to understand the simplification process, since it gives some insights into how fractions are constructed and "deconstructed."

You will notice that the term *canceling* is never used in this text. Students tend to learn canceling improperly and apply it incorrectly. For example, in $\frac{x+3}{3}$, they might cancel the 3s and get x as an answer. If you focus on rewriting using factors instead, as in the example $\frac{3x+3}{3} = \frac{3(x+1)}{3} = \frac{3}{3}(x+1) = (x+1)$, students actually see what's happening mathematically rather than learning a rote elimination of numbers and variables.

 Think & Discuss

Give students a minute to work out for themselves whether the fractions in each pair are equivalent. Encourage them to share how they reached their conclusions. Students will likely suggest substituting values. This can be a good test and will help prove by counterexample that the middle equation is incorrect. However, it cannot prove that the first and third are correct; to do this, algebra must be used.

About the
Mathematics

These examples were carefully chosen. Not all simplified versions of an algebraic fraction are equivalent; for example, $\frac{3a^2}{a}$ is not truly equivalent to $3a$, because the first expression is undefined when $a = 0$. Such expressions are sometimes said to be *equivalent almost everywhere,* because there is a finite number of values for which they do not give the same result. This is a subtle point that is more likely to confuse your students than help them. However, try to keep to the term *simplified* throughout the rest of this lesson, and avoid referring to simplified fractions as *equivalent.*

If there are problems in which students disagree and you suspect it will take too long to resolve the issues, leave the discussion for now and return to it after you have gone through the Example on page 404 and Problem Set C.

5. Now use your calculator to make a table and a graph for
$y = \frac{100}{x+5} + \frac{120}{x-5}$. Use values of x from $^-10$ to 10 and values
of y from $^-100$ to 100. For the table, start with $x = {}^-10$ and
use an increment of 1.

How do the graph and the table show the values of x for which the
expression does not make *mathematical sense*?
Possible answer: The table gives an error at those values. The
graph has vertical (or nearly vertical) lines at $x = {}^-5$ and $x = 5$.

Share & Summarize Answers

1. Possible answer: Mathematical sense involves only whether values will work in the expression, not whether they make sense in the situation. For example, if a pack of gum costs 55 cents, I can buy x packs of gum for $55x$ cents. Since any number for x will give a value for the expression, it makes mathematical sense. However, in the context of the given situation, only whole numbers make sense.

Share Summarize

1. When you are looking at an expression for a situation, what is the difference between *mathematical sense* and *sense in the context of the situation*? Give examples if it helps you make your point.

2. Consider the auction situation in Problem Set B.

a. What did you have to think about when trying to determine the values that made *mathematical* sense?

b. What did you have to think about when trying to determine the values that made sense in the *context* of the situation?

2a. what values would make a denominator equal to 0 (those values would not make mathematical sense)

Investigation 2

2b. Possible answer: What the variables and the expression represented: x is the number of comic books, so it must be positive and an integer. The expression stood for the total amount of money paid, so it had to be positive; since the friends paid $220 altogether, it also had to be equal to $220.

Investigation 2 ▶ Rearranging Algebraic Fractions

When you work with numeric fractions, you sometimes want to write
them in different ways. For example, to calculate $\frac{1}{2} + \frac{1}{3}$, it's helpful to
rewrite the problem as $\frac{3}{6} + \frac{2}{6}$.

Think Discuss   See Additional Answers.

Tamika tried to write equivalent expressions for three algebraic
fractions. Which of these are correct, and which are incorrect?
How do you know?

$$\frac{3}{12m} = \frac{1}{4m} \qquad \frac{2}{m+2} = \frac{1}{m+1} \qquad \frac{2x}{x^2} = \frac{2}{x}$$

Additional Answers
Think & Discuss

The first and third are correct; the second is incorrect. Possible explanation: In the correct fractions, the numerator and the denominator have been multiplied or divided by the same number. The second fraction isn't like that, which you can see by substituting a number such as 2 for m: $\frac{2}{2+2} = \frac{1}{2}$, but $\frac{1}{2+1} = \frac{1}{3}$.

1 If students mention an abrupt change of sign, ask them to consider $y = \frac{1}{x^2}$.

2 If students have trouble with Question 1, suggest they answer Question 2 first.

3 Give students a minute to consider their answers individually before discussing.

Develop

It is extremely helpful to compare students' work with simplifying algebraic fractions to their understanding of numeric fractions. With the class, work through the two methods of removing common factors that are mentioned in the text on page 404, before the Example. These two methods will be generalized for algebraic fractions.

Example

Now go through the Example with the class. You may want to stress that when we divide a numerator and a denominator by a common factor, we are essentially multiplying by 1. Another way to think about this is that when we factor out a common factor from a numerator and a denominator, we are factoring out 1.

The expressions Tamika wrote correctly are *simplified* versions of the original fractions. In a simplified fraction, the numerator and the denominator have no factors in common.

There are several strategies for simplifying fractions. For example, to simplify $\frac{15}{18}$, you can factor the numerator and the denominator:

$$\frac{15}{18} = \frac{3 \cdot 5}{3 \cdot 6} = \frac{3}{3} \cdot \frac{5}{6} = \frac{5}{6}$$

Another method is to divide the numerator and the denominator by a common factor, in this case 3:

$$\frac{15}{18} = \frac{\frac{15}{3}}{\frac{18}{3}} = \frac{5}{6}$$

You can also use these strategies to simplify algebraic expressions.

1 Work through the numeric examples so the class can make connections with the algebraic fractions.

2 • Discuss the Example with the class.

• Point out that dividing the numerator and denominator by a common factor is the same as multiplying by 1.

EXAMPLE

• To simplify $\frac{5}{5x + 15}$, factor the numerator and the denominator.

$$\frac{5}{5x + 15} = \frac{5}{5(x + 3)} = \frac{5}{5} \cdot \frac{1}{x + 3} = \frac{1}{x + 3}$$

Or, divide the numerator and the denominator by their common factor.

$$\frac{5}{5x + 15} = \frac{\frac{5}{5}}{} = \frac{1}{x + 3}$$

• To simplify $\frac{5a^2}{10a}$, factor the numerator and the denominator.

In Two Steps

$$\frac{5a^2}{10a} = \frac{5 \cdot a^2}{5 \cdot 2 \cdot a} = \frac{5}{5} \cdot \frac{a^2}{2 \cdot a} = \frac{a^2}{2a}$$

$$\frac{a^2}{2a} = \frac{a \cdot a}{2 \cdot a} = \frac{a}{a} \cdot \frac{a}{2} = \frac{a}{2}$$

In One Step

$$\frac{5a^2}{10a} = \frac{5 \cdot a \cdot a}{5 \cdot 2 \cdot a} = \frac{5}{5} \cdot \frac{a}{a} \cdot \frac{a}{2} = \frac{a}{2}$$

Or, divide both the numerator and the denominator by their common factors.

In Two Steps

$$\frac{5a^2}{10a} = \frac{\frac{5a^2}{5}}{} = \frac{a^2}{2a} = \frac{\frac{a^2}{a}}{\frac{2a}{a}} = \frac{a}{2}$$

In One Step

$$\frac{5a^2}{10a} = \frac{\frac{5a^2}{5a}}{} = \frac{a}{2}$$

1 **Problem Set C** Suggested Grouping: Pairs

In this problem set, students simplify fractions with variables in them, using the technique of finding common factors.

In **Problem 1,** students may concentrate on either the variables or the numbers and forget that they need to find common factors of both.

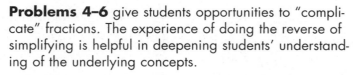

On the **Spot**
Assessment

In **Problem 2,** watch for students who remove the 2 from $2a$ only, rather than getting $2(a + 2)$. The same is true for **Problem 3,** where students may consider x^2 only. If students are convinced that $\frac{2}{2a + 4} = \frac{1}{a + 4}$, have them substitute numbers for a in both expressions to prove that they are not equivalent.

Problems 4–6 give students opportunities to "complicate" fractions. The experience of doing the reverse of simplifying is helpful in deepening students' understanding of the underlying concepts.

2 In **Problems 7–9,** you may want to discuss with the whole class that looking at factors across the products *before* multiplying can make finding the answer easier. For a numeric example, $\frac{5}{6} \cdot \frac{6}{4} = \frac{5 \cdot 6}{6 \cdot 4} = \frac{5 \cdot 6}{4 \cdot 6} = \frac{5}{4} \cdot \frac{6}{6} = \frac{5}{4}$. Students will likely find shortcuts to perform these operations.

3 In **Problems 10–12,** students are asked to divide fractions by fractions. It is worth mentioning the "Remember" in the margin: dividing by a fraction is the same as multiplying by its reciprocal.

Alternatively, students can rewrite both fractions, using a common denominator for the two fractions, and then concentrate on the resulting numerators. For example, $\frac{3}{4} \div \frac{5}{7} = \frac{21}{28} \div \frac{20}{28} = \frac{21}{20}$.

4 **Problem Set Wrap-Up** You may want to review student answers for Problem Set C to be sure students understand the simplification process before they continue to Problem Set D.

5 **Problem Set D** Suggested Grouping: Pairs

In this problem set, students analyze number tricks to see whether they are always true. In doing so, they write and simplify algebraic fractions, making use of the skills they have just learned.

Several problems make use of common mistakes when students are squaring. **Problem 1** involves squaring $2x$, which for many students is not trivial.

In **Problem 2,** students must square $(x + 2)$. Again, watch for students who give the all-too-common, incorrect answer of $x^2 + 4$. You may want to ask them to write the square as a product of two binomials and use the distributive property, or ask them to show you that their answer is correct using a rectangle diagram.

★ indicates multi-step problem

4. Possible answer:

$\dfrac{2}{6 + 2a}$ and $\dfrac{5a}{15a + 5a^2}$

5. Possible answer:

$\dfrac{x^2}{2x}$ and $\dfrac{4x}{8}$

6. Possible answer:

$\dfrac{10y^2z}{2yz^2}$ and $\dfrac{20y}{4z}$

Remember

Dividing $\dfrac{a}{b}$ by $\dfrac{c}{d}$ is the same as multiplying $\dfrac{a}{b}$ by the reciprocal of $\dfrac{c}{d}$:

$$\dfrac{\frac{a}{b}}{\frac{c}{d}} = \dfrac{a}{b} \cdot \dfrac{d}{c}$$

9. $\dfrac{2(d - 1)}{3d}$ or

$\dfrac{2d - 2}{3d}$

10. $\dfrac{5}{9a(a - 4)}$ or

$\dfrac{5}{9a^2 - 36a}$

Problem Set C

Simplify each fraction.

1. $\dfrac{6x^2y}{18x}$ $\dfrac{xy}{3}$ **2.** $\dfrac{2}{2a + 4}$ $\dfrac{1}{a + 2}$ **3.** $\dfrac{x}{x^2 + 2x}$ $\dfrac{1}{x + 2}$

Write two fractions that can be simplified to the given fraction.

4. $\dfrac{1}{3 + a}$ **5.** $\dfrac{x}{2}$ **6.** $\dfrac{5y}{z}$

Find each product. Simplify your answers.

7. $\dfrac{1}{2d} \cdot \dfrac{4}{3}$ $\dfrac{2}{3d}$ **8.** $\dfrac{1}{2} \cdot \dfrac{-2}{d - 5}$ $\dfrac{-1}{d - 5}$

9. $\dfrac{-4(d - 1)}{3} \cdot \dfrac{-1}{2d}$ **10.** $\dfrac{1}{3(a - 4)} \div \dfrac{3a}{5}$

11. $\dfrac{\frac{a}{7}}{\frac{3a}{5}}$ $\dfrac{5}{21}$ **12.** $\dfrac{\frac{1}{a}}{\frac{1}{a + 1}}$ $\dfrac{a + 1}{a}$

You will now use what you have learned to analyze several number tricks.

Problem Set D

Brian made up four number tricks. For each, do the following:

- Check whether or not the trick *always* works. If it always works, explain why.

- If it doesn't always work, does it work with only a few exceptions? If so, what are the exceptions? Explain why it works for all numbers other than those exceptions.

- If it never works or works for only a few numbers, explain how you know.

★ **1.** *Number Trick 1:* Pick a number, any number. Multiply it by 2 and square the result. Add 12. Then divide by 4 and subtract the square of the number you chose at the beginning. Your answer is 3.

★ **2.** *Number Trick 2:* Pick a number, any number. Add 2 to it and square the result. Multiply the new number by 6 and then subtract 24. Divide by your chosen number. Divide again by 6, and then subtract 4. Your answer is your chosen number.

Problem Set D Answers

1. It always works. If you choose x, you get the expression $\dfrac{(2x)^2 + 12}{4} - x^2$, which simplifies to $x^2 + 3 - x^2$, or 3, for any value of x.

2. It works for all numbers except 0. If you choose x, you get the expression $\dfrac{6(x + 2)^2 - 24}{6x} - 4$, which simplifies to $\dfrac{6x^2 + 24x}{6x} - 4 = x + 4 - 4 = x$. It doesn't work for 0 because you can't divide by 0.

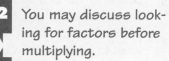

1 You may have students work in pairs.

2 You may discuss looking for factors before multiplying.

3 Point out the "Remember."

4 Be sure students understand the simplification process.

5 You may have students work in pairs.

6 Watch for students who calculate $(x + 2)^2$ incorrectly.

Problem 4 is interesting because it works for all numbers *except* ⁻3. Students should be able to figure out why this is true: if the number were ⁻3, the trick would involve division by 0.

Share & Summarize

These questions emphasize some of the common mistakes made when students simplify fractions. You may want to let students work on them in pairs, and then conduct a full-class discussion of the solutions.

Troubleshooting This investigation concentrates on skills in working with algebraic fractions. This topic will certainly reappear in later years, and there is no need to spend a lot of time on it at this point. You can give students additional examples to work on if you feel it would be helpful, but in general, it is fine to go on to the next lesson, in which students will be adding and subtracting algebraic fractions.

On Your Own Exercises

Practice & Apply: 4–19, pp. 407–408
Connect & Extend: 22–26, pp. 409–410
Mixed Review: 27–36, p. 410

3. It doesn't work in general. If you choose x, you get $\frac{3x-4}{2} + 5$. Solving $\frac{3x-4}{2} + 5 = 6$ gives $x = 2$, so the only number this works for is 2.

★ **3.** *Number Trick 3:* Pick a number, any number. Multiply your number by 3 and then subtract 4. Divide by 2 and add 5. The result is 6.

★ **4. Challenge** *Number Trick 4:* Pick a number, any number. Add 6 to it and multiply the result by the chosen number. Then add 9. Now divide by 3 more than the chosen number, and then subtract the chosen number. Your answer is 3.

It works for all numbers except $^-3$. If you choose x, you get the expression $\frac{(x+6)x+9}{x+3} - x$, which simplifies to $\frac{x^2+6x+9}{x+3} - x = \frac{(x+3)^2}{x+3} - x = x + 3 - x = 3$. You can't use $^-3$ because that would mean you are dividing by 0.

Share & Summarize

Evan simplified each fraction as shown. Check his answers. If he did a problem correctly, say so. If he didn't, explain what is wrong and how to find the right answer.

1. $\frac{3}{x+3} = \frac{1}{x+1}$

2. $\frac{a}{a+4} = \frac{1}{4}$

3. $\frac{5a}{3} \div \frac{3}{a} = \frac{5a}{3} \cdot \frac{a}{3} = \frac{5a^2}{9}$ correct

4. $\frac{12t^2}{35} \cdot \frac{21}{16t} = \frac{9t}{20}$ correct

1. Incorrect; $\frac{3}{x+3}$ can't be simplified because you can't factor a 3 out of $x+3$.

2. Incorrect; $\frac{a}{a+4}$ can't be simplified because you can't factor an a out of $a+4$.

1 You may have students work in pairs and then discuss solutions.

Teacher Notes

On Your Own Exercises

Practice & Apply

1. Consider this equation.

$$y = \frac{2 - x}{(x - 2)(x + 1)}$$

a. For what values of x is y undefined? $2, {}^-1$

b. Explain how you could use the information from Part a to help you sketch a graph of the equation.

2. Every morning a restaurant manager buys $300 worth of fresh fish at the market. One morning she buys fish that is selling for d dollars per pound. The next morning the price has risen $2 per pound.

a. Write an expression for the quantity of fish, in pounds, the manager purchased on the first morning. $\frac{300}{d}$

b. Write an expression for the quantity of fish, in pounds, the manager purchased on the second morning. $\frac{300}{d + 2}$

c. Write an equation for the total quantity of fish the manager purchased on these two days. $\frac{300}{d} + \frac{300}{d + 2}$

d. For what values of d, if any, does your expression from Part c not make *mathematical* sense? $0, {}^-2$

e. For what additional values of d, if any, does your expression not make sense in the situation?

3. Every Friday a delivery person drives her truck 120 miles into the city to make a pickup and then drives back. On one particular Friday, she drove into the city at the posted speed limit, s. However, on the return trip, she was slowed by road construction and had to travel 15 miles per hour below the speed limit.

a. Write an expression for the time it took her to drive into the city.

b. Write an expression for the time her return trip took. $\frac{120}{s - 15}$

c. Write an equation for her total driving time for the round trip.

d. For what values of s, if any, does your expression from Part c not make *mathematical* sense? $0, 15$

e. For what additional values of s, if any, does your expression not make sense in the situation? Possible answer: $s \leq 0$, values that are too large or small for a speed limit, such as $s < 10$ and $s > 80$, or that are not whole numbers

Remember

rate · time = distance

or

$$time = \frac{distance}{rate}$$

1b. Possible answer: The graph will approach the lines $x = 2$ and $x = {}^-1$ but never touch them.

2e. Possible answer: $d \leq 0$, very large values, and values that could not represent dollars and cents

3a. $\frac{120}{s}$ **3c.** $\frac{120}{s} + \frac{120}{s - 15}$

Simplify each fraction.

4. $\frac{12m}{2m}$ 6

5. $\frac{2x}{4xy}$ $\frac{1}{2y}$

6. $\frac{20a^2b}{16ab^2}$ $\frac{5a}{4b}$

7. $\frac{3k}{k^2 - 6k}$ $\frac{3}{k - 6}$

 impactmath.com/self_check_quiz

Investigation 1,
pp. 401–403
Practice & Apply: 1–3
Connect & Extend: 20, 21

Investigation 2,
pp. 403–406
Practice & Apply: 4–19
Connect & Extend: 22–26

Assign Anytime
Mixed Review: 27–36

Exercises 2 and 3:
In answering **Part e** for each of these, students will need to consider issues of domain for the context given. In Exercise 2, they need to think about reasonable values of d that could represent the price of fish per pound, and in Exercise 3 they need to think about reasonable speed limits.

Exercises 4–7:
Watch for students who do not remove common factors correctly.

Exercises 4–7 Extension:
You may want to ask students what values are not possible for the denominators. You may also want to ask what values for the *variables* are not possible. Exercise 7 will be more of a challenge, since students will not learn to solve quadratics using factoring until Chapter 7.

Exercises 8–11 Extension:
You may want to ask students what values are not possible for the denominators. It will be more difficult in these exercises than in Exercises 4–7 to give values for the variables, although it might be worth pointing out that the denominator in Exercise 9 can never be 0.

Exercise 15:
You might want to ask students what steps they took to find the quotient. Many will, by habit, find the reciprocal of the divisor and multiply; however, since the dividend and divisor are the same, the answer has to be 1. Encourage students to look for such shortcuts.

Exercise 17:
Students need to notice that $(x - 2)$ and $(2 - x)$ are opposites; that is, $-(x - 2) = (2 - x)$. Students will be confronted with these kinds of pairings often, and it is important that they have some facility in recognizing them. You might create additional examples to show them, and try to include them whenever you can.

Exercise 19:
Watch for students who incorrectly square $x + 3$ and get $x^2 + 9$ instead of $x^2 + 6x + 9$. Use a rectangle diagram, if necessary, to model the correct answer.

Exercise 20:
Students may guess that y will be undefined when $k = 0$, but they may not see that y is also undefined when $k = 1$. Encourage them to use the distributive property to rewrite $k^2 - k$ as $k(k - 1)$ to see both solutions. This previews solving quadratic equations by factoring, which students will learn in Chapter 7.

★ indicates multi-step problem

Simplify each fraction.

18. It works for all numbers but 0. If you choose n, you get the expression $\frac{(n - 1)^2 - 1}{n} + 2$, which simplifies to $\frac{n^2 - 2n + 1 - 1}{n} + 2 = n - 2 + 2 = n$. It doesn't work for 0 because you can't divide by 0.

8. $\frac{1 + a}{a(1 + a)}$ $\frac{1}{a}$

9. $\frac{3(x + 1)}{6}$ $\frac{x + 1}{2}$

10. $\frac{nm}{m^2 + 2m}$ $\frac{n}{m + 2}$

11. $\frac{3ab}{a^2b^2 - 3ab}$ $\frac{3}{ab - 3}$

Find each product or quotient. Simplify your answers.

12. $\frac{1}{3} \cdot \frac{1}{a}$ $\frac{1}{3a}$

13. $\frac{4}{3} \cdot \frac{d}{2}$ $\frac{2d}{3}$

14. $\frac{1}{5a} \cdot \frac{3a^2}{2}$ $\frac{3a}{10}$

15. $\frac{1}{a} \div \frac{1}{a}$ 1

16. $\frac{m}{4} \div \frac{4}{m}$ $\frac{m^2}{16}$

17. $\frac{-1(x - 2)}{3(2 - x)}$ $\frac{1}{3}$

19. It works for all numbers but $^-1$. If you choose n, you get the expression $\frac{(n + 3)^2 - 4}{n + 1} - 5$, which simplifies to $\frac{n^2 + 6n + 9 - 4}{n + 1} - 5 = \frac{(n + 1)(n + 5)}{n + 1} - 5 = n + 5 - 5 = n$. It doesn't work for $^-1$ because that would mean you are dividing by 0.

For the number tricks in Exercises 18 and 19, do the following:

- Check whether the trick *always* works. If it does, explain why.

- If it doesn't always work, does it work with only a few exceptions? If so, what are the exceptions? Explain why it works for all numbers other than those exceptions.

- If it never works or works for only a few numbers, explain how you know.

★ **18.** Pick a number. Subtract 1 and square the result. Subtract 1 again. Divide by your number. Add 2. The result is your original number.

★ **19.** Pick a number. Add 3 to it, and square the result. Subtract 4. Divide by the number that is 1 more than your chosen number. Subtract 5 from the result. The result is your chosen number.

Connect & Extend

20. Consider this equation.

$$y = \frac{2k^2 - 3k}{k^2 - k}$$

a. For what values of k, if any, does y not have a value? $0, 1$

20b. Possible answer: The graph will approach $x = 0$ and $x = 1$ but never touch or cross these x-values.

b. Explain what will happen to a graph of the equation at the values you found in Part a.

21. Physical Science All objects attract each other with the force called *gravity*. The English mathematician Isaac Newton discovered this formula for calculating the gravitational force between two objects:

$$F = G\left(\frac{Mm}{r^2}\right)$$

In the formula, F is the gravitational force between the two objects, M and m are the masses of the objects, r is the distance between them, and G is a fixed number called the *gravitational constant*.

408 CHAPTER 6 Working with Expressions

In your
own words

Describe a situation that can be represented by an algebraic fraction. (Look at the problems in this lesson if you need ideas.) Discuss the values for which your expression does not make mathematical sense and the values for which your expression does not make sense in the context of the situation.

24a. $\frac{2}{5}$; This value would make the denominator 0.

24b. $x < \frac{2}{5}$; The expression will be positive only when the denominator is positive; that is, when $2 - 5x > 0$, or $x < \frac{2}{5}$.

24c. $x > \frac{2}{5}$; The expression will be negative only when the denominator is negative; that is, when $2 - 5x < 0$, or $x > \frac{2}{5}$.

a. How does the gravitational force between two objects change if the mass of one of the objects doubles? If the mass of one of the objects triples?   It doubles. It triples.

b. How does the gravitational force between two objects change if the distance between the objects doubles? If the distance triples?

c. Suppose the masses of two objects is doubled and the distance between the objects is doubled as well. How does this affect the gravitational force between the objects?

Simplify each expression.

22. $\frac{4k - 2}{2k^2 + 4k - 2}$ $\frac{2k - 1}{k^2 + 2k - 1}$

23. $\frac{(u - 3)(u + 2)(u - 1)}{-1(3 - u)(1 - u)}$ $^{-}u - 2$

24. Consider this equation.

$$y = \frac{24}{2 - 5x}$$

a. For what values of x does y not have a value? Explain.

b. For what values of x will y be positive? Explain.

c. For what values of x will y be negative? Explain.

d. For what values of x will y equal 0? Explain.
none; Possible explanation: A fraction $\frac{a}{b}$ can equal 0 only if $a = 0$.

21b. It is divided by 4. It is divided by 9.

21c. It doesn't. The gravitational force is the same.

Exercise 21:
Students may not be comfortable working with direct and inverse variation involving multiple variables. If they are having difficulty understanding what happens when the mass of one object doubles, you may want to encourage them to choose actual numbers for all the variables to see the effect of changing some of the numbers.

Exercise 22:
After removing the common factor of 2, students may try to find a way to rewrite the denominator as a product of two binomials. If they express frustration at not being able to, let them know that this quadratic expression can't be rewritten in that way, and that they will learn more about recognizing when it's possible and when it's not in Chapter 7.

25a.

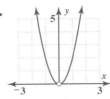

26. All values except 0 and $^-1$. $\frac{1}{m} > \frac{1}{m+1}$ when $m < m+1$ for all values of m. However, $\frac{1}{m}$ has no value when $m = 0$, and $\frac{1}{m+1}$ has no value when $m = ^-1$.

36b. Possible answer: 475; the middle data point is the highest of the four points in the 400–499 range.

25. The equation $y = \frac{(x+1)^2}{x+1}$ can be simplified to $y = x + 1$ for all values of x except $^-1$ (which makes the denominator 0). The graph of $y = \frac{(x+1)^2}{x+1}$ looks like the graph of $y = x + 1$, but with an open circle at the point where $x = ^-1$.

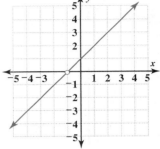

Use this idea to graph each equation.

a. $y = \frac{4x^3}{2x}$ **b.** $y = \frac{4x^2 + 2x}{2x}$

See Additional Answers.

26. For what values of m is it true that $\frac{1}{m} > \frac{1}{m+1}$? Explain.

Evaluate each expression.

27. $\frac{2}{3} + \frac{5}{8}$ $\frac{31}{24}$, or $1\frac{7}{24}$ **28.** $\frac{3}{10} - \frac{1}{4}$ $\frac{1}{20}$ **29.** $\frac{3}{7} - \frac{8}{3}$

30. $\frac{2}{3} \cdot \frac{5}{8}$ $\frac{5}{12}$ **31.** $\frac{3}{10} \div \frac{1}{4}$ $\frac{6}{5}$, or $1\frac{1}{5}$ **32.** $\frac{3}{7}\left(\frac{8}{3}\right)$ $\frac{8}{7}$, or $1\frac{1}{7}$

Rewrite each expression using a single base and a single exponent.

33. $27x^3$ $(3x)^3$ **34.** $a^{12} \cdot (a^2)^{-7}$ **35.** $\frac{32}{c^5}$

36. Statistics Gerry surveyed five fast-food restaurants about the number of calories in the various types of sandwiches they sold. He put his results in a histogram. For example, the first bar in his graph reveals that two of the sandwiches had from 200 to 299 calories.

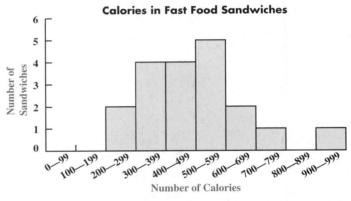

Calories in Fast Food Sandwiches

a. On how many different sandwiches did Gerry gather data?   19

b. Estimate the median for these data. Explain your answer.

c. What does the histogram tell you about the sandwiches at these restaurants?   See Additional Answers.

Additional Answers
25b.

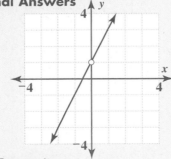

36c. Possible answer: The least number of calories is between 200 and 300, and there are only two sandwiches in this category. One of the sandwiches has between 900 and 1,000 calories. However, most are around 500 calories.

6.5

Adding and Subtracting Algebraic Fractions

Objectives

▶ To add and subtract algebraic fractions using common denominators

▶ To use the graphs of equations containing algebraic fractions to estimate solutions

▶ To solve equations containing algebraic fractions

Overview (pacing: about 4 class periods)

This lesson focuses on addition and subtraction of algebraic fractions. Students use the technique of finding common denominators, just as they would in combining unlike numeric fractions. In the last investigation, students solve equations with algebraic fractions using a variety of techniques, including rewriting with common denominators, graphing, and "clearing" fractions (multiplying both sides by a common denominator).

Advance Preparation

In Investigation 1, you may want to give copies of Master 47 to students.
A transparency of Master 48 may be helpful for going over the Example that introduces Problem Set G.

Lesson Planner

	Summary	Materials	On Your Own Exercises	Assessment Opportunities
Investigation 1 page T411	Students learn the basic process of adding and subtracting algebraic fractions using simple, one-term denominators.	• Master 47	Practice & Apply: 1–8, pp. 421–422 Connect & Extend: 26–30, p. 423 Mixed Review: 47–57, pp. 424–425	On the Spot Assessment, page T412 Share & Summarize, pages T413, 413 Troubleshooting, page T413
Investigation 2 page T414	Students extend their understanding of adding and subtracting fractions, including binomial and factored denominators.		Practice & Apply: 9–16, p. 422 Connect & Extend: 31–38, p. 423 Mixed Review: 47–57, pp. 424–425	Share & Summarize, pages T417, 417 Troubleshooting, page T417
Investigation 3 page T417	Students solve equations involving algebraic fractions.	• Graphing calculators • Transparency of Master 48	Practice & Apply: 17–25, p. 422 Connect & Extend: 39–46, p. 424 Mixed Review: 47–57, pp. 424–425	On the Spot Assessment, page T418 Share & Summarize, pages T420, 420 Troubleshooting, page T420 Informal Assessment, page 425 Quick Quiz, page 425

1 Let the class know that this final lesson in Chapter 6 focuses on the two remaining operations—addition and subtraction—of algebraic fractions. Their knowledge of adding and subtracting numeric fractions will be of great benefit in thinking about the problems in this lesson. Have them go right into the Think & Discuss to make this connection more apparent.

2 ### Think & Discuss
Give students a minute to use the fractions given to create an addition problem and try to find the sum. Then demonstrate one to the class, letting students describe to you how they would go about finding the sum. For some problems, such as $\frac{3}{8} + \frac{3}{10}$, students may have various ways to find a common denominator. You may want to ask for different strategies.

Repeat this for the remaining questions, giving students a minute to write and solve their own problems before demonstrating to the class. Stress the use of finding a common denominator, since this technique mirrors what they will be doing with algebraic fractions.

Investigation 1

In this investigation, students will use a variety of methods to find common denominators as they add and subtract algebraic fractions. Note that finding the least common denominator is not essential; in fact, finding the least common denominator is not always the most efficient way to combine fractions. An alternative strategy is to multiply the given denominators and, if necessary, simplify the result at the end. It is important to be flexible in evaluating how students approach these problems; for this reason, the Example in the text before Problem Set B illustrates strategies students might use to create common denominators.

3 ### Problem Set A Grouping: Pairs
In this problem set, students add and subtract fractions with variables in the denominator, and they begin to think about how they would find common denominators in those cases.

Problem 1 uses only numeric fractions to help students reacquaint themselves with the method of adding and subtracting fractions. You can have students copy the table, or give them Master 47.

6.5

Adding and Subtracting Algebraic Fractions

You have added and subtracted fractions in which the numerator and denominator are both numbers. In this lesson, you will apply what you know to add fractions involving variables.

Think & Discuss

Consider these fractions and mixed numbers.

$$1\frac{1}{2} \qquad \frac{2}{3} \qquad \frac{3}{8} \qquad \frac{3}{10} \qquad 2\frac{5}{12}$$

• Choose any two of the numbers and add them. Describe how you found the common denominator and the sum.   Answers will vary.

• Choose two of the remaining fractions, and subtract the lesser from the greater. Describe how you found the common denominator and the difference.   Answers will vary.

• Finally, subtract the remaining fraction from 10. Describe how you found the common denominator and the difference.
Answers will vary.

Investigation Combining Algebraic Fractions

You will now use what you know about fractions with numbers to add and subtract algebraic fractions—fractions that involve variables.

Problem Set A

1. Copy and complete this addition table.

+	$\frac{8}{5}$	$\frac{3}{2}$	$\frac{3}{4}$
$\frac{1}{2}$	$\frac{21}{10}$	2	$\frac{5}{4}$
$\frac{1}{4}$	$\frac{37}{20}$	$\frac{7}{4}$	1
$\frac{3}{5}$	$\frac{11}{5}$	$\frac{21}{10}$	$\frac{27}{20}$

LESSON 6.5   Adding and Subtracting Algebraic Fractions   **411**

---

1 Tell students they will add and subtract algebraic fractions

2 • For each part, give students a minute to try it on their own, and then demonstrate for the class.

• Stress finding common denominators.

3 Have students work in pairs.

1

In **Problem 2,** watch for students who combine $\frac{100}{w} + \frac{100}{w}$ and get $\frac{200}{2w}$. It is common to make the mistake of adding the denominators as well as the numerators when adding fractions. You can provide counterexamples by using numeric values for w, or by simplifying $\frac{200}{2w}$ to $\frac{100}{w}$, which means the result is the same as the pieces they were adding together. Students may make this error throughout this problem set, and it is a good idea to draw attention to this as a class if you see enough mistakes.

In **Problem 5,** some students may use the common denominator of $6x^2$, which is not the least common denominator, but certainly will work. Do not discourage them from using $6x^2$. They can always simplify at the end.

You might compare methods for finding a common denominator for **Problems 6 and 7.** In each case, one denominator is 2 times the other.

In **Problem 8,** students may use 48 as the common denominator and get $-\frac{10}{48}$ as an answer. This is an acceptable answer.

2 ## Example
Have students explain in their own words the three strategies used here. Each of the strategies has merit, and students can choose whichever feels best for doing the problems in Problem Set B.

If a discussion of finding common denominators by comparing factors has not yet occurred, you may want to prompt such a discussion at this time.

Find each sum or difference.

2. $\dfrac{100}{w} + \dfrac{100}{w}$ $\dfrac{200}{w}$

3. $\dfrac{100}{w} - \dfrac{100}{w}$ 0

4. $\dfrac{100}{w} + \dfrac{100}{w} + \dfrac{100}{w}$ $\dfrac{300}{w}$

5. $\dfrac{1}{2x} + \dfrac{2}{3x}$ $\dfrac{7}{6x}$

6. $\dfrac{m}{3} + \dfrac{m}{6}$ $\dfrac{m}{2}$

7. $\dfrac{y}{p} + \dfrac{1}{2p}$ $\dfrac{2y+1}{2p}$

8. $\dfrac{5}{8} - \dfrac{5}{6}$ $-\dfrac{5}{24}$

9. $\dfrac{3}{2x} - \dfrac{3}{2y}$ $\dfrac{3y-3x}{2xy}$

10. Dave can type an average of *n* words per minute. Write an expression for the number of minutes it takes Dave to type

a. 400 words.

b. 200 words.

c. 1,000 words.

d. Add your expressions from Parts a, b, and c. What does the sum represent in terms of the typing situation?

When you add or subtract algebraic fractions, there are many ways to find a common denominator.

10a. $\dfrac{400}{n}$

10b. $\dfrac{200}{n}$

10c. $\dfrac{1,000}{n}$

10d. $\dfrac{1,600}{n}$; the time it takes Dave to type 1,600 words

EXAMPLE

Evan, Tala, and Lucita have different methods for adding $\dfrac{14}{8x}$ and $\dfrac{3}{4x}$.

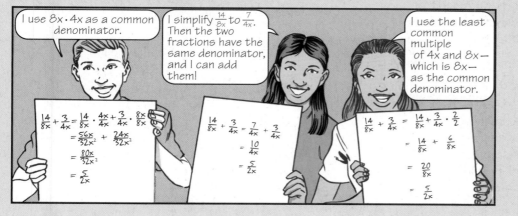

Keep the three methods above in mind as you work on the next problem set.

1 Watch for students who answer $\dfrac{200}{2w}$ for Problem 2.

2
- Have students explain the three strategies in their own words.
- You may mention finding common denominators by comparing factors.

1 Problem Set B Grouping: Pairs

This problem set allows students to become more proficient in their chosen method from the Example. Students may find these problems more difficult than those in Problem Set A. ■

For **Problem 1,** you can have students copy the table or use Master 47, which reproduces the table.

In **Problems 2–4,** students are given fractions that can be simplified before they find common denominators. This is a good strategy but not a necessary one. Some students may prefer to find common denominators immediately.

2 **Problem 5c** may pose some difficulties for students, since it involves division by a fraction. Remind students that they can think about multiplying 40 by the reciprocal of $\frac{5}{6n}$.

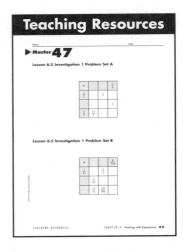

Share & Summarize

3 In general, when students create their own problems, they tend to be more interested in doing them! You may want to write some of their examples on the board, especially those that are more challenging.

4 Ask students to explain how they found their problems for **Question 2.** They will probably reveal some interesting ways of thinking about how to work backward.

Troubleshooting If students are having difficulty adding and subtracting algebraic fractions, they will get more practice in the next two investigations. If necessary, you can give them additional problems to work on.

 **Additional Examples** Find each sum or difference.

$$\frac{6}{4c} - \frac{7}{12c} \quad \frac{11}{12c}$$

$$\frac{5}{10y} + \frac{3}{y^2} \quad \frac{y + 6}{2y^2}$$

On Your Own Exercises

Practice & Apply: 1–8, pp. 421–422
Connect & Extend: p. 423
Mixed Review: pp. 424–425

Problem Set B

1. Copy and complete this addition table.

+	$\frac{1}{2x}$	$\frac{5}{3x}$	$\frac{8}{15x}$
$\frac{1}{3x}$	$\frac{5}{6x}$	$\frac{2}{x}$	$\frac{13}{15x}$
$\frac{3}{4x}$	$\frac{5}{4x}$	$\frac{29}{12x}$	$\frac{77}{60x}$
$\frac{1}{10x}$	$\frac{3}{5x}$	$\frac{53}{30x}$	$\frac{19}{30x}$

Find each sum or difference.

2. $\frac{6}{3x^2} - \frac{2}{2x^2}$ $\frac{1}{x^2}$

3. $\frac{2}{4t} - \frac{2t}{3}$ $\frac{3 - 4t^2}{6t}$

4. $\frac{3}{6m} + \frac{4m}{8m^2}$ $\frac{1}{m}$

5. Camila and Lakita earn money on the weekends by painting people's houses. It takes Camila $2n$ minutes to paint 1 square meter by herself; it takes Lakita $3n$ minutes.

   a. Write an expression for how much area Camila paints in 1 minute. Do the same for Lakita. $\frac{1}{2n}, \frac{1}{3n}$

   b. How much area will the friends paint in 1 minute if they work together? Write your expression as a single algebraic fraction. $\frac{5}{6n}$

   c. If the friends are working together to paint a room with 40 m^2 of wall, how much time will the job take? Show how you found your answer. $40 \div \frac{5}{6n} = 48n$ min

---

Share & Summarize

Consider these five terms.

$$c \qquad 2 \qquad 3 \qquad 2c^2 \qquad 3c^2$$

1. Create four addition or subtraction problems involving fractions whose numerator and denominator are made from these terms (for example, $\frac{c}{2} + \frac{3}{3c^2}$). Use each term only once in a problem. Then, exchange problems with your partner, and solve your partner's problems.

2. Use the terms to create an addition or a subtraction problem with a sum or difference of 3. Possible answer: $\frac{3}{2} + \frac{3c^2}{2c^2}$

1. Possible problems: $\frac{3}{c} + \frac{3c^2}{2} = \frac{6 + 3c^3}{2c}$,
$\frac{3}{2} + \frac{3c^2}{2c^2} = 3$, $\frac{c}{2} - \frac{3}{2c^2} = \frac{c^3 - 3}{2c^2}$,
$\frac{3c^2}{3} - \frac{2}{c} = \frac{c^3 - 2}{c}$

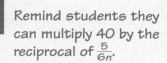
LESSON 6.5 Adding and Subtracting Algebraic Fractions **413**

Investigation 2

This investigation continues looking at adding and subtracting algebraic fractions but concentrates on a more formal, algebraic method of multiplying through by a particular fraction.

Briefly explain to students that they will be learning more about adding and subtracting algebraic fractions in this investigation, working with expressions that are a bit more complicated. Then set students to work on Problem Set C. As this investigation is somewhat lengthy, keep an eye on students' progress.

Problem Set C Suggested Grouping: Pairs
In this problem set, students examine an interesting number pattern when adding two fractions with unit numerators and with denominators that differ by 1.

In **Problem 2,** if students don't see how the sum in Problem 1a fits the pattern, you may need to encourage them to leave the sum as the fraction $\frac{3}{2}$ rather than writing it as a mixed number.

Problems 3 and 4 ask students to articulate the pattern by focusing their attention on the denominators and numerators, respectively. They should combine these observations in a conjecture for **Problem 5.**

In **Problem 7,** students need to find a common denominator for $\frac{1}{m}$ and $\frac{1}{m+1}$ in order to prove their conjectures. Make the connection to numeric fractions to help students realize that a common denominator is simply the product of the denominators. If students are struggling with this, you may want to bring the class together and wrap up the problem set, continuing to the Example on page 415.

Problem Set Wrap-Up Review student answers to Problems 1–6, and to Problem 7 if possible. A sample proof for Problem 7 is given in the Example on page 415.

3. The denominator of the sum is the product of the denominators of the addends.

4. The numerator of the sum is the sum of the denominators of the addends.

Now you will learn more about adding and subtracting algebraic fractions.

Problem Set C

1. Compute each sum without using a calculator.

a. $\frac{1}{1} + \frac{1}{2}$ $\frac{3}{2}$ **b.** $\frac{1}{2} + \frac{1}{3}$ $\frac{5}{6}$ **c.** $\frac{1}{3} + \frac{1}{4}$ $\frac{7}{12}$ **d.** $\frac{1}{4} + \frac{1}{5}$ $\frac{9}{20}$

2. Look for a pattern in the sums in Problem 1. Use it to find $\frac{1}{5} + \frac{1}{6}$ without actually calculating the sum. $\frac{11}{30}$

3. In each part of Problem 1, how does the denominator of the sum relate to the denominators of the two fractions being added?

4. In each part of Problem 1, how does the numerator of the sum relate to the denominators of the two fractions added?

5. Use the patterns you observed to make a conjecture about this sum.

Possible answer: It's equal to $\frac{m + 1 + m}{m(m + 1)}$. $\qquad \frac{1}{m} + \frac{1}{m + 1}$

7. Possible answer: $\frac{1}{m}$ and $\frac{1}{m + 1}$ have a common denominator of $m(m + 1)$, so the sum is $\frac{m + 1}{m(m + 1)} + \frac{m}{m(m + 1)} = \frac{m + 1 + m}{m(m + 1)}$.

6. Consider again the sum $\frac{1}{5} + \frac{1}{6}$.

a. If this sum is equal to $\frac{1}{m} + \frac{1}{m + 1}$, what is the value of m? 5

b. Use your conjecture for Problem 5 and the value of m from Part a to find the sum of $\frac{1}{5} + \frac{1}{6}$. Does the result agree with your prediction in Problem 2? Possible answer: $\frac{5 + 1 + 5}{5(6)} = \frac{11}{30}$; yes

c. To check your result, calculate the sum by finding a common denominator and adding. $\frac{6}{30} + \frac{5}{30} = \frac{11}{30}$

7. Prove It! Try to prove that your conjecture is true.

1 You may have students work in pairs.

2 Problem-Solving Strategy

Look for a pattern

3 If students struggle with the proof, wrap up the problem set and use the Example on page 415 for the proof.

Develop

Example

You can discuss this Example with the class as a continuance of the wrap-up for Problem Set C, possibly even using Problems 1 and 2 of Problem Set D as part of the discussion.

If enough students were able to find their own proof for Problem 7 of Problem Set C, however, you may prefer to let students read the Example and continue to Problem Set D, which asks specific questions about the process in the Example.

Problem Set D Suggested Grouping: Pairs

Students analyze a correct and an incorrect approach to finding a common denominator. The correct approach involves multiplying through by a fraction. This concept was presented in the initial Think & Discuss.

You may prefer to use **Problems 1 and 2** as part of a class discussion (see the Example notes above) and then let partners work on **Problem 3.** Otherwise, have partners answer these three problems.

Problem Set Wrap-Up

Before moving on to the Example on page 416, discuss with the class Ben's method for adding the fractions. Ben makes a common mistake when he adds 1 to both the numerator and the denominator of the fraction. You can provide a simple counterexample.

Does $\frac{2}{3}$ equal $\frac{2+1}{3+1}$?

Most students will see immediately that adding 1 to both the numerator and the denominator changes the value of the fraction.

EXAMPLE

Here's how Lydia thought about the sum of $\frac{1}{m}$ and $\frac{1}{m+1}$.

"When I add $\frac{1}{m}$ and $\frac{1}{m+1}$, I use a common denominator of $m(m+1)$, the product of the two denominators."

$$\frac{1}{m} + \frac{1}{m+1} = \frac{1}{m} \cdot \frac{m+1}{m+1} + \frac{1}{m+1} \cdot \frac{m}{m}$$

$$= \frac{m+1}{m(m+1)} + \frac{m}{m(m+1)}$$

$$= \frac{m+1+m}{m(m+1)}$$

$$= \frac{2m+1}{m(m+1)}$$

1 Discuss the proof if necessary, or let students read it and continue with Problem Set D.

Problem Set D

Discuss Lydia's strategy with your partner. Make sure you understand how each line follows from the previous line.

1. to get a common denominator of $m(m+1)$

1. Why did Lydia multiply the first fraction by $\frac{m+1}{m+1}$?

2. to get a common denominator of $m(m+1)$

2. Why did she multiply the second fraction by $\frac{m}{m}$?

3. Ben says, "I have an easier method for adding $\frac{1}{m}$ and $\frac{1}{m+1}$. Here's what I did."

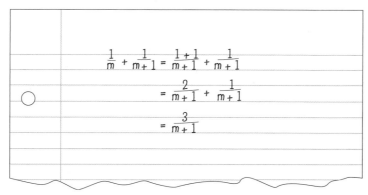

$$\frac{1}{m} + \frac{1}{m+1} = \frac{1+1}{m+1} + \frac{1}{m+1}$$

$$= \frac{2}{m+1} + \frac{1}{m+1}$$

$$= \frac{3}{m+1}$$

3. No; he didn't find a common denominator correctly. He added 1 to the numerator and denominator of the first fraction, which changes the value of the fraction.

Is Ben's method correct? Explain.

2 You may have students work in pairs, or discuss Problems 1 and 2 as a class before letting pairs complete Problem 3.

3 Discuss Ben's incorrect method with the class.

LESSON 6.5 Adding and Subtracting Algebraic Fractions **415**

Example

Read through the Example with the class. Mention that it would have been fine to find the common denominator in the first step if students didn't see that the first fraction could be simplified, and ask what the denominator would have been in that case. Then point out that at the end, however, they would find that their expression could be simplified further. Also note that there is no reason to multiply out the two binomials in the denominator.

Problem Set E Suggested Grouping: Pairs

In this problem set, students are asked to add or subtract algebraic fractions that have binomials in the denominators. Stress that students should try to organize their work carefully in setting up the problems and in multiplying numerators and denominators by the same expression. Problems like these can occupy a good deal of space on the page, and often students who are careless or less organized in their work have great difficulty obtaining correct answers.

In **Problems 2 and 6,** watch for students who fail to distribute the negative sign correctly in doing the subtraction. It is worth the time to go over one of these problems carefully on the board.

In **Problems 4 and 5,** students might notice that they can simplify one of the fractions before they construct a common denominator.

When adding or subtracting algebraic fractions, it is often easiest to leave the numerator and the denominator in factored form. Knowing what the factors are allows you to recognize and identify common factors more easily.

EXAMPLE

Find this sum:

$$\frac{2x}{x(x-1)} + \frac{5}{(x-1)(x+2)}$$

The factored denominators make it easy to simplify the first fraction and then to find a common denominator.

You can simplify the first fraction by dividing the numerator and the denominator by x. Then $(x-1)(x+2)$ can be used as a common denominator of the resulting fractions.

$$\frac{2x}{x(x-1)} + \frac{5}{(x-1)(x+2)} = \frac{2}{x-1} + \frac{5}{(x-1)(x+2)}$$

$$= \frac{2}{x-1} \cdot \frac{x+2}{x+2} + \frac{5}{(x-1)(x+2)}$$

$$= \frac{2(x+2)+5}{(x-1)(x+2)}$$

$$= \frac{2x+9}{(x-1)(x+2)}$$

1 • Read the Example with the class.

• Point out that students could find the common denominator without simplifying first.

• Note there is no reason to expand the denominator.

2 You may have students work in pairs.

3 You may want to go over Probem 2 or 6 to be sure students are distributing the negative sign properly.

Problem Set E

Find each sum or difference. Simplify your answers if possible.

1. $\frac{1}{m} + \frac{2}{m+1}$ $\frac{3m+1}{m(m+1)}$

2. $\frac{4}{m} - \frac{1}{m-1}$ $\frac{3m-4}{m(m-1)}$

3. $\frac{4}{b+2} + \frac{b}{b+3}$ $\frac{b^2+6b+12}{(b+2)(b+3)}$

4. $\frac{2(x+1)}{x(x+1)} - \frac{1}{x-3}$ $\frac{x-6}{x(x-3)}$

5. $\frac{10}{x+4} + \frac{3x}{9x^2}$ $\frac{31x+4}{3x(x+4)}$

6. $\frac{2x}{x-1} - \frac{x+1}{x+3}$ $\frac{x^2+6x+1}{(x-1)(x+3)}$

Problem 7 is similar to the addition problems students analyzed in Problem Set C.

1 Share & Summarize

You may want to have students come to the board to present their ways of thinking about this subtraction problem. It is good experience for them to verbalize the processes they use to compute the difference.

Troubleshooting If students are having difficulty adding and subtracting algebraic fractions, you may want to create a few more examples for them to work on or have them create their own examples.

On Your Own Exercises

Practice & Apply: 9–16, p. 422
Connect & Extend: 31–38, p. 423
Mixed Review: 47–57, pp. 424–425

Investigation 3

Here students solve equations with algebraic fractions. They learn how to "clear" fractions by multiplying both sides by a common denominator. They also check their answers to make sure the denominators are not 0 for the solutions they find.

2 Think & Discuss

Write the two equations on the board, and ask students to volunteer ways they might solve each equation.

$$\frac{x}{2} = \frac{9}{6} \qquad \frac{50}{3.6} = \frac{11}{m}$$

Problem-Solving Strategies There are many strategies students might propose.

- In the first equation, multiply both sides by 2 to "undo" dividing by 2.

- In the first equation, multiply both sides by 12 to clear 6 and 2 from the denominators.

- In the first equation, multiply both sides by 6 to clear the denominators.

- In the second equation, multiply both sides by $3.6m$ to clear the denominators.

- In the second equation, rewrite the proportion as $\frac{3.6}{50} = \frac{m}{11}$, and then multiply both sides by 11.

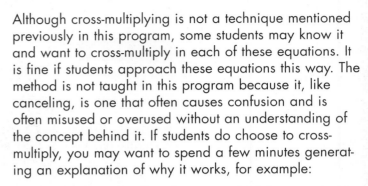

Although cross-multiplying is not a technique mentioned previously in this program, some students may know it and want to cross-multiply in each of these equations. It is fine if students approach these equations this way. The method is not taught in this program because it, like canceling, is one that often causes confusion and is often misused or overused without an understanding of the concept behind it. If students do choose to cross-multiply, you may want to spend a few minutes generating an explanation of why it works, for example:

In the equation $\frac{a}{b} = \frac{c}{d}$, cross-multiplying means you multiply the denominator of each fraction by the numerator of the other and set the two products equal: $bc = ad$.

Consider what you would get if you found a common denominator. What is the common denominator? *bd*

How would you rewrite $\frac{a}{b}$ using the common denominator? How would you rewrite $\frac{c}{d}$? Multiply $\frac{a}{b}$ by $\frac{d}{d}$ to get $\frac{ad}{bd}$; multiply $\frac{c}{d}$ by $\frac{b}{b}$ to get $\frac{bc}{bd}$.

We now have the equation $\frac{ad}{bd} = \frac{bc}{bd}$. Suppose we know that bd is just a number, like 3. Then we would have $\frac{ad}{3} = \frac{bc}{3}$. When you have two equivalent fractions with the same denominator, what does that tell you about the numerators? *They have to be equal.*

That means $ad = bc$, which is what cross-multiplying gave us.

7. Consider these subtraction problems.

$$\frac{1}{2} - \frac{1}{3} \qquad \frac{1}{3} - \frac{1}{4} \qquad \frac{1}{4} - \frac{1}{5}$$

a. Find each difference. $\frac{1}{6}, \frac{1}{12}, \frac{1}{20}$

b. Use the pattern in your answers to Part a to solve this subtraction problem without actually calculating the difference. $\frac{1}{30}$

$$\frac{1}{5} - \frac{1}{6}$$

7c. $\frac{1}{m(m + 1)}$ or $\frac{1}{m^2 + m}$

c. Use the pattern to find this difference.

$$\frac{1}{m} - \frac{1}{m + 1}$$

d. Prove It! Use algebra to show that your answer to Part c is correct.

$$\frac{1}{m} - \frac{1}{m + 1} = \frac{m + 1}{m(m + 1)} - \frac{m}{m(m + 1)} = \frac{m + 1 - m}{m(m + 1)} = \frac{1}{m(m + 1)}$$

Share & Summarize

In the Example on page 415, Lydia explains how she thinks about adding algebraic fractions. Compute the following difference, and explain how *you* think about figuring it out. $\frac{x - 1}{2x(x + 1)}$; Explanations will vary.

$$\frac{1}{x + 1} - \frac{1}{2x}$$

1 You may have students present their thinking.

Investigation ▶3 Solving Equations with Fractions

You have already solved equations involving algebraic fractions. For example, in earlier grades, you have solved proportions such as these:

$$\frac{x}{2} = \frac{9}{6} \qquad \frac{50}{3.6} = \frac{11}{m}$$

2 Ask volunteers how they might solve these.

Think & Discuss

Describe some ways you could solve each of these equations.

$$\frac{x}{2} = \frac{9}{6} \qquad \frac{50}{3.6} = \frac{11}{m}$$

Possible answer: For the first equation, multiply both sides by 12 to get $6x = 18$, and then divide both sides by 6 to get $x = 3$; or multiply both sides by 6 to get $3x = 9$, and then divide both sides by 3. For the second equation, multiply both sides by 3.6 to get $50m = 39.6$, and then divide both sides by 50 to get $m = 0.792$.

3 If students know about and want to use cross-multiplying, help them understand why it works.

LESSON 6.5 Adding and Subtracting Algebraic Fractions **417**

Problem Set F Grouping: Pairs

In this problem set, students practice using their own methods of choice to solve some simple equations involving algebraic fractions. None of these problems have variables in the denominator. The next problem set will introduce equations with variables in the denominator and the considerations they involve.

Problem-Solving Strategies Students might invent several ways to solve equations containing algebraic fractions. None of these should be discouraged at this point. It is helpful to expose students to a variety of appropriate methods for solving these equations so that they don't rely on one rote way. Students might:

- use methods already learned, such as backtracking and doing the same thing to both sides

- think about the two sides of the equation as equivalent fractions and look for a factor to multiply the numerator and denominator of one fraction by to get a common denominator

- use methods for solving proportion problems, such as multiplying both sides of the equation by one of the denominators

- graph the two sides to see where a solution would fall

In **Problem 1,** watch for students who multiply both sides by 4 but forget to multiply 4 by both x and -8 on the right side of the equation.

Problems 5 and 6 require a little more thought. Students need to reverse the operation in each of these to find a solution: to discover what must be added to something to produce a result requires the subtraction operation.

Problem 7 presents a graphing approach to solve equations. It is important to point out to students that they need to answer **Part c** to be sure their estimate is correct, because the graphing approach does not guarantee an exact solution.

Problem Set Wrap-Up You may want to go over student answers before continuing.

Problem Set F

Solve each equation using any method you like. You may want to use different methods for different equations.

1. $\dfrac{3x - 6}{4} = x - 8$ 26

2. $\dfrac{t}{2} + \dfrac{t}{3} = {}^-1$ $-\dfrac{6}{5}$, or $-1\dfrac{1}{5}$

3. $\dfrac{4a}{5} - \dfrac{2 - a}{4} = 30$ $\dfrac{610}{21}$, or $29\dfrac{1}{21}$

4. $\dfrac{p}{5} - p = {}^-0.4$ 0.5

5. What fraction added to $\dfrac{2x - 1}{4}$ equals $\dfrac{x^2 - 4}{4}$? $\dfrac{x^2 - 2x - 3}{4}$

6. What fraction subtracted from $\dfrac{k + 3}{5}$ equals $\dfrac{k - 3}{15}$? $\dfrac{2k + 12}{15}$

7. Evan estimated the solution of the equation $\dfrac{n + 7}{2} + \dfrac{n}{3} = 10$ by finding the intersection of the graphs of these two equations.

$$y = \dfrac{n + 7}{2} + \dfrac{n}{3} \qquad\qquad y = 10$$

   a. Explain why Evan's method works.

   b. Graph both equations in the same window of your calculator, and use the graphs to estimate the solution.

   c. Check your estimate by solving the original equation using whatever method you prefer.   7.8

All the equations in Problem Set F contain one or more fractions with variables in the numerator. When you solve equations with variables in the denominators, you need to check that the "solutions" you find do not make any denominators in the original equation equal to 0.

7a. Possible answer: The intersection includes all the points where $y = \dfrac{n + 7}{2} + \dfrac{n}{3}$ and $y = 10$. So for every intersection point, $\dfrac{n + 7}{2} + \dfrac{n}{3} = 10$.

7b.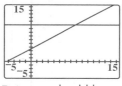

Estimates should be about 7.8.

1 ▸ Example

Bring the class together to go over the Example, which presents the simple and easy equation-solving strategy of clearing the fractions.

2 ▸

You may want to display a transparency of Master 48, draw the graph of the parabola $y = 5x^2 + 12x + 4$ on the board, or project the graphing calculator image on the overhead, and have students estimate the solution or solutions. (There is no need to take more time in letting all students graph the parabola on their own calculators.)

3 ▸

It is *vital* that students check the solution in the original equation. Stress that $^-2$ is not a solution of the original equation since the denominator would be 0.

Teaching Resources

▸ Master **48**

Lesson 6.5 Investigation 3 Example

66 CHAPTER 6 Working with Expressions   TEACHING RESOURCES

Solve the equation $\frac{5x + 10}{x + 2} = \frac{3}{x + 1}$.

One way to solve this equation is to "clear" the fractions by multiplying both sides by a common denominator of all the fractions in the equation—

$$\frac{(x + 2)(x + 1)}{1} \cdot \frac{5x + 10}{x + 2} = \frac{3}{x + 1} \cdot \frac{(x + 2)(x + 1)}{1}$$

—and then simplify the resulting equation:

$$\frac{x + 2}{x + 2} \cdot (x + 1)(5x + 10) = 3(x + 2) \cdot \frac{x + 1}{x + 1}$$

$$1 \cdot (x + 1)(5x + 10) = 3(x + 2) \cdot 1$$

$$5x^2 + 15x + 10 = 3x + 6$$

Rearranging the equation to set one side equal to 0 will allow you to solve it by graphing.

$$5x^2 + 12x + 4 = 0$$

In this case, the simplified equation is quadratic. You can estimate a solution by graphing $y = 5x^2 + 12x + 4$ and finding the points where $y = 0$.

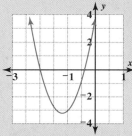

The solutions are approximately $^-2$ and $^-0.4$. Check these values *in the original equation.* Since $^-2$ makes the denominator of $\frac{5x + 10}{x + 2}$ equal to 0, it is *not* a solution of the original equation. The number $^-0.4$ makes the original equation true, so $^-0.4$ is a solution, $^-2$ is not.

1 Go over the Example with the class.

2 Problem-Solving Strategy

Use a graph

3 Stress the importance of checking solutions.

LESSON 6.5 Adding and Subtracting Algebraic Fractions **419**

Problem Set G Grouping: Pairs

This problem set includes problems with variables in the denominator.

Some students may want to first write both sides of an equation over a common denominator, and then clear the fractions by setting the numerators equal to each other. For example, in Problem 1, they would multiply the left side by $\frac{k-3}{k-3}$ and the right side by $\frac{7}{7}$, and then, since the denominator on both sides is $7(k-3)$, they would set the numerators equal to each other; in effect, they are multiplying both sides by $7(k-3)$. You may want to point this out, but encourage them to work the problems as they prefer.

Problem 4 is worth a class discussion, perhaps as a Problem Set Wrap-Up. If students notice that $a^2 - 4$ is equivalent to $(a - 2)(a + 2)$, they will see that the simplest common denominator is $(a - 2)(a + 2)$. If they do not recognize the expression as the difference of two squares, they will still get the right answer but it will take longer. This is a good place to reinforce that if they are skillful in recognizing algebraic patterns in expressions, they can be much more efficient in solving them. After all, one of the reasons for learning algebra is to make life simpler!

Share & Summarize

Have students work in pairs and discuss how they would explain their solutions. After they come to agreement, have them write their explanation down. You might use it as a portfolio entry or have students submit it for extra credit. Ask students to present their solutions to the class.

Troubleshooting If students are having difficulty solving equations with algebraic fractions, go back to some simpler examples like those in the Think & Discuss on page 417. Encourage students to articulate the ways in which they are thinking about solving these equations and to try to identify one solution method that seems to make sense. Provide similar problems so students can use this method again.

On Your Own Exercises

Practice & Apply: 17–25, p. 422
Connect & Extend: 39–46, p. 424
Mixed Review: 47–57 pp. 424–425

As you solve the equations that follow, be sure to check that your solutions don't make any of the denominators in the original equation equal 0.

MATERIALS
graphing calculator
(optional)

Problem Set G

Solve each equation using whatever method you like. You may want to use different methods for different equations. For some, you may need to use a graph to estimate solutions.

1. $\dfrac{10}{7} = \dfrac{k+1}{k-3}$ $\dfrac{37}{3}$

2. no solution (The only apparent solution, 3, makes the denominator 0.)

2. $\dfrac{6-2x}{x-3} = 8$

3. $\dfrac{2}{g+1} - \dfrac{2}{g-1} = 4$ 0

4. $\dfrac{20-a}{a^2-4} = \dfrac{5}{a-2} + \dfrac{3}{a+2}$ $\dfrac{16}{9}$

5. $0 = \dfrac{2}{s+3} + \dfrac{s}{s+2}$ $^-1, ^-4$

6. no solution (The only apparent solution, $^-5$, makes the denominator 0.)

6. $\dfrac{^-60-12z}{z+5} = ^-120$

Share Summarize

Choose one problem from Problem Set G and explain how you solved it so that a student who was absent could understand.
Possible answer: For Problem 6, I multiplied both sides by $z + 5$ to eliminate the fraction. That gave me $^-60 - 12z = ^-120z - 600$. I added $120z$ and 60 to both sides to get $108z = ^-540$. I then divided both sides by 108 to get $z = ^-5$. Then I substituted $^-5$ into the original equation, which gave a denominator of 0, so there isn't a solution.

3 • Have students work in pairs and write their agreed-upon answers.

• You might have some present their explanations.

Teacher Notes

Practice  **Apply**

Find each sum or difference.

1. $\frac{9}{8} - \frac{8}{9}$ $\frac{17}{72}$

2. $\frac{x}{4} + \frac{y}{2}$ $\frac{x + 2y}{4}$

3. $\frac{2xy}{3} - \frac{1}{6}$ $\frac{4xy - 1}{6}$

4. $\frac{1}{x} + \frac{2}{x^2}$ $\frac{x + 2}{x^2}$

5. $\frac{c}{a} - \frac{a}{c}$ $\frac{c^2 - a^2}{ac}$

6. Marcus and his sister Annette have part-time jobs after school at the grocery store. When she's stacking cans in a display at the end of an aisle, Annette can put 500 cans up in z minutes. Marcus works half as fast as Annette, stacking 500 cans in $2z$ minutes.

   a. Write an expression for how many cans Marcus stacks in 1 minute. $\frac{500}{2z}$ or $\frac{250}{z}$

   b. Write an expression for how many cans Annette stacks in 1 minute. $\frac{500}{z}$

6c. $\frac{750}{z}$

   c. Working together, how many cans can Marcus and Annette stack in 1 minute? Express your answer as a single algebraic fraction.

   d. The store manager has asked the two to create a display using 750 cans. How long will it take them? z minutes

7. Esperanza and Jasmine are making the same 300-mile drive in separate cars. Esperanza drives an average of n miles per hour. Jasmine drives 1.5 times as fast.

7a. $\frac{300}{1.5n}$, or $\frac{200}{n}$

   a. Write an expression for the time it takes Jan to drive the 300 miles.

7b. $\frac{300}{n} - \frac{300}{1.5n}$, or $\frac{300}{n} - \frac{200}{n}$, or $\frac{100}{n}$

   b. Assume Jasmine and Esperanza left at the same time. Write an expression for the difference in time between Jasmine's arrival at the final destination and Esperanza's arrival.

7c. $\frac{200}{n} + \frac{300}{n}$, or $\frac{500}{n}$

   c. Write an expression for the total time both women spent traveling.

On Your Own Exercises

Investigation 1,
   pp. 411–413
Practice & Apply: 1–8
Connect & Extend: 26–30

Investigation 2,
   pp. 414–417
Practice & Apply: 9–16
Connect & Extend: 31–38

Investigation 3,
   pp. 417–420
Practice & Apply: 17–25
Connect & Extend: 39–46

Assign Anytime
Mixed Review: 47–57

Exercise 6d:
This exercise asks students to solve an equation. Though students don't focus on solving equations until Investigation 3, they should be able to simplify the equation to $\frac{1,500}{2z} = 750$ or even $\frac{750}{z} = 750$. At that point, they should see that the answer is $z = 1$.

Exercise 7:
This exercise might confuse students if they do not think about the relationship between distance, rate, and time. If they have difficulty, suggest that they substitute a number for n and then think about calculating the time it takes. In **Part b,** if they don't realize that Esperanza's time is greater than Jasmine's time, they will get a negative answer.

Exercise 8:
You will have to decide whether unsimplified answers are acceptable in this table. Since there is no instruction to indicate that the answers have to be in lowest terms, you may not want to stress that simplest form is necessary.

Exercises 17–22:
Make sure students check their solutions in each of these exercises.

Exercise 21:
Students may want to combine all of the terms with denominator $w + 5$ before they look to clear fractions.

8. Copy and complete this addition table.

+	$\dfrac{5}{2x}$	$\dfrac{4}{x}$	$2x$
$\dfrac{1}{4x}$	$\dfrac{11}{4x}$	$\dfrac{17}{4x}$	$\dfrac{8x^2 + 1}{4x}$
$-\dfrac{2}{3x}$	$\dfrac{11}{6x}$	$\dfrac{10}{3x}$	$\dfrac{-2 + 6x^2}{3x}$
$\dfrac{3 + x}{2}$	$\dfrac{x^2 + 3x + 5}{2x}$	$\dfrac{x^2 + 3x + 8}{2x}$	$\dfrac{5x + 3}{2}$

Find each sum or difference.

9. $\dfrac{1}{m} - \dfrac{2}{m + 1}$ $\dfrac{1 - m}{m(m + 1)}$

10. $\dfrac{4}{m} + \dfrac{1}{m + 1}$ $\dfrac{5m + 4}{m(m + 1)}$

11. $\dfrac{3}{d} + \dfrac{4}{d + 1}$ $\dfrac{7d + 3}{d(d + 1)}$

12. $\dfrac{3}{c} - \dfrac{4}{c - 1}$ $\dfrac{-c - 3}{c(c - 1)}$

13. $\dfrac{a}{a + 4} + \dfrac{3a}{5}$ $\dfrac{3a^2 + 17a}{5(a + 4)}$

14. $\dfrac{x^2}{x^2 - 1} - \dfrac{1}{x^2 - 1}$ 1

15. $\dfrac{5}{k} - \dfrac{5}{k + 1}$ $\dfrac{5}{k(k + 1)}$

16. $\dfrac{2y - 1}{4} - \dfrac{y}{2}$ $-\dfrac{1}{4}$

Solve each equation using any method you like.

17. $\dfrac{2x}{3} + \dfrac{1}{4} = x - 1$ $\dfrac{15}{4}$

18. $\dfrac{v - 2}{3} + \dfrac{v}{2} = 10$ $\dfrac{64}{5}$

19. $\dfrac{n + 1}{n - 1} = 3$ 2

20. $\dfrac{2 - u}{u + 1} = 5$ $-\dfrac{1}{2}$

21. $\dfrac{8}{w + 5} - \dfrac{2}{w + 5} = \dfrac{2}{w} + \dfrac{1}{w + 5}$ $\dfrac{10}{3}$

22. $\dfrac{3}{c - 1} + \dfrac{3}{c + 1} = \dfrac{21 - c}{c^2 - 1}$ 3

23. What fraction added to $\dfrac{r + 1}{r}$ equals 1? $-\dfrac{1}{r}$

24. What fraction subtracted from $\dfrac{2 - x}{7}$ is equal to $\dfrac{x}{14}$? $\dfrac{4 - 3x}{14}$

25. What fraction subtracted from $\dfrac{1}{v}$ is equal to $\dfrac{3v}{2}$? $\dfrac{2 - 3v^2}{2v}$

Connect & Extend

26. Economics Meg earns $70 for w hours of picking fruit. Her friend Rashid, who is more experienced and works faster, earns $80 for w hours. Together they earn $1,000 in a week.

Write a brief explanation for each expression.

a. $\dfrac{70}{w}$ **b.** $\dfrac{80}{w}$ **c.** $\dfrac{70}{w} + \dfrac{80}{w}$

d. $\dfrac{150}{w}$ **e.** $1,000 \div \dfrac{150}{w}$ **f.** $1,000 \div \dfrac{70}{w}$

g. $1,000 \div \dfrac{80}{w}$

Find each sum or difference.

27. $\dfrac{c}{ab} - \dfrac{a}{bc}$ $\quad \dfrac{c^2 - a^2}{abc}$

28. $\dfrac{2x}{2y} + \dfrac{y}{x}$ $\quad \dfrac{x^2 + y^2}{xy}$

29. $\dfrac{G + 1}{G - 1} - \dfrac{2}{G + 1}$ $\quad \dfrac{G^2 + 3}{G^2 - 1}$

30. $\dfrac{4 - 2y}{6} + \dfrac{y}{4}$ $\quad \dfrac{8 - y}{12}$

31. $\dfrac{1}{x^2 y} + \dfrac{1}{xy}$ $\quad \dfrac{1 + x}{x^2 y}$

32. $\dfrac{1}{p} + \dfrac{1}{p^2} + \dfrac{1}{y}$ $\quad \dfrac{py + y + p^2}{p^2 y}$

33. $\dfrac{1}{xc} + 1 - \dfrac{1}{c}$ $\quad \dfrac{1 + xc - x}{xc}$

34. $\dfrac{a + 1}{1} + \dfrac{1}{a - 1}$ $\quad \dfrac{a^2}{a - 1}$

35. $2 - \dfrac{2}{s + 1} - \dfrac{s}{s + 1}$ $\quad \dfrac{s}{s + 1}$

36. $\dfrac{1}{m} + \dfrac{1}{m + 1} + \dfrac{1}{m + 2}$ $\quad \dfrac{3m^2 + 6m + 2}{m(m + 1)(m + 2)}$

37. $\dfrac{1}{m} - \dfrac{1}{m + 1} - \dfrac{1}{m + 2}$ $\quad \dfrac{2 - m^2}{m(m + 1)(m + 2)}$

38. Ms. Diaz drove 135 miles to visit her mother. She knew the speed limit increased by 10 mph after the first 75 miles, but she couldn't remember what the speed limits were.

a. Write an expression representing the amount of time it will take Ms. Diaz to drive the first 75 miles if she travels the speed limit of x mph. $\dfrac{75}{x}$

b. Write an expression representing the amount of time it will take her to drive the remaining 60 miles at the new speed limit. $\dfrac{60}{x + 10}$

c. Write an expression for Ms. Diaz's total driving time. Combine the parts of your expression into a single algebraic fraction. $\dfrac{75}{x} + \dfrac{60}{x + 10} = \dfrac{135x + 750}{x(x + 10)}$

26a. Meg's hourly pay rate

26b. Rashid's hourly pay rate

26c. their hourly pay rate if they work together

26d. their hourly pay rate if they work together

26e. total hours it takes both working together to earn $1,000

26f. total hours it takes Meg working alone to earn $1,000

26g. total hours it takes Mollie working alone to earn $1,000

Exercise 26:
This exercise is a good tool to assess students' understanding of the concept of a variable, as well as how facile they are interpreting a situation in mathematical symbols. This is a good problem to go over with the class.

Exercise 29:
Students need to pay attention to distributing $^-2$ over $G - 1$. This may cause some errors.

Exercise 36:
Students will get practice combining like terms in this exercise. Watch for students who compute $m^2 + m^2 + m^2$ as m^6.

★ indicates multi-step problem

In your
own words

Write an addition
problem involving
two algebraic
fractions with
different algebraic
expressions in
their denominators.
Explain step-by-
step how to add
the two fractions.

45. $\frac{51.75}{x} + \frac{40.5}{2x + 2} =$
$\frac{162}{2x + 2}$; $5.75 per
hour at the market,
$13.50 tutoring

46b. $\frac{Ax - A + Bx + B}{x^2 - 1}$

46c. The numerators on
both sides of the
original equation
must be equal, so
$Ax + Bx = 5x$ and
$^-A + B = 1$.

Mixed Review

Solve each equation using any method you like.

39. $\frac{p + 2}{2} + \frac{p - 1}{5} = p + 1$ $^-\frac{2}{3}$

40. $\frac{r - 8}{3} + \frac{r - 5}{2} = r - 5$ $^-1$

41. $\frac{T - 1}{4} + \frac{2 - T}{3} + \frac{T + 1}{2} = 3$ 5

42. $\frac{v - 2}{4} + \frac{2}{v - 1} + \frac{1}{2} = \frac{v^2 - 9}{4v - 4}$ 17

43. $\frac{Z - 5}{2} - \frac{3}{Z + 5} = \frac{(Z + 1)(Z - 3)}{2Z + 10}$ 14

44. $\frac{3}{x - 3} + \frac{4}{x + 3} = \frac{21 - x}{x^2 - 9}$ no solution

★ **45.** Jing earns x dollars per hour
bagging groceries at the local
market. She also works as a math
tutor. Her hourly tutoring rate is
$2 more than twice her hourly rate
at the market.

Last week Jing earned $51.75 at the
market and $40.50 tutoring. She realized
that if she had spent all her working hours
that week tutoring, she would have earned
$162! Write and solve an equation to find
Jing's hourly rate for each job.

46. For two numbers A and B,

$$\frac{5x + 1}{x^2 - 1} = \frac{A}{x + 1} + \frac{B}{x - 1}$$

a. What is a common denominator for $\frac{A}{x + 1}$ and $\frac{B}{x - 1}$? $x^2 - 1$

b. Find the sum $\frac{A}{x + 1} + \frac{B}{x - 1}$ using the common denominator you
found in Part a. Write the sum without parentheses.

c. Explain why you can use this system to find the values of A and B:

$$A + B = 5$$
$$^-A + B = 1$$

d. Solve the system to find A and B. $A = 2, B = 3$

Evaluate without using a calculator.

47. $\sqrt{(^-18)^2}$ 18 **48.** $^-\sqrt{7^2}$ $^-7$ **49.** $^-(\sqrt{64})^2$ $^-64$ **50.** $(^-\sqrt{49})^2$ 49

424 CHAPTER 6 Working with Expressions

51. a and d, b and f

51. Which of the following are equal? Find all matching pairs.

    a. 12   **b.** 12^{-1} **c.** $4\sqrt{\frac{1}{9}}$

    d. $4\left(\frac{1}{3}\right)^{-1}$ **e.** $\sqrt{\frac{4}{9}}$ **f.** the reciprocal of 12

52. Geometry This figure has both reflection symmetry and rotation symmetry.

    a. How many lines of symmetry does it have?   5

    b. What is the angle of rotation?   72°

Just the facts

The U.S. Mint decided to issue 5 state quarters each year in the order in which they ratified the Constitution and joined the Union. The quarter for New York, the 11th state admitted to the Union, was the first issued in the year 2001.

53. A figure has an area of a cm². An enlargement of the figure using a scale factor of f would have what area? af^2 cm²

Rewrite each equation in the form $y = mx + b$.

54. $2(y + x) + 1 = 3x - 2y + 3$ $y = \frac{1}{4}x + \frac{1}{2}$

55. $6y + \frac{3}{7}x - 2 = 0$ $y = -\frac{1}{14}x + \frac{1}{3}$

56. $8 = {}^{-}(3x + 4) + (4 - y) - (2y + 10)$ $y = {}^{-}x - 6$

57. In 1999 the United States began making a series of quarters whose reverse sides are designed by different states. Chris began collecting the quarters, separating them from the rest of his spare change.

By the time the fourth state's quarters were minted, Chris already had several Delaware, New Jersey, and Pennsylvania quarters. Counting them, he discovered he had 3 times as many Delaware quarters as Pennsylvania quarters. The number of New Jersey quarters he had was 7 more than half the number of Delaware quarters.

  ★ **a.** Choose a variable, and use it to express the number of quarters of each type that Chris had.

  ★ **b.** Altogether Chris had saved $12.75 in quarters. Write and solve an equation to find how many of each type of quarter he had.
    $0.25(p + 3p + 1.5p + 7) = 12.75$, $p = 8$; 8 Pennsylvania quarters, 24 Delaware quarters, 19 New Jersey quarters

57a. Pennsylvania: p;
    Delaware: $3p$;
    New Jersey: $1.5p + 7$

Informal Assessment
Students should be able to:

✔ add and subtract algebraic fractions using common denominators

✔ use the graphs of equations containing algebraic fractions to estimate solutions

✔ solve equations containing algebraic fractions

Quick Quiz

1. Find each sum or difference.
  a. $\frac{4}{5} + \frac{5}{4}$ $\frac{41}{20}$
  b. $\frac{r}{8} - \frac{r}{16}$ $\frac{r}{16}$
  c. $\frac{10}{y^2} + \frac{9}{2y}$ $\frac{20 + 9y}{2y^2}$

2. Zach can peel p apples in an hour. Emma can peel $2p$ apples in an hour. Write an expression, and then simplify it, for the total number of hours they will take if they each peel 100 apples. $\frac{100}{p} + \frac{100}{2p}$, or $\frac{150}{p}$

3. Find each sum or difference.
  a. $\frac{1}{t} + \frac{3}{t-2}$ $\frac{4t-2}{t(t-2)}$
  b. $\frac{2x}{x+1} - \frac{1}{x-4}$ $\frac{2x^2 - 9x - 1}{(x+1)(x-4)}$
  c. $\frac{x}{2x-3} + \frac{1}{3-2x}$ $\frac{x-1}{2x-3}$ or $\frac{1-x}{3-2x}$

4. Solve each equation.
  a. $\frac{r}{5} - \frac{r}{6} = {}^{-}2$ ${}^{-}60$
  b. $\frac{3}{d^2 - 9} = \frac{1}{d+3} - \frac{1}{d-3}$ no solution

5. What fraction added to $\frac{g}{g+1}$ equals 2? $\frac{g+2}{g+1}$

Chapter Summary
This summary helps students recall the major topics of the chapter.

Vocabulary
Students should be able to explain each of the terms listed in the vocabulary section.

Problem-Solving Strategies and Applications
The questions in this section help students review and apply the important mathematical ideas and problem-solving strategies developed in the chapter. The questions are organized by mathematical highlights. The highlights correspond to those in "The Big Picture" chart on page 355a.

Question 3:
Students will need to use the coordinates of the given points to find the lengths of the various segments that define the shaded and unshaded regions.

VOCABULARY
binomial
expanding
like terms

1. $x^2 + 9x + 18$

2. $3t^2 + 2t - 1$

Chapter Summary

This chapter focused on expanding and simplifying algebraic expressions. Two main themes were using the distributive property and working with algebraic fractions.

You solved problems that involved multiplying binomials, requiring you to use the distributive property to expand the product and then to simplify by combining like terms. Turning your attention to algebraic fractions, you discovered you could simplify, add, and subtract them using the same methods you use for numeric fractions.

You concluded the chapter by solving equations that required you to apply all your new skills.

Strategies and Applications

The questions in this section will help you review and apply the important ideas and strategies developed in this chapter.

Using geometric models to expand expressions

1. Draw a rectangle diagram that models the expression $(x + 3)(x + 6)$. Use it to expand the product of these binomials.

2. Draw a rectangle diagram that models the expression $(3t - 1)(t + 1)$. Use it to expand the product of these binomials.

3. Consider this graph.

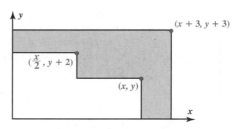

a. Write an expression for the area of the unshaded region. $xy + x$

b. Write an expression, with and without parentheses, for the area of the shaded region. $(x + 3)(y + 3) - (xy + x) = 2x + 3y + 9$

 impactmath.com/chapter_test

★ indicates multi-step problem

4. Use the distributive property to expand the first part and multiply the binomials in the second part, and then combine like terms; $3 - 3x$.

5. $-2xy - x^2 - y^2$

6a. $2x^2 + 70x$ in^2

6b. $2x^2 + 64x - 96$ in^2

7a. The expanded expression is $a^2x^2 + 2abx + b^2$. You can show this works by applying the distributive property twice: $(ax + b)(ax + b) = ax(ax + b) + b(ax + b) = a^2x^2 + abx + abx + b^2 = a^2x^2 + 2abx + b^2$.

8a. The expanded expression is $a^2x^2 - 2abx + b^2$. You can show this works by applying the distributive property twice: $(ax - b)(ax - b) = ax(ax - b) - b(ax - b) = a^2x^2 - abx - abx + b^2 = a^2x^2 - 2abx + b^2$.

9a. The expanded expression is $a^2x^2 - b^2$. You can show this works by applying the distributive property twice: $(ax + b)(ax - b) = ax(ax - b) + b(ax - b) = a^2x^2 - abx + abx - b^2 = a^2x^2 - b^2$.

Using the distributive property to expand expressions

4. Describe the steps required to simplify $x(1 - x) + (1 - x)(3 - x)$. Give the simplified expression.

5. Simplify the expression $(x^2 - 1)(y^2 - 1) - (1 + xy)(1 + xy)$.

6. *Molding* is a strip of wood placed along the base of a wall to give a room a "finished" look. The diagram shows a floor plan of a room with 1-inch-thick molding along the edges. Measurements are in inches.

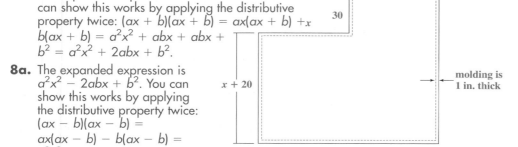

★ **a.** Write an expression for the floor area before the molding was installed. Simplify your expression as much as possible.

★ **b.** Write an expression for the remaining floor area after the molding was installed. Simplify your expression as much as possible.

Expanding expressions of the forms $(ax + b)^2$, $(ax - b)^2$, and $(ax + b)(ax - b)$

7. Consider expressions of the form $(ax + b)^2$.

    a. Describe a shortcut for expanding such expressions, and explain why it works.

    b. Use your shortcut to expand $(x + 13)^2$. $x^2 + 26x + 169$

8. Consider expressions of the form $(ax - b)^2$.

    a. Describe a shortcut for expanding such expressions, and explain why it works.

    b. Use your shortcut to expand $\left(\frac{x}{2} - 1.5\right)^2$. $\frac{x^2}{4} - 1.5x + 2.25$

9. Consider expressions of the form $(ax + b)(ax - b)$.

    a. Describe a shortcut for expanding such expressions, and explain why it works.

    b. Use your shortcut to expand $(xy + 3)(xy - 3)$. $x^2y^2 - 9$

Review and Self-Assessment **427**

Question 6:
There are many ways to think about constructing the floor areas, and students will need to be careful. It may be helpful for them to sketch the room diagram, add segments to divide the room into two rectangles, and then label the sides of each rectangle. For **Part a,** for example, the room can be split into rectangles with dimensions $2x$ by $x + 20$ and 30 by x, or into rectangles with dimensions x by $x + 20$ and x by $x + 50$.

★ indicates multi-step problem

10. Rewrite $24 \cdot 26$ as the product of two binomials, and then use the "difference of squares" pattern to compute the product.
$(25 - 1)(25 + 1) = 625 - 1 = 624$

Simplifying expressions involving algebraic fractions

Simplify each expression, and explain each step.

11, 12. See Additional Answers.

11. $\dfrac{-3x}{9 - 6x}$

12. $\dfrac{15xy}{3x^3y^3}$

Solving equations involving algebraic fractions

13. Consider the equation $\dfrac{1}{x+1} + \dfrac{2}{x-1} = \dfrac{8}{x^2-1}$.

13a. Possible answer: Multiply both sides by the common denominator $(x + 1)(x - 1) = x^2 - 1$.

   a. Describe the first step you would take to solve this equation.

   b. Solve the equation. $\dfrac{7}{3}$

14. Consider the equation $\dfrac{k}{k-1} - \dfrac{5}{2} = \dfrac{1}{k-1}$.

   a. Solve the equation. There is no solution.

14b. There is the possibility that a value or values can't be permitted since they would make a denominator 0.

   b. Explain why it is especially important to check your solutions when solving equations containing algebraic fractions.

15. Every week a freight train delivers grain to a harbor 156 miles away. Last week the train traveled to the harbor at an average speed of s miles per hour. On the return trip, the train had empty cars and was able to travel an average of 16 miles per hour faster.

   a. Write an expression for the time it took the train to reach the harbor. $\dfrac{156}{s}$

   b. Write an expression for the time the return trip took. $\dfrac{156}{s + 16}$

★ **c.** The round trip took 10.4 hours. Write an equation to find the value of s. Solve your equation. $\dfrac{156}{s} + \dfrac{156}{s + 16} = 10.4$, $s = 24$

Additional Answers

11. $\dfrac{-3x}{9 - 6x} = \dfrac{-3x}{3(3 - 2x)}$ Factor out 3 from the denominator.

       $= \dfrac{3}{3} \cdot \dfrac{-x}{3 - 2x}$ Factor out 1 in the form $\dfrac{3}{3}$.

       $= \dfrac{-x}{3 - 2x}$ Simplify.

12. $\dfrac{15xy}{3x^3y^3} = \dfrac{3xy(5)}{3xy(x^2y^2)}$ Factor out $3xy$ from the numerator and denominator.

       $= \dfrac{3xy}{3xy} \cdot \dfrac{5}{x^2y^2}$ Factor out 1 in the form $\dfrac{3xy}{3xy}$.

       $= \dfrac{5}{x^2y^2}$ Simplify.

Demonstrating Skills

Rewrite each expression without parentheses.

16. $^-6(x + 1) + 2(5 - x) - 9(1 - x)$ $x - 5$

17. $^-a(1 - 3a) - (2a^2 - 5a)$ $a^2 + 4a$

18. $(2b + 1)(4 + b)$ $2b^2 + 9b + 4$

19. $(x + 1)(5 - x)$ $5 + 4x - x^2$

20. $(2c - 8)(c - 2)$ $2c^2 - 12c + 16$

21. $(2x + y)(y - xy)$ $2xy - 2x^2y + y^2 - xy^2$

22. $(L - 8)^2$ $L^2 - 16L + 64$

23. $(x - xy)(x + xy)$ $x^2 - x^2y^2$

Simplify each expression.

24. $\dfrac{14x^2y^2}{2xy}$ $7xy$

25. $(5xy - 2)(1 - 2x)$ $5xy - 10x^2y + 4x - 2$

26. $(d + 2)(1 - d) + (1 - 2d)(3 - d)$ $d^2 - 8d + 5$

27. $\dfrac{5n}{n - 1} + \dfrac{3n}{2n - 2}$ $\dfrac{13n}{2n - 2}$

28. $\dfrac{b}{3} + \dfrac{b - 1}{b + 1} - \dfrac{b}{2b + 2}$ $\dfrac{2b^2 + 5b - 6}{6(b + 1)}$

29. $\dfrac{1}{k - 1} - \dfrac{1}{k + 2}$ $\dfrac{3}{(k - 1)(k + 2)}$

Solve each equation.

30. $\dfrac{3}{x + 4} = \dfrac{2}{x - 4}$ 20

31. $\dfrac{^-2x + 2}{x - 1} = ^-3$ no solution

CHAPTER 7

Solving Quadratic Equations

Chapter Overview

In this chapter, students work with solving equations, mostly quadratic equations. They begin by using backtracking to solve quadratics of a particular form as well as equations requiring taking reciprocals, square roots, and changes of sign. Next they learn how to solve some quadratic equations by *factoring* and using the zero product property (when a product is equal to 0, at least one of the factors must be equal to 0). They follow up with methods that work with nonfactorable equations: completing the square and using the quadratic formula.

 the **Big Picture**

Chapter 7 Highlights	Links to the Past	Links to the Future
Using backtracking to undo square roots, squares, reciprocals, and changes of sign (7.1)	**Courses 1 and 2 and Chapter 4:** Using backtracking to solve (linear) equations **Chapter 2:** Working with quadratic relationships	**High School and College:** Working with inverse functions
Solving quadratic equations by factoring (7.2)	**Chapter 6:** Expanding binomial products **Chapter 6:** Working with squared binomials and differences of squares	**High School and College:** Solving polynomial equations
Solving quadratic equations by completing the square (7.3)	**Chapter 2:** Working with quadratic relationships	**High School and College:** Working with quadratic relationships
Understanding and applying the quadratic formula (7.4)	**Courses 1 and 2:** Applying formulas	**Chapter 8:** Using *x*-intercepts **Chapter 8, High School, and College:** Working with functions **High School and College:** Working with polynomials

Planning Guide

Lesson Objectives	Pacing	Materials	NCTM Standards	Hot Topics
7.1 Solving by Backtracking page 431b • To backtrack to undo taking the square root of a number • To backtrack to undo taking the reciprocal of a number • To backtrack to undo changing the sign of a number • To use backtracking to find solutions to equations with powers and square roots • To understand that some equations have more than one solution	3 class periods	• Scientific calculators	1, 2, 7, 8	
7.2 Solving by Factoring page 441b • To understand the zero product property • To solve quadratic equations in factored form • To solve quadratic equations by factoring the difference of two squares and perfect square trinomials • To solve quadratic equations by factoring quadratic trinomials	4 class periods	• Graphing calculators (optional)	2, 6, 9, 10	
7.3 Completing the Square page 455b • To solve equations of the form $a(x + b)^2 + c = d$ • To identify perfect square trinomials • To complete quadratic expressions to make them perfect squares • To solve quadratic equations by completing the square	3 class periods	• Graphing calculators (optional)	2, 9	
7.4 The Quadratic Formula page 465b • To understand the origin of the quadratic formula • To use the quadratic formula to solve quadratic equations • To understand when the quadratic formula is appropriate to solve equations and when factoring is appropriate • To understand how to apply the quadratic formula to specific situations • To understand the significance of $b^2 - 4ac$ in the quadratic formula	4 class periods	• Graphing calculators (optional) • Ruler • Graph paper (optional)	2, 6, 7, 9	

Key to NCTM Curriculum and Evaluation Standards: 1=Number and Operations, 2=Algebra, 3=Geometry, 4=Measurement, 5=Data Analysis and Probability, 6=Problem Solving, 7=Reasoning and Proof, 8=Communication, 9=Connections, 10=Representation

Assessment Opportunities

Standard Assessment

Impact Mathematics offers three types of formal assessment. The Chapter 7 Review and Self-Assessment in the Student Edition serves as a self-assessment tool for students. In the Teacher's Guide, a Quick Quiz at the end of each lesson allows you to check students' understanding before moving to the next lesson. The Assessment Resources include blackline masters for chapter and quarterly tests.

- **Student Edition** Chapter 7 Review and Self-Assessment, pages 483–485
- **Teacher's Guide** Quick Quizzes, pages A662, 455, 465, 482
- **Assessment Resources** Chapter 7 Test Form A, pages 195–197; Chapter 7 Test Form B, pages 198–200

Ongoing Assessment

Impact Mathematics provides numerous opportunities for you to assess your students informally as they work through the investigations. Share & Summarize questions help you determine whether students understand the important ideas of an investigation. If students are struggling, Troubleshooting tips provide suggestions for helping them. On the Spot Assessment notes appear throughout the teaching notes. They give you suggestions for preventing or remedying common student errors. Assessment Forms in the Assessment Resources provide convenient ways to record student progress.

- **Student Edition** Share & Summarize, pages 435, 438, 444, 448, 450, 459, 461, 468, 471, 475
- **Teacher's Guide** On the Spot Assessment, pages T436, T444, T457, T459, T467 Troubleshooting, pages T435, T438, T444, T448, T450, T459, T461, T468, T471, T475
- **Assessment Resources** Chapter 7 Assessment Checklists, pages 294–295

Alternative Assessment, Portfolios, and Journal Ideas

The alternative assessment items in *Impact Mathematics* are perfect for inclusion in student portfolios and journals. The In Your Own Words feature in the Student Edition gives students a chance to write about mathematical ideas. The Performance Assessment items in the Assessment Resources provide rich, open-ended problems, ideal for take-home or group assessment.

- **Student Edition** In Your Own Words, pages 440, 453, 464, 481
- **Assessment Resources** Chapter 7 Performance Assessments, pages 201–202

Assessment Resources

The Assessment Resources provide a chapter test in two equivalent forms, along with additional performance items. The performance items can be used in a variety of ways. They are ideal for take-home assessment or in-class group assessment.

- Chapter 7 Test Form A, pages 195–197
- Chapter 7 Test Form B, pages 198–200
- Chapter 7 Performance Assessment, pages 201–202
- Chapter 7 Assessment Solutions, pages 203–205

Ch. 6 Test Form A

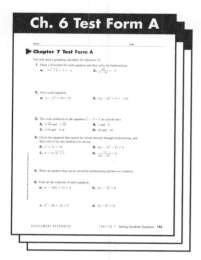

Ch. 6 Test Form B

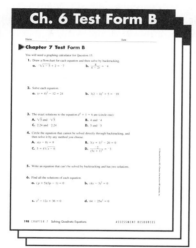

Ch. 6 Perf. Assess

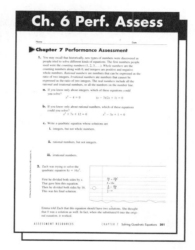

Additional Resources

- **Math Skills Maintenance Workbook,** 1, 2, 3, 4, 25, 28
- **StudentWorks™ CD-ROM**
- **Reading and Writing in the Mathematics Classroom**
- **Using the Internet in the Mathematics Classroom**

ExamView® Pro

Use ExamView® Pro Testmaker CD-ROM to:

- Create Multiple versions of tests.
- Create Modified tests for Inclusion students with one mouse click.
- Edit existing questions and Add your own questions.
- Build tests aligned with state standards using built-in State Curriculum Correlations.
- Change English tests to Spanish with one mouse click and vice versa.

CHAPTER 7

Introduce

Students have worked with quadratic relationships as early as Chapter 2, and possibly before. Review the applications highlighted under "Super Models," and ask whether students know of other relationships that might be quadratic. Trajectories and areas are likely to be the most prominent applications in students' minds.

Think About It

You may want to have students actually draw the path of the football on paper or on the chalkboard. They should describe the shape as an upside-down, U-shaped curve.

Solving Quadratic Equations

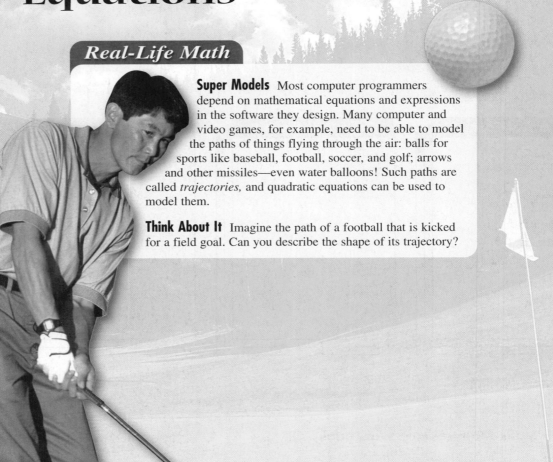

Real-Life Math

Super Models Most computer programmers depend on mathematical equations and expressions in the software they design. Many computer and video games, for example, need to be able to model the paths of things flying through the air: balls for sports like baseball, football, soccer, and golf; arrows and other missiles—even water balloons! Such paths are called *trajectories,* and quadratic equations can be used to model them.

Think About It Imagine the path of a football that is kicked for a field goal. Can you describe the shape of its trajectory?

Family Letter

Dear Student and Family Members,

Our next chapter in mathematics deals with solving quadratic equations. Quadratic equations involve the square of the main variable and can be written in the form $ax^2 + bx + c = 0$, where a, b, and c are constants.

Quadratic equations are an important topic in mathematics and science. They are used to describe the movement of objects in space, such as the motion of basketballs, automobiles, satellites, and rockets. They are also used to determine the shapes of radar antennae, satellite dishes, and mirrors used in telescopes.

We will learn and practice three important methods for solving quadratic equations: solving perfect squares, solving equations by factoring, and using the quadratic formula.

- We will learn to recognize perfect square quadratics, which are equivalent to a simple linear expression multiplied by itself:

$$x^2 + 4x + 4 = (x + 2)(x + 2) = (x + 2)^2$$
$$4x^2 - 12x + 9 = (2x - 3)(2x - 3) = (2x - 3)^2$$

- Another important method is solving quadratic equations by factoring. This is useful when a quadratic equation is equivalent to the product of two different linear expressions:

$$x^2 - 8x + 15 = (x - 5)(x - 3)$$
$$2x^2 - 8x - 10 = (2x + 2)(x - 5)$$

- A third method is to use the quadratic formula. The quadratic formula is useful because it can be used to solve any quadratic equation written in the form $ax^2 + bx + c = 0$, not just those that are perfect squares or easily factored.

Vocabulary Along the way, we'll be learning about two new vocabulary terms:

factoring   **trinomial**

What can you do at home?

Knowledge of quadratic equations will allow your student to master one of the most important topics in algebra. The work is abstract, but the power that comes from mastery will help students in all their future algebraic work. Encourage your student to show you the problems we are working on and to explain the methods he or she is learning to use.

impactmath.com/family_letter

431

Another version of the Family Letter, available in English and Spanish, is found in the Teaching Resources. You may want to send a copy of this letter home with your students.

Teaching Resources

familyletter

CHAPTER 7 SOLVING QUADRATIC EQUATIONS

Dear Family,

Our next chapter in mathematics deals with solving quadratic equations. Quadratic equations involve the square of the main variable and can be written in the form

$$ax^2 + bx + c = 0$$

where a, b, and c are constants. The work in this chapter pulls together much of what students have learned in earlier chapters: their knowledge of quadratic relationships from Chapter 2; equation-solving skills from Chapter 4; and methods for multiplying, factoring, and simplifying algebraic expressions from Chapter 6.

Quadratic equations are an important topic in mathematics and science. They are used to describe the movement of objects in space, such as the motion of basketballs, automobiles, satellites, and rockets. They are also used to determine the shapes of radar antennae, satellite dishes, and mirrors used in telescopes.

Students learn and practice three important methods for solving quadratic equations: solving perfect squares, solving equations by factoring, and using the quadratic formula.

- Students learn to recognize perfect square quadratics, which are equivalent to a simple linear expression multiplied by itself:

$$x^2 + 4x + 4 = (x + 2x)(x + 2) = (x + 2)^2$$
$$4x^2 - 12x + 9 = (2x - 3)(2x - 3) = (2x - 3)^2$$

- Another important method is solving quadratic equations by factoring. This is useful when a quadratic equation is equivalent to the product of two different linear expressions:

$$x^2 - 8x + 15 = (x - 5)(x - 3)$$
$$2x^2 - 8x - 10 = (2x + 2)(x - 5)$$

- A third method is to use the quadratic formula. The quadratic formula is useful because it can be used to solve any quadratic equation written in the form $ax^2 + bx + c = 0$, not just those that are perfect squares or easily factored.

Knowledge of quadratic equations will allow your child to master one of the most important topics in algebra. The work is abstract, but the power that comes from mastery will help students in all their future algebraic work. Encourage your child to show you the problems we are working on and to explain the methods he or she is learning to use.

TEACHING RESOURCES   CHAPTER 7 Solving Quadratic Equations **67**

Mathematical Background

Quadratic equations are significant for several reasons. Quadratic equations have practical applications, primarily in physics, where they are used to describe the motion of objects subject to gravity, and in geometry, where they sometimes arise in calculations involving area. All quadratic equations can be solved exactly. In addition, there are methods for rewriting quadratic equations so they can be solved more easily, and some of these methods can be extended to other types of equations as well.

Quadratic equations can be written in at least three general forms; each form can be expressed in terms of the others. The most common form of a quadratic equation is

$$ax^2 + bx + c = 0$$

where x is the variable and a, b, and c are constants that may be positive or negative. Two other general forms are often used in special cases:

$$(x + h)^2 = k$$

$$(mx + n)(px + q) = 0$$

Solving Quadratic Equations In Chapter 2, students found approximate solutions to quadratic equations. In this chapter, they are introduced to three general methods for finding exact solutions to quadratic equations: backtracking, factoring, and using the quadratic formula. The first two methods are relatively simple to remember and carry out, but they can be used for only a limited number of quadratic equations. The quadratic formula can be used for all quadratic equations, but it is a "rote" method, difficult to remember and involving several complex calculations. (A fourth method, completing the square, is also introduced in this chapter but is used mainly as a way to derive the quadratic formula.)

Equations of the Form $(x + h)^2 = k$ Quadratic equations that can be easily rewritten in the form $(x + h)^2 = k$ are quite simple to solve; students begin with this form, using the backtracking method. Some students may use a similar process but abandon the flowcharts that are characteristic of the backtracking method.

If the equation is first rewritten in this form, solving becomes a simple matter of taking the square root of both sides and then subtracting h from both sides of the result.

Equation	Rewritten as $(x + h)^2 = k$	Solution
$2(x - 4)^2 + 5 = 7$	$(x - 4)^2 = 1$	$x - 4 = \pm 1$; $x = 5$ or $x = 3$
$(3t - 2)^2 - 20 = 30$	$(3t - 2)^2 = 50$	$3t - 2 = \pm\sqrt{50} = \pm 5\sqrt{2}$; $t = \frac{2}{3} + \frac{5\sqrt{2}}{3}$ or $t = \frac{2}{3} - \frac{5\sqrt{2}}{3}$
$\sqrt{(2p - 3)^2 - 5} = 2$	$(2p - 3)^2 = 9$	$2p + 3 = \pm 3$; $p = {}^-3$ or $p = 0$

The $\pm$ sign is required because both the positive and the negative square root satisfy the equation.

Solving Quadratic Equations by Factoring A larger—but still limited—class of quadratic equations can be solved by factoring. Factoring involves rewriting a quadratic expression as the product of two binomial expressions:

$$(mx + n)(px + q) = 0$$

• **Teaching notes continued on page A682**

7.1

Solving by Backtracking

Objectives

▸ To backtrack to undo taking the square root of a number

▸ To backtrack to undo taking the reciprocal of a number

▸ To backtrack to undo changing the sign of a number

▸ To use backtracking to find solutions to equations with powers and square roots

▸ To understand that some equations have more than one solution

Overview (pacing: about 3 class periods)

In this lesson, students revisit a useful equation-solving technique: solving by backtracking. This technique uses flowcharts to represent the process of "undoing" operations. This lesson extends the set of operations that can be undone to include powers and reciprocals.

Advance Preparation

It is assumed students will have access to scientific calculators; no other preparation is needed.

Lesson Planner

	Summary	Materials	On Your Own Exercises	Assessment Opportunities
Investigation 1 page T433	Students review backtracking with linear equations and learn inverse operations for reciprocals and squaring.	• Scientific calculators	Practice & Apply: 1–7, p. 439 Connect & Extend: 18, 19, pp. 439–440 Mixed Review: 23–35, pp. 440–441	Share & Summarize, pages T435, 435 Troubleshooting, page T435
Investigation 2 page T436	Students use backtracking to solve equations involving powers, including simple quadratic equations.		Practice & Apply: 8–17, p. 439 Connect & Extend: 20–22, p. 440 Mixed Review: 23–35, pp. 440–441	On the Spot Assessment, page T436 Share & Summarize, pages T438, 438 Troubleshooting, page T438 Informal Assessment, page 441 Quick Quiz, page A662

1 Begin by asking students to think about the ways in which they solved linear equations.

> What operations do you know how to "undo" in order to solve any linear equation, $y = mx + b$? **addition, subtraction, multiplication, and division**

Explain that in this lesson, students will be examining other kinds of equations and looking at how to undo other operations.

Think & Discuss

This Think & Discuss will raise students' awareness that there are operations other than addition, subtraction, multiplication, and division that can be undone. The questions here set the stage for topics that are addressed thoroughly in the investigations that follow, so there is no need to expect students to be totally comfortable with the answers or that they will derive the correct answers on their own. It is important, however, that students use the same kind of thinking that they did when they backtracked using the four standard operations. Undoing is a key mathematical process, and students need to be able to think in this way.

2 In all of these questions, it may be helpful to use a specific numeric example to bring home the point. For example, in undoing finding the reciprocal of a number, you might start with 5, find its reciprocal $\left(\frac{1}{5}\right)$, and then undo the process to get the original number (5) by finding the reciprocal's reciprocal.

Solving by Backtracking

As you know, backtracking is a step-by-step process of undoing operations. To solve a linear equation by backtracking, you must know how to undo addition, subtraction, multiplication, and division. To use backtracking to solve nonlinear equations, however, you have to undo other operations as well.

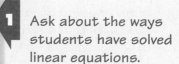
1 Ask about the ways students have solved linear equations.

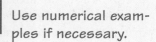
2 Use numerical examples if necessary.

① Possible answer: If you think division undoes multiplication, you could start with a number like 6 and multiply it by a number like 7. To check, divide the result, 42, by the second number, 7, and see if the result is the number you started with, 6.

② find the positive nth root of the result

Think & Discuss

How would you check to make sure that one operation really *does* undo another? Give an example to illustrate your thinking.   See ①.

What would you do to undo each of these operations?

• finding the square roots of a number   square the results

• finding the reciprocal of a number   find the reciprocal of the result

• changing the sign of a number   change the sign of the result

• raising a positive number to the nth power, such as 2^3 See ②.

Just the facts

Quadratic equations are used in many contexts. For example, $h = 1 + 2t - 4.9t^2$ might give the height in meters at time t seconds of someone jumping on a trampoline with an initial velocity of 2 m/s.

Investigation 1

In this investigation, students examine equations with square roots and reciprocals. They also look at the operation of "change sign," which on most calculators is designated as $+/-$, and learn how to undo this operation. The investigation builds the foundation for the rest of the lesson, in which students study how to solve quadratic equations. This investigation intentionally begins with students' intuitive ideas about the undoing process so that they can generalize undoing and relate it to new operations.

Although all of the examples in this investigation may be solved in a variety of ways—some of which may, in fact, seem simpler than backtracking—students should solve them via backtracking in order to focus on the undoing process.

Problem Set A **Suggested Grouping: Pairs**

 In this first problem set, students consider several equations and their related flowcharts. Begin with a class discussion about the cartoon, and answer **Problems 1 and 2** as a class.

 If students think that Ben and Kai are constructing the same equation, have them substitute numbers for x to see how the results are different.

As an alternative to beginning with the cartoon, you may find it interesting to ask students how they might think about solving $\sqrt{2x - 11} = 5$. If a student says she knows that $2x - 11$ must equal 25 (since its square root is 5), it is important to acknowledge that perspective and insight, and then explain that backtracking is a way to get to exactly that insight. You can then challenge students to see how backtracking leads to that same conclusion.

 Students can complete the problem set in pairs.

Investigation Backtracking with New Operations

In this investigation, you will try out the ideas about undoing operations from the Think & Discuss.

Problem Set A

Ben is solving the equation $\sqrt{2x - 11} = 5$.

Kai said Ben's flowchart should really be like this:

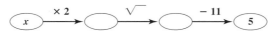

1. What is wrong with Kai's flowchart?

2. What equation would you solve by backtracking with Kai's flowchart? $\sqrt{2x} - 11 = 5$

3. Consider the equation $\sqrt{3x + 7} = 8$.

   a. Draw a flowchart for the equation.

   b. Use backtracking to find the solution. Check your answer by substituting it back into the equation.   19

3a.

1. Possible answer: The "− 11" is in the wrong place; he's taking the square root of $2x$ and then subtracting 11, instead of subtracting 11 before taking the square root.

Remember

The $\sqrt{}$ sign refers to the nonnegative square root of a number, if one exists.

1. **Problem-Solving Strategy**

   Work backward

2. If students think both flowcharts are correct, have them substitute values for x.

3. You may have students work in pairs on the rest of the problem set.

Develop

Problem 4 presents some interesting challenges for students: if you enter this expression into a calculator, you might do the operations in a different order. If you use the calculator's parentheses, though, you can often enter expressions like this as written.

The important thing to recognize here is that the flowchart shows the order you would use if you substituted a value for s: first subtract 2 and then, essentially, "divide the result into" 24. Note that the flowchart method has no way of designating "division into," so the method that is used is to take the reciprocal of the result and multiply that by 24. If students have trouble understanding the flowchart, you might ask them to actually perform the flowchart calculations with a specific number.

About the Mathematics

The operation of finding the reciprocal is different from operations students are more familiar with, because it is a *unary* operation, meaning it involves only one number. On the other hand, multiplication and addition, for example, are *binary* operations because two numbers are multiplied or added.

Performing an operation with a single number may be particularly confusing if students use a calculator, so be certain students understand how to use the reciprocal key on their calculators, usually designated $\frac{1}{x}$ or x^{-1}.

In **Problem 5,** students examine another flowchart that begins with the variable. To make sense of the flowchart, students may need to first "tell the story" of the variable: take p and subtract it from 3. Point out that, again, the flowchart has no way of indicating how to subtract p from something. Therefore, it's necessary to take p, find its opposite by changing its sign, and add it to 3. This problem makes a nice connection with the work students did with signed numbers, looking at the subtraction of a number as addition of its opposite.

Students may want to know why they can't write the flowchart as they would read it. If so, tell them that this is a good question and that they will address it in **Problem 5b.**

As an extension to **Problem 6,** you might ask if there are any other operations that undo themselves. Students should recognize that taking the reciprocal is one such operation.

In **Problem 7b,** you may want to point out to students that, to undo multiplying a number by $^-1$, they can simply repeat the multiplication by $^-1$ because $^-1$ is its own *multiplicative inverse,* or reciprocal. That is, multiplying $^-1$ by itself gives 1, so if you multiply a number by $^-1 \cdot {}^-1$, you are in effect multiplying the number by 1.

As an extension, you may want to ask if there are any other numbers with this property (the number is its own reciprocal). The number 1 is the only other such number.

Problem Set Wrap-Up Review student answers to Problem 5b as a class. You may also want to give students an example equation and have them help you create a flowchart for it on the board. Problem 1 of Problem Set B could also be used for this purpose; see the notes on page T435.

Additional Examples Create a flowchart for each equation.

$$4 - x = 32$$

$$\frac{30}{8 - x} = 5$$

4. This flowchart is for the expression $\frac{24}{s-2}$.

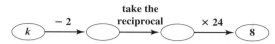

a. Try using the flowchart with a few numbers to see how it works. Record your results. Possible answer: $5 \rightarrow 3 \rightarrow \frac{1}{3} \rightarrow \frac{24}{3}$, or 8

b. This flowchart is for the equation $\frac{24}{k-2} = 8$.

Backtrack to find the solution. Check that your solution is correct by substituting it into the equation. 5

5. This flowchart is for the equation $3 - p = 1$. The symbol $+/-$ means to take the opposite of the value—that is, to change its sign.

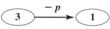

a. Solve the equation using backtracking. 2

5b. You would have to add a variable as part of the back-tracking, which can't be done.

b. Ben made this flowchart for $3 - p = 1$, but he got stuck when he tried to backtrack. Why can't you use his flowchart to solve the equation?

6. This flowchart is for the expression $\frac{2(3-t)}{4}$.

6a. Possible answer:
$5 \rightarrow {}^-5 \rightarrow {}^-2 \rightarrow$
${}^-4 \rightarrow {}^-1$

a. Try the flowchart with a few numbers to see how it works.

b. This flowchart is for the equation $\frac{2(3-t)}{4} = 5$.

Backtrack to find the solution, and check that it is correct. ${}^-7$

6c. "Change sign" undoes itself.

c. What operation undoes the "change sign" operation?

7. You can think of changing the sign of a number as multiplication by ${}^-1$. For example, ${}^-x = {}^-1 \cdot x$.

7a. divide by the same number

a. How do you usually undo multiplication by a number?

b. What does your answer to Part c of Problem 6 suggest about another way to undo multiplication by ${}^-1$?
You can undo multiplication by ${}^-1$ by multiplying by ${}^-1$.

1 You may want students to substitute a value for s and find the result using the flowchart.

2 You may need to have students explain what happens to p.

3 You may wish to introduce the term *multiplicative inverse*.

4 Discuss Problem 5b with the class.

Problem Set B Suggested Grouping: Pairs

In this problem set, students solve a variety of equations that contain reciprocals and, in some cases, require subtracting the variable. Unlike the problems in Problem Set A, most of these require students to create flowcharts on their own.

It may be challenging for students to think of expressions such as $\frac{4}{x}$ as the process of selecting x, taking its reciprocal, and then multiplying by 4. In fact, this kind of flexibility in thinking about such expressions should be encouraged whenever possible.

It may be worthwhile to go over **Problem 1** as a class, since it requires that students use the reciprocal key on their calculators. Prompt students to help you write the flowchart for Problem 1 on the board:

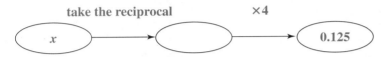

To undo the process by working backward, divide by 4 and then take the reciprocal. (You may want to have students guess the answer before they take the reciprocal so that they use their estimation skills.)

You might explain that there are other ways of solving this problem, which students may recall from their work with proportions and ratios from Course 2, but the focus is on backtracking here because of its applications later on.

Problem 6 requires that students go from the flowchart to the equation, the reverse of what they did in Problems 1–5. Their answers may take less simplified forms than the one given in the book, such as $\frac{1}{2x+1} \times 30 = 6$, which of course is fine.

Share & Summarize

These questions require students to write their own equations that can be solved by backtracking. You may want to write some of the more interesting creations on the board and assign them for homework or extra credit.

As an extension, you might add the following to the class discussion:

> With your partner, decide whether one of the equations you created was harder to solve than another. If so, see if you can explain why one was harder.

> Can you write an equation using these operations that cannot be solved by backtracking?

Troubleshooting If students are having difficulty with the flowcharts for these problems, go back to one of the first examples and have them create the appropriate flowchart. It may help if they choose a number for the variable and go through, step by step, recording the operation at each stage.

Taking reciprocals is likely to be the most challenging part of this investigation. If students find that part difficult, you can still go on to the next lesson since it deals with powers, which are more closely related to the square root content. Students will have other opportunities to work with reciprocals.

 On Your Own Exercises

Practice & Apply: 1–7, p. 439
Connect & Extend: 18, 19, pp. 439–440
Mixed Review: 23–35, pp. 440–441

Problem Set B

Solve each equation by backtracking.

1. $\frac{4}{x} = 0.125$ 32

2. $\frac{8 - z}{2} = 9$ $^-10$

3. $\frac{7 - m}{2} = 3$ 1

4. $5\left(20 - \frac{a}{4}\right) = 85$ 12

5. Consider this equation.

$$\frac{12}{3s - 1} = 6$$

a. Draw a flowchart for the equation.   See below.

b. Solve the equation by backtracking, and check your solution.   1

6. Katie drew this flowchart.

6a. $\frac{30}{2x + 1} = 6$

a. What equation can be solved using Katie's flowchart?

b. Solve the equation, and check your solution.   2

Share & Summarize

In this investigation, you learned how to undo taking the square root of a number, taking the reciprocal of a number, and changing the sign of a number.

1. Write an equation that can be solved by backtracking that uses all three of these operations. Find the solution of your equation.

2. Exchange equations with a partner, and try to solve your partner's equation. Check your answer by substitution.   Answers will vary.

1. Possible answer:
$\frac{20}{\sqrt{2 - x}} = 5$,
$x = {^-}14$

Problem Set B Answer

5a.

1 You may have students work in pairs, perhaps after going over Problem 1 as a class.

Problem-Solving Strategy

Work backward

2 You may want to assign students' creations for homework.

Investigation 2

In this investigation, students will use backtracking to solve simple quadratic equations. Specifically, they will be asked to think about the operation that undoes squaring. This investigation is a preview to the rest of the chapter, which involves methods that allow students to solve *all* quadratic equations. Although students have seen examples of equations that have two solutions, they have mostly been in the context of guess-check-and-improve.

 Remind students of their backtracking work in Investigation 1, and then move directly into the Think & Discuss.

Think & Discuss

The first questions are straightforward, and students should feel comfortable with the idea of having two solutions to $x^2 = 9$. They may need some assistance in thinking about the flowchart; in particular, creating a flowchart that shows two possible outcomes for an operation will be new to them.

It is important that students realize that in working backward, they need to think about all the numbers that, when squared, equal 25. Their representation here will mirror the steps they perform in later lessons when they take the square root of both sides of an equation.

 Students may not think of all three methods for recording multiple backtracking paths given in the answer to the last question. You may want to suggest any methods they omit. Of course, they may think of other methods not listed. Let them choose whatever method they prefer. This should be a matter of individual preference.

 Problem Set C Suggested Grouping: Pairs

In this problem set, students work with equations with powers of 2 or greater, as well as equations with square roots. Although the equations vary in type, all can be solved by backtracking. There are also problems that involve inverse square relationships, that is, relationships that have a squared term in the denominator.

 On the **Spot Assessment**

Problem 1 is very similar to the question students explored in the Think & Discuss. If students are having difficulty, they will probably not be able to go further in the problem set. You may want to check answers to this problem by quickly moving around the room before students continue. If necessary, conduct a group or class discussion with some additional examples.

Additional Examples Draw a flowchart for each equation, and then solve by backtracking.

$(x - 3)^2 = 49$ $10, {}^-4$

$144 = (F + 20)^2$ ${}^-8, {}^-32$

$(2 + x)^3 = 27$ 1

 Problems 2–4 are each in the form $a(x - b)^2 + c = d$, where a, b, and d are positive and c is positive or negative. Students need to think carefully about the order of the operations, which is good practice for the more formal equation solving. You might suggest they think about the variable first—as if they were substituting a value and then evaluating the expression for that value. Most likely, the step that will cause trouble is whether they should multiply by the constant before the binomial or square first. In Problem 2, for example, should they multiply $(b - 4)$ by 2 or square it first? Remind students that raising a number to a power is done before multiplication in the order of operations.

Investigation 2 ▶ Backtracking with Powers

In this investigation, you will extend the types of equations for which you can use backtracking.

① Two; positive numbers have both a positive and a negative square root.

② subtract 2 and then square

④ The square step; when you square a number and its opposite, you get the same number, so there are two possible entries for the oval before the square step.

⑤ Possible answers: Draw a line to divide the ovals in half and write one answer in each section. *Or,* draw a second set of ovals below the existing ones, and write the alternate path in them. *Or,* write both possibilities in each oval, separated by a comma. The solutions are 7 and ⁻3.

Think & Discuss

This flowchart is for the equation $x^2 = 9$.
To solve this equation by backtracking, you must undo the "square" operation by taking the square root.

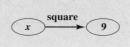

- How many solutions are there for $x^2 = 9$? How do you know?

    See ①.

Now consider the equation $(d - 2)^2 = 25$.

- Write the operations, in order, that you would use to evaluate the expression $(d - 2)^2$ for some value of d.   See ②.

- Draw a flowchart for the equation $(d - 2)^2 = 25$.   See ③, above.

- This equation has two solutions. Which step in your flowchart makes it possible for there to be two answers? Explain.   See ④.

- As you backtrack beyond the step that makes two answers possible, there are two possible values for each oval. Think of a way you might show two values at each step, and then find both of the equation's solutions.   See ⑤.

Problem Set C

1a.

1. Consider the equation $(a + 5)^2 = 25$.

  a. Draw a flowchart for the equation.

  b. Solve $(a + 5)^2 = 25$ by backtracking, and check your answer by substitution. Can you find more than one backtracking path (and so more than one solution)? 0, ⁻10; Yes, there are two solutions.

For each equation, draw a flowchart. Solve the equation using backtracking, and check your answers.

  2. $2(b - 4)^2 + 5 = 55$ See Additional Answers.

  3. $3(c - 5)^2 - 5 = 7$ See Additional Answers.

1 Remind students of their work on Investigation 1.

2 You may want to suggest methods that students don't think of.

3 You may have students work in pairs.

4 Check that students are able to do Problem 1.

5 Help students think about order of operations.

Additional Answers
Problem Set C

2. Solutions: 9, ⁻1

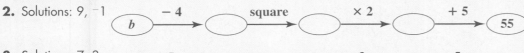

3. Solutions: 7, 3

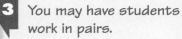

Problem 5 involves both squaring and taking the square, and both need to be undone in the process of working backward. This is a good problem to review as a class if there is time.

Problems 6 and 7 have binomials raised to the third and fourth powers, respectively, and this may be the first time students have encountered such equations. In working backward through **Problem 6,** they will eventually need to ask themselves, "What number cubed is 8?"

Problem 8 involves an inverse square relationship, a relationship of the form $y = \frac{a}{x^2}$, where a is a constant. Students may recall previous work they have done with inverse relationships; you may even want to ask them what their graphs looked like. In answering **Part d,** they will need to use both squaring and taking the reciprocal in creating their flowcharts. Note that the second solution, -54.77, does not make sense in the context of the problem since distance must be positive. You may need to point out this reasoning to students.

About the Mathematics

Another example of an inverse square relationship is Newton's law of universal gravitation, which states that the weight of a body, W, varies inversely with the square of its distance, d, from the center of the earth, or $W = \frac{k}{d^2}$, where k is a constant.

Problem Set Wrap-Up A class discussion of some of the solutions to Problems 2–7 would help students who are having difficulty raising an expression to a power and creating flowcharts involving powers, and would help you assess their understanding of these processes.

Just the facts

The unit *foot-candle* measures the amount of light falling on 1 square foot of area. It was originally defined using a standardized candle burning 1 foot away from a surface.

8a. Because the variable d is being squared and is in the denominator.

8c. The closer an object is to the light source, the brighter it is; the farther it is from the light source, the less bright it is.

8e. 54.77; An object 54.77 ft from this light source has a brightness of 120 foot-candles.

Solve each equation.

4. $(d - 2)^2 - 20 = 44$ 10, ⁻6   **5.** $\sqrt{(2p - 3)^2} - 5 = 2$ 3, 0

6. $3(6 - T)^3 - 1 = 23$ 4   **7.** $(e - 3)^4 = 81$ 6, 0

8. When filmmakers make movies outside at night, they often use floodlights to brighten the actors and the scenery. The relationship between the brightness of an object F (measured in *foot-candles*) and its distance d (measured in feet) from the light source follows an *inverse square law*. For a particular 2,000-watt floodlight, the formula might be

$$F = \frac{360{,}000}{d^2}$$

a. Why do you think this is called an inverse square law?

b. Find the brightness for $d = 10, 20, 30,$ and 50.   3,600; 900; 400; 144

c. Explain the effect on an object's brightness of moving closer to or farther from the light source.

d. Draw a flowchart for the brightness formula.

e. Use backtracking to solve the equation

$$120 = \frac{360{,}000}{d^2}$$

What does the answer tell you?

Problem Set ⁸ᵈ **D**

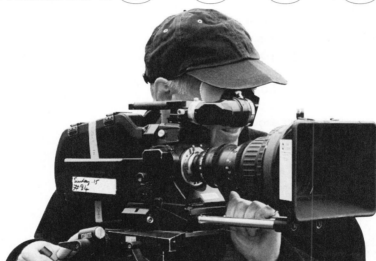

$d \xrightarrow{\text{square}} \bigcirc \xrightarrow{\substack{\text{take the} \\ \text{reciprocal}}} \bigcirc \xrightarrow{\times\, 360{,}000} F$

1 You may need to point out that one solution doesn't make sense in the context.

2 Discuss some of the solutions to Problems 2–7.

Problem Set D Suggested Grouping: Pairs
In this problem set, students work with equations whose
solutions are irrational numbers.

Problem-Solving Strategies Students may approach
Problem 1a in different ways:

- Some may show that these are solutions by direct substitution:

$$(3 + \sqrt{5} - 3)^2 - 5 = (\sqrt{5})^2 - 5 = 5 - 5 = 0$$
$$(3 - \sqrt{5} - 3)^2 - 5 = (^-\sqrt{5})^2 - 5 = 5 - 5 = 0$$

- Other students may backtrack to find the solution,
using this flowchart:

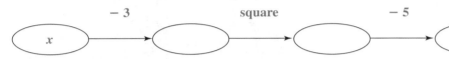

In Problem 1b, students are told that the decimal form
of an irrational number must be an approximation. You
may want to remind them of the definition of an *irrational number* (numbers that cannot be written as the
ratio of two integers) from Chapter 3.

In any case, one question to consider is why one might use
a decimal approximation over an exact solution. This is a
good time to explain that the form they use will depend on
the purpose. In most practical contexts, such as those involving measurement, the decimal approximation will be more
useful, and the issue will be the degree of accuracy needed
for the particular context. A situation in which an exact
answer is preferable may be one in which you will be
doing a further calculation with your result, or in which you
might not know the level of precision necessary, or in which
you want to be able to check the accuracy of your answer.

Share & Summarize
This question is an assessment of working backward to
undo squaring and of getting two solutions.

Troubleshooting You may want to present some simple linear equations to review the undoing process with
the class. For some students, you may want to create
some flowcharts with squaring, and have students work
backward through them with specific numbers to check
that they are thinking about undoing correctly. If squaring and taking the square root seem to be the problem,
you may need to review these concepts.

On Your Own Exercises

Practice & Apply: 8–17, p. 439
Connect & Extend: 20–22, p. 440
Mixed Review: 23–35, pp. 440–441

1. Consider this equation.

$$(x - 3)^2 - 5 = 0$$

1a. See below.

a. Show that $3 + \sqrt{5}$ and $3 - \sqrt{5}$ are solutions of this equation.

b. The values $3 + \sqrt{5}$ and $3 - \sqrt{5}$ are *exact* solutions of the equation. Because $\sqrt{5}$ is an irrational number, when you write it in a decimal form, you are giving an *approximation,* no matter how many decimal places you use.

Write each solution from Part a as a decimal accurate to two places. 5.24, 0.76

For each equation, give the exact solutions and the approximate solutions correct to two decimal places.

2. $h^2 - 5 = 45$ $\sqrt{50}, ^-\sqrt{50}$ or 7.07, $^-$7.07

3. $(2m - 3)^2 + 7 = 9$

4. $3(J + 5)^2 - 2 = 7$ $\sqrt{3} - 5, ^-\sqrt{3} - 5$ or $^-$3.27, $^-$6.73
$\frac{\sqrt{2} + 3}{2}, ^-\frac{\sqrt{2} + 3}{2}$ or 2.21, 0.79

Share

Summarize See below.

Use backtracking to solve this equation. Explain what you did at each step, and make note of any places you had to be particularly careful.

$$2(3b - 4)^2 + 1 = 19$$

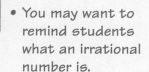

1 You may have students work in pairs.

2 • You may want to remind students what an irrational number is.

• You might discuss when to use exact solutions versus approximations.

3 Assess students' understanding of undoing squares and getting two solutions.

Problem Set D Answer

1a. $(3 + \sqrt{5} - 3)^2 - 5 = (\sqrt{5})^2 - 5 = 5 - 5 = 0$
$(3 - \sqrt{5} - 3)^2 - 5 = (^-\sqrt{5})^2 - 5 = 5 - 5 = 0$

Share & Summarize Answer

First, draw a flowchart for the equation.

Backtrack through the flowchart, beginning at 19 and undoing each step: $19 - 1 = 18$, $18 \div 2 = 9$, the square roots of 9 are 3 and $^-$3, $3 + 4 = 7$ and $^-3 + 4 = 1$, $7 \div 3 = \frac{7}{3}$ and $1 \div 3 = \frac{1}{3}$. You must be careful when undoing the squaring, because there are two numbers that can give the same square.

Teacher Notes

On Your Own Exercises

Practice & **Apply**

1. Consider the equation $-\sqrt{2x-1} = -7$.
   a. Draw a flowchart for the equation.   See below.
   b. Solve the equation by backtracking.   25

Solve each equation.

2. $\sqrt{3x+1} = 4$ 5

3. $\frac{2}{3p-1} = 5$ $\frac{7}{15}$

4. $\sqrt{a} = 1.5$ 2.25

5. $\sqrt{2-q} = 2.5$ $^{-}4.25$

6. $5\sqrt{\frac{z}{5}-1} = 4$ 8.2

7. $\frac{9}{4-7d} = 18$ 0.5

8. $2(x-4)^2 + 5 = 7$ 5, 3

9. $b^2 - 5 = 44$ 7, $^{-}7$

10. $c^2 - 20 = 44$ 8, $^{-}8$

11. $(L-2)^2 - 5 = 44$ $^{-}5$, 9

12. $(q-2)^2 + 8 = 44$ 8, $^{-}4$

13. $y^3 = 27$ 3

14. $3(2w-3)^2 - 5 = 70$ 4, $^{-}1$

15. $(2t-3)^2 - 20 = 44$ 5.5, $^{-}2.5$

16. $y^3 = ^{-}27$ $^{-}3$

17. $(x+2)^3 = 64$ 2

Connect & **Extend**

18. A man controlling a robot with a camera eye has just sent it into a burning house to retrieve a safe full of money. He has given it this set of commands:

```
Forward 20 feet.
Right turn.
Forward 15 feet.
Left turn.
Forward 30 feet.
Right turn.
Forward 25 feet.
Pick up safe.
```

The robot is now standing in the burning house holding the safe, but the robot controller has been overcome by smoke and you have been asked to get the robot back. Use what you know about backtracking to write a set of commands that will bring the robot back out of the burning house with the safe.

1a.

On Your Own Exercises

Investigation 1,
   pp. 433–435
Practice & Apply: 1–7
Connect & Extend: 18, 19

Investigation 2,
   pp. 436–438
Practice & Apply: 8–17
Connect & Extend: 20–22

Assign Anytime
Mixed Review: 23–35

Exercises 2–7:
Although these exercises do not require flowcharts, it is expected that some students will use them. You may need to suggest their use to students who find these equations difficult to solve but did not use them.

Exercises 8–17:
These exercises are good for class discussion about solution strategies. Ask some students to present their methods; you may be surprised by the variety, from flowcharts, to working backward in their heads, to thinking about what was done last and then figuring out how to undo that operation first.

Exercise 18 Extension:
Have students write directions to go from your classroom to another part of the school, such as the gym. Then have them give those directions to a partner, and have the partner reverse the directions to get from that place to the classroom.

back 25 ft, left turn, back 30 ft, right
turn, back 15 ft, left turn, back 20 ft

Exercise 19:

Ask students to try the same experiment on other irrational numbers, such as $\sqrt{3}$ or $\sqrt{5}$. It would be helpful to explain to them that their knowledge of nonrepeating decimals is essential in thinking about these kinds of problems, and that calculators have limitations because of restrictions both in their memory and, more to the point in this case, their available display space.

Exercise 20:

This is a good exercise to preview students' work in solving quadratic equations, since they will need to develop methods for solving problems that cannot be solved by backtracking.

Exercise 22:

This exercise connects to the definition of the absolute value of x. You may want to point out to students that $|x|$ always has the same value as $\sqrt{x^2}$.

In y o u r
own **words**

Explain how you can decide whether an equation can be directly solved by backtracking. Then give an example of an equation that can be solved directly by backtracking and an example of one that cannot.

19. Possible answer: No. The operations undo each other exactly, but her calculator gives only an approximation for $\sqrt{2}$. When it squares this value, the answer is not exactly 2.

19. Mary Ann used her calculator to find $\sqrt{2}$, wrote down the result, and then cleared the calculator. She then used her calculator to square the number she had written down, and got 1.99998.

Mary Ann concluded that squaring doesn't exactly undo taking the square root. Do you agree with her? What would you tell her?

20. Many equations cannot be solved directly by backtracking. Some have the variable stated more than once; others involve variables as exponents.

Here are some equations that can't be solved directly by backtracking.

$$f^2 = f + 1 \qquad x = \sqrt{x} + 1 \qquad k^2 + k = 0$$
$$1.1^B = 2 \qquad \tfrac{1}{x} = x^2 + 2$$

For each equation below, write *yes* if it can be solved directly by backtracking and *no* if it cannot.

a. $5 = \sqrt{x - 11}$ yes   **b.** $4^d = 9$ no

c. $3g^2 = 5$ yes   **d.** $\sqrt{x + 1} = x - 4$ no

21. Use backtracking to solve the equations in Parts a and b.

a. $(3x + 4)^2 = 25$ $\frac{1}{3}, -3$

b. $(3x + 4)^2 = 0$ $-\frac{4}{3}$

c. How many solutions did you find for each equation? Can you explain the difference? See Additional Answers.

22. Use backtracking to solve the equations in Parts a and b.

a. $(\sqrt{x})^2 = 5$ 5

b. $\sqrt{x^2} = 5$ 5, $^-5$

c. How many solutions did you find for each equation? Can you explain the difference? See Additional Answers.

Mixed Review

Expand each expression.

23. $3(3a - 7)$ $9a - 21$ **24.** $^-2b(8b - 0.5)$ $^-16b^2 + b$

25. $9c(^-8 + 7c)$ $^-72c + 63c^2$ **26.** $(d + 3)(d + 6)$ $d^2 + 9d + 18$

27. $(2e - 4)(e - 6)$ **28.** $(3f + 10)(9f - 1)$

29. $(g + 7)^2$ $g^2 + 14g + 49$ **30.** $(3h - 1)^2$ $9h^2 - 6h + 1$

27. $2e^2 - 16e + 24$
28. $27f^2 + 87f - 10$

440 CHAPTER 7 Solving Quadratic Equations

Additional Answers

21c. Two solutions to Equation a, one to Equation b. This is because a positive number like 25 has two square roots, one positive and one negative, but 0 has only one square root, 0.

22c. One solution to Equation a, two to Equation b. In Equation a, you first take the square root, so the solution must be a positive number. For Equation b, you first square, so the solution could be a negative number. If x is negative, say $^-5$, then $\sqrt{x^2}$ is not the same as x. In this case, it is 5.

31. $(2j + 2)^3$ $8j^3 + 24j^2 + 24j + 8$ **32.** $(3k - 2m)^2$

$9k^2 - 12km + 4m^2$

Geometry Find the area of each rectangle.

33. $2d$ $8d^2$ **34.** $1.75d$ $1.575d^2$

$4d$ $0.9d$

35b. Possible answer: A square meter of temperate rainforest produces about 57% of the plant material that a square meter of tropical rainforest produces. A square meter of tropical rainforest produces almost twice as much plant material as a square meter of temperate rainforest.

Remember
1 km = 1,000 m
1 kg = 1,000 g

35. **Life Science** The table lists the approximate amount of dry plant material that each type of habitat produces in 1 year.

Habitat	Plant Material (grams) Produced per Square Meter
Coral reef	2,500
Tropical rainforest	2,200
Temperate rainforest	1,250
Savannah	900
Open sea	125
Semidesert	90

Source: *Ultimate Visual Dictionary of Science.* London: Dorling Kindersley Limited, 1998.

a. One gram is equivalent to 0.035 ounce, and 1 meter is equivalent to 1.09361 yards. Determine how many ounces of plant material per square yard the typical coral reef produces in 1 year. Show how you found your answer.

b. Write two different statements comparing the amount of plant material produced in a tropical rainforest to that produced in a temperate rainforest.

c. The Baltic Sea covers approximately 422,000 square kilometers.

35a. $2,500 \text{ g/m}^2 \times 0.035 \text{ oz/g} = 87.5 \text{ oz/m}^2$,
and $87.5 \text{ oz/m}^2 \times \frac{1 \text{ m}^2}{1.09361^2 \text{ yd}^2} \approx 73.2 \text{ oz/yd}^2$

35c. See Additional Answers.

Quick Check

Informal Assessment
Students should be able to:

✔ backtrack to undo taking the square root of a number

✔ backtrack to undo taking the reciprocal of a number

✔ backtrack to undo changing the sign of a number

✔ use backtracking to find solutions to equations with powers and square roots

✔ understand that some equations have more than one solution

• **Quick Quiz on page A684**

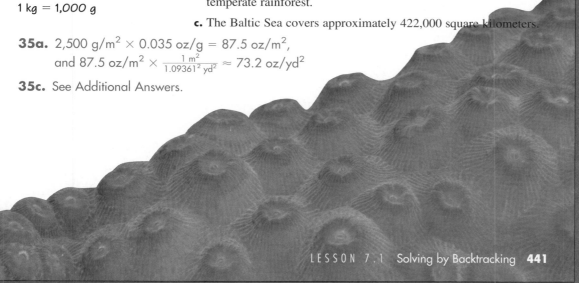

LESSON 7.1 Solving by Backtracking **441**

Additional Answers

35c. 5.275×10^{10} kg; Possible explanation: $125 \text{ g/m}^2 \times \frac{1 \text{ kg}}{1,000 \text{ g}} \times \frac{1,000^2 \text{ m}^2}{1^2 \text{ km}^2} = 125,000 \text{ kg/km}^2$, and
$125,000 \text{ kg/km}^2 \times 422,000 \text{ km}^2 = 5.275 \times 10^{10}$ kg

Teacher Notes

7.2

Solving by Factoring

Objectives

▶ To understand the zero product property

▶ To solve quadratic equations in factored form

▶ To solve quadratic equations by factoring the difference of two squares and perfect square trinomials

▶ To solve quadratic equations by factoring quadratic trinomials

Overview (pacing: about 4 class periods)

In this lesson, students solve quadratic equations by factoring. They begin by learning the zero product property (if $ab = 0$, either a or b, or both, must be 0). By the end of the lesson, students will likely appreciate that factoring is one of the simplest methods for solving quadratics, one that requires little time and effort. Factoring, however, is not a method that can be used to solve all quadratics, and students will learn other methods in later lessons.

Advance Preparation

No advance preparation is required.

	Summary	Materials	On Your Own Exercises	Assessment Opportunities
Investigation 1 page T442	Students solve equations written as the product of factors as well as equations that need to be factored first, particularly differences of squares and perfect square trinomials.	• Graphing calculators (optional)	Practice & Apply: 1–14, p. 451 Connect & Extend: 33–40, p. 452 Mixed Review: 47–57, p. 455	On the Spot Assessment, page T444 Share & Summarize, pages T444, 444 Troubleshooting, page T444
Investigation 2 page T445	Students are exposed to factoring trinomials of the form $x^2 + bx + c$ in order to gain facility with solving quadratics.		Practice & Apply: 15–24, p. 451 Connect & Extend: 41–44, pp. 452–453 Mixed Review: 47–57, p. 455	Share & Summarize, pages T448, 448 Troubleshooting, page T448
Investigation 3 page T448	Students solve quadratic equations that necessitate rearranging terms before they can be factored.		Practice & Apply: 25–32, p. 451 Connect & Extend: 45, 46, p. 454 Mixed Review: 47–57, p. 455	Share & Summarize, pages T450, 450 Troubleshooting, page T450 Informal Assessment, page 455 Quick Quiz, page 455

1 Write the following equation on the board:

$$(x - 2)(x + 5) = 0$$

Ask students if they can solve this by backtracking. Most will say they can't. Explain that in this lesson, they will learn how to solve such equations.

Think & Discuss

In this Think & Discuss, students become aware of the zero product property: if the product of two (or more) real numbers is 0, at least one of those numbers must be 0. The first question asks them what must be true about the factors; give them time to think about this. If no student ventures a guess, you might prompt them with such questions as the following:

2

> Do you think one of the numbers could be 1? What would the other number be? *yes, 0*

> Are those the only two numbers that work? *No; 0 and anything will work.*

When students consider $k(k - 3) = 0$, some may become confused if they think k is both 3 and 0 at the same time. Explain that in this case, k can be *either* 0 or 3. Encourage them to try both values in the original equation to check.

3 For the third part, some students may not agree that 2 and $^-5$ are the only solutions of the quadratic equation. You might ask them to graph the equations $y = x(x - 3)$ and $y = (x - 2)(x + 5)$ on their graphing calculators. To solve these equations, students need to look for the points where each graph crosses the x-axis, where $y = 0$. They will easily see that each parabola touches the axis in only two places; therefore they should agree that there are only two possible solutions.

Investigation 1

In this investigation, students use the zero product property to solve equations written as the product of factors set equal to 0. They also solve equations that need to be factored first, concentrating on those equations that contain a difference of two squares or a perfect square trinomial.

4 **Problem Set A** Grouping: Individuals

These problems are fairly straightforward and should not take students long to do, since they are all in factored form, like the example in the Think & Discuss. Allow about 5 minutes for students to complete this problem set.

5 Note that **Problem 5** contains three binomial factors. You may need to help students realize that the zero product property still holds. Try having them enclose two factors with brackets, [ ], and ask whether they can consider the third factor to be multiplied by the *result* in the brackets. Prompt them to apply the zero product property to that product.

You might also write an equation using the product of three variables, $abc = 0$, and ask what happens if one variable is 0. Then ask whether it's possible for all three variables to be nonzero and yet still have a product of 0.

Problem Set Wrap-Up After students have completed Problem Set A, briefly review their answers, especially to Problem 5, as a class.

Solving by Factoring

Some quadratic equations can be solved easily by backtracking. A second solution method, factoring, can be used to solve other quadratic equations fairly easily.

When a quadratic equation consists of a product of two factors on one side of the equal sign and 0 on the other side, such as

$$(x - 2)(x + 5) = 0$$

the solutions can be found exactly. This is because 0 has a special property.

1 Write this equation on the board, and ask if students can use back-tracking to solve it.

① 0, 3; Possible explanation: No other values will make one of the factors equal to 0.

② 2, ⁻5; Possible explanation: I found the value of *x* that makes *x* − 2 equal to 0, and did the same for *x* + 5.

Think & Discuss

If the product of two factors is 0, what must be true about the factors? At least one of them must be 0.

Find all the values of *k* that satisfy the equation $k(k - 3) = 0$. Explain how you know you've found them all. See ①.

Now find all the values of *x* that satisfy $(x - 2)(x + 5) = 0$. Explain how you found them. See ②.

2 Prompt students as needed.

3 Problem-Solving Strategy

Use a graph

Investigation Factoring Quadratic Expressions

You will now use the ideas from the Think & Discuss to solve some equations written as a product equal to 0.

Problem Set A

Find all the solutions of each equation.

1. $(t - 1)(t - 3) = 0$ 1, 3

2. $(s + 1)(2s + 3) = 0$ ⁻1, ⁻1.5

3. $x(3x + 7) = 0$ 0, $-\frac{7}{3}$

4. $(p + 4)(p + 4) = 0$ ⁻4

5. Using the same idea, find the solutions of this equation. ⁻0.5, ⁻8, 1

$$(2x + 1)(x + 8)(x - 1) = 0$$

4 Have students work on their own.

5 Help students reason with the three factors as needed.

Point out that the equations in Problem Set A were all written as products equal to 0. In that form, the equations should have been easy to solve.

One visual way to introduce the Think & Discuss is to write the expression $(x - 3)(x + 2)$ on the board. Remind students that in Chapter 6 they learned to expand expressions like this, and have them help you write the equivalent expression $x^2 - x - 6$. Then cover the original (factored) expression. Let students know that in this investigation, they will be reversing (or undoing) this expansion, taking an expression like $x^2 - x - 6$ and rewriting it as the product of two binomials. (At this, uncover the factored expression.) Explain that this process is called *factoring*, because they are creating an expression written as factors.

 Think & Discuss

Work through the questions as a group. As much as possible, have volunteers show how they would expand or factor the expressions. This activity uses terms students have seen before, *binomial* and *difference of two squares*, and also new terms, *trinomial* and *perfect square trinomial*. Be sure students understand these terms; it may help to post the terms with definitions and examples for reference during the chapter.

Be sure to discuss the last question; students' answers will give you a good idea of their understanding of this basic idea. Students may have trouble expressing the value of b, however; you may find it helpful to write $ax^2 + bx + c = (mx + n)^2$ on the board to give them something more concrete to compare. Ask them,

How is the value of b related to m and n? $b = 2mn$
What must the value of m be? $\sqrt{a}$
What must the value of n be? $\pm\sqrt{c}$
Now write b in terms of a and c. $b = \pm 2\sqrt{a}\sqrt{c}$

You have seen how easily you can solve equations that are written as a product of factors equal to 0. Sometimes you can rewrite an equation in this form to make the solution easy to find.

In Chapter 6, you learned how to *expand* a product of two binomials, such as $(x + 3)(x - 2)$. The reverse of this process—rewriting an expression as a product of factors—is called **factoring.** For example, the expression $x^2 + x - 6$ can be factored to $(x + 3)(x - 2)$.

1 Introduce the concept of factoring.

VOCABULARY
factoring

① Because $9x^2 = (3x)^2$, and $16 = 4^2$, one subtracted from the other is the difference of two perfect squares.

Think & Discuss

2 Work through the questions with the class.

You may recall from Chapter 6 that the expression $(3x + 4)(3x - 4)$ can be rewritten as $9x^2 - 16$ when it is expanded. An expression such as $9x^2 - 16$ is called a *difference of two squares*. Can you explain why?   See ①.

Now think about reversing the expansion. How would you factor $4a^2 - 25$? That is, how would you rewrite it as the product of two factors? $(2a + 5)(2a - 5)$

VOCABULARY
trinomial

② Because it can be expressed as the square of a binomial.

In Chapter 6, you also learned how to square a binomial and rewrite it as a **trinomial,** an expression with three unlike terms. For example:

$$(x - 5)^2 = x^2 - 10x + 25 \qquad (b + 5)^2 = b^2 + 10b + 25$$

Rewrite each trinomial below as the square of a binomial.

$$(c + 2)^2 \quad c^2 + 4c + 4 \qquad\qquad 16d^2 - 8d + 1 \quad (4d - 1)^2$$

Remember

Subtracting a term means the coefficient is negative. For example, in the expression $16x^2 - 8x + 1$, the coefficient of x is $^-8$.

A trinomial such as $16d^2 - 8d + 1$ is called a *perfect square trinomial.* Can you explain why?   See ②.

Which of these four trinomials are perfect squares? $x^2 + 6x + 9$ and $49s^2 - 28s + 4$

$$x^2 + 6x + 9 \qquad\qquad k^2 - 8k + 25$$

$$4y^2 + 4y + 4 \qquad\qquad 49s^2 - 28s + 4$$

Just by looking at the coefficients, how can you tell whether *any* trinomial in the form $ax^2 + bx + c$ is a perfect square?
The values of a and c are perfect squares, and $b = \pm 2(\sqrt{a})(\sqrt{c})$.

3 Use the last question to assess how well students understand.

Develop

Problem Set B Suggested Grouping: Pairs

This problem set focuses on identifying whether expressions in quadratic equations are the differences of two squares or perfect square trinomials. In the second part of the problem set, students work with more general forms of these special cases.

On the **Spot** **Assessment**

In **Problem 2,** watch for the common mistake of thinking that the *sum* of two squares can be factored. If students believe they have found factors, tell them they can always check their factors by expanding *carefully.* They will likely catch their errors this way. They also might try evaluating the expressions (original and after factoring) for a few test values.

Problem 8 is another equation involving the sum of two squares. At this point, you may want to ask students what they can say about factoring the sum of two squares. (It can't be done.)

If students are having difficulty with the general form in **Problem 10,** you may want to have them concentrate on the first and last terms of the trinomial: a^2 and $4b^2$. They should think about these terms as perfect squares and try to find the binomial factors by thinking about the square roots of these terms, a and $2b$.

About the **Mathematics**

There is only one solution to Problem 10, but it is what is known as a *multiple solution* (or a *solution of multiplicity 2*), since there are two factors of $(a - 2b)$.

Share & Summarize

These questions assess students' understanding of the two forms, differences of two squares and perfect square trinomials. You might ask students, if there is time, why quadratic equations in these forms are easy to solve. You may want to collect the various examples and use them as additional problems for the class, if needed.

Troubleshooting If students are having difficulty with these special forms of quadratics, work additional examples by using the expressions generated in the Share & Summarize.

On Your Own Exercises

Practice & Apply: 1–14, p. 451
Connect & Extend: 33–40, p. 452
Mixed Review: 47–57, p. 455

1. $(x + 8)(x - 8) = 0;$ $x = 8, ^-8$

2. This is the sum of two squares, not the difference; and it is not a perfect square trinomial because it has no middle term.

3. $^-64$ is not the square of a (real) number so the expression can't be a perfect square trinomial.

4. $(k - 8)^2 = 0, k = 8$

5. $(3y + 1)(3y - 1) = 0; y = \frac{1}{3}, ^-\frac{1}{3}$

6. $(3m + 1)^2 = 0,$ $m = ^-\frac{1}{3}$

7. $^-1$ is not the square of any (real) number so the expression can't be a perfect square trinomial.

Just the facts

Quadratic equations are often used to describe how the position of a moving object changes over time. For example, the equation $d = 25 - 3t^2$ might describe how many meters an accelerating hyena is from a rabbit after t seconds if it began running toward the rabbit from 25 meters away.

Problem Set B

In Problems 1–8, determine whether the quadratic expression to the left of the equal sign is the difference of two squares, or a perfect square trinomial. If it is, rewrite it in factored form and solve the equation. If it isn't in one of these special forms, explain how you know it isn't.

1. $x^2 - 64 = 0$

2. $p^2 + 64 = 0$

3. $x^2 - 16x - 64 = 0$

4. $k^2 - 16k + 64 = 0$

5. $9y^2 - 1 = 0$

6. $9m^2 + 6m + 1 = 0$

7. $9g^2 - 4g - 1 = 0$

8. $y^2 + 9 = 0$ See below.

Each equation below has two variables. If the quadratic expression is the difference of two squares, or a perfect square trinomial, rewrite the equation in factored form and solve for a. If it is in neither special form, explain how you know it isn't.

9. $a^2 + 9b^2 = 0$ This is the sum of two squares, so it's neither form.

10. $a^2 - 4ab + 4b^2 = 0$ $(a - 2b)^2 = 0; a = 2b$

11. $4a^2 - b^2 = 0$ $(2a + b)(2a - b) = 0; a = \frac{b}{2}, ^-\frac{b}{2}$

Share & Summarize

1. Give an example of a perfect square trinomial. Then give an example of a quadratic expression that is the difference of two squares. Explain how you know that your expressions are in the correct forms.   See below.

2. Explain why the only solutions of $4x^2 - 9 = 0$ are $x = 1.5$ and $x = ^-1.5$.   See Additional Answers.

Problem Set B Answer

8. This is the sum of two squares, not the difference; and it is not a perfect square trinomial because it has no middle term.

Share & Summarize Answer

1. Possible answer: $x^2 + 12x + 36$ and $x^2 - 81$; $x^2 + 12x + 36$ can be rewritten as the square of a binomial, $(x + 6)^2$; x^2 and 81 are both perfect squares (of x and 9), so $x^2 - 81$ is the difference of two squares.

444 CHAPTER 7   Solving Quadratic Equations

Additional Answers
Share & Summarize

2. $4x^2 - 9 = 0$ can be rewritten as $(2x - 3)(2x + 3)$. This is equal to 0 only when one of the factors is equal to 0, so the only values of x that satisfy the equation are those that make $2x - 3$ or $2x + 3$ equal to 0, that is, $x = 1.5, ^-1.5$.

Investigation 2

There is legitimate debate about how much factoring should be emphasized. Some say factoring is no longer a necessary skill and should take little (if any) time in the mathematics curriculum.

This investigation on techniques of factoring quadratic trinomials of the form $x^2 + (m + n)x + mn$ is included for more than one reason. Factoring makes solving some quadratics quite simple, especially when the coefficient of x^2 is 1, and students are capable of great facility in factoring such forms. Learning factoring also reinforces sums and products as the building blocks of our number system, and some students enjoy factoring as a mental exercise akin to crossword puzzles and logic games.

The approach here is to expect mastery when factoring basic forms but not to emphasize the topic beyond what is necessary. Like knowing certain algorithms, factoring is a skill that helps to develop mathematical flexibility and efficiency.

Some teachers find algebra tiles a helpful manipulative in teaching factoring. When the coefficients of the terms in quadratic trinomials are negative, however, algebra tiles become more difficult to use as a model and are probably not worth the effort. ■

1 You might introduce this investigation by having the class read together the introductory material on page 445. Ask them to look at the expression $x^2 + 8x + 12$:

> Is this a perfect square trinomial? How do you know?

> Can you still factor it into the product of two binomials?

Give students a chance to work on this, and ask them to share strategies. When you get a factored form of the expression, draw a connection between the general form in the text, $(x + m)(x + n)$, and have students verify that the original expression is $x^2 + (m + n)x + mn$. Then move into the Example.

Example

2 If you had students try to factor the expression, ask them to compare the explanation given in the text with their own ideas. If you didn't, you might ask students to find the values of m and n and verify that the general forms given above the Example fit the specific equations given here.

Even if students seem confused at this point, let them go on to Problem Set C. The problem set offers similar problems that they will be able to work on together.

Access for all **Learners**

Extra Challenge As you begin to study the factors of numbers, a nice excursion that involves factoring is the *Russian Peasant algorithm.* Students find the algorithm interesting and should be able to explain why it works.

The Russian Peasant algorithm is a way to multiply two integers by repeatedly doubling and halving the numbers. Create a two-column table, labeling the columns "Halve" and "Double." Write one of the factors to be multiplied in either column, and the other factor in the other column. Then halve the number in the first column, rounding down to the nearest integer; double the number in the second column. Halve and double the new numbers in the same way, continuing until the number in the "Halve" column is 1. For example, consider $41 \cdot 7$:

Halve	Double
41	7
20	14
10	28
5	56
2	112
1	224

Now cross out any row in which there is an even number in the "Halve" column. (In the example, the rows with 20, 10, and 2 would be crossed out.) Add the remaining numbers in the "Double" column; the resulting sum is the product of the original expression. In the example, $7 + 56 + 224 = 287 = 41 \cdot 7$.

As long as the number in the "Halve" column is even, the product of the corresponding pairs are equal when you move to the next step (for example, $20 \cdot 14 = 10 \cdot 28$) because the factor of 2 is moved from the first number to the second. If you have only even numbers until you reach the point where the "Halve" number is 1, the product of 1 and the number in the "Double" column is equal to the product of the original numbers.

When the number being halved is odd, rounding down makes the new product less than the previous product by the amount in the double column: $5 \cdot 56 = (4 + 1) \cdot 56 = 4 \cdot 56 + 56 = 2 \cdot 112 + 56$. So, you "lose" that amount in the process and have to add it back at the end.

Investigation 2 ▶ Practice with Factoring

If a quadratic expression is equal to 0 and can be factored easily, finding its factors is an efficient way to solve the equation. In this investigation, you will learn some new strategies for determining whether a quadratic expression can easily be factored and for factoring it when you can. For example, consider this expression:

$$x^2 + 8x + 12$$

If such an expression can be factored, it can be rewritten as the product of two linear expressions:

$$(x + m)(x + n)$$

Multiplying terms gives

$$x^2 + (m + n)x + mn$$

You can use this idea to help factor any quadratic expression for which a, the coefficient of the squared variable, is equal to 1.

EXAMPLE

Can $x^2 + 8x + 12$ be factored? If so, solve the equation $x^2 + 8x + 12 = 0$.

First compare the expanded form of $(x + m)(x + n)$ with the given expression:

$$x^2 + 8x + 12$$
$$x^2 + (m + n)x + mn$$

If $x^2 + 8x + 12$ can be factored into the form $(x + m)(x + n)$, the product of m and n must be 12, and their sum must be 8. The only two numbers that fit these conditions are 6 and 2. This means that the expression *can* be factored and that the equation can be rewritten as

$$(x + 2)(x + 6) = 0$$

So, the equation $x^2 + 8x + 12 = 0$ has two solutions, $^-2$ and $^-6$.

In this investigation, you will consider only cases in which m and n are integers.

---

1 Read the text with the class.

2 Present the Example in one of two ways:

• Have students try to factor the expression and compare it to the Example.

• Have students verify the general forms above using specific values for m and n.

Problem Set C Suggested Grouping: Pairs

In **Problems 1–6,** students expand the product of two binomials using the general form,

$$(x + m)(x + n) = x^2 + (m + n)x + mn$$

In using this form, they should be able to expand these expressions quickly and accurately. The idea here is to bypass writing out the separate terms of the expansion and to use the general form to think about the coefficient of x as the sum of m and n and the constant term as the product of m and n. This will help students feel more comfortable when they reverse the process and factor.

For problems in which the operation of subtraction appears in one of the binomials, you may suggest that students rewrite the subtraction as addition of the opposite of the number. For example, students may rewrite **Problem 3** as $(x + {}^-4)(x + {}^-5)$, which makes it clearer that m is $^-4$ and n is $^-5$.

In **Problems 7–10,** students are given a quadratic trinomial and asked to find the binomial factors. Again, students should identify what the product and sum of m and n are for each problem. For example, in **Problem 7,** students should state that $m + n$ is 7 and mn is 6 and then determine that the only two numbers that satisfy these conditions are 6 and 1.

Problems 11 and 12 take this one step further by asking students to solve quadratic equations by first factoring the quadratic expressions.

Problem Set Wrap-Up If you find that students are still confused, particular in Problems 7–12, you may want to bring them together to discuss how they found values for m and n in specific problems. If it seems that students understand the process but simply have trouble finding the required numbers, the Think & Discuss on page 447 will give them a way to organize their work.

Problem Set C

For Problems 1–6, do the following:

- Think of the expression as a special case of $(x + m)(x + n)$, and state the values of m and n.

- Use the fact that $(x + m)(x + n) = x^2 + (m + n)x + mn$ to expand the expression.

1. $m = 7, n = 1;$
$x^2 + 8x + 7$

2. $m = 2, n = 5;$
$x^2 + 7x + 10$

3. $m = {}^-4, n = {}^-5;$
$x^2 - 9x + 20$

4. $m = 2, n = {}^-3;$
$x^2 - x - 6$

5. $m = {}^-2, n = 3;$
$x^2 + x - 6$

6. $m = 5, n = {}^-4;$
$x^2 + x - 20$

1. $(x + 7)(x + 1)$ **2.** $(x + 2)(x + 5)$

3. $(x - 4)(x - 5)$ **4.** $(x + 2)(x - 3)$

5. $(x - 2)(x + 3)$ **6.** $(x + 5)(x - 4)$

For Problems 7–10, use the fact that $(x + m)(x + n) = x^2 + (m + n)x + mn$ to do the following:

- Determine what $m + n$ and mn equal. From this, find the values of m and n.

- Rewrite the expression as a product of two binomials. You may want to expand the product to check your result.

7. $x^2 + 7x + 6 = (x + \_\_)(x + \_\_)$ $(x + 6)(x + 1)$

8. $x^2 - 7x + 6 = (x - \_\_)(x - \_\_)$ $(x - 6)(x - 1)$

9. $x^2 - 4x - 12 = (x - \_\_)(x + \_\_)$ $(x - 6)(x + 2)$

10. $x^2 + 4x - 12 = (x - \_\_)(x + \_\_)$ $(x - 2)(x + 6)$

Use the method demonstrated in the Example on page 445 to solve these equations.

11. $x^2 - 10x + 16 = 0$ 2, 8 **12.** $x^2 + 6x - 16 = 0$ 2, $^-$8

Just the facts

The quadratic equation $x = 10t + \frac{1}{2}(2.5)t^2$ describes the distance in meters traveled by a motorcycle that began from a certain point with velocity 10 m/s and increased its speed, or accelerated, at a rate of 2.5 m/s².

1 You may have students work in pairs.

2 Beginning with Problem 3, you may need to have students rewrite subtraction as adding the opposite.

3 If necessary, discuss how students found values for m and n in specific problems.

1 Think & Discuss

Have students come together as a class to read Kai's approach to factoring. In essence, Kai is doing the same thing students did in Problems 7–12 of Problem Set C, but he is using a systematic approach to find all of the possible factor pairs. If students are already using this systematic approach, you can go through this quickly and move right on to Problem Set D.

2 Problem Set D   Suggested Grouping: Pairs

In this problem set, students factor quadratic trinomials by systematically listing factors of the constant term. If some students think that the expression in **Problem 6**
3
can be factored, encourage them to check their work by expanding the binomials they come up with.

In **Problems 8–11,** students explore expressions that have a common factor that can be removed before they attempt to factor into binomial products. A general rule of thumb is to look for such common factors before attempting to simplify any expression.

The challenge problems, **Problems 12 and 13,** introduce quadratic trinomials in which the coefficient of x^2 is a number other than 1. There are only two of these, since often it is counterproductive to take the time to figure out all the combinations of factors of the leading coefficient and constant term. The quadratic formula, which students will learn in Lesson 7.4, and technology such as computer algebra systems (found on higher-level graphing calculators and in mathematical software), are more reasonable solution tools. It is important, however, that students have some exposure to the process for factoring these kinds of quadratic trinomials. If students need some additional examples or scaffolding of Problems 12 and 13, you may want to provide the following:

$$2x^2 + 3x + 1 = (2x + \underline{\quad})(x + \underline{\quad})$$

$$3r^2 - 17r + 10 = (3r - \underline{\quad})(r - \underline{\quad})$$

$$4t^2 + 5t + 1 = (\underline{\quad} + 1)(\underline{\quad} + 1)$$

$$2x^2 + 3x - 2 = (2x \underline{\quad} \underline{\quad})(x \underline{\quad} \underline{\quad})$$

Access
for all Learners

Extra Challenge For students who enjoy factoring and view such problems as puzzles, here is an additional challenge problem:

$$9r^3 + 24r^2 + 12r \quad 3r(3r + 2)(r + 2)$$

Think & Discuss

Kai organized the possibilities for factoring trinomials.

1 Read and discuss Kai's approach.

Use Kai's approach to factor these expressions.

$$x^2 + 11x + 10 \qquad\qquad x^2 - 7x + 10 \qquad\qquad x^2 - 3x - 10$$
$$(x + 10)(x + 1) \qquad\qquad (x - 2)(x - 5) \qquad\qquad (x + 2)(x - 5)$$

Explain what happens if you use Kai's approach with $x^2 + 6x + 10$. This expression can't be factored. The factors of 10 are 10 and 1, or 5 and 2. The factors must both be positive or both be negative, and there is no sum of these that equals 6. So the expression can't be factored using integers.

Problem Set D

2 You may have students work in pairs.

Factor each quadratic expression using Kai's method, or state that it can't be factored using his method.

1. (x + 5)(x + 1)
2. (b + 5)(b − 1)
3. (w − 1)²
4. can't be factored
5. (s − 12)(s + 2)
6. can't be factored

1. $x^2 + 6x + 5$ **2.** $b^2 + 4b - 5$

3. $w^2 - 2w + 1$ **4.** $t^2 + 9t - 18$

5. $s^2 - 10s - 24$ **6.** $c^2 - 4c + 5$

7. Use Kai's approach to solve the equation $w^2 + 4w - 12 = 0$. 2, ⁻6

3 Encourage students to check their answers by expanding their factored expressions.

If every term of a quadratic expression has a common factor, rewriting it can make factoring easier. For example, $2x^2 + 12x + 10$ can be rewritten as $2(x^2 + 6x + 5)$, which factors to $2(x + 1)(x + 5)$.

Find the common factor for each expression below, and then factor the expression as much as possible.

8. 3(a² + 6a + 5) = 3(a + 5)(a + 1)
9. 2(b² + 4b − 5) = 2(b + 5)(b − 1)
10. 4(x² − 2x + 2); can't be factored further
11. 5(t² + 5t − 14) = 5(t + 7)(t − 2)

8. $3a^2 + 18a + 15$ **9.** $2b^2 + 8b - 10$

10. $4x^2 - 8x + 8$ **11.** $5t^2 + 25t - 70$

Challenge Sometimes a quadratic expression can be factored even though the coefficient of x^2 is not 1 and the terms do not have a common factor. For example, $2x^2 - 9x + 9$ can be factored as $(2x - 3)(x - 3)$. Use strategies like those you've used before to factor these expressions.

12. $3x^2 - 11x - 4$ **13.** $8x^2 + 2x - 3$
    $(3x + 1)(x - 4)$ $(4x + 3)(2x - 1)$

1 Share & Summarize

It may be helpful to write the steps students suggest on the board so the whole class can discuss them and decide whether they agree.

It is important that students begin to make some generalizations about the signs of the terms in the trinomials and what they reveal about the signs of the factors. For example, if the middle term is negative and the constant is positive (such as $x^2 - 5x + 6$), you can conclude that factors of the constant term will both be negative. If both the middle and constant terms are negative, one factor must be positive and one must be negative. If the middle term is positive and the constant is negative, one factor must be positive and one factor must be negative.

As an extra challenge, you might ask students to think about what to do when the coefficient of x^2 is negative. You might offer an example, such as $-x^2 + x + 12$. Many students have difficulty deciding what to do with the negative coefficient, especially when it is -1.

Troubleshooting The next investigation continues with factoring, and students will be learning more generalizable techniques later in the chapter. Students should have some grasp on the concept, even if they aren't very proficient with the technique. There is certainly no shortage of factoring examples for you to supply for students if they just need practice, but be careful not to dwell on this topic more than is necessary.

If students are having conceptual difficulty, you might review some of the rectangle diagrams used in Chapter 6, perhaps using algebra tiles as well.

On Your Own Exercises

Practice & Apply: 15–24, p. 451
Connect & Extend: 41–44, pp. 452–453
Mixed Review: 47–57, p. 455

Investigation 3

In this investigation, students continue to solve quadratic equations, but ones that necessitate rearranging terms before they can be factored.

Think & Discuss

Introduce the investigation by having students read the cartoon in the Think & Discuss.

Discuss the cartoon and questions. Combining like terms on one side of an equation should not be a new idea, but it is important that students understand that they cannot use the zero product property unless the product is 0. This point is reinforced in Problem 9 of Problem Set E.

Investigation ▷3 Solving Quadratics by Factoring

Share & Summarize   See margin.

If you are given a quadratic expression to factor, what steps would you follow to factor it or to determine that it can't be factored using integers?

Sometimes you must rearrange the terms in a quadratic expression to see how—or if—the expression can be factored.

Think & Discuss

Mrs. Torres gave his class a number puzzle.

Why is Tamika's suggestion a good one? What quadratic equation should the class find when they finish rearranging?   See ①, above left.

Can the quadratic expression be factored? If so, what are the factors?
yes, $(x - 5)(x - 3)$

What numbers could Mrs. Torres have started with? Check your answer in his original number puzzle.   5 or 3

Problem Set E Suggested Grouping: Pairs

In this problem set, students work with a variety of quadratic equations that require rearranging before they can be factored. Some of these equations are developed in contexts; others, like those in the beginning, are used to practice the skill of getting all terms set equal to 0.

In all of these problems, students can make the coefficient of the squared term positive or negative.

Problem-Solving Strategies For example, in **Problem 1:**

- Students could subtract $6a$ from both sides and then subtract a^2. In doing so, they would be faced with factoring $-a^2 - 2a + 3 = 0$. Most students will not like the look of this trinomial; they may multiply through by -1 or factor out -1.

- Other students may think ahead and keep the coefficient positive by moving all terms over to the right side.

You may want to quickly scan **Problems 2–4** with the class to see what their first steps would be to keep the squared term positive, if students agree this is an easier form to work with.

Students at first may not think that **Problem 4** represents a quadratic equation. If necessary, suggest they try to rearrange the equation to eliminate the fraction.

In **Problem 6,** students end up with the equation $(x - 1)^2 = 0$. A graph is a good way to show that there is only one solution to this equation; graphs of quadratics in the form $y = (x + h)^2$ are parabolas with vertices that are on the x-axis at $x = -h$.

Problem 7 introduces a context that makes negative solutions of the quadratic equation unreasonable.

Remember

When solving an equation involving algebraic fractions, always check that the apparent solutions don't make any denominators in the original equation equal to 0.

1. $a^2 + 2a - 3 = 0$, $(a + 3)(a - 1) = 0$; $a = 1, ^-3$

2. $b^2 - 4b - 12 = 0$, $(b - 6)(b + 2) = 0$; $b = ^-2, 6$

3. $c^2 + 7c + 12 = 0$, $(c + 4)(c + 3) = 0$; $c = ^-4, ^-3$

4. $d^2 - 5d + 6 = 0$, $(d - 3)(d - 2)$; $d = 3, 2$

5. $x^2 - 2x - 3 = 0$, $(x - 3)(x + 1) = 0$; $x = 3, ^-1$

6a. $x(x + 2) = 4x - 1$, $x^2 - 2x + 1 = 0$, $(x - 1)^2 = 0$; $x = 3$

6b. Kenyon's puzzle resulted in a quadratic expression that is a perfect square set equal to 0, so it has only one solution because 0 has only one square root.

7b. $w^2 + 2w - 15 = 0$, $(w + 5)(w - 3) = 0$; $w = 3, ^-5$; Since $^-5$ can't be the length of a rug, only 3 makes sense.

Problem Set E

Rearrange each equation so you can solve by factoring. Find the solutions.

1. $4a + 3 = 6a + a^2$

2. $b^2 - 12 = 4b$

3. $c(c + 4) + 3c + 12 = 0$

4. $d + \frac{6}{d} = 5$

5. $\frac{(x + 3)(x - 2)^2}{x - 2} = 3x - 3$ (Hint: Simplify the fraction first.)

6. Kenyon challenged his teacher, Ms. Hiroshi, with a number puzzle: "I'm thinking of a number. If you multiply my number by 2 more than the number, the result will be 1 less than four times my number."

   a. Write an equation for Kenyon's puzzle, and then use factoring to solve it. Check that your answer fits the puzzle.

   b. Kenyon expected his teacher to find two solutions to his puzzle. Why didn't she?

7. A rectangular rug has an area of 15 square meters. Its length is 2 meters more than its width.

   a. Write an equation to show the relationship between the rug's area and its width. $w(w + 2) = 15$, where $w =$ width

   b. Solve your equation. Explain why only one of the solutions is useful for finding the rug's dimensions.

   c. What are the dimensions of the rug?   5 m by 3 m

1 You may have students work in pairs.

2 You may want to quickly discuss what first steps will keep a positive coefficient on the quadratic term.

In **Problem 10d,** students will probably use the following steps:

$$x^2 + 3x - 10 = 30$$
$$x^2 + 3x - 40 = 0$$
$$(x + 8)(x - 5) = 0$$
$$x = {}^-8, 5$$

Problem Set Wrap-Up Discuss **Problem 10** with the class. Gabriela's reasoning reveals a common misconception. Her correct guess is a lucky one, since her reasoning is incorrect. If the product of two or more numbers multiply to any number other than 0 (in this case, 10), there is an infinite number of possibilities for both numbers, but the two numbers will be related. (For example, if one is 2, the other must be 5; if one is $\frac{3}{10}$, the other must be $\frac{1}{3}$.) The beauty of the zero product property is that you can draw a conclusion about what *one* of the numbers must be *independent of* what the other might be; if the first number is 0, it doesn't matter what the second number is—the product will be 0.

Share & Summarize

You may want to have students work in small groups on these questions and then trade questions with other groups. Challenge them to decide whether it is likely that an equation they make up by just choosing numbers will factor.

Troubleshooting If students are having difficulty with these problems, you might first determine where the problem lies (finding solutions from the factored form of a quadratic equation, factoring quadratic expressions, or rearranging equations in order to factor) and then review the appropriate problem sets.

On Your Own Exercises

Practice & Apply: 25–32, p. 451
Connect & Extend: 45, 46, p. 454
Mixed Review: 47–57, p. 455

8. $x + 20 = x^2$,
$(x - 5)(x + 4) = 0$;
$x = 5, \, ^-4$

9. $x^2 + (x + 1)^2 =$
145; $x = 8$ or $^-9$;
The integers are 8
and 9, or $^-9$ and
$^-8$.

8. When 20 is added to a number, the result is the square of the number. What could the number be? Show how you found your answer.

9. The sum of the squares of two consecutive integers is 145. Find all possibilities for the integers. Show how you found your answer.

10. Gabriela was trying to solve the equation $(x + 1)(x - 2) = 10$. This is how she reasoned:

> Two factors of 10 are 5 and 2.
>
> So, $x + 1 = 5$ must be one solution of the equation.
>
> That means $x = 4$.
>
> I'll check: $(4 + 1)(4 - 2) = 5 \cdot 2 = 10$.
>
> It checks!

10c. $x^2 - x - 2 = 10$,
$x^2 - x - 12 = 0$,
$(x - 4)(x + 3) =$
0; $x = 4, \, ^-3$

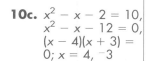

Just the facts

The quadratic equation $K = \frac{1}{2}(64)v^2$ gives the kinetic energy of a skydiver with a mass of 64 kg (about 141 lb) falling through the sky with velocity v in m/s.

a. What would have happened if Gabriela had guessed that $x - 2 = 5$? She'd get $x = 7$, which doesn't satisfy the equation.

b. Do you think Gabriela's method is an efficient way to solve quadratic equations? Explain.   No; it doesn't always work.

c. Solve Gabriela's equation, $(x + 1)(x - 2) = 10$. Start by expanding and then rearranging. Check each solution.

d. Solve $(x + 5)(x - 2) = 30$. $^-8, \, 5$

Share & Summarize See below.

1. Make up a problem involving area that requires solving a quadratic equation.

2. Try to solve your problem by factoring. If you can, give the solutions of the equation and then answer the question. If not, explain why the expression can't be factored.

1. Possible answer: A rug is 4 times as long as it is wide and has an area of 16 square feet. What are its length and width?

2. Possible answer: In the above case, with w as width, $4w^2 = 16$, $4w^2 - 16 = 0$, $(2w + 4)(2w - 4) = 0$; $w = 2$ or $^-2$. The negative solution has no meaning in this problem, so the answer is width = 2 ft, length = 8 ft.

1 Discuss Problem 10 with the class.

2 You may have students work in small groups and trade problems with other groups.

Teacher Notes

On Your Own Exercises

Practice & Apply

5. difference of squares; $(x + 7)(x - 7)$; $x = 7, {}^-7$

8. perfect square trinomial; $(x - 7)^2$; $x = 7$

9. difference of squares; $(7 + x)(7 - x)$; $x = 7, {}^-7$

10. perfect square trinomial; $(x + 7)^2$; $x = {}^-7$

12. perfect square trinomial; $(ax + 2b)^2 = 0$; $x = \frac{{}^-2b}{a}$

13. difference of squares; $(mx + n)(mx - n)$; $x = \frac{n}{m}, \frac{{}^-n}{m}$

17. Can't be factored because none of the factors of 6 (6 and 1, or 3 and 2) have a difference of 2.

21. Can't be factored because none of the factors of 30 (30 and 1, 15 and 2, 10 and 3, or 6 and 5) have a sum of 15.

22. $(n - 14)(n - 3) = 0$, $n = 3, 14$

25. $(x - 3)(x + 7) = 0$; $x = 3, {}^-7$

26. Can't be solved by factoring (no factors of 12 add to 3).

27. $(e - 12)(e - 2) = 0$; $e = 12, 2$

28. $(g - 8)^2 = 0$; $g = 8$

29. $(u - 4)(u + 9) = 0$; $u = 4, {}^-9$

Solve each equation.

1. $(x + 5)(x + 7) = 0$ ${}^-5, {}^-7$

2. $(x - 5)(x + 7) = 0$ $5, {}^-7$

3. $(x - 5)(x - 7) = 0$ $5, 7$

4. $(x + 5)(x - 7) = 0$ ${}^-5, 7$

In Exercises 5–14, determine whether the expression on the left of the equal sign is a difference of squares or a perfect square trinomial. If it is, indicate which and then factor the expression and solve the equation for x. If the expression is in neither form, say so.

5. $x^2 - 49 = 0$

6. $x^2 + 49 = 0$ neither form

7. $x^2 + 14x - 49 = 0$ neither form

8. $x^2 - 14x + 49 = 0$

9. $49 - x^2 = 0$

10. $x^2 + 14x + 49 = 0$

11. $a^2x^2 + 4ab + b^2 = 0$

12. $a^2x^2 + 4abx + 4b^2 = 0$

13. $m^2x^2 - n^2 = 0$ neither form

14. $m^2x^2 + n^2 = 0$ neither form

Factor each quadratic expression that can be factored using integers. Identify those that cannot, and explain why they can't be factored.

15. $d^2 - 15d + 54$ $(d - 9)(d - 6)$

16. $g^2 - g - 6$ $(g - 3)(g + 2)$

17. $z^2 + 2z - 6$

18. $h^2 - 3h - 28$ $(h - 7)(h + 4)$

19. $2x^2 - 8x - 10$ $2(x - 5)(x + 1)$

20. $3c^2 - 9c + 6$ $3(c - 2)(c - 1)$

Solve each equation by factoring using integers, if possible. If an equation can't be solved in this way, explain why.

21. $k^2 + 15k + 30 = 0$

22. $n^2 - 17n + 42 = 0$ $(2b - 1)(b - 10) = 0$, $b = 0.5, 10$

23. Challenge $2b^2 - 21b + 10 = 0$

24. Challenge $8r^2 + 5r - 3 = 0$ $(8r - 3)(r + 1) = 0$; $r = \frac{3}{8}, {}^-1$

25. $4x + x^2 = 21$

26. $h^2 + 12 = 3h$

27. $14e = e^2 + 24$

28. $g^2 + 64 = 16g$

29. $u^2 + 5u = 36$

30. $(x + 3)(x - 4) = 30$

31. $\dfrac{(x + 1)^3}{x + 1} = 5x + 5$ (Hint: Simplify the fraction first.)

32. Carlos multiplied a number by itself and then added 6. The result was five times the original number. Write and solve an equation to find his starting number. $n^2 + 6 = 5n$; $n = 2$ or 3

30. $(x - 7)(x + 6) = 0$; $x = 7, {}^-6$

31. $(x + 1)(x - 4) = 0$; $x = 4$

 impactmath.com/self_check_quiz

On Your Own Exercises

Investigation 1,
pp. 442–444
Practice & Apply: 1–14
Connect & Extend: 33–40

Investigation 2,
pp. 445–448
Practice & Apply: 15–24
Connect & Extend: 41–44

Investigation 3,
pp. 448–450
Practice & Apply: 25–32
Connect & Extend: 45, 46

Assign Anytime
Mixed Review: 47–57

Exercise 9:
Students may not be used to seeing the constant term as the first term in the difference of two squares. You may want to show them how to rewrite this expression as ${}^-(x^2 - 49) = {}^-(x + 7)(x - 7)$.

Exercises 19 and 20:
It will help students to take out the common factor before they factor the trinomial.

Exercises 23 and 24:
These are challenge exercises because the coefficient of the squared term is not 1.

Exercises 25–31:
In each of these exercises, students need to rearrange the equation to set the quadratic expression equal to 0. In Exercise 31, the possible solution ${}^-1$ must be thrown out since $\frac{(x + 1)^3}{x + 1}$ would be undefined.

Exercise 33:
This exercise brings up an interesting question about domain when it comes to factoring expressions. In fact, $4x^2 - 7$ can be factored, but not over the integers. When factoring polynomials, you usually assume that the domain is integers. You may want to reassure students that they need only focus on integers in the investigations.

Note that in **Part a,** $-\sqrt{7}$ is also a possible answer, although it's unlikely students will think of it. Either answer should lead students to the ultimate goal in **Part b.**

Exercise 34:
This exercise is a good review of area and area formulas.

Exercises 35–40
These exercises extend students' work with factoring. They reveal some interesting patterns for differences of squares of the form $x^{2n} - 1$, where n is an integer.

Connect & Extend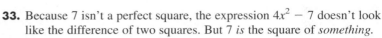

33. Because 7 isn't a perfect square, the expression $4x^2 - 7$ doesn't look like the difference of two squares. But 7 *is* the square of *something*.

a. What is 7 the square of?

33b. By thinking of 7 as a "square" (of $\sqrt{7}$), $4x^2 - 7$ can be thought of as the difference of two squares: $(2x + \sqrt{7})(2x - \sqrt{7})$.

b. How can you use your answer to Part a to factor $4x^2 - 7$ into a product of two binomials?

34. Geometry Each of these expressions represents one of the shaded areas below.

i. $D^2 - d^2$ **ii.** $\pi(r + w)^2 - \pi r^2$

iii. $(d + w)^2 - d^2$ **iv.** $4r^2 - \pi r^2$

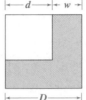 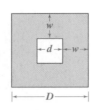 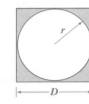 

Figure A   Figure B   Figure C   Figure D

34a. i. Figure B
ii. Figure D
iii. Figure A
iv. Figure C

a. Match each expression with one of the shaded areas so that *every* figure is matched to a different expression.

b. Write each expression in factored form. Factor out common factors, if possible.

34b. i. $(D + d)(D - d)$
ii. $\pi w(2r + w)$
iii. $w(2d + w)$
iv. $r^2(4 - \pi)$

Factor the expression on the left side of each equation as much as possible, and find all the possible solutions. It will help to remember that $x^4 = (x^2)^2$, $x^8 = (x^4)^2$, and $x^3 = x(x^2)$.

35–38. See below.

35. $x^4 - 1 = 0$ **36.** $x^8 - 1 = 0$

37. $x^3 - 16x = 0$ **38.** $x^3 - 6x^2 + 9x = 0$

39, 40. See Additional Answers.

39. $x^4 - 2x^2 + 1 = 0$ **40.** $x^4 + 2x^2 + 1 = 0$

Solve each equation. Be sure to check your answers. (Hint: Try factoring the numerator first.)

41. $x - 7 = 0; x = 7$
42. $x - 10 = 0; x = 10$

41. $\dfrac{x^2 + 6x + 9}{x + 3} = 10$ **42.** $\dfrac{16x^2 - 81}{4x + 9} = 31$

35. $(x^2 + 1)(x^2 - 1) = (x^2 + 1)(x + 1)(x - 1) = 0; x = 1, ^-1$
36. $x^8 - 1 = (x^4 + 1)(x^4 - 1) = (x^4 + 1)(x^2 + 1)(x + 1)(x - 1) = 0; x = 1, ^-1$
37. $x^3 - 16x = x(x^2 - 16) = x(x + 4)(x - 4) = 0; x = 0, 4, ^-4$
38. $x^3 - 6x^2 + 9x = x(x^2 - 6x + 9) = x(x - 3)(x - 3) = 0; x = 0, 3$

452 CHAPTER 7 Solving Quadratic Equations

Exercises 35–40
Extension:
Factor $x^{16} - 1$ as much as possible.
   $(x^8 + 1)(x^4 + 1)(x^2 + 1)(x + 1)(x - 1)$

Additional Answers

39. $x^4 - 2x^2 + 1 = (x^2 - 1)^2$
$= (x + 1)(x - 1)(x + 1)(x - 1) = 0;$
$x = 1, ^-1$

40. $x^4 + 2x^2 + 1 = (x^2 + 1)^2 = 0;$ no solutions

List the steps you
would follow to
solve a quadratic
equation by factor-
ing, or to decide
that it can't be
solved that way.

43a. $(a + 2)(a - 2)$; 2, -2

43d. $\frac{5}{2 - 2}$ is undefined;
$\frac{5}{-2 - 2} = -\frac{5}{4}$

43e. Possible answer:
When I simplified, I
removed one of the
factors that made
the original expression
undefined.

43. Challenge When you simplify algebraic expressions, sometimes
the simplified expression is not equivalent to the original for all
values of the variable. For example, consider this expression:

$$\frac{5a + 10}{a^2 - 4}$$

a. Factor the denominator. For what values of a is the expression
undefined? That is, for what values is the denominator equal to 0?

b. Now write the expression above using factored forms for both the
numerator and denominator. Be sure to look for common factors
in the terms. $\frac{5(a + 2)}{(a + 2)(a - 2)}$

c. Simplify the fraction. $\frac{5}{a - 2}$

d. Now try to evaluate the fraction using each value that made the
original expression undefined. (You found those values in Part a.)

e. You should have seen in Part d that the simplified fraction is not
equivalent to the original fraction for *all* values of a. Explain why
this happened.

f. When you simplify an algebraic fraction, you should note any
values of the variable that make the simplified fraction unequal
to the original. For example, the fraction $\frac{x(x + 1)}{3x}$ can be simplified
as $\frac{x + 1}{3}$, where $x \neq 0$.

Simplify the fraction $\frac{2m + 1}{4m^2 - 1} \cdot \frac{1}{2m - 1}$, where $m \neq {}^-0.5$ or 0.5

44. The Numkenas built a small, square patio from square bricks with
sides of length 1 foot. They bought just enough bricks to build the
patio, but after they built it they decided it was too small.

To extend the length and width of the patio by d feet, they had to
buy 24 more bricks. The original side length of the patio was 5 feet.

44a.

a. Draw a diagram to represent this situation. Be sure to show both
the original patio and the new one.

b. Write an equation to represent this situation. $(5 + d)^2 - 5^2 = 24$

c. Simplify your equation and solve it to find d, the amount by
which the patio's length and width were increased. Check your
answer. $25 + 10d + d^2 - 25 = 24$; $d^2 + 10d - 24 = 0$;
$(d + 12)(d - 2) = 0$; $d = 2$ ($d = {}^-12$ is meaningless
in this situation.)

Exercise 45:

It may not be obvious to students that they have to set each of the possible triangular numbers equal to $\frac{1}{2}(n^2 + n)$. You may want to mention this to students.

Observant students may realize it isn't obvious that when the expression can't be factored using integers, the number must not be triangular. Since n has to be a counting number, clearly *one* of the roots has to be an integer, but that doesn't explain why the other would have to be as well. If students ask, you can give them the following explanation. The mathematics behind the explanation isn't beyond your students, but it may take them some thought to understand it.

Consider the general equation, $T = \frac{1}{2}(n^2 + n)$. An equivalent equation is $\frac{1}{2}(n^2 + n - 2T) = 0$. If you can factor this (using integers or nonintegers), you get an equation of the form $\frac{1}{2}(n + a)(n + b) = 0$, where $a + b = 1$. (Refer to page 445 if necessary.) For T to be a triangular number, the equation must have an integer solution, so at least one of a and b must be an integer.

Suppose a is an integer. Then b must also be an integer, because $b = 1 - a$ and the difference of two integers (1 and a) is always an integer.

Exercise 46:

See the notes above for Exercise 45; the same issue applies here.

45a. $n^2 + n - 110 = 0$, $(n + 11)(n - 10) = 0$; $n = 10$ ($n = {}^-11$ doesn't make sense in this situation.)

45b. $n^2 + n - 240 = 0$, $(n + 16)(n - 15) = 0$; $n = 15$ ($n = {}^-16$ doesn't make sense.)

45c. $n^2 + n - 300 = 0$, can't be factored; 150 is not a triangular number.

45d. $n^2 + n - 400 = 0$, can't be factored; 200 is not a triangular number.

45e. $n^2 + n - 420 = 0$, $(n + 21)(n - 20) = 0$; $n = 20$ ($n = {}^-21$ doesn't make sense.)

46a. $n^2 - 3n - 40 = 0$, $(n - 8)(n + 5) = 0$; $n = 8$ ($n = {}^-5$ can't be the number of sides of a polygon.)

46b. $n^2 - 3n - 60 = 0$; Can't be factored; there is no polygon with 30 diagonals.

46c. $n^2 - 3n - 70 = 0$, $(n - 10)(n + 7) = 0$; $n = 10$ ($n = {}^-7$ can't be the number of sides of a polygon.)

46d. $n^2 - 3n - 100 = 0$; Can't be factored; no polygon has 50 diagonals.

45. The *triangular numbers* are a sequence of numbers that begins

$$1, 3, 6, 10, \ldots$$

The numbers in this sequence represent the number of dots in a series of triangular shapes.

Triangle 1 Triangle 2 Triangle 3 Triangle 4

T, the number of dots in Triangle n, is given by this quadratic equation:

$$T = \tfrac{1}{2}(n^2 + n)$$

Some of the following numbers are triangular numbers. For each possible value of T, set up an equation and try to solve it for n by factoring. If an equation cannot be factored using integers, T cannot be a triangular number. Indicate which numbers are not triangular.

a. 55 **b.** 120 **c.** 150 **d.** 200 **e.** 210

46. Geometry In Chapter 2, you learned that the number of diagonals in an n-sided polygon is given by the equation $D = \frac{n^2 - 3n}{2}$. Some examples are shown below.

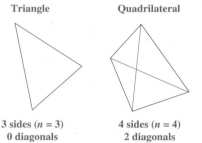

Triangle Quadrilateral Pentagon

3 sides ($n = 3$) 4 sides ($n = 4$) 5 sides ($n = 5$)
0 diagonals 2 diagonals 5 diagonals

Some of the following numbers are the number of diagonals in a polygon. For each possible value of D, set up an equation and try to solve it for n by factoring. If an equation can't be factored using integers, D cannot be the number of diagonals in a polygon. Indicate which values cannot be the number of diagonals in a polygon.

a. 20 **b.** 30 **c.** 35 **d.** 50 **e.** 54

46e. $n^2 - 3n - 108 = 0$; $(n - 12)(n + 9) = 0$; $n = 12$ ($n = {}^-9$ can't be the number of sides of a polygon.)

Mixed Review

Solve each equation by doing the same thing to both sides.

47. $\frac{3k-5}{5} + k = 5 + k$ 10

48. $7.5a - 6 = 5a + 4$ 4

Determine whether the points in each set are collinear. Explain how you know.

49. $(^-2, 13)$, $(1.5, ^-4.5)$, $(3, ^-12)$

50. $(^-1, ^-4.2)$, $(3, 0.6)$, $(4, 1.6)$

49. collinear; Possible explanation: The line through the first two points has the equation $y = ^-5x + 3$, and $(3, ^-12)$ satisfies this equation.

50. not collinear; Possible explanation: The line through the first two points has the equation $y = 1.2x - 3$, but the third point doesn't satisfy this equation.

Determine whether the values in each table could represent a linear relationship, a quadratic relationship, or neither. Explain your answers.

51.

x	$^-3$	$^-2$	$^-1$	0	1	2	3
y	$^-12.6$	$^-9.2$	$^-5.8$	$^-2.4$	1	4.4	7.8

52.

x	$^-3$	$^-2$	$^-1$	0	1	2	3
y	$^-24$	$^-13$	$^-6$	0	4	5	6

53.

x	$^-3$	$^-2$	$^-1$	0	1	2	3
y	0	$^-2$	$^-2$	0	4	10	18

51. Linear; first differences are constant.

52. Neither; neither first nor second differences are constant.

53. Quadratic; second differences are constant.

54. Astronomy A light-year, the distance light travels in one year, is 5.88×10^{12} miles. Answer these questions without using your calculator.

a. The star Alpha Centauri is about 4 light-years from Earth. Write this distance in miles, using scientific notation. 2.352×10^{13} mi

b. The star Betelgeuse is about 500 light-years from Earth. Write this distance in miles, using scientific notation. 2.94×10^{15} mi

c. Suppose a light beam went from Earth to Betelgeuse, and another light beam went from Earth to Alpha Centauri. How much farther did the beam going to Betelgeuse have to travel?
   2.91648×10^{15} mi

Tell whether each figure has reflection symmetry, rotation symmetry, or both.

55.

rotation symmetry

56.

both

57.

reflection symmetry

Quick Check

Informal Assessment
Students should be able to:

✔ understand the zero product property

✔ solve quadratic equations in factored form

✔ solve quadratic equations by factoring the difference of two squares and perfect square trinomials

✔ solve quadratic equations by factoring quadratic trinomials

Quick Quiz

1. Find all solutions to each equation.

   a. $(y + 3)(2y - 4) = 0$
   $^-3, 2$

   b. $r^2 - 81 = 0$ $^-9, 9$

   c. $16y^2 + 8y + 1 = 0$
   $^-\frac{1}{4}$

2. Factor each expression, if possible. If an expression can't be factored, explain why not.

   a. $x^2 + 8x + 7$
   $(x + 7)(x + 1)$

   b. $c^2 - 2c - 35$
   $(c - 7)(c + 5)$

   c. $d^2 + 100$ Cannot be factored; sums of squares aren't factorable.

3. Solve each equation by factoring.

   a. $x^2 + 6x = 2x + 21$ $^-7, 3$

   b. $r(r + 1) + 2r = 18$ $^-6, 3$

4. A number and its square differ by 20. Find all numbers for which this is true. $^-4, 5$

• **continued at left**

Teacher Notes

7.3

Completing the Square

Objectives

▶ To solve equations of the form $a(x + b)^2 + c = d$

▶ To identify perfect square trinomials

▶ To complete quadratic expressions to make them perfect squares

▶ To solve quadratic equations by completing the square

Overview (pacing: about 3 class periods)

In this lesson, students learn to complete the square, a technique that (unlike factoring) can be used to solve any quadratic equation. Completing the square is introduced by examples in which students do the same thing to both sides. This is a useful strategy to emphasize as a context for the steps in completing the square, which can sometimes be complicated. Initially, students complete the square on quadratics whose leading coefficient is 1; then they look at factoring out the leading coefficient.

Some people contend that the technique of completing the square is virtually obsolete because the quadratic formula can always be used to solve quadratics. However, if students are simply given the quadratic formula without seeing the derivation, it may reinforce misconceptions that important theorems arise out of thin air and that mathematics is like magic. The power of algebra is clear in this derivation, and since students can grasp the underlying thinking without too much difficulty, they may recognize their own mathematical power.

Advance Preparation

No advance preparation is required.

	Summary	Materials	On Your Own Exercises	Assessment Opportunities
Investigation 1 page T457	Students learn to complete expressions to make them perfect squares.	• Graphing calculators (optional)	Practice & Apply: 1–9, p. 462 Connect & Extend: 22, 23, p. 463 Mixed Review: 27–36, p. 465	On the Spot Assessment, pages T457, T459 Share & Summarize, pages T459, 459 Troubleshooting, page T459
Investigation 2 page T459	Students develop the technique of solving quadratic equations by completing the square.		Practice & Apply: 10–21, p. 462 Connect & Extend: 24–26, pp. 463–464 Mixed Review: 27–36, p. 465	Share & Summarize, pages T461, 461 Troubleshooting, page T461 Informal Assessment, page 465 Quick Quiz, page 465

1 Explain to students that in this lesson they will be learning a technique to solve quadratic equations that can be used when factoring fails. Remind them that they have "done the same thing to both sides" to write a series of equivalent equations in forms that are easier to solve than the original.

Example

2 Write the equation $\sqrt{3m + 7} = 5$ on the board, and ask:

> How would you solve this?

If necessary, refer students to the Example. If they suggest proceeding in the same way, you might ask:

> Why are both sides squared in the first step?

As students provide their suggestions for what to do at each step, stress the fact that they are doing the same thing to both sides in each instance. Then go on to the questions in the Think & Discuss.

Think & Discuss

3 Discuss these questions as a class. Students may not have thought before about the kinds of things that can or cannot be done to both sides of an equation. This is an important realization, and you may find that students are curious about this.

4 The questions here emphasize that doing the same thing to both sides should not be done mechanically. It is only correct if the operation changes the value of both sides in the same way. In the case of the fractions, $\frac{x}{2} = \frac{2x}{4}$, since the denominators of the fractions are different, adding 1 to the numerator adds different values to each side.

5 Students need to understand the last question in particular, since it connects to the work they will be doing in completing the square. For such equations as $w^2 = 36$, when taking the square root of both sides, there are two values to consider; in this case, 6 and $^-6$.

Completing the Square

Factoring is a very useful tool for solving equations. But factors and squares are not always easy to find. In Lessons 7.3 and 7.4, you will learn some techniques that will enable you to solve *every* quadratic equation.

You have used "doing the same thing to both sides" to solve linear equations. In this strategy, you write a series of equivalent equations that have the same solutions as the original equation but are easier to solve. You can also use this strategy with equations that contain square roots.

EXAMPLE

Solve $\sqrt{3m + 7} = 5$.

$3m + 7 = 25$	after squaring both sides
$3m = 18$	after subtracting 7 from both sides
$m = 6$	after dividing both sides by 3

Think & Discuss

Why are both sides squared in the first solution step of the Example?
to remove the square root from the left side

In general, what kinds of "same things" do you know you can do to both sides to solve an equation? See ①.

Would you get an equivalent equation if you added 1 to the numerator of the fractions on both sides of an equation? Try it with $\frac{x}{2} = \frac{2x}{4}$.
See ②.

What happens to an equation—such as $x = 2$—when you multiply both sides by x? Does the new equation have the same solutions?
See ③.

What happens to the set of solutions when you multiply both sides of an equation—such as $x = 2$—by 0? See ④.

What effect would squaring both sides have on an equation? For example, begin with $x = 5$. See ⑤.

When you take the square root of both sides of an equation, what should you do to keep the same set of solutions? For example, begin with $w^2 = 36$. Unless one side of the equation is 0, you will need to consider two values when you take the square root. For the equation $w^2 = 36$, take the square root of both sides to get the solutions 6 and ⁻6.

① add or subtract the same number or expression; multiply or divide both sides by the same number or expression as long as its value isn't 0; square both sides

② No; for example, $\frac{x}{2} = \frac{2x}{4}$ is true for all x. But $\frac{x+1}{2} = \frac{2x+1}{4}$ is equivalent to $4x + 4 = 4x + 2$, which is never true.

③ No; in this case, the new equation is $x^2 = 2x$, which has solutions of 2 and 0, while 2 is the only solution of the original equation.

④ After multiplying, the equation becomes $0 = 0$, which is always true no matter what x is. All numbers are solutions to the multiplied equation, even though the original equation might have had only a few (or no) solutions.

⑤ Since any number squared is equal to its negative squared, you might add to the set of solutions. For example, $x = 5$ has only one solution, but $x^2 = 25$ has two solutions, 5 and ⁻5.

Investigation 1

In this investigation, students learn the crucial step in completing the square: determining what constant term must be added to make a quadratic expression a perfect square. When students become facile at this, they will be ready to use the full technique of completing the square to solve equations.

Example

Before turning to the student text, write the equation in the Example on the board, $x^2 + 2x + 1 = 7$, and challenge students to solve it. Some will first subtract 7 from both sides and then try to factor $x^2 + 2x - 6 = 0$. They will soon discover that $x^2 + 2x + 6$ cannot be factored. This is good justification for developing another method for solving quadratics, so it is worth the time to let them experiment a bit before you suggest an alternative strategy.

Some may notice that $x^2 + 2x + 1$ is a perfect square trinomial, or $(x + 1)^2$. Therefore, the equation can be rewritten $(x + 1)^2 = 7$. This equation can be solved by taking the square root of both sides.

Stress to students that whenever they take the square root of both sides of an equation, they need to think about the fact that a number has both a positive and a negative square root.

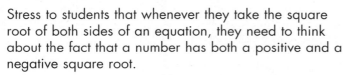

Interestingly, it is common to write the $\pm$ sign to designate two possible roots on one side of an equation only, even though one could reasonably assert that both sides should have the $\pm$ sign. If this issue does not come up, it is probably not worth mentioning. But if students ask, affirm their observation and help them think the consequences through by writing the following on the board:

$(x + 1) = 7$ $^-(x + 1) = 7$

$(x + 1) = ^-7$ $^-(x + 1) = ^-7$

Ask if any of these equations are equivalent to any others. Students should realize that there are two equivalent pairs. You can then point out that $x + 1 = \pm 7$ adequately represents all four possibilities, so it's really only necessary to use the $\pm$ sign for one side.

In this particular problem, you may also want students to think about an estimate for their irrational answer, since $^-1 \pm \sqrt{7}$ probably doesn't have much meaning for them as written. Ask them to substitute their estimates into the original equation to see if they are close.

Problem Set A Suggested Grouping: Pairs

In this problem set, students are given equations in which the quadratic expressions are already written as squares of binomials. In each problem, they may have to get the squared binomial terms alone on one side of the equation before they take the square root of each side to get the answer.

On the **Spot**
Assessment

Watch for students who forget to take both the positive and negative square roots of the constant term. You may want to circulate around the room to check that students are getting two answers in each problem (except for Problems 4 and 8). You might have them use their graphing calculators to graph the left-hand side of an equation, and then ask where the y-value for the graph is equal to the right-hand side. If they consider only one such point, ask whether there are any other possibilities.

Discourage students from leaving their answers in a form such as 3 ± 6 as in **Problem 1.** They should be able to evaluate this answer as 9 or $^-3$.

In **Problems 4 and 8,** students will get equations in which the square of a number equals a negative number. They should begin to see by inspection when this situation occurs and not have to go much beyond the first step to recognize that there will be no real-number solutions.

In **Problem 5,** it may help some students if you ask them to think about order of operations in undoing this equation. It is easier to subtract 5 first and then divide by 2 to solve this equation.

In **Problem 9,** it is fine for students to leave the fraction under the radical sign. At this stage, simplifying radical expressions is not an expectation.

Problem 10 allows students to attach more meaning to the irrational expressions they found in Problems 7 and 9.

Investigation 1 Finding Perfect Squares

If you can rearrange a quadratic equation into a form with a quadratic expression that is a perfect square on one side and a constant on the other side, you can solve the equation by taking the square root of both sides.

EXAMPLE

Solve the equation $x^2 + 2x + 1 = 7$.

First, notice that $x^2 + 2x + 1$ is equal to $(x + 1)^2$, so the equation $x^2 + 2x + 1 = 7$ can be solved by taking the square root of both sides:

$$(x + 1)^2 = 7$$
$$\sqrt{(x + 1)^2} = \sqrt{7} \text{ or } ^-\sqrt{7}$$

To write "$\sqrt{7}$ or $^-\sqrt{7}$" more easily, use the $\pm$ symbol: $\pm\sqrt{7}$ refers to both numbers, $\sqrt{7}$ and $^-\sqrt{7}$.

$$\sqrt{(x + 1)^2} = \pm\sqrt{7}$$
$$x + 1 = \pm\sqrt{7}$$
$$x = ^-1 \pm \sqrt{7}$$

So the solutions are $^-1 + \sqrt{7}$ and $^-1 - \sqrt{7}$.

Remember

An *exact solution* does not involve approximations. For example, $x = \sqrt{2}$ is an exact solution of $x^2 = 2$, while $x = 1.414$ is an approximate solution to the nearest thousandth.

Problem Set A

Find exact solutions of each equation, if possible, using any method you like.

1. $(x - 3)^2 = 36$ 9, $^-3$
2. $(k - 1)^2 - 25 = 0$ 6, $^-4$
3. $2(r - 7)^2 = 32$ 11, 3
4. $(a - 4)^2 + 2 = 0$ no solution
5. $2(b - 3)^2 + 5 = 55$ 8, $^-2$
6. $3(2c + 5)^2 - 63 = 300$ 3, $^-8$
7. $(x - 4)^2 = 3$ $4 \pm \sqrt{3}$
8. $2(r - 3)^2 = ^-10$ no solution
9. $4(x + 2)^2 - 3 = 0$ $^-2 \pm \sqrt{\frac{3}{4}}$, or $^-2 \pm \frac{\sqrt{3}}{2}$
10. Find approximate solutions of the equations in Problems 7 and 9 to the nearest hundredth. 7. 5.73, 2.27; 9. $^-1.13$, $^-2.87$

1 Write the equation on the board, and challenge students to solve it.

2 Stress that when taking the square root of both sides, both roots need to be considered.

3 You may have students work in pairs.

4 Watch for students who forget to use both roots.

LESSON 7.3 Completing the Square **457**

Develop

1 **Problem Set B** **Suggested Grouping: Pairs**
In this problem set, students review recognizing whether
a quadratic trinomial is a perfect square. These problems should not take long to do.

2 **Problem 3** asks students to generalize how to decide
whether an expression is a perfect square. This is an
important generalization that previews the Example and
problem set that follow. You may want to have students
talk about this as a whole class.

3 **Example**
Be sure to review this Example with students before they
continue to Problem Set C.

Students may think of a shortcut to finding the constant
term being added: take half the middle term and square
it. However, this strategy works only when the coefficient
of the squared term is 1.

To use the solution method demonstrated in the Example on page 457, you need to be able to recognize quadratic expressions that can be rewritten as perfect squares. You worked with such *perfect square trinomials* in the last lesson.

Problem Set B

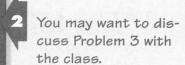

1 You may have students work in pairs.

1. Which of these are perfect squares?   a, e, f, and h

a. $x^2 + 6x + 9$ **b.** $b^2 + 9$ **c.** $x^2 + 6x + 4$

3. If the expression is in the form $ax^2 + bx + c$, the coefficient of x^2 and the constant c should both be perfect squares. The coefficient of x should be ± 2 times the product of the square roots of these two perfect squares.

d. $m^2 + 12m - 36$ **e.** $m^2 - 12m + 36$ **f.** $y^2 + y + \frac{1}{4}$

g. $r^2 - 16$ **h.** $1 + 2r + r^2$ **i.** $y^2 - 2y - 1$

2. Which of these are perfect squares?   a, d, and f

a. $4p^2 + 4p + 1$ **b.** $4q^2 + 4q + 4$ **c.** $4s^2 - 4s - 1$

d. $4t^2 - 4t + 1$ **e.** $4v^2 + 9$ **f.** $4w^2 + 12w + 9$

3. Describe how you can tell whether an expression is a perfect square, without factoring it.

2 You may want to discuss Problem 3 with the class.

Suppose you know the x^2 and x terms in a quadratic expression, and you want to make it into a perfect square trinomial by adding a constant. How can you find the missing term?

3 Read the Example with the class.

> **EXAMPLE**
>
> If $x^2 + 20x + $ ___ is a perfect square, then
>
> $$x^2 + 20x + \underline{\quad} = (x + ?)^2$$
>
> Since the middle term of the expansion is twice the product of the coefficient of x and the constant term in the binomial being squared,
>
> $$20 = (2)(1)(?)$$
> $$10 = ?$$
>
> So the perfect square must be $(x + 10)^2$, or $x^2 + 20x + 100$.

Just the facts

The quadratic equation $W = \frac{1}{2}kx^2$ describes the amount of work (in a unit called *Joules*) needed to stretch a spring x cm beyond its normal length. The value of k depends on the spring's strength.

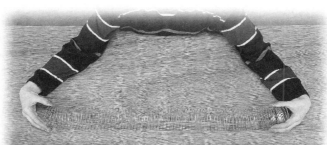

Problem Set C Suggested Grouping: Pairs

In this problem set, students need to find the constant term that will make an unfinished quadratic expression into a perfect square.

Problem 3 is worth discussing as a class. Some students might use the constant -1.5; others might use $-\frac{3}{2}$. While both are correct, it is clear that squaring a fraction is easier than squaring a decimal. Encourage them to consider keeping the numbers to be squared in fraction form in such problems.

Problems 4, 5, and 6 provide an additional challenge since the coefficients of the squared terms are not 1. Using the method from the Example on page 458 for Problem 4, they will get the equation $10 = 2(5)(?)$; the missing number is therefore 1 and the constant to add is 1^2, or 1.

On the Spot Assessment

Watch for students who add 25 to Problem 4 and get $(5m + 5)^2$ for the factored expression. These students may also get 16 and $(4r - 4)^2$ for Problem 5, and 36 and $(2z - 6)^2$ for Problem 6. These students are using the shortcut mentioned in the notes for the Example on page 458, without considering the fact that the coefficient of the squared term is not 1.

You might ask them to expand their factored expressions as a check; when they realize their answers are incorrect, you can ask (or point out) how these problems are different from the Example equation.

Share & Summarize

These questions underscore the general principle for finding perfect square trinomials. You may want to stress the general form in Question 2 ($ax^2 + bx + c$) and help students understand that b will be equal to twice the positive or negative square root of ac if the expression is a perfect square trinomial.

Troubleshooting If students are having difficulty with these problems, give them additional problems that involve finding perfect square trinomials in which the coefficient of the squared term is equal to 1. You may want to have them start again by squaring binomials to

see what is happening. For example, begin with $(ax + b)^2$, or even just $(x + b)^2$, and ask students to draw some conclusions from looking at the coefficients of the resulting terms.

On Your Own Exercises

Practice & Apply: 1–9, p. 462
Connect & Extend: 22, 23, p. 463
Mixed Review: 27–36, p. 465

Investigation 2

In this investigation, students develop the technique of completing the square to solve quadratic equations. Unlike Investigation 1, they will work with expressions that are not perfect squares and transform them into perfect squares by adding or subtracting a constant.

Introduce the investigation by reminding students of the work they did in Problem Set C creating perfect square trinomials.

Example

Write the expression $x^2 + 6x + 10$ on the board. Ask students if this is a perfect square trinomial. After they acknowledge that it is not, ask if there is a way to rewrite this expression so that it *contains* a perfect square.

Students should see that if they look only at $x^2 + 6x$, the constant that needs to be added to create a perfect square is 9. If necessary, cover up the $+ 10$ and ask them if they can create a perfect square from the remaining terms. Point out that $x^2 + 6x + 10$ can be rewritten as $x^2 + 6x + 9 + 1$; they should be able to see that this is $(x + 3)^2 + 1$.

Explain to students that they can use this technique on any quadratic equation. By the end of this investigation, they will combine it with their work from Problem Set A (solving an equation by doing the same thing to both sides) to solve quadratic equations.

Problem Set C

Complete each quadratic expression to make it a perfect square. Then write the completed expression in factored form.

1. $x^2 - 18x + \underline{81}$, $(x - 9)^2$ **2.** $x^2 + 22x + \underline{121}$, $(x + 11)^2$

3. $k^2 - 3k + \underline{\frac{9}{4}}$, $\left(k - \frac{3}{2}\right)^2$ **4.** $25m^2 + 10m + \underline{1}$, $(5m + 1)^2$

5. $16r^2 - 8r \boxplus \underline{1}$, $(4r - 1)^2$ **6.** $4z^2 - 12z \boxplus \underline{9}$, $(2z - 3)^2$

1 You may have students work in pairs.

Share & Summarize

1. If you can get a quadratic equation into the form $expression^2 = constant$, you can solve it by taking the square root of both sides.

1. Why is it useful to look for perfect squares in quadratic expressions?

2. How can you recognize a perfect square trinomial?
If a trinomial is in the form $ax^2 + bx + c$, b should be equal to $\pm 2\sqrt{ac}$.

2 Stress the general form in Question 2.

Investigation 2 Solving Quadratics by Completing the Square

In Problem Set A, you learned that it is easy to solve a quadratic equation with a perfect square on one side and a constant on the other. You also solved equations that had a perfect square with a constant added or subtracted. A technique called *completing the square* can be used to rearrange quadratic equations into this form.

In Problem Set C, you found the constant that should be added to transform a quadratic expression into a perfect square. Using the same idea, some expressions that are not perfect squares can be rewritten as perfect squares with a constant added or subtracted.

3 Remind students of their work creating perfect square trinomials in Problem Set C.

EXAMPLE

$x^2 + 6x + 10$ is not a perfect square. For $x^2 + 6x + \underline{\quad}$ to be a perfect square, the added constant must be 9, because $x^2 + 6x + 9$ is a perfect square. (Can you see why?)

This means $x^2 + 6x + 10$ is 1 more than a perfect square. We can use this to rewrite the expression as a square plus 1:

$$x^2 + 6x + 10 = (x^2 + 6x + 9) + 1$$
$$= (x + 3)^2 + 1$$

4 Write $x^2 + 6x + 10$ on the board, and help students see how to rewrite it using a perfect square.

Develop

1 **Problem Set D** Suggested Grouping: Pairs
In this problem set, students are asked to rewrite each quadratic expression as the square of a binomial with a constant either added or subtracted. These problems lay the foundation for solving by completing the square, and students should feel comfortable doing them before they go on. If necessary, spend extra time on this first step in completing the square; it will be time well spent.

In **Problems 1–4,** students rewrite the constant term as the sum (or difference) of two constants to create a perfect square. Students are given the perfect square constant to help them get started.

In **Problems 5–8,** students have to figure out the perfect square term themselves. These problems depend upon students' facility with addition of signed numbers, and you may find that arithmetic errors cause more of a problem than finding the correct constant term to complete the square. In either case, they are a good review for these operations on signed numbers.

2 **Problem Set Wrap-Up** Review the answers to Problem Set D, especially Problems 5–8. If students are having trouble, or if they do not seem comfortable with this process, let them work some additional examples, individually or in pairs. As noted before, the extra time spent now will help with the rest of this investigation as well as the derivation of the quadratic formula.

> **Additional Examples** Rewrite each expression as a square with a constant added or subtracted.

$s^2 + 8s - 14 = s^2 + 8s + 16 - 30$
$\qquad\qquad\quad = (s + 4)^2 - 30$

$t^2 - 10t + 35 = t^2 - 10t + 25 + 10$
$\qquad\qquad\quad = (t - 5)^2 + 10$

$4x^2 + 16x - 1 = 4x^2 + 16x + 16 - 17$
$\qquad\qquad\quad = (2x + 4)^2 - 17$

$16y^2 - 8y + 3 = 16y^2 - 8y + 1 + 2$
$\qquad\qquad\quad = (4y - 1)^2 + 2$

3 Before students move on to Problem Set E, pull the class together to read the cartoon. In this cartoon, Marcus and Lydia solve a quadratic equation using the technique of completing the square.

When approaching an equation, students may prefer to check first to see whether the quadratic expression factors, since many find factoring to be an easier method. For the equation in the cartoon, factoring does in fact work: $(x - 10)(x + 4) = 0$. If students point this out, you may want to tell them that they can use completing the square as well, and you can even use their factoring technique to confirm that Marcus and Lydia's answer is correct. Be sure they know that in the next problem set, the purpose is to practice *that* technique, even if the quadratics factor.

The method used in the cartoon is one of two popular methods for completing the square. The other method is to add 40 to both sides immediately to get $x^2 - 6x = 40$; then add 9 to both sides to complete the square, $x^2 - 6x + 9 = 49$; and then finish the problem in the same way as in the cartoon. Some students may find this easier, but it can cause difficulty for students if they tend to forget to add 9 to both sides of the equation.

4 **Problem Set E** Suggested Grouping: Pairs
In this problem set, students solve quadratic equations by completing the square.

Since there are many steps in solving an equation using this technique, it may be helpful to go over **Problem 1** as a class before students continue, to make sure they are on the right track.

Problem 3 requires some sophisticated numerical work in the last steps. Students produce the equation $3m + 1 = \pm 3$. Subtracting 1 from the right side gives $^-1 + 3$ and $^-1 - 3$, which is 2 and $^-4$. It may help students to actually write $^-1 + 3$ and $^-1 - 3$ before trying to simplify. The last step is to divide by 3. Make sure students think about these steps in the right order.

Problem Set D

Rewrite each expression as a square with a constant added or subtracted.

1. $x^2 + 6x + 15 = x^2 + 6x + 9 + \underline{\ 6\ } = (x + 3)^2 + \underline{\ 6\ }$
2. $k^2 - 6k + 30 = k^2 - 6k + 9 + \underline{21} = (k - 3)^2 + \underline{21}$
3. $s^2 + 6s - 1 = s^2 + 6s + 9 - \underline{10} = (s + \underline{\ 3\ })^2 - \underline{10}$
4. $r^2 - 6r - 21 = r^2 - 6r + 9 \boxminus \underline{30} = (r \boxminus \underline{\ 3\ })^2 \boxminus \underline{30}$
5. $m^2 + 12m + 30 \quad (m + 6)^2 - 6$
6. $h^2 - 5h \quad \left(h - \frac{5}{2}\right)^2 - \frac{25}{4} \text{ or } (h - 2.5)^2 - 6.25$
7. $9r^2 + 18r - 20 \quad (3r + 3)^2 - 29$
8. $9n^2 - 6n + 11 \quad (3n - 1)^2 + 10$

Marcus and Lydia want to solve the equation $x^2 - 6x - 40 = 0$.

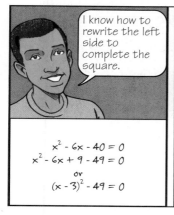

This method of solving equations is called *completing the square*.

Problem Set E

Find exact solutions of each equation by completing the square.

1. $x^2 - 8x - 9 = 0$
2. $w^2 - 8w + 6 = 0$
3. $9m^2 + 6m - 8 = 0$

1. $x^2 - 8x + 16 - 25 = 0$
$(x - 4)^2 - 25 = 0$
$(x - 4)^2 = 25$
$x - 4 = \pm 5$
$x = 9, \ ^-1$

2. $w^2 - 8w + 16 - 10 = 0$
$(w - 4)^2 - 10 = 0$
$(w - 4)^2 = 10$
$w - 4 = \pm\sqrt{10}$
$w = 4 \pm \sqrt{10}$

3. $9m^2 + 6m + 1 - 9 = 0$
$(3m + 1)^2 - 9 = 0$
$(3m + 1)^2 = 9$
$3m + 1 = \pm 3$
$m = \frac{2}{3}, \ \frac{-4}{3}$

460 CHAPTER 7 Solving Quadratic Equations

1 You may have students work in pairs.

2 Discuss students' answers and spend extra time on this first step, if needed.

3 Read the cartoon with the class.

4 You may have students work in pairs after discussing Problem 1 as a class.

Develop

Problem Set F Suggested Grouping: Pairs
In this problem set, students solve more challenging quadratic equations by completing the square. In all of these problems, the squared term has a coefficient other than 1.

Problem 1 outlines a strategy for how to approach these problems, and it would be helpful to do this problem with the class on the board before students proceed to the other problems. Essentially, students need to divide through by the leading coefficient (the coefficient of the squared term) before they complete the square. Once they divide through by that term, they are back to the form they are accustomed to and can complete the square.

Problem 3 presents a more challenging situation. Dividing through by 18 would give the middle term a fractional coefficient. Of course, it is possible to think about halving this fraction and squaring it, but **Part b** suggests an alternative approach: dividing by 2 so that the coefficient of x^2 is 9, which is a perfect square. Of course, not every number has a perfect square factor, so this method cannot always be used. But in this case, it's an efficient strategy.

In **Part c,** students will end up with a "messy" answer. Make sure they understand that when they solve the equation $3x = 1 \pm \sqrt{\frac{5}{2}}$ they need to divide the entire expression on the right side by 3 (or multiply it by $\frac{1}{3}$). You may need to use whole numbers to remind them of this; for example, show them the equation $2x = 4 \pm 6$ to illustrate that both 4 and 6 must be divided by 2.

Problems 4 and 5 bring up the issue of the number of possible solutions to a quadratic equation. Students may know from previous work with graphs that quadratic equations may have zero, one, or two solutions; in Lesson 7.4, they will learn how to determine the number of solutions using a numerical method.

> ### Access
> #### for all **Learners**
> **For Early Finishers** Ask students to write three equations of their own; one with no solutions, one with one solution, and one with two solutions.

Share & Summarize

These questions focus on the techniques of solving equations by completing the square. If you need more problems, collect students' answers to **Question 1** and use them for additional practice.

Troubleshooting If students are having difficulty with these problems, use examples like those they may have written in the Share & Summarize to provide additional practice. For students who are struggling, it is appropriate to have them just focus on quadratics that have squared terms with coefficient 1. Of course, those students may need extra help understanding the derivation of the quadratic formula in Lesson 7.4.

On Your Own Exercises

Practice & Apply: 10–21, p. 462
Connect & Extend: 24–26, pp. 463–464
Mixed Review: 27–36, p. 465

What can you do if the coefficient of the squared variable is not a square? One approach is to first do the same thing to each side to produce an equivalent equation with 1—or some other square number—as the coefficient of the squared variable.

Problem Set F

1. To solve $2x^2 - 8x - 1 = 0$, you could divide both sides by 2, which gives the equivalent equation $x^2 - 4x - \frac{1}{2} = 0$. Complete the solution by solving this equivalent equation.

2. Use the method from Problem 1 to solve $2m^2 - 12m + 7 = 0$.

3. Consider the equation $18x^2 - 12x - 3 = 0$.

   a. Try dividing the equation by 18 to make the coefficient of x^2 equal to 1. $x^2 - \frac{2}{3}x - \frac{1}{6} = 0$

   b. Now think about the coefficient 18. Find another number you could divide 18 by to get a perfect square. Divide the equation by that number. $2; 9x^2 - 6x - \frac{3}{2} = 0$

   c. Use your answer to Part a or Part b to solve the equation.

4. Explain why $x^2 + 64 = 16x$ has only one solution.

5. Explain why $g^2 - 4g + 11 = 0$ has no solutions.

Share & Summarize

1. Give an example of a quadratic equation that is not a perfect square but that is easy to solve by completing the square. Solve your equation.

2. Suppose you have an equation in the form $y = ax^2 + bx + c$ for which the coefficient of x^2 is not a perfect square. How can you solve the equation? Illustrate your answer with an example.

Problem Set F Answers

1. $x^2 - 4x + 4 - \frac{9}{2} = 0$
   $(x - 2)^2 - \frac{9}{2} = 0$
   $(x - 2)^2 = \frac{9}{2}$
   $x - 2 = \pm \frac{3}{\sqrt{2}}$
   $x = 2 \pm \frac{3}{\sqrt{2}}$

2. $m^2 - 6m + \frac{7}{2} = 0$
   $m^2 - 6m + 9 - \frac{11}{2} = 0$
   $(m - 3)^2 - \frac{11}{2} = 0$
   $(m - 3)^2 = \frac{11}{2}$
   $m - 3 = \pm \sqrt{\frac{11}{2}}$
   $m = 3 \pm \sqrt{\frac{11}{2}}$

3c. Possible solution:
   $9x^2 - 6x - \frac{3}{2} = 0$
   $(3x - 1)^2 - \frac{5}{2} = 0$
   $(3x - 1)^2 = \frac{5}{2}$
   $3x - 1 = \pm \sqrt{\frac{5}{2}}$
   $3x = 1 \pm \sqrt{\frac{5}{2}}$
   $x = \frac{1}{3}\left(1 + \sqrt{\frac{5}{2}}\right),$
   $\frac{1}{3}\left(1 - \sqrt{\frac{5}{2}}\right)$

4. If you rewrite the equation as $x^2 - 16x + 64 = 0$, the left side is already a perfect square.
   $(x - 8)^2 = 0$
   $x - 8 = 0$ (Zero has only one square root.)
   $x = 8$ is the only solution.

5. $g^2 - 4g + 4 + 7 = 0$
   $(g - 2)^2 + 7 = 0$
   $(g - 2)^2 = -7$
   The next step would involve taking the square root of a negative number, which can't be done.

Share & Summarize Answers

1. Possible answer: $4x^2 - 4x - 15 = 0$. Complete the square by adding 1 to both sides:
   $4x^2 - 4x + 1 - 15 = 1$
   $(2x - 1)^2 = 16$
   $2x - 1 = \pm 4$
   $x = \frac{5}{2}, -\frac{3}{2}$

2. Divide through by the leading coefficient so that the equation is in the form $x^2 + \frac{b}{a}x + \frac{c}{a} = 0$. For example, $2x^2 + 4x - 10 = 0$ becomes $x^2 + 2x - 5 = 0$. It's now easy to complete the square: $x^2 + 2x - 5 + 1 = 1$, so $(x + 1)^2 = 6$.

1 You may have students work in pairs after discussing Problem 1 as a class.

2 Watch for division or multiplication errors.

3 You might use students' examples for additional practice.

LESSON 7.3   Completing the Square   **461**

On Your Own Exercises

On Your Own Exercises

Investigation 1,
pp. 457–459
Practice & Apply: 1–9
Connect & Extend: 22, 23

Investigation 2,
pp. 459–461
Practice & Apply: 10–21
Connect & Extend: 24–26

Assign Anytime
Mixed Review: 27–36

Exercises 1–6:
In these exercises, students are given equations in which the expressions are already in factored form; in other words, they enter the problems after the squares have been completed. These are a good assessment tool for students who are having difficulty taking the square root of both sides of an equation and finding the two solutions.

Exercises 10–15:
At times students confuse *expressions* with *equations*. Exercises 10–15 present expressions; there is no equal sign in them. Students are asked to rewrite the expressions, not to solve equations. It may be worthwhile to point out the difference.

Exercises 20 and 21:
In these exercises, students need to divide through by 2 so that the coefficient of the squared term is 1. Watch for students who try to complete the square before they do this division. If they try this, ask them to substitute their answers into the original equation.

Practice & Apply

Solve each equation.

1. $(x + 3)^2 = 25$ $2, \ ^{-}8$

2. $(r - 8)^2 + 3 = 52$ $15, 1$

3. $(2m + 1)^2 - 4 = 117$ $5, \ ^{-}6$

4. $3(x - 3)^2 = 30$

5. $^{-}2(y - 7)^2 + 4 = 0$

6. $4(2z + 3)^2 - 2 = \ ^{-}1$

5. $7 \pm \sqrt{2}$

6. $^{-}\frac{5}{4}, \ ^{-}\frac{7}{4}$

7. $x^2 - 8x + 16, (x - 4)^2$

8. $b^2 + 9b + \frac{81}{4}, \left(b + \frac{9}{2}\right)^2$

9. $81d^2 - 90d + 25, (9d - 5)^2$

Complete each quadratic expression so that it is a perfect square. Then write the completed expression in factored form.

7. $x^2 - 8x \ \square$ ___

8. $b^2 + 9b \ \square$ ___

9. $81d^2 - 90d \ \square$ ___

Rewrite each expression as a square with a constant added or subtracted.

10. $r^2 - 6r + 1 = r^2 - 6r + 9 + \underline{\ ^{-}8} = (r \ \boxed{-} \ \underline{3} \ )^2 - \underline{\ 8}$

11. $r^2 + 6r + 6 = (r \ \boxed{+} \ \underline{3} \ )^2 \ \boxed{-} \ \underline{3}$

12. $p^2 - 16p + 60 \quad (p - 8)^2 - 4$

13. $g^2 - 3g - 1 \quad (g - 1.5)^2 - 3.25$

14. $a^2 + 10a + 101 \quad (a + 5)^2 + 76$

15. $4x^2 + 4x + 2 \quad (2x + 1)^2 + 1$

16. $m^2 + 2m + 1 - 12 = 0$
$(m + 1)^2 - 12 = 0$
$m + 1 = \pm\sqrt{12}$
$m = \ ^{-}1 \pm 2\sqrt{3}$

17. $b^2 - 6b - 7 = 0$
$b^2 - 6b + 9 - 16 = 0$
$(b - 3)^2 - 16 = 0$
$b - 3 = \pm\sqrt{16}$
$b = 7, \ ^{-}1$

18. $x^2 - 6x + 5 = 0$
$x^2 - 6x + 9 - 4 = 0$
$(x - 3)^2 - 4 = 0$
$x - 3 = \pm\sqrt{4}$
$x = 1, 5$

Solve each equation by completing the square.

16. $m^2 + 2m - 11 = 0$

17. $b^2 - 3b = 3b + 7$

18. $x^2 - 6x = \ ^{-}5$

19. $a^2 + 10a + 26 = 0$

20. $2x^2 + 4x - 1 = 0$

21. $2u^2 + 3u - 2 = 0$

19. no solutions

20. $x^2 + 2x - \frac{1}{2} = 0$
$x^2 + 2x + 1 - \frac{3}{2} = 0$
$(x + 1)^2 - \frac{3}{2} = 0$
$x + 1 = \pm\sqrt{\frac{3}{2}}$
$x = \ ^{-}1 \pm \sqrt{\frac{3}{2}}$

21. $u^2 + \frac{3}{2}u - 1 = 0$
$u^2 + \frac{3}{2}u + \frac{9}{16} - \frac{25}{16} = 0$
$\left(u + \frac{3}{4}\right)^2 - \frac{25}{16} = 0$
$u + \frac{3}{4} = \pm\frac{5}{4}$
$u = \ ^{-}2, \frac{1}{2}$

Just the facts

The acceleration, in m/s², of a bicyclist coasting down a hill might be given by the quadratic equation $a = 0.12 - 0.0006v^2$, where v is the bike's velocity in m/s.

impactmath.com/self_check_quiz

Connect & Extend

22. Stephen, Consuela, and Kwame each made up a number puzzle for their teacher, Mr. Karnowski.

- Stephen said, "I'm thinking of a number. If you subtract 1 from my number, square the result, and add 5, you will get 4."
- Consuela said, "I'm thinking of a number. If you subtract 1 from my number, square the result, and add 1, you will get 1."
- Kwame said, "I'm thinking of a number. If you double the number, subtract 5, square the result, and add 1, you will get 10."

After thinking about the puzzles, Mr. Karnowski said, "One of your puzzles has one solution, one of them has two solutions, and one doesn't have a solution."

Whose puzzle is which? Write an equation for each puzzle, and explain your answer. See below left.

23. Sports Brianna and Lucita are playing tennis. On one volley, the height of the ball h, in feet, could have been described with the following equation, where t is the time in seconds since Brianna hit the ball:

$$h = {}^{-}16(t-1)^2 + 20$$

Assuming Lucita will let the ball bounce once, when will it hit the ground? Write and solve an equation to help you answer this question. Give your answer to the nearest hundredth of a second.

24. When you start the process of completing the square for an equation, you may be able to tell whether the equation has solutions without solving it.

a. Express each of these using a perfect square plus a constant. Without solving, decide whether the equation has a solution, and explain your answer.

i. $x^2 + 6x + 15 = 0$

ii. $x^2 + 6x + 5 = 0$

24a. i. $(x+3)^2 + 6 = 0$; no solution; Possible explanation: $(x+3)^2$ would have to be $^{-}6$, and a square can't be negative.

b. State a rule for determining whether an equation of the form $(x+a)^2 + c = 0$ has solutions. Explain your rule.
If $c > 0$, the equation has no solutions because $(x+a)^2$ must be ≥ 0 and if you add a positive number, the result can't be 0. If $c \leq 0$, there will be solutions because $(x+a)^2$ would have to equal ^{-}c, which is ≥ 0 and so has at least one square root.

23. $^{-}16(t-1)^2 + 20 = 0$; $t = 1 + \frac{\sqrt{5}}{2} \approx 2.12$ s ($t = 1 - \frac{\sqrt{5}}{2}$ is about $^{-}0.12$, which doesn't make sense in this situation.)

24a. ii. $(x+3)^2 - 4 = 0$; There will be solutions. Possible explanation: $(x+3)^2$ must be 4, which has two square roots.

22. Stephen's puzzle has no solution. The equation is $(x-1)^2 + 5 = 4$. An equivalent equation is $(x-1)^2 = {}^{-}1$. You cannot take the square root of a negative number. So, the puzzle has no solution.
Consuela's puzzle has one solution. The equation is $(x-1)^2 + 1 = 1$. An equivalent equation is $(x-1)^2 = 0$, and 0 has only one square root.
Kwame's puzzle has two solutions. The equation is $(2x-5)^2 + 1 = 10$. An equivalent equation is $(2x-5)^2 = 9$, and 9 has two square roots.

Exercise 22:
In each of the examples, students are asked to square a binomial expression. Watch for students who incorrectly square and, for example, get $x^2 - 1$ or $x^2 + 1$ from $(x-1)^2$.

Exercise 24:
This exercise previews a topic students will study later when they work with the quadratic formula. At times one is interested in the number of solutions of a quadratic equation, more than the exact value of those solutions. This is particularly helpful when graphing quadratic equations and looking at how many times they intersect the x-axis. (If there are no solutions to the associated quadratic equation, the parabola does not intersect the x-axis; one solution indicates it crosses the x-axis once; and two solutions indicate it crosses twice.)

LESSON 7.3 Completing the Square 463

★ indicates multi-step problem

Exercise 26:

Students may have seen this famous problem before, but it is so mathematically powerful that it is worth visiting more than once! In thinking about the answer to **Part f,** note that if n is even, each number appears in two pairs. If n is odd, each number except the middle one (which is $\frac{n+1}{2}$) appears in two pairs, and the middle number appears twice in one pair. For example, if $n = 5$, one of the pairs is 3 and 3:

1	2	3	4	5
5	4	3	2	1

So regardless of whether n is even or odd, each number appears twice.

25. Geometry A rectangular painting has an area of 25 square feet. One side is 2 feet longer than the other.

   a. Quickly estimate approximate values for the lengths of the painting's sides. Do your estimates give an area that is too large or too small?

  ★ **b.** Write an equation relating the sides and the area of the painting and solve it exactly by completing the square.

   c. Compare your answer in Part b to your approximation in Part a.

26. History When the famous German mathematician Gauss was a young boy, he amazed his teacher by rapidly computing the sum of the integers from 1 to 100. He realized that he could compute the sum without adding all the numbers, by grouping the 100 numbers into pairs.

To see a shortcut for finding this sum, look at two lists of 1 to 100, one in reverse order.

1	2	3	4	5	6	7	...	50	...	94	95	96	97	98	99	100
100	99	98	97	96	95	94	...	51	...	7	6	5	4	3	2	1

25a. Possible answer: 4 ft and 6 ft, which gives an area that is too small (24 ft^2 instead of 25 ft^2).

25b. See Additional Answers.

25c. Possible answer: $\sqrt{26} - 1 \approx 4.1$ and $\sqrt{26} + 1 \approx 6.1$; the approximation was a little smaller than the exact answer.

   a. What is the sum of each pair? 101

   b. How many pairs are there? 100

   c. What is the sum of all these pairs? $100(101) = 10{,}100$

   d. How many times is each of the integers from 1 to 100 counted in this sum? twice

   e. Consider your answers to Parts c and d. What is the sum of the integers from 1 to 100? $10{,}100 \div 2 = 5{,}050$

   f. Explain how you can use this same reasoning to find the sum of the integers from 1 to n for any value of n. Write a formula for s, the sum of the first n positive integers. See Additional Answers.

   g. Chloe added several consecutive numbers, starting at 1, and found a sum of 91. Write an equation you could use to find the numbers she added. Solve your equation by completing the square. Check your answer with the formula.

$$\frac{n(n+1)}{2} = 91 \qquad\qquad n = 13, {}^-14$$
$$n(n+1) = 182$$
$$n^2 + n + \tfrac{1}{4} = 182 + \tfrac{1}{4}$$
$$\left(n + \tfrac{1}{2}\right)^2 = 182.25$$
$$n + \tfrac{1}{2} = \pm\sqrt{182.25}$$
$$n = {}^-0.5 \pm 13.5$$

Additional Answers

25b. If x is the length of the shorter side, $x(x + 2) = 25$.
$$x^2 + 2x - 25 = 0$$
$$x^2 + 2x + 1 - 26 = 0$$
$$(x + 1)^2 = 26$$
$$x = {}^-1 \pm \sqrt{26}$$
Since x is the side of a rectangle, only the positive answer makes sense. The shorter side is $\sqrt{26} - 1$ ft; the longer side is $\sqrt{26} + 1$ ft.

26f. Write two rows of numbers 1 to n, one in reverse order. There are n pairs of numbers, and each pair adds to $n + 1$, so the sum of all the pairs is $n(n + 1)$. Since each number is counted twice, S is half of the sum of all the pairs, so $S = \frac{n(n+1)}{2}$.

Mixed Review

27. $a = 2$, $b = ^-7$, $c = 5$

28. $a = 9$, $b = ^-8$, $c = ^-2$

29. $a = 3.5$, $b = 2$, $c = 3$

30. $a = 1$, $b = 0$, $c = ^-1$

31. $a = 1$, $b = 0$, $c = 4$

32. $a = 3.5$, $b = 1$, $c = ^-7$

Identify the values of *a*, *b*, and *c* in each equation by rearranging it into the form of the general quadratic equation, $ax^2 + bx + c = 0$.

27. $2x^2 - 7x = ^-5$ **28.** $8a + 2 = 9a^2$

29. $4.5k^2 + 3k = ^-3 + k + k^2$ **30.** $^-m - 2 = m^2 - m - 3$

31. $4 = ^-p^2$ **32.** $7 - w^2 = w + 2.5w^2$

Graph each inequality on a separate grid like the one shown.

33. $y \geq x - 3$ **34.** $y < 3 - x$ **35.** $y \leq 1.5x + 3$

33.

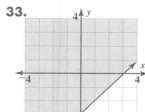

34.

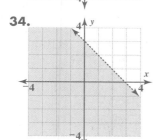

35.

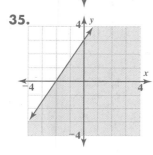

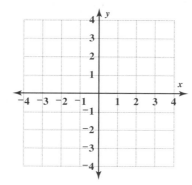

36. Geometry Match each solid to its name. (Hint: For the ones you are unsure of, think about what the term might mean.)

a. square pyramid N

b. cone K

c. cylinder P

d. triangular prism T

e. oblique prism R

f. hexagonal prism M

g. octahedron Q

h. tetrahedron S

i. hemisphere L

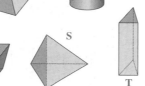

LESSON 7.3 Completing the Square **465**

Exercises 27–32:
Note that students may correctly use the opposites of each value. For example, in Exercise 30, students may use the equation $^-m^2 + 1 = 0$, giving $a = ^-1$ and $c = 1$, rather than $m^2 - 1 = 0$, giving $a = 1$ and $c = ^-1$.

Quick Check

Informal Assessment
Students should be able to:

✔ solve equations of the form $a(x + b)^2 + c = d$

✔ identify perfect square trinomials

✔ complete quadratic expressions to make them perfect squares

✔ solve quadratic equations by completing the square

Quick Quiz

1. Find exact solutions of each equation using any method you choose.

   a. $(x + 4)^2 = 49$
   $^-11, 3$

   b. $3(x - 5)^2 - 12 = 0$
   $3, 7$

2. Complete each quadratic expression to make it a perfect square.

   a. $x^2 - 16x + \underline{64}$

   b. $9r^2 + 6r + \underline{1}$

• **continued at left**

3. Solve each equation by completing the square.

   a. $c^2 + 6c - 9 = 0$ $^-3 \pm 3\sqrt{2}$

   b. $4m^2 - 12m - 7 = 0$ $\frac{7}{2}, -\frac{1}{2}$

   c. $2x^2 - 8x + 5 = 0$ $2 \pm \sqrt{\frac{3}{2}}$

4. Explain why $b^2 - 6b + 12 = 0$ has no solutions. **Completing the square gives** $(b - 3)^2 + 3 = 0$, **so** $(b - 3)^2$ **would have to be negative, which is impossible.**

Teacher Notes

The Quadratic Formula

Objectives

▶ To understand the origin of the quadratic formula

▶ To use the quadratic formula to solve quadratic equations

▶ To understand when the quadratic formula is appropriate to solve equations and when factoring is appropriate

▶ To understand how to apply the quadratic formula to specific situations

▶ To understand the significance of $b^2 - 4ac$ in the quadratic formula

Overview (pacing: about 4 class periods)

This lesson introduces one of the most famous formulas in all of mathematics, the quadratic formula. The beauty of the quadratic formula is that it can be used to solve any quadratic equation. While completing the square can also be used to solve any quadratic equation, the quadratic formula is more efficient. In fact, the technique of completing the square is used to derive the quadratic formula; the two techniques are inextricably connected.

Students are more likely to remember the quadratic formula and use it correctly if they have some understanding of its derivation. All too often students memorize the formula as if it were a jumble of letters and numbers with no intrinsic meaning. Students are not expected to reproduce the proof of the quadratic formula in this course, but they *should* understand the method by which it is derived.

Advance Preparation

No advance preparation is required.

Lesson Planner

	Summary	Materials	On Your Own Exercises	Assessment Opportunities
Investigation 1 page T467	Students gain experience using the quadratic formula. They explore whether equations can be solved using factoring, completing the square, or the quadratic formula.		Practice & Apply: 1–5, p. 479 Connect & Extend: 12–15, p. 480 Mixed Review: 20–25, p. 482	On the Spot Assessment, page T467 Share & Summarize, pages T468, 468 Troubleshooting, page T468
Investigation 2 page T469	Students use the quadratic formula to solve problems.	• Graphing calculators (optional)	Practice & Apply: 6, 7, p. 479 Connect & Extend: 16, 17, pp. 480–481 Mixed Review: 20–25, p. 482	Share & Summarize, pages T471, 471 Troubleshooting, page T471
Investigation 3 page T472	Students examine one part of the quadratic formula, $b^2 - 4ac$, which determines the number of possible solutions for an equation.		Practice & Apply: 8–11, p. 479 Connect & Extend: 18, 19, p. 481 Mixed Review: 20–25, p. 482	Share & Summarize, pages T475, 475 Troubleshooting, page T475 Informal Assessment, page 482 Quick Quiz, page 482
Lab Investigation page T475	Students discover the value of the golden ratio.	• Ruler • Graph paper (optional)		

The derivation of the quadratic formula may seem a little tedious for some of your students, so it may help if you give them some motivation for it. Begin by writing following equations on the board:

$$x^2 - 7x + 6 = 0$$

$$x^2 + 2x - 2 = 0$$

$$3x^2 + 7x - \frac{5}{3} = 0$$

For each equation, ask the class how they might try solving it. The first is easily factorable: $(x - 6)(x - 1) = 0$ so $x = 1$ or 6. The second isn't factorable, but completing the square is fairly simple: $(x + 1)^2 - 3 = 0$ so $x = {}^-1 \pm \sqrt{3}$. The third doesn't look particularly inviting using either method. If you feel comfortable doing so, you might reassure students by telling them that you find the equation a little intimidating, too!

Next, write the general quadratic equation on the board:

$$ax^2 + bx + c = 0$$

Tell the class that they are about to solve this general quadratic equation using the technique of completing the square. In doing so, they will see how one of the most famous formulas in mathematics, the quadratic formula, was developed. Tell students that the formula will let them solve *any* quadratic equation, including that third one.

You might explain that the algebra involved in the derivation is a little tricky, but they should not be as concerned with reproducing what you are doing as with understanding the general ideas behind the derivation.

At this point, go through the steps in the text for completing the square in each of the two columns, "General Equation" and "Specific Equation." It's helpful for students to see what the process looks like with specific numbers, since the operations with variables alone can be confusing.

It is most important that students understand the significance of the $\pm$ sign in the final equation: there are two possible solutions. Write the quadratic formula on the board, both using $\pm$ and with the two possible solutions separated as in the boxed text on page 467. Explain to students that it's helpful if they commit this formula to memory—it's that useful! At the end of class, you may want to have pairs of students quiz each other on it, after they write it on a notecard.

The Quadratic Formula

You have seen that some quadratic equations are easier to solve than others. Some can be solved quickly by factoring or by taking the square root of both sides. Any quadratic equation can be solved by completing the square, but it is not always obvious what has to be done.

Look again at the process of solving an equation by completing the square. The general quadratic equation

$$ax^2 + bx + c = 0$$

is solved below by completing the square. To help you see each step more easily, a specific quadratic equation is solved alongside the general equation.

General Equation	**Specific Equation**
$ax^2 + bx + c = 0$	$2x^2 + 8x + \frac{1}{2} = 0$

Step 1: Divide by a.

$$x^2 + \frac{b}{a}x + \frac{c}{a} = 0 \qquad\qquad x^2 + 4x + \frac{1}{4} = 0$$

Step 2: Complete the square.

$$x^2 + \frac{b}{a}x + \frac{b^2}{4a^2} + \frac{c}{a} - \frac{b^2}{4a^2} = 0 \qquad x^2 + 4x + 4 + \frac{1}{4} - 4 = 0$$

Step 3: Rearrange.

$$x^2 + \frac{b}{a}x + \frac{b^2}{4a^2} = \frac{b^2}{4a^2} - \frac{c}{a} \qquad x^2 + 4x + 4 = \frac{15}{4}$$

$$\left(x + \frac{b}{2a}\right)^2 = \frac{b^2 - 4ac}{4a^2} \qquad\qquad (x + 2)^2 = \frac{15}{4}$$

Step 4: Take the square root of both sides.

$$x + \frac{b}{2a} = \frac{\pm\sqrt{b^2 - 4ac}}{2a} \qquad\qquad x + 2 = \pm\frac{\sqrt{15}}{2}$$

Step 5: Subtract the constant added to x.

$$x = \frac{-b \pm \sqrt{b^2 - 4ac}}{2a} \qquad\qquad x = -2 \pm \frac{\sqrt{15}}{2}$$

1 Use specific examples to motivate the need for a general solution to quadratic equations.

2 Go through the steps, using the specific equation to give a concrete example.

3 Rewrite the formula with the two solutions separated (as on page 467) to emphasize that there are two.

Think & Discuss

Work through this problem slowly with the class, since this is their first time applying the formula, and it may take some getting used to!

The first step in using the formula is to identify a, b, and c. In this case, $a = 1$. Students often think that either $a = 0$ or $a = x^2$ in this case, so be careful. Remind them that a stands for the number multiplying the x^2 term, b is the number multiplying the x term, and c is the constant.

It is important that students also solve this equation using the technique of completing the square, to see for themselves that the quadratic formula often saves time and energy. In a sense, every time they complete the square, they are deriving the quadratic formula!

Investigation 1

In this investigation, students gain experience using the quadratic formula to solve quadratic equations. They also explore which types of equations can be solved using factoring and which have to be solved by using the formula or completing the square.

Students can move from the Think & Discuss directly into Problem Set A.

Problem Set A Suggested Grouping: Pairs

In this problem set, students solve a variety of equations using the quadratic formula. It is important that they understand that the equation must be in the form $ax^2 + bx + c = 0$ (that is, 0 must be alone on one side of the equation) before they apply the formula, and that they be able to correctly identify the values of a, b, and c.

Go over the values of a, b, and c for **Problem 1** as a class before setting students to work in pairs.

To drive home the point that there may be two solutions, have students write each solution separately. That is, instead of writing 1 ± 3, they would write $4, -2$.

Don't worry about whether students simplify the radical expressions that occur in many of these problems. You may, however, want to ask for approximations of their solutions if they are in radical form so that students have some idea of what these numbers mean.

On the Spot Assessment

One common point of confusion for students is working with the denominator in the formula, $2a$. In fact, the division by $2a$ should be done last in the sequence of steps in evaluating the quadratic formula. Students often write the formula incorrectly and don't realize that $2a$ divides both $-b$ and the square root term. After students have tried using the formula a few times, you might review the derivation, paying particular attention to this aspect.

Another common error is in the interpretation of $-b$. Some students incorrectly assume that the term $-b$ must always be negative. In fact, if b is negative, $-b$ will be positive. Encourage them to say "the opposite of b" when talking about the formula—and try to remember to do so yourself as well!

Yet another common error occurs when students perform the calculations to evaluate $b^2 - 4ac$. If either a or c is negative, students have difficulty with the subtraction sign before the 4 and how it applies to the other numbers. If they begin by writing $b^2 + -4ac$, they may make fewer mistakes.

In **Problem 3,** watch for students who incorrectly identify a as 3 since it is the first term. Remind students that a is the coefficient, or multiplier, of the squared term, and therefore a in this case is -1. You may need to go over Problem 3 with the whole class, at least to the point of identifying a, b, and c.

Problem 4 is the first of several problems in which the equation is not set equal to 0. Again, watch for students who begin to identify a, b, and c before they have isolated 0 on one side of the equation.

In **Problem 6,** watch for students who think that b is -12. Again, reinforce what a, b, and c stand for.

Just the facts

As early as the seventh century, Indian mathematicians solved quadratic equations by completing the square, and wrote down the quadratic formula.

This process gives us a formula that can be used to find the solutions of any quadratic equation.

The Quadratic Formula

The solutions of $ax^2 + bx + c = 0$ are

$$x = \frac{-b \pm \sqrt{b^2 - 4ac}}{2a}$$

That is, the solutions are

$$x = \frac{-b + \sqrt{b^2 - 4ac}}{2a} \quad \text{and} \quad x = \frac{-b - \sqrt{b^2 - 4ac}}{2a}$$

Think & Discuss

With $a = 1$, $b = 3$, and $c = -5$, the solutions are $x = \frac{-3 \pm \sqrt{9 + 20}}{2} = \frac{-3 + \sqrt{29}}{2}$ and $\frac{-3 - \sqrt{29}}{2}$.

Use the quadratic formula to solve this equation.

$$x^2 + 3x - 5 = 0$$

Now solve the equation by completing the square. Do you get the same answer? Which method seems easier?

The same answer is obtained by completing the square. Students may find the quadratic formula easier to use.

> **1** Work through this problem slowly with the class.

Investigation 1 Using the Quadratic Formula

1. $a = 2$, $b = 3$, $c = 0$; $\frac{-3 \pm 3}{4} = 0$ or $-\frac{3}{2}$

2. $a = 7$, $b = 1$, $c = -3$; $\frac{-1 \pm \sqrt{85}}{14}$

3. $a = -1$, $b = 2$, $c = 3$; $\frac{2 \pm 4}{2} = 3$ or -1

4. $a = 1$, $b = -6$, $c = -2$; $\frac{6 \pm \sqrt{44}}{2} = 3 \pm \sqrt{11}$

5. $a = 2$, $b = -1$, $c = 5$; $\frac{1 \pm \sqrt{-39}}{4}$; no solutions

6. $a = 1$, $b = 0$, $c = -12$; $\pm \frac{\sqrt{48}}{2} = \pm 2\sqrt{3}$

This investigation will help you learn to use the quadratic formula.

Problem Set A

For Problems 1–8, do the following:

- Identify the values of a, b, and c referred to in the quadratic formula. You may need to rewrite the equation in the form $ax^2 + bx + c = 0$.
- Solve the equation using the quadratic formula.

1. $2x^2 + 3x = 0$

2. $7x^2 + x - 3 = 0$

3. $3 - x^2 + 2x = 0$

4. $6x + 2 = x^2$

5. $2x^2 = x - 5$

6. $x^2 - 12 = 0$

7. $x^2 = 5x$

8. $x(x - 6) = 3$

7. $a = 1$, $b = -5$, $c = 0$; $\frac{5 \pm 5}{2} = 0$ or 5

8. $a = 1$, $b = -6$, $c = -3$; $\frac{6 \pm \sqrt{48}}{2} = 3 \pm 2\sqrt{3}$

> **2** You may have students work in pairs after identifying a, b, and c in Problem 1 with the class.

> **3** Watch for common errors.

Develop

In **Problem 9,** students are asked to determine whether a particular quadratic equation is easier to solve with factoring than with the formula. Since this equation is a simple one to factor, many will probably say that factoring is easier. Factoring also avoids the simplification errors that plague students when applying the quadratic formula. It is important for students to understand that both methods get them to the same solutions, but that they should use common sense in choosing one over the other.

Access for all Learners

Extra Challenge Here is the beginning of another derivation of the quadratic formula. Ask students to try to follow the steps and provide reasons for each step.

$$ax^2 + bx + c = 0$$
$$4a^2x^2 + 4abx + 4ac = 0$$
$$4a^2x^2 + 4abx + 4ac + b^2 = b^2$$
$$4a^2x^2 + 4abx + b^2 = b^2 - 4ac$$
$$(2ax + b)^2 = b^2 - 4ac$$

Then ask students to try to complete the derivation.

About the Mathematics

Students may be interested in knowing that there are, in fact, cubic and quartic formulas as well, but deriving them is quite complex and lengthy. Furthermore, it can be proved that it is *impossible* to derive a formula for solving equations of degree 5 and above.

Problem Set B Suggested Grouping: Pairs

In this problem set, students solve quadratic equations by any method they choose. Students should develop a good sense for choosing the most suitable technique for a given situation.

It might be interesting to poll the class to see how many students used each technique (factoring, completing the square, or the quadratic formula) in **Problems 1 and 2.** If students volunteer their answers, probe for why they chose a particular method. They should be developing a sense for whether quadratics factor; clearly, in these two problems, factoring will take less time.

Problem 6 involves some tricky calculations, and you will need to reinforce with students how careful they must be if they use the quadratic formula in evaluating $b^2 - 4ac$. In this case, $b^2 - 4ac = (-2)^2 - 4(3)(-2) = 4 + {}^-4(3)(-2) = 4 + 24 = 28$.

In **Problems 9 and 10,** students who use the quadratic formula must be sure to get an expression equal to 0 before they identify a, b, and c. Encourage students to try to keep the squared terms positive when they rearrange expressions on one side of an equation, especially if they are going to complete the square or factor.

Share & Summarize

You may want students to give examples of equations that are easiest to solve by each one of these methods. This is an important distinction that will serve them well later on. In general, factoring is fastest when the coefficient of the x^2 term and the constant term are prime or have only a couple of prime factors (and, of course, the expression is actually factorable).

Troubleshooting Students will have more experience in solving quadratic equations in the next investigation, so they may continue even if they are having some difficulties.

On Your Own Exercises

Practice & Apply: 1–5, p. 479
Connect & Extend: 12–15, p. 480
Mixed Review: 20–25, p. 482

9. Consider the equation $x^2 + 3x + 2 = 0$.

   a. Solve the equation by factoring. -2, -1

   b. Now use the quadratic formula to solve the equation.

   c. Which method seems easier?   Answers will vary.

   d. Which of Problems 1–8 could you have solved by factoring?

1, 3, and 7

Problem Set B

For each problem, do the following:

• Solve the equation using any method you like. Check your answers.

• If you did not solve the equation by factoring, decide whether you could have used factoring to solve it.

1. $x^2 - 5x + 6 = 0$ **2.** $w^2 - 6w + 9 = 0$

3. $t^2 + 4t + 1 = 0$ **4.** $x^2 - x + 2 = 0$

5. $k^2 + 4k + 2 = 0$ **6.** $3g^2 - 2g - 2 = 0$

7. $z^2 - 12z + 36 = 0$ **8.** $2e^2 + 7e + 6 = 0$

9. $x^2 + x = 15 - x$ **10.** $3n^2 + 14 = 8n^2 + 3n$

Share & Summarize

1. What is the connection between the quadratic formula and the process of completing the square?

2. You have learned several methods for solving quadratic equations: backtracking, factoring, completing the square, and the quadratic formula.

   a. Which of these can be used with only some quadratic equations? factoring and backtracking

   b. Which can be used with all quadratic equations?

3. When you are given a quadratic equation to solve, how do you choose a solution method?

Possible answers: Factoring is convenient when the factors are easy to find. Backtracking is convenient for an equation in the form $a(bx + c)^2 + d = e$. Completing the square is easy when the coefficient of the x^2 term is 1 and the coefficient of the x term is even. Otherwise, the quadratic formula is likely to be the easiest method.

Investigation 2

In this investigation, students use the quadratic formula to solve problems involving quadratic equations. Although students have solved quadratic equations before this chapter, they were limited to approximations using graphs or guess-check-and-improve. They should derive some satisfaction at this stage knowing that they now have the power to solve any quadratic equation and obtain exact solutions.

Tips
from Teachers

"You may want to use students' accomplishment in learning such a famous formula as a reason for celebration! For example, when none of my students have dietary concerns, I have found that a cake with the formula written on it is a welcome treat."

Problem Set C Suggested Grouping:
Pairs or Small Groups

In this problem set, students are given contexts that require the solution of quadratic equations. The key point here (other than additional practice with the quadratic formula) is that, at times, contexts impose domain restrictions on the solutions. Students are asked to check whether their answers make sense in the context of the problem.

In **Problem 1,** for example, since the context is length of the side of a rectangle, only positive solutions should be considered. Of course, another issue that arises is the degree of accuracy needed in the answer. Encourage students to imagine they are actually ordering this material: would they really ask for a length as an irrational number?

In **Problem 3,** students need to realize that when the ball returns to the ground, the value of h is 0. This isn't always obvious to students. They should also note that there are two times at which the ball is on the ground: at the beginning when the ball leaves the ground ($t = 0$) and when it returns to the ground after the bounce ($t = 1.875$).

★ indicates multi-step problem

Investigation 2 ▶ Applying the Quadratic Formula

In Chapter 4 you examined quadratic equations in specific situations and estimated solutions using a graphing calculator. Now you will apply the quadratic formula to solve them exactly.

Problem Set C

In some of these problems, the quadratic formula will give two solutions. Make sure your answers make sense in the problem's context.

1. Josefina, a tapestry maker, has a client who wants a tapestry with an area of 4 square meters. Josefina decides it will have a rectangular shape and a length 1 meter longer than its width.

   a. Write an equation representing the client's requirements and Josefina's decision.

   ★ **b.** Use the quadratic formula to find the width and the length of the tapestry. Express your answer in two ways, exactly and to the nearest centimeter.

★ 2. Another client wants a rectangular tapestry with an area of 6 m², but she insists the length be exactly 2 m longer than the width.

   Write and solve an equation that represents this situation. Give exact dimensions of the tapestry, and then estimate the dimensions to the nearest centimeter.

★ 3. Jesse threw a superball to the ground, and it bounced straight up with an initial speed of 30 feet per second. The height h in feet t seconds after the ball left the ground is given by the formula $h = 30t - 16t^2$. Write and solve an equation to find the value of t when the ball returns to the ground.

   $16t^2 - 30t = 0$; $t = 0$ or $t = 1\frac{7}{8}$. Since $t = 0$ is when the ball left the ground, the ball returns to the ground after $1\frac{7}{8}$ s, or 1.875 s.

Sidebar answers (left margin):

1a. $x(x + 1) = 4$ or $x^2 + x - 4 = 0$, where x is the width in meters

1b. $x = \frac{-1 \pm \sqrt{17}}{2}$;

Only the positive solution makes sense in this context, so the width is $\frac{-1 + \sqrt{17}}{2}$ m ≈ 156 cm, and the length is $\frac{1 + \sqrt{17}}{2}$ m ≈ 256 cm.

2. $x(x + 2) = 6$ or $x^2 + 2x - 6 = 0$, where x is the width in meters; $x = ^-1 \pm \sqrt{7}$; Only the positive solution makes sense in this context, so the width is $\sqrt{7} - 1$ m ≈ 165 cm, and the length is $\sqrt{7} + 1$ m ≈ 365 cm.

Right margin notes:

1 You may have students work in pairs or small groups.

2 Ask students to consider their answer in terms of actually ordering the material.

Problem 4 may be challenging. Be sure students understand that in **Part a,** they need to give a general equation for the ball's height above the ground after t seconds. Some may be tempted to write $5 = 30t - 16t^2$, making the incorrect assumption that they are finding the time at which the ball reached 5 feet. In **Part b,** note that again only the positive solution makes sense.

Problem Set D Suggested Grouping:
                  Pairs or Small Groups

This problem set involves a context that, although fictitious, has some interesting aspects that might appeal to students. However, its main purpose is to provide a setting within which students can practice their skills in solving quadratics.

★ indicates multi-step problem

Remember

Motion equations such as $h = 30t - 16t^2$ and $h = {}^-16t^2 + 20$ only give estimates of an object's position because they ignore air resistance.

4b. $5 + 30t - 16t^2 = 0$ or $16t^2 - 30t - 5 = 0$;

$t = \dfrac{30 \pm \sqrt{1{,}220}}{32}$;

Only the positive solution makes sense in this context, so

$t = \dfrac{30 + \sqrt{1{,}220}}{32} \approx$ 2.03 s.

4. When an object is thrown straight upward, its height h in feet after t seconds can be estimated using the formula $h = s + vt - 16t^2$, where s is the initial height (at $t = 0$) and v is the initial velocity. In Problem 3, s was 0 feet and v was 30 feet per second, so the ball's height was estimated by $h = 30t - 16t^2$.

Suppose Jesse threw the ball upward instead of bouncing it, so that the ball's height when $t = 0$ was 5 ft above the ground but the initial velocity was still 30 ft/s.

a. Write an equation describing the height h of Jesse's ball after t seconds. $h = 5 + 30t - 16t^2$

★ **b.** Write and solve an equation to find how long it takes the ball to reach the ground.

★ **5.** If an object is dropped with an initial velocity of 0, its height can be approximated by adding its starting height to $^-16t^2$, which represents the effect of gravity. For example, the height of a rock dropped from 20 feet above the ground can be approximated by the formula $h = {}^-16t^2 + 20$.

Write and solve an equation to determine how many seconds pass until a rock dropped from 100 ft hits the ground.

$^-16t^2 + 100 = 0$ or $100 = 16t^2$; $t = 2.5$ s ($t = {}^-2.5$ makes no sense in this context.)

Problem Set D

The town of Seaside, which now has only a few small hotels, is considering allowing a large tourist resort to be built along the oceanfront. Some residents are in favor of the plan because it will bring income to the community. Others are against it, saying it will disrupt their lifestyle. The state tourism board has a formula for computing the overall tourism rating T of an area based on two factors: U, the uniqueness rating, and A, the amenities rating.

1. The amenities rating scale, A, is used to assess the attractiveness of a tourist destination, including how easy it is to find a place to stay. Seaside currently has a rating of 5. It is estimated that for every 100 beds the resort opens to tourists, A will increase by 2 points.

If the resort has p hundreds of beds, what is the estimate for the new amenities rating? $A = 5 + 2p$

2. The uniqueness rating scale, U, is used to assess the special features that will attract tourists. Seaside currently has a high uniqueness rating, 20, because dolphins are often sighted close to the local beaches. A committee has gathered evidence that an increase in tourists will keep dolphins from coming near shore. They estimate that for every 100 beds in the resort, U will drop by 2 points.

If the resort has p hundreds of beds, what is the estimate for the new uniqueness rating? $U = 20 - 2p$

1 Be sure students understand that Part a asks for a general equation.

2 You may have students work in pairs or small groups.

In **Problem 3,** students use the expressions they wrote in Problems 1 and 2 to form the equation $100 + 30p - 4p^2 = 100$ in **Part c.** If there were no change in the tourism rating, it would mean that the product of A and U would equal 100.

In **Problem 3d,** students are asked for the number of beds that would result in a value of T less than 100. Using a graphing calculator, students could graph $y = 100 + 30x - 4x^2$ and $y = 100$ and observe where on the graph of $y = 100 + 30x - 4x^2$ the values of y are less than 100. A good viewing window would be Xmin = 0, Xmax = 18, Xscl = 2, Ymin = 0, Ymax = 180, Yscl = 10. Students could use a similar technique to answer the second question in **Part e.**

Access
for all **Learners**

Extra Challenge Ask students to find the number of beds to be added that would give the maximum tourism rating. *375 beds*

Share & Summarize
This question is not asking students to derive the formula but merely to describe how they would go about using the formula.

1 ▶ **Troubleshooting** If students are still having difficulty, you may want to give them specific values of a, b, and c and ask them to find the solutions using the quadratic formula. In this way, you can see whether they are having problems with calculation. If they do not have difficulty with the calculations, ask them to make up a problem with an area context (these seem the most simple in terms of setting up the equations and solving them) and solve it, explaining each step to you.

On Your Own Exercises

Practice & Apply: 6, 7, p. 479
Connect & Extend: 16, 17, pp. 480–481
Mixed Review: 20–25, p. 482

3b. $(5 + 2p)(20 - 2p)$ or $100 + 30p - 4p^2$

3c. $100 + 30p - 4p^2 = 100$; $p = 0$ and $p = 7.5$

3d. The rating decreases when $100 + 30p - 4p^2 < 100$, or $30p - 4p^2 < 0$, which occurs when $p < 0$ or $p > 7.5$. So a decrease in beds or an increase of more than 750 would decrease T.

3e. i. $100 + 30p - 4p^2 = 140$; $p = \frac{15 \pm \sqrt{65}}{4} \approx$ 5.77 or 1.73

3. The overall tourism rating, T, is computed by multiplying A and U.

   a. What is the town's current tourism rating?   100

   b. Write an expression in terms of p for the estimated tourism rating if p hundreds of beds are added.

   c. Use your expression from Part b to decide for what values of p there would be no change in the tourism rating. (Hint: Write and solve an equation.)

   d. For what numbers of beds would the resort create a decrease in the tourism rating?

   e. Seaside's town council believes that the disruption to the town's lifestyle could not be justified unless the development resulted in an increase in the tourism rating to at least 140 points.

     i. Use your expression from Part b to decide for what values of p you would expect to achieve a tourism rating of 140 points.

     ii. What values of p would give a tourism rating *over* 140 points?
       values between 5.77 and 1.73

   f. What would you advise the council to do?   Add between 173 and 577 beds.

Share & Summarize

Explain the steps involved in using the quadratic formula to solve an equation. If the equation is quadratic, express it in the form $ax^2 + bx + c = 0$ and then substitute the values of a, b, and c into the formula $x = \frac{-b \pm \sqrt{b^2 - 4ac}}{2a}$.

1 You may want to give students values for a, b, and c to be sure they understand the calculations needed.

LESSON 7.4 The Quadratic Formula **471**

Investigation 3

In this investigation, students examine one part of the quadratic formula, $b^2 - 4ac$. This is known as the *discriminant* because $b^2 - 4ac$ discriminates among the possible number of real solutions to a quadratic equation. If the discriminant is 0, the square root term disappears, and the single solution is $\frac{-b}{2a}$. If the discriminant is any positive number, there will be two solutions because there are two roots (thus the $\pm$ sign before the square root). If the discriminant is negative, there will be no real solutions.

This part of the quadratic formula is a useful tool in that it saves time in answering the question "How many solutions does this quadratic equation have?"

 1 Explain the scenario before the Think & Discuss about the ball, and the fact that the important question in this example is not "What are the solutions?" but "Does this equation have any solutions?"

 2 The term *discriminant* is not used in the text, but you may wish to introduce it to your students.

 ## Think & Discuss

3 Have students work in groups to answer these questions. You might create three columns on the board (0 solutions, 1 solution, 2 solutions) and have each group put their examples in the appropriate columns.

Then you might ask students whether they can see any patterns within each column. In the "one solution" examples, students may see that all are perfect squares when written as $ax^2 + bx + c = 0$. The other two columns may be mysteries, however. Tell them they will discover the answers in this investigation.

If you keep the student examples on the board, you can refer back to them at the end of Problem Set E if students need more convincing that $b^2 - 4ac$ is connected to the number of solutions a quadratic equation has.

Problem Set E Suggested Grouping: Small Groups

4 In this problem set, students are given several equations that they know have zero, one, or two solutions and are asked to examine the value of $b^2 - 4ac$ in each case.

Investigation 3 ▶ What Does $b^2 - 4ac$ Tell You?

In some situations, you might be more interested in knowing *how many* solutions a quadratic equation has than exactly what the solutions *are*. For example, suppose you are thinking about the height of a thrown ball at various times. You could solve a quadratic equation to find at what time the ball reaches a certain height. But if you want to know only *whether* it reaches that height and don't care about *when* it does, the question you want to answer is

Does this equation have any solutions?

You need only part of the quadratic formula—the expression $b^2 - 4ac$—to answer this question.

Remember

The quadratic formula is

$$x = \frac{-b \pm \sqrt{b^2 - 4ac}}{2a}.$$

① Possible answer: $x^2 + 25 = 0$; $x^2 \geq 0$ so $x^2 + 25 \geq 25$, which means $x^2 + 25$ can never be equal to 0.

② Any quadratic equation that is a perfect square set equal to 0, such as $(x + 3)^2 = 0$, has one solution.

Think & Discuss

You have seen examples of quadratic equations that have no solutions. Sometimes this is easy to tell without using the quadratic formula. Give an example of such an equation, and explain how you know that it doesn't have solutions. See ①.

Some quadratic equations have exactly one solution. Give some examples. See ②.

Of course, many quadratic equations have two solutions. Give an example. Possible answer: $x^2 + x - 6 = 0$, or $(x - 2)(x + 3) = 0$

Problem Set E

You will now investigate the relationship between the value of $b^2 - 4ac$ and the number of solutions of $ax^2 + bx + c = 0$.

1. The equation $x^2 + 1 = 0$ has no solutions.

   a. Explain why this is true.

   b. What is the value of $b^2 - 4ac$ for this equation? Is it positive, negative, or 0? $^-4$, negative

   c. Give another example of a quadratic equation that you know has no solutions. Find the value of $b^2 - 4ac$ for your example: is it positive, negative, or 0? Equations will vary; the value of $b^2 - 4ac$ will be negative.

1a. Possible answer: $x^2 \geq 0$, so $x^2 + 1 \geq 1$, so $x^2 + 1$ can't be equal to 0.

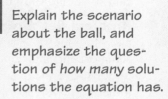

1 Explain the scenario about the ball, and emphasize the question of *how many* solutions the equation has.

2 You may want to introduce the term *discriminant*.

3 Problem-Solving Strategies

   • Make an organized list

   • Look for a pattern

4 You may have students work in small groups.

By the time students finish **Problem 3,** they should be forming some conjectures about the value of $b^2 - 4ac$ and its relation to the number of solutions.

 Problem Set Wrap-Up You may want to bring the class together to discuss **Problem 4** as a way of summarizing their findings. You will need to refer to the quadratic formula and the significance of the $\pm$ sign in indicating two roots (when the value under the radical sign is positive).

It would be beneficial to write the following on the board so students have a record of this connection:

If $b^2 - 4ac < 0$, there are no solutions.

If $b^2 - 4ac = 0$, there is one solution.

If $b^2 - 4ac > 0$, there are two solutions.

2a. $x^2 + 2x - 15 = 0$, $b^2 - 4ac = 64$, positive

2b. Equations will vary; the value of $b^2 - 4ac$ will be positive.

3a. 0

3b. Equations will vary; the value of $b^2 - 4ac$ will be 0.

Just the facts

The acceleration of the passengers on this carnival ride might be given by the quadratic equation $a = 0.2v^2$, where a is the acceleration toward the center of the ride in m/s², and v is the velocity in m/s.

2. The equation $(x - 3)(x + 5) = 0$ has two solutions.

   a. Express this equation in the form $ax^2 + bx + c = 0$ and find the value of $b^2 - 4ac$. Is it positive, negative, or 0?

   b. Give another example of a quadratic equation with two solutions. Find the value of $b^2 - 4ac$ for your equation.

3. The expression $x^2 + 2x + 1$ is a perfect square trinomial since it is equal to $(x + 1)^2$. The equation $x^2 + 2x + 1 = 0$ has one solution.

   a. Is the value of $b^2 - 4ac$ for this equation positive, negative, or 0?

   b. Give another example of a quadratic equation with one solution. Is the value of $b^2 - 4ac$ for your equation positive, negative, or 0?

4. As you know, a quadratic equation can have zero, one, or two solutions. This problem will help you explain the connection between the value of $b^2 - 4ac$ and the number of solutions an equation has.

   a. Where does the expression $b^2 - 4ac$ occur in the quadratic formula?   under the radical sign

   b. What value or values must $b^2 - 4ac$ have for the quadratic formula to give no solutions? Explain.   See Additional Answers.

   c. What value or values must $b^2 - 4ac$ have for the quadratic formula to give one solution? Explain.   See Additional Answers.

   d. What value or values must $b^2 - 4ac$ have for the quadratic formula to give two solutions? Explain.
   Positive values; if the expression is positive, there are two square roots (when you add and subtract $\sqrt{b^2 - 4ac}$ you get two different values).

 Discuss Problem 4 as a class, and write the results on the board.

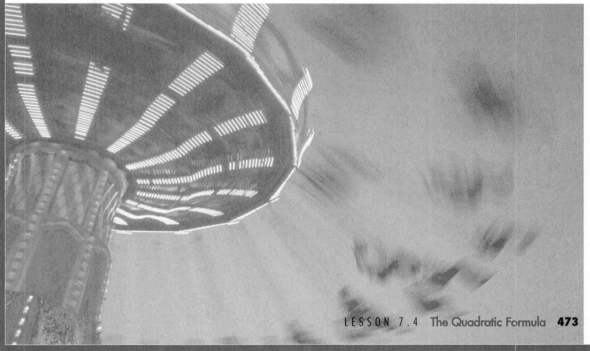

Additional Answers

4b. Negative values; if the expression is negative, you're trying to take the square root of a negative number, so there are no solutions.

4c. 0; if the expression is 0, there is only one square root (you add and subtract 0, which gives the same value for the solution).

Problem Set F Suggested Grouping: Small Groups

In this problem set, students evaluate $b^2 - 4ac$ to determine the number of solutions for problems with and without situational contexts.

Problems 1 and 2 present two equations without a situation to allow students to practice using $b^2 - 4ac$ without distraction. These should be relatively simple for students to complete.

In **Problem 3b,** students may also write the answer in the form $8t^2 - 15t + 50 = 0$. Note that students need only find the value of $b^2 - 4ac$ to answer **Problem 3d.** Since it is negative, there will be no solutions. If students want a visual representation of this, you can have them look at the graph of $y = -16x^2 + 30x$ to see if y ever reaches 100. This is actually a preview for Problem 4.

In **Problem 4,** students need to understand that if M is the maximum height reached by the ball, only one value of t will satisfy the equation $-16t^2 + 30t - M = 0$, since that value is the highest point on the parabola (the vertex). For **Part g,** they will have to substitute the value of M into that equation and solve for t. Students may be clever, however, and realize that since $b^2 - 4ac = 0$, the quadratic formula reduces to $-\frac{b}{2a}$; they can find the solution quickly this way.

Problem Set F

Find the number of solutions each equation has.

1. $2x^2 - 9x + 5 = 0$ 2

2. $3x^2 - 7x + 9 = 0$ 0

In Problem Set C, Jesse bounced a superball with a velocity of 30 feet per second as it left the ground. The ball's height is given by the formula $h = 30t - 16t^2$, where t is time in seconds since the ball left the ground.

3. You can use your knowledge of the quadratic formula to find how high the ball will travel. First look at whether the ball will reach 100 feet.

    a. What equation would you solve to find if and when the height of the ball reaches 100 feet? $30t - 16t^2 = 100$

3b. $-16t^2 + 30t - 100 = 0$ or $16t^2 - 30t + 100 = 0$

    b. Write your equation in the form $at^2 + bt + c = 0$.

    c. What is the value of $b^2 - 4ac$ for your equation? $-5,500$

3d. No; the value of $b^2 - 4ac$ is negative, so the equation has no solutions.

    d. Will the ball reach a height of 100 feet? Explain.

4. Challenge This graph of $h = 30t - 16t^2$ can help you determine just how high the ball will go.

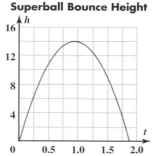

Superball Bounce Height

    a. Suppose M is the maximum height reached by the ball. Write an equation to represent when the ball is at this height.

    b. Write your equation in the form $at^2 + bt + c = 0$.

    c. How many solutions will this equation have? Hint: Look at the graph.   1

    d. What do you know about the value of $b^2 - 4ac$ for a quadratic equation with the number of solutions that this equation has?

    e. Use your answer to Part d to help you find the value of M. Show how you found your answer.

    f. How high does the ball travel?   about 14.06 ft

    g. Write and solve an equation to find how long it takes the ball to reach this height.

4a. $30t - 16t^2 = M$

4b. $-16t^2 + 30t - M = 0$ or $16t^2 - 30t + M = 0$

4d. It must be 0.

4e. $b^2 - 4ac = 900 - 64M = 0$, $M = \frac{900}{64} = \frac{225}{16} \approx 14.06$

4g. $-16t^2 + 30t - \frac{225}{16} = 0$; $t = \frac{15}{16} \approx 0.94$ s

1 You may have students work in small groups.

2 You might have students graph $y = {}^-16x^2 + 30x$ to see if it ever reaches 100 feet.

Share & Summarize

Question 2 may be tricky for students. If it helps, you may want to ask them to rewrite the equation, substituting d for y: $d = ax^2 + bx + c$. Subtracting d from both sides gives $ax^2 + bx + (c - d) = 0$, so the expression to look at is $b^2 - 4a(c - d)$.

Troubleshooting If students are having difficulty understanding the role of $b^2 - 4ac$, you can still move on, since they should be able to solve a quadratic equation to find the number of solutions, if necessary.

On Your Own Exercises

Practice & Apply: 8–11, p. 479
Connect & Extend: 18, 19, p. 481
Mixed Review: 20–25, p. 482

Lab Investigation

Suggested Grouping: Small Groups

In this lab, students explore a topic in mathematics that dates back to the early Greeks: the golden ratio. In the investigation, students will use some of the tools they have developed recently: solving proportions and solving quadratic equations. Students may find the applications to art, architecture, and other branches of mathematics appealing. The lab ends with an exploration of the connection between the golden ratio and the Fibonacci sequence.

Materials and Preparation

Each student will require a ruler. Graph paper would also be helpful.

Introduce

Explain to students that they will be exploring a topic quite famous in mathematics and will be able to use their tools for solving quadratic equations. If students do not finish the lab in one period, you can assign any one of the parts as an independent project or as a piece to submit for a portfolio.

What Do You Like?

After students select which rectangles seem most pleasing to them and draw some of their own, you may want to pull the class together to talk about the golden rectangle and the golden ratio, as described at the bottom of page 475 and the top of page 476.

1. Write the equation in the form $ax^2 + bx + c = 0$ and compute $b^2 - 4ac$. If this value is positive, there are two solutions; if it is equal to 0, there is one solution; and if it is negative, there are no solutions.

1 You may want to have students substitute d for y and work with that equation.

Share & Summarize

1. Without actually solving it, how can you tell whether a quadratic equation has zero, one, or two solutions?

2. For a quadratic relationship in the form $y = ax^2 + bx + c$, how can you tell whether y ever has a certain value d?
Possible answer: Look at the value of $b^2 - 4a(c - d)$; if it's positive or 0, y is d for at least one x value; if it's negative, y is never d.

Lab Investigation ▶ The Golden Ratio

MATERIALS
- ruler
- graph paper (optional)

In this investigation, you will work with a ratio that has been important since the time of the early Greeks. The ratio arises in many surprising places, including mathematics, art, music, architecture, and genetics.

2 You may have students work in small groups.

What Do You Like?

1. Here are several rectangles. Which do you think is the most "appealing to the eye"? (You don't need reasons for your answers; just say which one you like.) Answers will vary.

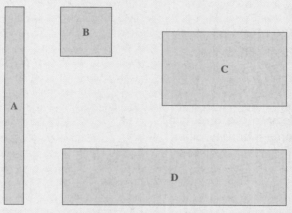

2. Rectangles and explanations will vary.

2. Draw some other rectangles that have a shape that is pleasing to you. Explain why you think one shape is more pleasing than another.

Many people think Rectangle C—and rectangles geometrically similar to it—is the most pleasing to the eye. It is called a *golden rectangle*, and the ratio of its sides (the ratio of the long side to the short side) is the *golden ratio*.

3 You may want to discuss the golden rectangle and the golden ratio with the class.

LESSON 7.4 The Quadratic Formula **475**

Develop

1 If you have an overhead projector, it may be helpful to actually construct the second rectangle ($x + 1$ by x) using two pieces of paper: a rectangle with dimensions 1 in. and 1.6 in., and a square with a side length of 1.6 in. (The length of x is approximately 1.618 inches.)

Before students answer questions in the next section, you may want to give them some historical data. Ancient Egyptians apparently used golden rectangles in religious buildings. Classical Greek sculptures, temples, and other works of art use the golden ratio in proportions for the human body: the ratio of the total height to the height of the navel approximates the golden ratio. In 1876, German psychologist Gustav T. Fechner was the first to conduct a psychological study to find out which rectangles people thought most pleasing. He found that most people preferred rectangles with the proportions of the golden ratio. On the other hand, there have been studies that claim to refute Fechner's findings.

Try It Out

The two rectangles pictured were created to be golden rectangles. When students measure their sides, they should get a ratio of approximately 1.62 to 1. In **Problem 4,** depending upon the rectangle they created, they may or may not get this ratio. It would be interesting to find out whether more students chose a rectangle approximating the golden rectangle than any other, as Fechner found with his study subjects. Some of your students may have created a "wild" rectangle just to be different. Don't worry about this.

Solve It

In **Problem 6,** students begin to solve the equation $\frac{x}{1} = \frac{x + 1}{x}$. When they multiply both sides of the equation by x, you might want to remind them that they are making the assumption that x cannot equal 0. Of course, this assumption is acceptable, because x is the length of a side of a rectangle and so must be positive. However, it's important that students remember that they must be careful not to accidentally multiply by 0 when solving equations.

In **Problems 7, 8, and 9,** students use the equation to calculate the golden ratio.

Remember

In similar figures, corresponding sides have lengths that share a common ratio and corresponding angles are congruent.

One special property of a golden rectangle is that, when you add a square to its longer side to form a new rectangle, the new shape is similar to the original. So, the new rectangle is a golden rectangle and its sides are in the golden ratio.

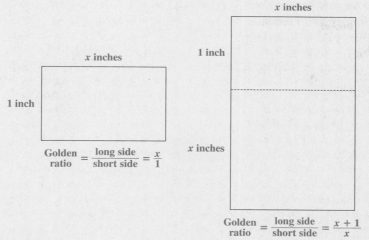

x inches

1 inch

$$\text{Golden ratio} = \frac{\text{long side}}{\text{short side}} = \frac{x}{1}$$

x inches

1 inch

x inches

$$\text{Golden ratio} = \frac{\text{long side}}{\text{short side}} = \frac{x + 1}{x}$$

1

- You may want to construct the second rectangle on an overhead projector.
- You also may want to give students some background about the golden rectangle.

Try It Out

3. approximately 1.62

4. Answers will vary.

3. Measure the dimensions of the two rectangles above and determine whether they have the same $\frac{\text{long side}}{\text{short side}}$ ratio. What is the ratio?

4. Now find the $\frac{\text{long side}}{\text{short side}}$ ratio of each rectangle you drew in Problem 2.

Solve It

5. The ratios of the two rectangles above must be equal. Write an equation setting the ratios equal to each other. That is, complete this equation:

$$\frac{x}{1} = \frac{x + 1}{x}$$

6. Now write your equation in the form $ax^2 + bx + c = 0$. (Hint: You will need to think about how to get x out of the denominator.)

7. Find the exact solutions of your equation, and then express the solutions to the nearest thousandth.

8. Do both of your solutions make sense? Explain.

9. What is the value of the golden ratio? approximately 1.618

2

You may want to poll students to see how close to the golden ratio they got.

6. $x^2 = x + 1$ or $x^2 - x - 1 = 0$

7. $\frac{1 \pm \sqrt{5}}{2}$; approximately 1.618, ⁻0.618

8. Only 1.618 makes sense; the side lengths of a rectangle must be positive.

Going Further

In **Problem 12,** students create a sequence of rectangular drawings whose dimensions mirror the Fibonacci sequence. In creating these drawings, you may want to have them work on graph paper. Make sure students understand they are to alternate adding a square to the side and then to the bottom of each step.

10. Compare the value of the golden ratio with the ratios you measured in Question 3. What do you notice? The values are very close.

11. Answer will vary.

11. Now compare the value of the golden ratio to the measurements you made of your own rectangles in Question 4. What do you notice?

Going Further

1 You may want to give students graph paper.

12. Using graph paper or ordinary paper and a ruler, you can draw a rectangle that's almost a golden rectangle.

a. *Step 1:* Start with a square with side lengths of 1 unit in the top left corner of your page. What is the ratio of the sides? Since this is a square, the ratio is $\frac{1}{1}$ or 1.

b. *Step 2:* Add another square next to the first to make a larger rectangle. What is the ratio of the long side to the short side of this new rectangle? $\frac{2}{1}$ or 2

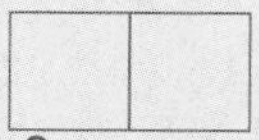

c. *Step 3:* Add a square next to the longer side of your rectangle to make an even larger rectangle. What is the $\frac{\text{long side}}{\text{short side}}$ ratio of this new rectangle? $\frac{3}{2}$ or 1.5

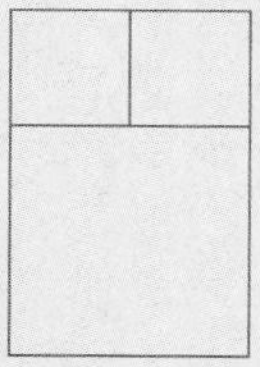

12d. Answer will vary, but the ratio should be close to the golden ratio.

d. Repeat Step 3 as many times as you can on your paper. What is the ratio for the final rectangle you make? Compare this value to the golden ratio you calculated in Problem 9.

Step 4

Step 5

LESSON 7.4 The Quadratic Formula **477**

Students may be surprised when they discover in **Problem 13** that the smaller dimensions form the Fibonacci sequence. You may want to ask why the dimensions, after the first two, reflect the summations $1 + 1, 2 + 1, 3 + 2, 5 + 3$, and so on.

In **Problems 14 and 15,** students calculate the ratios of consecutive Fibonacci numbers and discover that they get closer and closer to the golden ratio.

Finding Out More

This is a good question to assign as extra credit or as a long-term homework assignment, since it requires that students do research into the topic of the golden ratio.

13. 13 and 21; Possible explanation: For each new number, add the two previous numbers.

14. $\frac{F_4}{F_3} = \frac{3}{2} = 1.5$

$\frac{F_5}{F_4} = \frac{5}{3} = 1.667$

$\frac{F_6}{F_5} = \frac{8}{5} = 1.6$

$\frac{F_7}{F_6} = \frac{13}{8} = 1.625$

$\frac{F_8}{F_7} = \frac{21}{13} \approx 1.615$

$\frac{F_9}{F_8} = \frac{34}{21} \approx 1.619$

$\frac{F_{10}}{F_9} = \frac{55}{34} \approx 1.618$

15. They seem to be getting closer and closer to the golden ratio.

Just the **facts**

The Fibonacci sequence is named for its discoverer, Leonardo Fibonacci (also known as Leonardo Pisano), who was born about 1170 A.D. in the city of Pisa (Italy). He was one of the first people to introduce the Hindu-Arabic number system—which uses the digits 0 to 9 and a decimal point—into Europe.

13. Look at the dimensions of the rectangles you made in Problem 11.

- The first is 1×1.

- The next four are 1×2, 2×3, 3×5, and 5×8.

- Listing only the smaller dimension in each rectangle gives the *Fibonacci sequence:*

$$1, 1, 2, 3, 5, 8, \ldots .$$

Look for a pattern in the Fibonacci sequence. What are the next two numbers? How did you find them?

14. Compute the sequence of ratios of Fibonacci numbers up to the ratio $\frac{\text{tenth Fibonacci number}}{\text{ninth Fibonacci number}}$, or $\frac{F_{10}}{F_9}$. The first two are computed below.

$$\frac{F_2}{F_1} = \frac{1}{1} = 1 \qquad\qquad \frac{F_3}{F_2} = \frac{2}{1} = 2$$

15. Compare the ratios to the golden ratio. What do you notice?

Finding Out More

16. The golden ratio and the Fibonacci numbers appear in many contexts both inside and outside mathematics. For example, pineapples have scales in sets of 8, 13, and 21 rows.

Look for answers to some of these questions at the library or on the Internet.   Answers will vary.

- How do the golden ratio and the Fibonacci sequence appear in the natural world?

- How has the golden ratio been used by Leonardo da Vinci and other artists?

- How is the golden ratio applied in architecture?

- How is the golden ratio used in music?

1 You may want to ask *why* the dimensions are connected to the sums $1 + 1$, $2 + 1$, $3 + 2$, and so on.

2 You may want to assign this as extra credit or a long-term project.

Teacher Notes

On Your Own Exercises

★ indicates multi-step problem

Practice & Apply

Solve each equation using the quadratic formula, if possible.

1. $2x^2 + 5x = 0$

2. $5x^2 + 7x + 4 = 0$

3. $c^2 - 10 = 0$ $\pm\frac{\sqrt{40}}{2}$, or $\pm\sqrt{10}$

4. $b^2 + 10 = 0$

1. $\frac{-5 \pm \sqrt{25}}{4}$, or -2.5 and 0

2. $\frac{-7 \pm \sqrt{49 - 80}}{10}$; no solutions

4. $\pm\frac{\sqrt{-40}}{2}$; no solutions

5. factoring: $9x^2 - 16 = (3x - 4)(3x + 4)$, $x = \pm\frac{4}{3}$;
quadratic formula:
$\pm\frac{\sqrt{576}}{18} = \pm\frac{24}{18} = \pm\frac{4}{3}$

5. Solve the equation $9x^2 - 16 = 0$ by factoring and by using the quadratic formula.

6. Geometry The area of a photograph is 320 square centimeters. Its length is 2 cm more than twice its width. Write and solve an equation to find its dimensions. See Additional Answers.

7. Physical Science Suppose that, at some point into its flight, a particular rocket's height h, in meters, above sea level t seconds after launching depends on t according to the formula $h = 2t(60 - t)$.

   a. How many seconds after launching will the rocket return to sea level? 60 s

   b. Write and solve an equation to find when the rocket will be 1,200 m above sea level. See Additional Answers.

Find the number of solutions to each quadratic equation without actually solving the equation. Explain how you know your answers are correct.

8. no solutions because $b^2 - 4ac$ is negative (-8)

9. two solutions because $b^2 - 4ac$ is positive (16)

10. one solution because $b^2 - 4ac$ is 0

8. $x^2 + 2x + 3 = 0$

9. $x^2 - 2x - 3 = 0$

10. $9x^2 + 12x + 4 = 0$

11. A ball is thrown upward with a starting velocity of 40 feet per second from 5 feet above the ground. The equation describing the height h of the ball after t seconds is $h = 40t - 16t^2 + 5$.

   a. Will the ball travel as high as 100 feet? Explain.

   b. Will it travel as high as 15 feet? Explain.

  ★ **c. Challenge** Find the ball's maximum height. 30 ft

11a. No; to find when it might, you'd solve $40t - 16t^2 + 5 = 100$ or $-16t^2 + 40t - 95 = 0$, but since $b^2 - 4ac = -4{,}480$, which is negative, the equation has no solutions.

11b. Yes; to find whether it will, you'd solve $40t - 16t^2 + 5 = 15$ or $-16t^2 + 40t - 10 = 0$; since $b^2 - 4ac = 960$, which is positive, the equation has solutions.

 impactmath.com/self_check_quiz

LESSON 7.4 The Quadratic Formula **479**

On Your Own Exercises

Investigation 1,
  pp. 467–468
Practice & Apply: 1–5
Connect & Extend: 12–15

Investigation 2,
  pp. 469–471
Practice & Apply: 6, 7
Connect & Extend: 16, 17

Investigation 3,
  pp. 472–475
Practice & Apply: 8–11
Connect & Extend: 18, 19

Assign Anytime
Mixed Review: 20–25

Exercises 1–4:
You might want to suggest that it's probably a good idea to calculate $b^2 - 4ac$ first for any problem students do using the quadratic formula, since if it's negative there is no need to go further, and if it's positive or 0, they will need the calculation anyway. Students will look into this expression more in Investigation 3.

Exercise 4:
Students may notice by inspection that this equation has no solutions.

Additional Answers

6. If $w =$ width, then $w(2w + 2) = 320$, or $2w^2 + 2w - 320 = 0$; $\frac{-1 \pm \sqrt{641}}{2}$; the width is about 12.16 cm (-13.16 doesn't make sense in the context) and the length is about 26.32 cm.

7b. $-2t^2 + 120t - 1{,}200 = 0$; $\frac{60 \pm 20\sqrt{3}}{2} = 30 \pm 10\sqrt{3}$ or approximately 12.68 s and 47.32 s

• **Teaching notes continued on page A684**

Exercise 12:

This exercise brings up an interesting point about the number of equations with a particular set of solutions. In fact, there are an infinite number of quadratic equations with solutions 8 and -1.5. All of these equations are of the form $0 = a(x - 8)(x + 1.5)$, where a is any constant. You may want to bring this point up with students. In fact, the family of graphs with equations of the form $y = a(x - 8)(x + 1.5)$ all have the same x-intercepts (at 8 and -1.5) but different widths.

Exercises 14:

This problem relies on students' understanding that 0 is the only number that, when squared, is 0. Therefore, $x^2 - 2x - 2 = 0$; this equation can be solved using the quadratic formula or completing the square.

Connect & Extend

12a, b. See below.

12c. Possible answers: An advantage of using the quadratic formula is that you can be sure it will work. A disadvantage is that it can be extra work to rearrange an equation into the form $ax^2 + bx + c = 0$ and then apply the formula.

13a. Possible answer: $x = 1$

13b. $3x^2 + 1 = 4x$ or $3x^2 - 4x + 1 = 0$; $x = \frac{4 \pm \sqrt{16 - 12}}{6} = \frac{4 \pm 2}{6}$; $x = 1$ or $\frac{1}{3}$

14. The left side is equal to 0 when $x^2 - 2x - 2 = 0$, so the solutions are $1 \pm \sqrt{3}$.

12. When Lourdes solved the equation $2x^2 - 13x = 24$, she was surprised to find that the solutions were exactly 8 and -1.5. Ben said he thought this meant the equation could have been solved by factoring.

  a. Write a quadratic equation in factored form that has the solutions 8 and -1.5.

  b. Expand the factors to write an equation without parentheses. Was Ben correct? (Hint: If your equation contains a fraction, try multiplying by its denominator to get only integers for coefficients.)

  c. Write one advantage and one disadvantage of using the quadratic formula to solve the equation $2x^2 - 13x = 24$.

13. Consider the equation $3x + \frac{1}{x} = 4$.

  a. Do you see any obvious solutions to this equation?

  b. Now solve the equation using the quadratic formula. (Hint: First write an equivalent quadratic equation.) Check your solutions in the original equation.

Challenge Although these equations are not quadratic, the quadratic formula can help you solve them. Try to solve them, and explain your reasoning.

14. $(x^2 - 2x - 2)^2 = 0$ **15.** $x^3 - 2x^2 - 2x = 0$

16. History Here is a problem posed by the 12th-century Indian mathematician Bhaskara:*

The eighth part of a troop of monkeys, squared, was skipping in a grove and delighted with their sport. Twelve remaining monkeys were seen on the hill, amused with chattering to each other. How many were there in all?

That is, take $\frac{1}{8}$ of the entire troop and square the result. That number of monkeys, along with the 12 on the hill, form the entire troop. How many monkeys are there in the troop? Show your work. See Additional Answers.

12a. Possible answers: $(x - 8)(x + 1.5) = 0$ or $(x - 8)(2x + 3) = 0$

12b. $x^2 - 6.5x - 12 = 0$ or $2x^2 - 13x - 24 = 0$; Yes, he was correct.

15. Possible answer: The equation can be factored as $x(x^2 - 2x - 2) = 0$; at least one of the factors must be equal to 0 for the equation to be true. The first factor gives $x = 0$; the second gives $x = 1 \pm \sqrt{3}$. There are three solutions: 0, $1 + \sqrt{3}$, and $1 - \sqrt{3}$.

*Source: Victor Katz. *A History of Mathematics: An Introduction*. Reading, Mass.: Addison-Wesley, 1998.

480 CHAPTER 7 Solving Quadratic Equations

Additional Answers

16. Let m stand for the number of monkeys in the troop. Then $\left(\frac{m}{8}\right)^2 + 12 = m$, or $\frac{m^2}{64} + 12 = m$, or $m^2 + 768 = 64m$, or $m^2 - 64m + 768 = 0$. Using the quadratic formula, $m = \frac{64 \pm \sqrt{64^2 - 4(768)}}{2} = \frac{64 \pm \sqrt{1,024}}{2} = \frac{64 \pm 32}{2} = 16$ or 48. Both answers make sense.

In your
own
words

Describe the relationship between the graph of $y = ax^2 + bx + c$ and solutions of the equation $ax^2 + bx + c = d$. If the equation $ax^2 + bx + c = d$ has no solutions, what does that mean about the graph?

18c. no; Possible explanation: If $x^2 - x + 1 = 0$, $b^2 - 4ac = -3$, and there are no solutions.

18d. yes; Possible explanation: If $x^2 - x - 1 = 0$, $b^2 - 4ac = 5$, and there are two solutions.

18e.

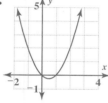

18f. If m is the minimum, $x^2 - x - m = 0$ has exactly one solution. So, $b^2 - 4ac = 1 + 4m$ must be 0, so $4m = -1$ and $m = -0.25$.

17. In Chapter 4, you solved inequalities involving linear relationships. For this problem, use the same ideas to solve inequalities involving quadratic relationships.

   a. First use the quadratic formula to solve $x^2 - 3x - 7 = 0$.

   b. Use the information from Part a to help graph $y = x^2 - 3x - 7$. You may want to plot some additional points.   See Additional Answers.

   Use your solutions and graph to solve each inequality.

   c. $x^2 - 3x - 7 < 0$ $-1.54 < x < 4.54$ **17a.** $\frac{3 \pm \sqrt{9 + 28}}{2} =$

   d. $x^2 - 3x \geq 7$ $x \leq -1.54$ or $x \geq 4.54$ $\frac{3 \pm \sqrt{37}}{2} \approx 4.54$

   e. $x^2 - 3x \leq 7$ $-1.54 \leq x \leq 4.54$ and -1.54

18. Consider the quadratic relationship $y = x(x - 1)$.

   a. For what values of x is $y = 0$? 0, 1

   b. Is y positive or negative for x values between those you listed in Part a? negative

   c. Can y ever be equal to -1? Explain.

   d. Can y ever be equal to 1? Explain.

   e. Sketch a graph of this relationship.

   f. Challenge Use your knowledge of the quadratic formula and your graph to find the *minimum* value of y.

19. **Challenge** You may have solved this problem in Chapter 4. Now you can use your knowledge of the quadratic formula to solve it in another way.

   Jermaine wants to construct a large picture frame using a 20-foot strip of wood.

   a. Express the height and area of the frame in terms of its width.

   b. Sketch a graph of the relationship between area and width. Is there a maximum area or a minimum area? See Additional Answers.

   c. Use the quadratic formula to find the maximum or minimum area for Jermaine's frame. Explain how you found your answer.

   d. What dimensions give this area? 5 ft by 5 ft

19a. If the width is w, the height is $\frac{1}{2}(20 - 2w) = 10 - w$. The area is $(10 - w)w = 10w - w^2$.

19c. If the frame has maximum area M, w satisfies the equation $10w - w^2 = M$ or $w^2 - 10w + M = 0$. For this equation, $b^2 - 4ac = 100 - 4M$. At the maximum, there is only one solution, so $100 - 4M = 0$ and $M = 25$.

LESSON 7.4 The Quadratic Formula **481**

Exercise 17:
Students need to understand that their answers to **Part a** are where the graph of the associated parabola crosses the x-axis (the x-intercepts). If they are confused by this, point out that when $y = 0$, the equation for the graph in **Part b** becomes the equation in Part a. It is a good idea to put both equations on the board

$$0 = x^2 - 3x - 7$$
$$y = x^2 - 3x - 7$$

and ask students about the difference between them. The first equation has at most two solutions. The second defines a relationship between x and y, and an infinite number of ordered pairs (x, y) satisfy this equation. These points lie on a parabola. The solutions to the first equation are the x-intercepts of the parabola associated with the second equation.

For **Part c,** students can look at the graph and ask themselves, "Where are the y values negative?" Likewise, for **Part d,** after they subtract 7 from both sides of the inequality, they can ask themselves, "Where are the y values positive or 0?" Note that the only difference between Parts c and e is the inclusion of the two endpoints of the interval.

Exercise 18f:
This exercise is similar to Problem 4 of Problem Set F; if students have trouble here, you might have them review how they solved that problem. They must substitute m, the minimum value of y, in the original equation; write the new equation in the form $ax^2 + bx + c = 0$; find $b^2 - 4ac$ in terms of m and set it equal to 0; and then solve for m.

Exercise 19:
The approach in this problem is very similar to the approach in Exercise 18.

• *Additional Answers on page A684*

Quick Check

Informal Assessment
Students should be able to:

✔ understand the origin of the quadratic formula

✔ use the quadratic formula to solve quadratic equations

✔ understand when the quadratic formula is appropriate to solve equations and when factoring is appropriate

✔ understand how to apply the quadratic formula to specific situations

✔ understand the significance of $b^2 - 4ac$ in the quadratic formula

Quick Quiz

1. For each equation, state the values of a, b, and c that would be used in the quadratic formula. Then use the quadratic formula to solve the equation.

   a. $3x^2 + x + 1 = 0$
   $a = 3$, $b = 1$, $c = 1$; no solution

   b. $x^2 - 7x = 2$ $a = 1$, $b = -7$, $c = -2$;
   $$\frac{7 \pm \sqrt{57}}{2}$$

   c. $x^2 - 12x + 36 = 0$
   $a = 1$, $b = -12$, $c = 36$; 6

Mixed Review

20. $B = 3(0.2^r)$
21. $B = 12(0.4^r)$

22. $b = 5{,}000(1.08)^t$

23. $b = c\left(\frac{15}{16}\right)^{24}$

24b. They increase, slowly at first and then more quickly.

25a. Possible answer: 40 blue, 60 orange

25b. Possible answer: 27 blue, 73 orange

482 CHAPTER 7 Solving Quadratic Equations

Write an equation to represent the value of B in terms of r.

20.

r	B
0	3
1	0.6
2	0.12
3	0.024
4	0.0048

21.

r	B
0	12
1	4.8
2	1.92
3	0.768
4	0.3072

In Exercises 22 and 23, write an equation to represent the situation.

22. **Economics** the balance b in a savings account at the end of any year t if $5,000 is deposited initially and the account earns 8% interest per year

23. **Life Science** the number of bacteria b left in a sample after 24 hours if one-sixteenth of the remaining colony of c bacteria dies every hour

24. Describe how the y values of each graph change as the x values increase.

   a. Graph a They increase at a steady rate.

   b. Graph b

   c. Graph c
   They decrease, quickly at first and then more slowly.

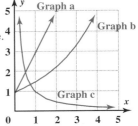

25. **Probability** Kendra fills a jar with 100 chips, some blue and some orange. She asks Ignacio to guess how many of each color are in the jar.

   a. Ignacio reaches in without looking and removes 10 chips, 4 blue and 6 orange. What reasonable guess might he make for the number of chips of each color in the jar?

   b. Ignacio takes out 5 more chips, and all are orange. What reasonable guess might he now make for the number of chips of each color in the jar?

   c. Kendra tells Ignacio there are actually three times as many orange chips as blue chips in the jar. How many of each are there?   25 blue, 75 orange

---

2. Write a quadratic equation that would be easier to solve by factoring than by using the quadratic formula. Possible answer: $x^2 - 4 = 0$

3. The base of a triangle is 4 cm more than twice the height. Find its base and height if the triangle's area is 15 cm². height = 3 cm, base = 10 cm

4. Find the number of solutions to each quadratic equation without actually solving the equation.

   a. $x^2 - 3x + 4 = 0$ none

   b. $x^2 + 16 = 0$ none

   c. $x^2 - 4x - 4 = 0$ 2

• **Quick Quiz continued on page A684**

Chapter Summary

Chapter Summary
This summary helps students recall the major topics of the chapter.

Vocabulary
Students should be able to explain each of the terms listed in the vocabulary section.

Problem-Solving Strategies and Applications
The questions in this section help students review and apply the important mathematical ideas and problem-solving strategies developed in the chapter. The questions are organized by mathematical highlights. The highlights correspond to those in "The Big Picture" chart on page 429a.

VOCABULARY
factoring
trinomial

Quadratic equations can be solved with several methods. In this chapter, you began with backtracking to solve quadratics of a particular form as well as equations requiring finding reciprocals, taking square roots, and changing signs. You also learned how to solve some quadratic equations by *factoring* and using the fact that when a product is equal to 0, at least one of the factors must be equal to 0.

As these methods don't work well for all quadratic equations, you also learned how to *complete the square* and to use the *quadratic formula*:

$$x = \frac{-b \pm \sqrt{b^2 - 4ac}}{2a}$$

Strategies and Applications

The questions in this section will help you review and apply the important ideas and strategies developed in this chapter.

Using backtracking to undo square roots, squares, reciprocals, and changes of sign

1. Identify the operation that undoes each given operation. Note the cautions, if any, you must take when undoing the given operation.

  a. taking the square root   **b.** taking the reciprocal

  c. changing sign   **d.** squaring

1a. squaring

1b. taking the reciprocal

1c. changing sign

1d. taking the square root; consider positive and negative roots

Indicate whether you can solve each equation directly by backtracking. If so, draw a flowchart and find the solution. If not, explain why not.

2. $\sqrt{2x + 3} - 4 = 7$ See below.

3. $\frac{24}{y - 7} = 4$ See below.

4. $3a - \sqrt{2a + 3} - 4 = 7$

5. $3(v - 1)^2 + v = 8$

6. $3 - (11w - 3) = 72$ See below.

7. $(4n + 5)^2 - 3 = 6$ See Additional Answers.

4. No; the input variable appears twice.

5. No; the input variable appears twice.

2. yes; 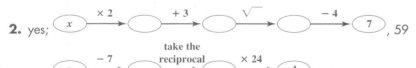 , 59

3. yes;  , 13

6. yes;  , $^-6$

Additional Answers

7. yes;  , $^-2$ and $^-0.5$

8. can't factor with integers; Possible explanation: This is $g^2 + 3g + 6 = 0$, but the factors of 6 are 1, 6 and 2, 3; neither pair adds to 3.

9. yes;
$81x^2 + 18x + 1 = 0$,
$(9x + 1)^2 = 0$,
$9x + 1 = 0$; $x = -\frac{1}{9}$

15. Possible answer:
$12x^2 + 5x - 3 = 0$

16. Complete the square using the equation $ax^2 + bx + c = 0$.

17. This is the quadratic formula, which works only if d is 0.

18. If the value is negative, there are no solutions; if it's 0, there is one solution; if it's positive, there are two solutions.

Just the facts

The air resistance of a particular race car (in a unit called Newtons) might be given by the quadratic equation $F = 0.4v^2$, where v is the car's velocity in m/s.

Solving quadratic equations by factoring

Tell whether you can solve each equation by factoring using integers. If you can, do so, and show your work. If not, explain why not.

8. $g^2 + 3g = -6$

9. $81x^2 + 1 = -18x$

10. $3k^2 - 5k - 12 = 12 + 2k^2$

11. $4w^2 - 9 = 0$

12. $(x + 5)(x - 1) = -8$

13. $2s^2 - 4s + 2 = 0$

10–13. See Additional Answers.

Solving quadratic equations by completing the square

14. Explain what it means to solve by "completing the square." Use the equation $4x^2 + 20x - 8 = 0$ to illustrate your explanation. See below.

15. Give an example of a quadratic equation that is possible, but not easy, to solve by completing the square.

Understanding and applying the quadratic formula

16. How was the quadratic formula derived? That is, what technique or method was used and on what equation?

17. Suppose a, b, c, and d are all numbers not equal to 0. Explain why the solutions of $ax^2 + bx + c = d$ are not $x = \frac{-b \pm \sqrt{b^2 - 4ac}}{2a}$.

18. How can you determine the number of solutions of a quadratic equation in the form $ax^2 + bx + c = 0$ using the value of $b^2 - 4ac$?

14. Possible answer: Completing the square means to write the equation as a perfect square with a number added or subtracted. For example, $4x^2 + 20x - 8 = 0$ can be rewritten $4x^2 + 20x + 25 - 33 = 0$, or $(2x + 5)^2 - 33 = 0$. Then you can solve by doing the same thing to both sides: $(2x + 5)^2 = 33$, so $2x + 5 = \pm\sqrt{33}$ and $x = \frac{-5 \pm \sqrt{33}}{2}$.

484 CHAPTER 7 Solving Quadratic Equations

Additional Answers

10. yes; $k^2 - 5k - 24 = 0$, $(k - 8)(k + 3) = 0$; $k = -3, 8$

11. yes; $(2w + 3)(2w - 3) = 0$; $w = \pm 1.5$

12. yes; $x^2 + 4x + 3 = 0$, $(x + 1)(x + 3) = 0$; $x = -1, -3$

13. yes; $2(s^2 - 2s + 1) = 0$, $2(s - 1)^2 = 0$; $s = 1$

Demonstrating Skills

Factor each expression.

19. $a^2 + 3a$ **20.** $2b^2 - 2$ **21.** $c^2 + 14c + 49$

22. $8d^2 - 8d + 2$ **23.** $e^2 + 8e - 9$ **24.** $f^2 + 7f + 10$

Write an expression equivalent to the given expression by completing the square.

25. $4g^2 + 12g - 3$ **26.** $h^2 - 10h + 7$ **27.** $2j^2 + 24j$

Tell how many solutions each equation has. (Do not solve them.)

28. $k^2 + 10 = 20k - 90$ 1

29. $2m^2 + 3m + 3 = {}^-5$ 0

Solve each equation, if possible.

30. $\sqrt{3n + 1} = 13$ 56

31. $\frac{60}{-(2p - 3)} = 12$ ${}^-1$

32. $(7q + 3)(q - 8) = 0$ $-\frac{3}{7}$, 8

33. $(10r + 4)(5r + 4) = {}^-2$ $-\frac{3}{5}$

34. $4s^2 + 3s - 40 = 3s - 41$ no solution

35. $t^2 - 100 = 0$ ± 10

36. $2u^2 - 4u = 14$

37. $9v^2 - 3 = 4v^2 + 32$

38. $5w^2 = 8w$ $0, \frac{8}{5}$

39. $3 - 9x - x^2 = 17$ ${}^-2$, ${}^-7$

19. $a(a + 3)$
20. $2(b + 1)(b - 1)$
21. $(c + 7)^2$
22. $2(2d - 1)^2$
23. $(e + 9)(e - 1)$
24. $(f + 5)(f + 2)$
25. $(2g + 3)^2 - 12$
26. $(h - 5)^2 - 18$
27. $2(j + 6)^2 - 72$

CHAPTER 8

Functions and Their Graphs

Chapter Overview

In this chapter, students get a formal introduction to a type of mathematical relationship called a *function.* A mathematical function produces a single output for each input and can be described with a graph or an equation.

Students will consider both the domain and range of various functions, and they will use graphs and equations to find the maximum and minimum values of functions. They will also learn how to translate graphs by modifying their function rules.

Much attention is focused on the graphs of quadratic functions. The line of symmetry and the coordinates of the vertex can be found by inspecting graphs and by completing the square of quadratic expressions. Using x-intercepts, along with the coordinates of the vertex, students can quickly and easily sketch the graphs.

In the second investigation, students will solve equations of the form $f(x) = g(x)$ by locating the points where the graphs of f and g intersect.

the **Big Picture**

Chapter 8 Highlights	Links to the Past	Links to the Future
Understanding functions and describing the domain and range of a function (8.1)	**Courses 1 and 2, Chapters 1–7:** Working with formulas and relationships **Course 2, Chapters 2 and 6:** Finding input values that make an expression undefined **Chapter 7:** Backtracking with equations that have no solution	**Trigonometry:** Understanding ranges of various trigonometric functions **Trigonometry:** Defining inverse trigonometric functions using restricted domains **High School and College:** Working with polynomial and other functions
Finding the maximum and minimum values of quadratic functions (8.1, 8.2)	**Chapter 2:** Working with quadratic equations **Chapter 7:** Solving quadratic equations	**Precalculus:** Finding local and absolute maxima and minima of functions
Understanding and using graphs of quadratic functions (8.2)	**Chapter 2:** Working with quadratic equations **Chapter 2:** Solving quadratic equations using graphs and tables **Chapter 5:** Performing translations	**High School:** Graphing trigonometric and other functions
Solving equations involving two functions (8.2)	**Course 2:** Using graphs to estimate solutions of equations **Chapter 4:** Solving systems of equations graphically	**High School and College:** Defining regions on a coordinate plane using multiple equations **High School and College:** Solving polynomial equations

Lesson Objectives	Pacing	Materials	NCTM Standards	Hot Topics
8.1 Functions page 487b • To understand the definition of a function • To understand different ways of representing functions • To identify functions in a variety of contexts and representations • To describe the domain of a given function • To find the maximum or minimum value of a function from its graph	5 class periods	• Graphing calculators • Transparency of Master 49 (optional) • 5-inch-by-8-inch cards • Rulers • Scissors • Tape	2, 6, 7, 9, 10	
8.2 Graphs of Functions page 513b • To understand how horizontal and vertical translations of a graph are related to the equation of the function • To specify the range of a function and understand the relationship between the range of a function and its maximum or minimum point • To use *x*-intercepts and completing the square to find the line of symmetry and vertex of a parabola • To use graphs to find approximate solutions to equations	5 class periods	• Tracing paper • Graphing calculators • Overhead graphing calculator (optional) • Master 50 (optional) * • GeoMirrors	2, 3, 6, 7, 9, 10	

* Included in Impact Mathematics Manipulative Kit

Key to NCTM Curriculum and Evaluation Standards: 1=Number and Operations, 2=Algebra, 3=Geometry, 4=Measurement, 5=Data Analysis and Probability, 6=Problem Solving, 7=Reasoning and Proof, 8=Communication, 9=Connections, 10=Representation

Standard Assessment

Impact Mathematics offers three types of formal assessment. The Chapter 8 Review and Self-Assessment in the Student Edition serves as a self-assessment tool for students. In the Teacher's Guide, a Quick Quiz at the end of each lesson allows you to check students' understanding before moving to the next lesson. The Assessment Resources include blackline masters for chapter and quarterly tests.

- **Student Edition** Chapter 8 Review and Self-Assessment, pages 538–541
- **Teacher's Guide** Quick Quizzes, pages 512, 537
- **Assessment Resources** Chapter 8 Test Form A, pages 211–214; Chapter 8 Test Form B, pages 215–218

Ongoing Assessment

Impact Mathematics provides numerous opportunities for you to assess your students informally as they work through the investigations. Share & Summarize questions help you determine whether students understand the important ideas of an investigation. If students are struggling, Troubleshooting tips provide suggestions for helping them. On the Spot Assessment notes appear throughout the teaching notes. They give you suggestions for preventing or remedying common student errors. Assessment Forms in the Assessment Resources provide convenient ways to record student progress.

- **Student Edition** Share & Summarize, pages 492, 496, 499, 502, 517, 522, 524, 527
- **Teacher's Guide** On the Spot Assessment, pages T493, T500, T517 Troubleshooting, pages T492, T496, T499, T502, T517, T522, T524, T527
- **Assessment Resources** Chapter 8 Assessment Checklists, page 296

Alternative Assessment, Portfolios, and Journal Ideas

The alternative assessment items in *Impact Mathematics* are perfect for inclusion in student portfolios and journals. The In Your Own Words feature in the Student Edition gives students a chance to write about mathematical ideas. The Performance Assessment items in the Assessment Resources provide rich, open-ended problems, ideal for take-home or group assessment.

- **Student Edition** In Your Own Words, pages 511, 535
- **Assessment Resources** Chapter 8 Performance Assessments, pages 219–220

Assessment Resources

The Assessment Resources provide a chapter test in two equivalent forms, along with additional performance items. The performance items can be used in a variety of ways. They are ideal for take-home assessment or in-class group assessment.

- Chapter 8 Test Form A, pages 211–214
- Chapter 8 Test Form B, pages 215–218
- Chapter 8 Performance Assessment, pages 219–220
- Chapter 8 Assessment Solutions, pages 221–224

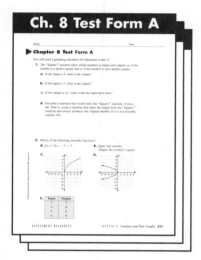

Ch. 8 Test Form A

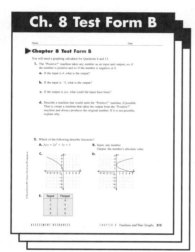

Ch. 8 Test Form B

Ch. 8 Perf. Assess

Additional Resources

- **Math Skills Maintenance Workbook,** 25, 28, 33, 34
- **StudentWorks™ CD-ROM**
- **Reading and Writing in the Mathematics Classroom**
- **Using the Internet in the Mathematics Classroom**

ExamView® Pro

Use ExamView® Pro Testmaker CD-ROM to:

- Create Multiple versions of tests.
- Create Modified tests for Inclusion students with one mouse click.
- Edit existing questions and Add your own questions.
- Build tests aligned with state standards using built-in State Curriculum Correlations.
- Change English tests to Spanish with one mouse click and vice versa.

CHAPTER 8

Introduce

A map is an excellent visual example of the use of functions. For each location on Earth, a map has a corresponding location. And the methods by which maps are created—called *projections*—are functions themselves.

Read the section titled "Flattening the Globe" with your students. You may want to tell students that the mathematical objects they are about to study, functions, are also called *mappings*. (Projections of Earth are actually a special kind of mapping, because each map point can be traced back to exactly one point on Earth. This is not always true with functions.)

Think About It

A net is a two-dimensional representation of a three-dimensional object.

Functions and Their Graphs

Real-Life Math

Flattening the Globe Creating an accurate map of the world is difficult to do because you must show a three-dimensional surface using only two dimensions. Mathematical functions called *projections* help cartographers create maps. A projection assigns every point on a three-dimensional globe to a point on a two-dimensional surface, in effect *flattening* the globe.

There are many different types of projections, some of which create very interesting maps. The Mercator projection you see in the background of these two pages exaggerates the areas of landmasses farthest from the equator, such as Greenland and Antarctica. On this type of map, Greenland looks like it is almost the size of Africa, when in fact it has only about 7% of Africa's area. Goode's interrupted projection reduces this distortion, but breaks the oceans and Antarctica into pieces.

Think About It In geometry, you studied nets. How are nets of geometric solids similar to projections?

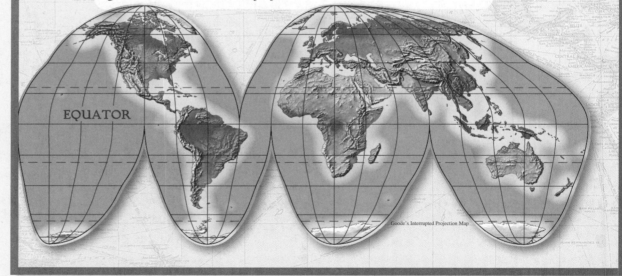
EQUATOR

Goode's Interrupted Projection Map

Family Letter

Dear Student and Family Members,

Our next chapter is about functions and their graphs. The concept of functions is central to algebra and has been a major thread throughout this course, although the term *function* has not yet been used.

One useful way to think about a function is as a machine that takes some input (a number or something else) and produces an output. The output must be *unique*, meaning you get only one output for a particular input. Also, the output must be *consistent*: you get that output every time you use the same input. For example, in this machine, if 3 is the input, it goes into the machine and is multiplied by 5, so the output is 15. Every time you input 3 you will get the same answer, 15.

Functions are often expressed as mathematical sentences. For example, each of these rules describes the function represented by the machine above: multiply by 5.

$$y = 5x \qquad f(x) = 5x \qquad g(t) = 5t$$

Once we have looked at functions using input-output machines, we will go on to use graphs for finding the maximum and minimum values of functions. We will also use functions to solve problems. For instance, if you have 6 meters of fencing for a rabbit pen and you want the greatest area possible, you can use the function $A(L) = L(3 - L)$ to determine that each side of the pen should have 1.5 meters of fencing.

Vocabulary Along the way, we be learning about these new vocabulary terms:

domain	**range**
function	**x-intercepts**

What can you do at home?

During the next few weeks, your student may show interest in functions and their graphs. You might help him or her think of some situations that can be represented as functions, like the following.

Input: the total restaurant bill   Output: the tip at 15%
Input: the side length of a square   Output: the area of that square
Input: number of adult moviegoers   Output: the total cost for tickets at $8.00 each

Another version of the Family Letter, available in English and Spanish, is found in the Teaching Resources. You may want to send a copy of this letter home with your students.

Mathematical Background

The concept of a function is perhaps the most important and unifying idea in all of modern mathematics. Because functions play such a critically important role, the NCTM *Principles and Standards for School Mathematics* calls for including the study of functions at *all* grade levels (K–12) as one of their five content standards, Standard 2: Patterns, Functions, and Algebra.

Functions and Function Machines

The following wonderful analogy is used in this chapter to help make the idea of a function clear. Think of a function as a machine with one input slot and one output slot. When you put an object in the input slot, the machine produces a corresponding output.

Call the machine *f* and the input *x*. Then the corresponding output is denoted by *f(x)*. This is most often read "*f* of *x*," but it can also be read "the *value* of *f* at *x*" or "the *image* of *x* under *f*."

The concept of a function is one that students have already been working with, unknowingly, not just in this course but in previous mathematics work as well. However, students often focus on the *process* of assigning an output value to an input value; a richer concept of function, which will become more important as students advance in their mathematics studies, uses functions as mathematical objects themselves, much in the same way that *numbers* are mathematical objects. This notion can be difficult for students to grasp, especially when they are first introduced to function notation.

In addition to helping students start to think of a function as an object itself, the machine analogy can help them think about many of the basic ideas relating to functions in a "concrete" way.

The machine model can help students when they study equivalent functions in more advanced mathematics courses. By thinking of function machines as "black boxes"—meaning machines that we know *only* in terms of their input-output behavior without looking at the internal mechanism by which they actually transform the input into the output—students can focus on the relationship and not on the evaluation process. For example, the functions $f(x) = |x|$ and $g(x) = \sqrt{x^2}$ are equivalent because they produce identical outputs for the same inputs. However, the *processes* by which these two are evaluated are very different; in fact, one cannot algebraically transform one function into the other except by recognizing that they are equivalent functions.

• *Teaching notes continued on page A685*

8.1

Functions

Objectives

▶ To understand the definition of a function

▶ To understand different ways of representing functions

▶ To identify functions in a variety of contexts and representations

▶ To describe the domain of a given function

▶ To find the maximum or minimum value of a function from its graph

Overview (pacing: about 5 class periods)

The concept of a function is central to algebra and has been a major thread throughout this course, though the term *function* has not been used before. Now that students have developed an intuitive sense of what a function is, they can be introduced to the formal definition. Functions are often troublesome since students disconnect them from the relationships they have already studied.

In this lesson, students work with functions using familiar relationships and a familiar metaphor: the input-output machine from their study of exponents in Course 2. You may want to point out this consistency to students. The lesson also includes functions other than numerical, so students get a broad view of what functions are and do.

Some students may grasp this new material quickly while others struggle. Throughout the lesson you will find "Extra Challenge" and "Early Finishers" problems to keep those students engaged. When there are multiple steps to be repeated for a problem, students who struggle might benefit from some support organizing their work.

Advance Preparation

You may want to prepare a transparency of Master 49 for Problem Set E.

	Summary	Materials	On Your Own Exercises	Assessment Opportunities
Investigation 1 page T490	Students look at functions using input-output machines.		Practice & Apply: 1–9, pp. 504–506 Connect & Extend: 23–26, p. 510 Mixed Review: 36–50, pp. 512–513	Share & Summarize, pages T492, 492 Troubleshooting, page T492
Investigation 2 page T492	Students describe functions using rules and graphs. They are introduced to function notation and domain.	• Graphing calculators • Transparency of Master 49 (optional)	Practice & Apply: 10–16, pp. 506–507 Connect & Extend: 27–30, pp. 510–511 Mixed Review: 36–50, pp. 512–513	On the Spot Assessment, page T493 Share & Summarize, pages T496, 496 Troubleshooting, page T496
Investigation 3 page T497	Students use graphs for finding approximate maximum and minimum values of functions.	• Graphing calculators	Practice & Apply: 17–20, pp. 507–508 Connect & Extend: 31–33, p. 511 Mixed Review: 36–50, pp. 512–513	Share & Summarize, pages T499, 499 Troubleshooting, page T499
Investigation 4 page T499	Students maximize area and minimize perimeter for rectangles.	• Graphing calculators	Practice & Apply: 21–22, pp. 508–509 Connect & Extend: 34, 35, pp. 511–512 Mixed Review: 36–50, pp. 512–513	On the Spot Assessment, page T500 Share & Summarize, pages T502, 502 Troubleshooting, page T502 Informal Assessment, page 512 Quick Quiz, page 513
Lab Investigation page T502	Students examine boxes of different sizes for a fixed surface area.	• 5-inch-by-8-inch cards • Rulers • Graphing calculators • Scissors • Tape		

Introduce

This lesson introduces students to the concept of a function by building on their knowledge of relationships between two variables.

Begin by asking students to consider the two graphs on page 488, one representing a relationship between the distance a car travels and the time it takes, and the other between the height of a ball and the horizontal distance the ball has traveled. Explain that students will now study these kinds of relationships once again, this time looking at a special set of relationships called *functions*.

1 Define a *function* as a relationship between an input variable and an output variable in which there is only one output for each input. The uniqueness of the output is a concept that often confuses students, and they will encounter this concept again later in the lesson. For now, just concentrate on the relationship between inputs and outputs. Ask students to identify the input and output for each of the graphs they examined.

Note: As they work through the chapter, you may find that students tend to think of functions as *processes* rather than *relationships*. Try to emphasize that the function is the machine itself, not the process of assigning the output to the input.

About the Mathematics

The more formal definition of a function focuses on ordered pairs, not producing outputs: a function is a relation in which, for each ordered pair, every *x*-coordinate has exactly one *y*-coordinate. While this definition is more accurate than treating a function like a process, it can be difficult for students to understand.

When formally describing a function, one should specify the domain. However, when students are first learning about functions, it's better to give them time to understand the greater concept first; for that reason, domain is not defined until Investigation 2. So, it's possible with these machines to try an input that has no output. (You may want students to think of a red light that goes on when the input is not allowable.) With a real, mathematical function, that is not possible: you simply cannot input something that is not in the domain.

2 Explain to students that one useful way to think about functions is to use the idea of a machine: it takes some input (a number or something else) and produces an output. Read together and discuss the introductory material, being sure students understand the two characteristics of functions described at the bottom of page 488 and the top of page 489. The two characteristics are as follows:

The output must be unique. A candy machine analogy is useful here. If you press the button on a candy machine for a Super Bar, you want only a Super Bar to come out, not an Extra Bar or some other bar.

8.1 Functions

In your study of algebra, you have analyzed many relationships between variables—relationships like these:

A car traveling along a highway at 55 miles per hour for t hours will cover a distance of $55t$ miles. This can be represented by the equation $d = 55t$.

When a quarterback throws a football, the height of the ball in yards when it has traveled d yards might be described by the equation $h = 2 + 0.8d - 0.02d^2$.

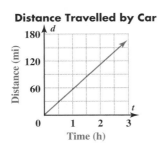

Distance Travelled by Car

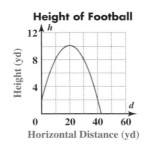

Height of Football

VOCABULARY
function

Many of the relationships you have studied, including those above, have a special name: they are called *functions*. In mathematics, a **function** is a relationship between an input variable and an output variable in which there is only one output for each input.

- In the car example, the input variable is the time spent on the highway. The output variable is the distance traveled. Since there can be only one distance traveled for any given time, the relationship is a function. In this case, the distance traveled is a *function of* the time.

- In the football example, the input variable is the horizontal distance the ball has traveled, and the output variable is the ball's height. Since there can be only one height for any given horizontal distance, the relationship is a function. In this case, the height is a *function of* the horizontal distance.

One way to think about a function is to imagine a machine that takes some input—a number, a word, or something else (depending on what the function is)—and produces an output.

For example, suppose you put 10 into a function machine for the football example. Since the machine is a function, the output must be *unique*. If you put 10 into the machine, it can give an output of 8, but it can't give both 8 and some other number.

1. • Introduce the term function.

   • Ask students to identify the inputs and outputs in the graphs above.

2. Discuss the machine model for functions.

488 CHAPTER 8 Functions and Their Graphs

LESSON 8.1 Functions **488**

The output must be consistent. Using the candy machine analogy, if you repeatedly press the button for a Super Bar, you want to get a Super Bar every time.

Point out that it is possible that two or more inputs will produce the same output. In the candy machine example, it is possible to have two buttons that say Super Bar. In the football example, the football-height machine will produce 8 when you put 10 or 30 into it. You can have students verify this.

End the introduction by asking students whether the square root relationship is a function. For example, you might say:

> Is a machine that outputs the square root of a positive number a function?

Students should answer no, since every positive number has two square roots. If you put in 16, the output can be 4 or ⁻4.

Think & Discuss

Have the class volunteer answers to the question of why there is only one possible output for each given input.

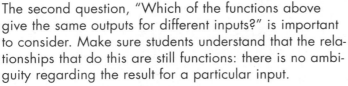

The second question, "Which of the functions above give the same outputs for different inputs?" is important to consider. Make sure students understand that the relationships that do this are still functions: there is no ambiguity regarding the result for a particular input.

In determining why the second set of relationships are not functions, make sure students give specific counterexamples. For instance, for the first example, if the number were 10, the output could be 5 or 6 or any other number less than 10. The output is not unique.

The "state in which a city can be found" function may be difficult for some students. They might not realize that many states can each have a city with the same name.

Extra Challenge You may want to challenge students to change each "nonfunction" into a function by altering either the input or the output definition. One example is given here for each relationship.

- Input: a number
  Output: 3 less than the number

- Input: a city name
  Output: the number of states that contain a city with that name

- Input: a whole number
  Output: the smallest factor of that number not equal to 1

- Input: the side length of a square
  Output: the area of that square

- Input: a person
  Output: the number of living grandparents that person has

- Input: a word
  Output: that word with the letters written backward

For a function machine, the output must be consistent. That is, the machine will always give the same output for the same input. If you get an output of 8 for an input of 10, then every time you put 10 into the machine, the output will be 8.

It *is* possible that two (or more) inputs will produce the same output. For example, the football-height function machine will produce 8 when you put 10 or 30 into it. (Try it!)

If more than one output is possible for a given input, the relationship is *not* a function. For example, a machine that outputs the square roots of a positive number can't be a function, because every positive number has *two* square roots.

① Every integer is either even or odd. No number is both even and odd, so no number would give more than one output.

input: 10
input: 30
$h = 2 + 0.8d - 0.02d^2$
output: 8

② The area of a square depends only on its side length. Given the side length, the area will be the square of that, so there is only one possible output for a given input.

Think & Discuss

③ Every social security number identifies a unique person. Every person has just one birth date.

④ Every word has one unique first letter.

Here are some examples of functions. For each function, explain why there is only one possible output for each input.

⑤–⑩: See Additional Answers.

- Input: a number
  Output: twice that number

For every number, there is only one number that is its double.

× 2

- Input: the name of a state
  Output: the state's capital

Every state has only one capital.

Capital?

- Input: an integer   See ①.
  Output: classification as even or odd

- Input: the side length of a square   See ②.
  Output: the area of that square

- Input: a person's social security number
  Output: that person's birth date   See ③.

- Input: a word   See ④.
  Output: the first letter of that word

Which of the functions above give the same outputs for different inputs? Explain.   See ⑤.

The following relationships are *not* functions. For each, explain why there might be more than one output for some inputs.

- Input: a number   See ⑥.
  Output: a number less than that number

- Input: a whole number   See ⑧.
  Output: a factor of that number

- Input: a person
  Output: the name of that person's grandparent
  Every person has four biological grandparents, so there are at least four possible outputs.

- Input: a city name   See ⑦.
  Output: the name of the state in which that city can be found

- Input: the side length of a rectangle   See ⑨.
  Output: the area of that rectangle

- Input: a word   See ⑩.
  Output: that word with the letters rearranged

• **Additional Answers continued on page A686**

Investigation 1

In this investigation, students look at functions using the machine metaphor. Function machines are not a new concept; they have been widely used as a way of introducing students to the structural approach to algebra, focusing on operations. Students have seen these machines in their work with exponents. In that case, the machines were identified by an operation and a number, such as "× 2."

Let students move directly from the Think & Discuss on page 489 into Problem Set A and through Problem Set C.

Problem Set A **Suggested Grouping: Pairs**
Make sure students understand how Function A works before they begin to answer the questions. When two machines are hooked together to form a more complicated function, the output of the first machine becomes the input of the second.

Hooking up two functions in this way emulates *composition of functions.* Here, the individual machines each use a single operation to produce their outputs. As noted earlier, students have used such machines, labeled with an operation and number; they have even worked with hookups in Course 2. Go over **Problem 1** together before they continue, to make sure they are using the machines correctly.

Problem 3 requires students to work backward to find the answer. It is important for students to notice that to "undo" the function machine, they need to subtract 7 first, and then take half of the answer. Their previous work in backtracking should be a help here.

The answer to **Problem 4** has to do with the fact that the function is linear rather than with the concept of a function. In general, a function could have more than one input for a specific output.

Problem 8 asks students to create a model of the process they used to solve Problem 3. It might be helpful for students to draw a hookup of Function A and its "undoing" function (so there should be four machines total) to check that they always get back the original number. In future mathematics courses, students will learn that this is called the *inverse* of the original function.

Extra Challenge Throughout Investigation 1, questions such as these are challenging and fun for the number-in, number-out machines:

What input produces itself as an output? (Such numbers are called *fixed points.*)

What input produces twice itself as an output?

If the output is positive, what can you say about the possible inputs?

Investigation Function Machines

You can describe a function in various ways—such as using words, symbols, graphs, or machines. In this investigation, you will think about functions as machines.

Problem Set A

Two machines that each perform one operation have been hooked together to form a more complicated function called Function A. Function A takes an input, doubles it, and then produces 7 more than that result as an output.

Function A

1. If the input is 5, what is the output?   17

2. If the input is ⁻4, what is the output?   ⁻1

3. If the output is ⁻10, what could the input have been?   ⁻8.5

4. Is there more than one answer to Problem 3? Explain why or why not.

5. If the input is some number *x*, what is the output?   2*x* + 7

6. Function A is called a *linear function*. Explain why that makes sense.

7. Function B is represented by this machine hookup. Is it the same as Function A? Explain.

Function B

8. If possible, describe a hookup that would "undo" Function A. That is, create a hookup so that if you put a number into Function A and then put the output into your hookup, you *always* get back your original number. If it isn't possible, explain why not.

4. no; Possible explanation: If you double a number, there's only one possible answer; when you add 7 to that answer, there's still only one possible result.

6. Possible answer: It's a linear relationship like those we've studied throughout the year. The graph of the function would be a line.

7. no; Possible explanation: The same input will produce different outputs in the two machines. For example, an input of 0 produces output 7 in Function A and output 14 in Function B; Function A = 2*x* + 7 and Function B = (*x* + 7)2.

1
- You may have students work in pairs.
- Be sure students understand how the hookup works.

2   Discuss Problem 1 with the class before they continue.

Problem-Solving Strategy

Work backward

Problem Set B Suggested Grouping: Pairs

In this problem set, students concentrate on the "Prime?" machine. This machine is a function, but there are several inputs that yield the same output.

Problem 4 is a bit tricky; in fact, 1 is not a prime number. A prime number is any number with two factors, itself and 1. Of course, 1 has only one factor: itself. Students may remember this from the work they did with stretching and shrinking machines in Course 2.

Problem 7 challenges students to come up with a machine that undoes the "Prime?" machine. This is an impossible task; if the output were *yes*, there would be an infinite number of inputs that could have given this result.

About the Mathematics

The prime machine is a case in which the inverse of a function is not a function. Only a function that has a *one-to-one correspondence*—for which each output can be matched to only one possible input—will have an inverse function. Whenever there is more than one input that can result in the same output, the inverse will not be a function.

 Problem Set C Suggested Grouping: Pairs

In this problem set, students look at the "3" machine, which takes input numbers and always outputs 3.

In **Problem 3,** students should realize that an infinite number of inputs can produce an output of 3.

 Problem 5 is a good problem to go over with the entire class. Students should note the similarity between the "3" machine and the "Prime?" machine: each machine gives a unique output for each input, but more than one input can result in the same output.

Problem 6 introduces the term *constant function*.

Problem 7 reinforces the idea from Problem 7 of Problem Set B: it is impossible to create a machine that undoes this function. This notion of when students can undo a function by creating another function will be important to them in future mathematics courses.

Access for all Learners

Early Finishers Ask students to describe a machine that outputs numbers but is not a function. **Possible answers: a machine that outputs a square root of the input; a machine that takes a sentence and outputs the number of letters in one of its words**

Problem Set B

The "Prime?" machine takes positive whole numbers as inputs and outputs *yes* if a number is prime and *no* if a number is not prime.

5. Any prime number; 2, 3, 5, 7, and 11 are the first few possibilities.

7. It's not possible. There is no way to know, just from the output *yes*, which prime number was entered. Likewise, there is no way to know from the output *no* which composite number was entered.

1. If the input is 3, what is the output? *yes*

2. If the input is 2, what is the output? *yes*

3. If the input is 100, what is the output? *no*

4. If the input is 1, what is the output? *no*

5. If the output is *yes*, what could the input have been?

6. Is there more than one answer to Problem 5? Explain why or why not. Yes; any prime number will produce the output *yes*.

7. If possible, describe a machine that would undo the "Prime?" machine. That is, create a machine that takes the output from the "Prime?" machine and always produces the original number. If it isn't possible, explain why not.

Problem Set C Answers

3. Any number; 0, $-\frac{1}{2}$, 101, and π are some examples.

4. Yes; every input produces the output 3, so it could have been any number.

5. For any input, there is only one possible output: 3. No input produces more than one output.

6. Possible answer: Because it always gives the same constant value as an output.

7. No machine will work. There is no way to know, just from the output 3, which number was entered.

Problem Set C

The "3" machine takes numbers as inputs and always outputs the number 3.

1. If the input is 17, what is the output? 3

2. If the input is $^-2$, what is the output? 3

3. If the output is 3, what could the input have been?

4. Is there more than one answer to Problem 3? Explain why or why not.

5. Explain why "3" is a function.

6. The function "3" is a *constant function*. Explain why that name makes sense.

7. If possible, describe a machine that would undo the "3" machine. That is, create a machine that takes the output from the "3" machine and always produces your original number. If it's not possible, explain why not.

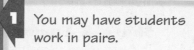

Share & Summarize

1 This is a good assessment question to see whether students understand that even though more than one input can result in the same output, the relationship is still a function, since there is a unique *output* for each input. You may need to clarify the machine's labeling: this is a machine whose output is the fourth power of the input (designated *x*).

You can extend this question by asking whether a machine that gives the fourth root of each input is a function. (No, because there are two fourth roots, one positive and one negative.)

Troubleshooting If students are having difficulty understanding the definition of a function, you may want to return to the beginning examples and help students try to cull the essence of the definition. The concept of *unique* and *consistent* is not trivial. Encourage students to come up with examples in their own lives that deal with uniqueness: they have unique fingerprints, a unique set of interests, and so on.

For some students, it may be helpful to focus on the idea of a unique output for each input; downplay the idea that an output can have different inputs until students are firm in their understanding, and then reintroduce it judiciously. If students grasp that each input must have a unique output, they will be able to recognize functions; the fact that several inputs can yield the same output doesn't interfere.

On Your Own Exercises

Practice & Apply: 1–9, pp. 504–506
Connect & Extend: 23–26, p. 510
Mixed Review: 36–50, pp. 512–513

Investigation 2

In this investigation, students describe functions using rules and graphs, making connections to the concept of input and output from the previous investigation. They are also introduced to function notation and the concept of the domain of a function.

Note: As this investigation is rather lengthy, it is important to move quickly through Problem Set D. If you want to break this investigation into two parts, a good stopping point is after Problem Set E and before the Example.

2 It is best to begin this investigation with a class discussion of the different ways to describe the function shown by the hookup:

$$y = 5x + 1 \qquad f(x) = 5x + 1 \qquad g(t) = 5t + 1$$

3 Explain that the symbol $f(x)$ is read "f of x" and means "apply function f to the value x" not "f times x." This is a common mistake, and you may need to repeat the information several times throughout this chapter.

In the rule $f(x) = 5x + 1$, x represents the input, $f(x)$ represents the output, and f is the name of the function. This is a notoriously difficult use of symbols for students to master.

Additional Example It may help students to revisit some functions from Investigation 1, name them, and practice the notation. For example, call the "Prime?" function p. (For brevity in notation, it's best to get used to using single letters to name functions.) Then $p(3) = yes$, $p(4) = no$, and so on.

In Problem Set A, you can use A for Function A and write:

$$A(x) = 2x + 7 \qquad A(0) = 2(0) + 7 = 7$$
$$A(1) = 2(1) + 7 = 9 \qquad A\left(-\tfrac{1}{2}\right) = 2\left(-\tfrac{1}{2}\right) + 7 = 6$$

Share & Summarize

Lucita and Ben are trying to decide whether $y = x^4$ is a function.

Who is correct, Ben or Lucita? Is $y = x^4$ a function? Explain how you know.

1 You may need to clarify the machine's labeling.

Investigation 2 Describing Functions with Rules and Graphs

Functions, like the one described by this hookup, are a type of rule that assigns one output value to each input value. You can often write such rules as algebraic equations, which is easier than drawing machines.

For example, each of these equations describes the same function as the one shown by the hookup: multiply the input by 5, and then add 1.

$$y = 5x + 1 \qquad f(x) = 5x + 1 \qquad g(t) = 5t + 1$$

Letters like f and g are often used to name functions. In the second rule above, the variable x represents the input, f is the name of the function, and $f(x)$ represents the output. The symbol $f(x)$ is read "f of x." It does *not* mean "f times x." Instead, it means "apply rule f to the value x." For example, $f(2) = 5(2) + 1 = 11$. This is illustrated below.

$x = 2 \qquad f \qquad f(x) = 11$

2 Discuss ways to describe the hookup.

3 Discuss function notation, f(x).

Develop

1 **Problem Set D** **Suggested Grouping: Pairs**
In this problem set, students are given a rule and asked
to identify correct symbolic representations, using the
function notation they just learned. Since they don't write
their own symbolic representations, this problem set
should not take long.

2 Make sure students understand why Kenneth's rule is a
function, as asked in **Problem 2.**

On the **Spot**
Assessment

In **Problem 3,** if students are having difficulty distinguishing these functions, have them tell the "story" of the number
for each symbolic form. For example, for $y = 2x^2 + 1$, the
story would be, "Take a number, square it, multiply by 2,
and then add 1."

There is a subtle difference between the rules given in
Parts b and c of Problem 3. It may be useful to point
out to students that the function notation form in Part c
draws attention to the fact that these are functions.

Access
for all **Learners**

Extra Challenge Ask students whether they can find a
rule that undoes Kenneth's rule. Is it a function? *Possible*
answer: Take the square root, subtract 1, and
divide by 2. This isn't a function, because when
you take the square root you don't know if you
want the positive or the negative root.

3 **Problem Set Wrap-Up** Briefly review student
answers to be sure students understand the uses of the
notation given here. They will use this notation more
extensively beginning with Problem Set F, so it is important that they recognize that symbols such as $f(x)$ refer to
a function.

4 **Problem Set E** **Suggested Grouping: Pairs**
In this problem set, students draw the graph of Kenneth's
rule and determine from a graph alone whether a relationship is a function.

Problem Set D

Kenneth is thinking about a rule to change one number into another number. He is wondering whether his rule is a function.

Double the number, add 1, and square the result.

1 You may have students work in pairs.

Problem Set D Answers

1. Possible table:

Input	Output
0	1
−1	1
1	9
$\frac{1}{2}$	4
−$\frac{1}{2}$	0

2. Yes; for each input, there is only one possible output.

1. Make an input/output table for Kenneth's rule, showing outputs for at least four inputs.

2. Is Kenneth's rule a function? How can you tell?

3. For Parts a–c, decide which functions describe Kenneth's rule.

a. $y = (2x + 1)^2$ $y = (2x + 1)^2$
$y = 2x^2 + 1$
$y = 2(x + 1)^2$
$y = (2x)^2 + 1$

b. $m = (2n + 1)^2$ All describe his rule.
$a = (2b + 1)^2$
$p = (2t + 1)^2$

c. $f(z) = 2(z + 1)^2$ $g(x) = (2x + 1)^2$ and $p(t) = (2t + 1)^2$
$g(x) = (2x + 1)^2$
$p(t) = (2t + 1)^2$
$j(k) = 1 + (2k)^2$

2 Make sure students understand why the rule is a function.

MATERIALS

graphing calculator

1b. Possible graph:

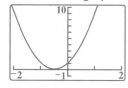

Problem Set E

You can graph a function with the input variable on the horizontal axis (the *x*-axis) and the output variable on the vertical axis (the *y*-axis).

1. Graph Kenneth's rule from Problem Set D on your calculator.

a. What did you enter into the calculator for the rule? $y = (2x + 1)^2$

b. Sketch the graph. Remember to label the minimum and maximum values on each axis.

3 Briefly discuss students' answers.

4 Problem-Solving Strategy

Use a graph

LESSON 8.1 Functions **493**

In **Problem 2,** students have to decide whether each graph represents a function. Of course, since the graphs describe a relationship, the only criterion students need to consider is whether a single input can have more than one output. You may want to display a transparency of Master 49, which reproduces the seven graphs. Alternatively, you might sketch the "nonfunctions" on the board so that you can circle points for which one input results in more than one output. **Part f,** which has only one input but an infinite number of outputs, is just about as "nonfunction" as you can get!

Teachers Resources

▶ Master **49**

Lesson 8.1 Investigation 2 Problem Set E

Problem 2

Example

Before students go on to Problem Set F, go over the Example so they see how to find the value of a function for different values of x. Do a quick informal assessment to check that they understand what $f(3)$ means, if $f(x) = x^2$. Remind them that this does not mean f times 3.

Remember

For a relationship to be a function, there can be only one output for a given input.

2. Graphs a, c, e, and g represent functions, because there is only one *y* value for each *x* value. Graphs b, d, and f do not, because a single *x* value produces more than one possible *y* value.

2. Decide which graphs below represent functions. Explain how you decided.

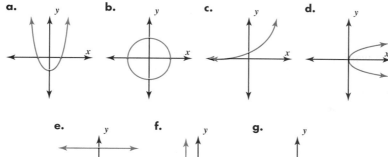

When you have a function such as $f(x) = x^2$, you may want to find the value of the function for different values of *x*.

1 Use drawings or a transparency to show why b, d, and f fail to be functions.

2 Show students how to evaluate a function for different x values.

EXAMPLE

Consider the function $f(x) = x^2$.

If $x = 3$, then $f(3) = 3^2 = 9$. Finding $f(3)$ is like putting 3 into this machine:

If $x = {}^-10$, then $f({}^-10) = ({}^-10)^2 = 100$.

Remember, $f(2)$ does not mean "*f* times 2." It means "use 2 as the input to machine *f*" or "evaluate the function *f* with the input 2."

Develop

Problem Set F **Suggested Grouping: Individuals**
This problem set deals with function notation, including interpreting expressions such as $f(2)$ and $f(-3)$. Letting students work on their own for this set will help you assess their understanding of the notation.

Students may need help with the notion of "a function of. . . ." In mathematics, one variable *is a function of* another variable when the value of the second variable depends on the value of the first:

- The time in the air is a function of how fast the ball was thrown upward.

- The circumference of a circle is a function of the diameter.

- It costs Jodi 35 cents to make a handmade note card, so her profit is a function of the selling price of each card.

- *y* is a function of *x*.

2 **Problem Set Wrap-Up** Review the answers to **Problems 1–3** quickly. It may help to poll the class for how many got each answer correct. If many students do not understand how to apply function notation, you might work through additional examples as a class.

Additional Examples

- The area of a square with side length s is $A(s) = s^2$. What does $A(9)$ represent? *the area of a square with side length 9 units* What is the value of $A(9)$? 9^2, *or 81, square units*

- Joely walked into a room, moving from the door to the other side of the room at a rate of 2 feet per second. Her distance in feet from the door t seconds after she entered the room was $d(t) = 2t$. What does $d(3)$ represent? *Joely's distance from the door at 3 seconds* What is the value of $d(3)$? $2(3)$, *or 6, feet*

3 After students seem to have a grasp on the concept and notation of functions, talk about the issue of allowable inputs, or *domain*, with them. Refer to Problem 3 of Problem Set F, when students should have recognized that only positive numbers make sense as inputs. Then remind them of the function with integer input and classification as even or odd for the output. Ask students why they think inputs are restricted to integers in this example, and then define *domain* for them: the set of allowable inputs to a function. If certain numbers are not allowed as inputs, they are not in the domain of the function.

3. no; Possible explanation: ⁻3 as an input would be 3 s before the jump, but a skydiver isn't falling before the jump, so the calculation won't tell you anything meaningful.

VOCABULARY
domain

1. $f(2)$ represents the distance a skydiver has fallen after 2 s. Its value is $4.9(2^2) = 19.6$ m.

Problem Set F

The distance fallen by skydivers, before they open their parachutes, is a function of the time since they fell from the aircraft. The function is approximated by $f(t) = 4.9t^2$, where t is the time in seconds and $f(t)$ is the distance in meters.

1. What does $f(2)$ represent in the skydiving situation? What is the numerical value of $f(2)$?

2. How far has a skydiver fallen after 10 seconds?   490 m

3. In the context of this situation, would it make sense to find the value of $f(⁻3)$? Explain your answer.

Some functions can have only certain inputs. In the skydiver problem, only positive numbers make sense as inputs, because the function measures how far a skydiver has fallen *after* jumping.

As another example, here is a function you considered earlier:

• Input: an integer
  Output: classification as even or odd

The input is described as "an integer" because non-integers, such as $\frac{3}{4}$ and ⁻12.92, don't make sense as inputs. It isn't reasonable to ask whether such numbers are even or odd.

The set of allowable inputs to a function is called the **domain** of that function. If some numbers are not allowed as inputs, we say they *are not in the domain* of the function.

1 You may have students work on their own.

2 Go over Problems 1–3 and assess whether students need more examples.

3 Discuss the *domain of a function*.

Think & Discuss

Use this question to assess students' understanding of domain. If necessary, ask students to check what happens when they enter $\frac{1}{0}$, or 0 followed by ⌐¹/ₓ⌐ or ⌐x¹⌐, into their calculators. They should get an error message.

About the Mathematics

There are really three ways to restrict domains. One is the implied restriction that comes from undefined results; for example, $g(x) = \frac{1}{x}$ has an implied restriction that $x \neq 0$, and $h(x) = \sqrt{x}$ has an implied restriction that $x \geq 0$. A second is a contextual restriction such as in the skydiver situation of Problem Set F: although $f(-3)$ can be calculated, an input of -3 is meaningless in the context of the problem. Students have had experience with both of these types of restrictions and will focus on them in Problem Set G.

The third type of restriction is explicit. For example, one can define a function k in this way: $k(s) = 3s + 4$, where $3 < s \leq 15$. The domain is restricted to $3 < s \leq 15$, but only because the definition made it so. Students will not encounter this type of restriction in this course, but it will be important in future courses. (For example, when discussing inverse relationships of trigonometric functions, such domain restrictions are used to ensure that the inverses will, in fact, be functions.)

 ## Problem Set G Suggested Grouping: Pairs

In this problem set, students are asked to identify the domains of functions given descriptions as rules and as input-output contexts.

In **Problem 1,** you may want to review the concept of real numbers with the class.

In **Problem 4,** some students may answer positive integers. This is acceptable, since students often work only with positive integers when factoring. Depending on your class, you may want to point out, or let students discuss, whether they should include 0 and negative integers in the domain.

About the Mathematics

Clearly, if $f > 0$ is a factor of a number, then $-f$ is also considered to be a factor. The number 0, however, is generally excluded from factor considerations, because it has no *unique prime factorization*. To write a factorization of 0, you must include 0 as a factor, and then there are an infinite number of possibilities, such as $0 \cdot 2, 0 \cdot 3, 0 \cdot 5 \cdot 7^2$, and so on.

A number a has a *unique prime factorization* if

- it can be written as $p_1 p_2 \cdots p_n$, where each p_i is prime

- for two prime factorizations $a = p_1 p_2 \cdots p_n$ and $a = q_1 q_2 \cdots q_n$, the factors p_i can be paired with factors q_k so that $p_i = \pm q_k$ in each pair

The second criterion is important. If you have two prime factorizations, they have to be basically the same after you rearrange the factors and perhaps multiply factors by -1. For example, -30 can be factored $2 \cdot -3 \cdot 5$ or $3 \cdot 2 \cdot -5$, but since you can pair the factors (2 and 2, -3 and 3, 5 and -5) so that each pair is equal in absolute value, the factorizations are considered to be the same.

As an extension for **Problem 6,** you might want to display two related graphs: $g(a) = 6a$ is a continuous line graph, but in the ant problem, the graph is a discrete set of points along that line (corresponding to whole number inputs).

 ## Share & Summarize

Question 1 reviews the different representations of a function. If you have students do this in small groups, you can assign a different representation to each group and have them come to the board to show their representations.

Troubleshooting If students are having difficulty with function notation or the concept of a domain, you may want to spend an additional day on this topic. Just by looking through this book (or others), you or your students should be able to find many examples of relationships that can be written as functions; you can then discuss different representations and domain restrictions.

 ## On Your Own Exercises

Practice & Apply: 10–16, pp. 506–507
Connect & Extend: 27–30, pp. 510–511
Mixed Review: 36–50, pp. 512–513

6a. 15,138

6b. Positive non-integers and negative numbers can't be inputs; you can't have a partial ant or negative ants.

Think & Discuss

Consider this function: $r(x) = \frac{1}{x}$.

What numbers are not in the domain of this function? Why?
0; $\frac{1}{0}$ is not a number, so there is no logical output.

Problem Set G

In Problems 1–5, describe the domain of the function.

1. $f(x) = x^2$ all real numbers

2. $g(t) = \sqrt{t}$ nonnegative numbers (positive or 0)

3. $R(x) = \frac{1}{1-x}$ all real numbers except 1

4. $e(n)$ is the number of factors of n.   integers

5. $q(p)$ is *yes* if p is evenly divisible by 3 and *no* if p is not evenly divisible by 3.   integers

6. The number of legs in an ant farm is a function of the number of ants in the farm. Specifically, the number of legs is 6 times the number of ants.

   a. If there are 2,523 ants in the farm, how many legs are there?

   b. What numbers cannot be inputs to this "number of legs" function? Explain your answer.

   c. You can describe this "number of legs" function using algebraic symbols. Let a be the number of ants, and write a function g so that $g(a)$ is the number of legs. $g(a) = 6a$

Share & Summarize

A particular function can be described in several ways, including using words, equations, tables, graphs, and machines.

1. Describe, write, or draw three representations of this function.

$$g(x) = 7 - 3x$$

2. Are any numbers not in the domain of $g(x) = 7 - 3x$? If so, which numbers?   no

1 Use this to assess students' understanding of domain.

2 You may have students work in pairs.

3 You may have students work in small groups and present their work to the class.

Investigation 3

An important, practical reason for representing situations using functions is optimization. In this investigation, students learn that maximum and minimum values of variables can be obtained graphically.

The intention here is not to develop a high level of efficiency in dealing with maximum and minimum values, but to see how the ideas of a function, particularly different representations of functions, can assist in estimating maxima and minima. Your students' next encounter with optimization will likely occur if they study precalculus, where exact procedures of finding maxima and minima will be developed using the concept of the derivative. It is helpful to think of this investigation as both dealing with some practical problems and as laying the foundation for a more thorough treatment of optimization later.

Students should work in pairs when using the graphing calculator, even if each student has access to one. Try to match students in a way that will save you time answering questions about the calculator: pair students who may need more help with students who have demonstrated facility with the calculator.

Students will use the Trace and Zoom features of the calculator to refine their estimates of maxima and minima. Some graphing calculators have built-in routines for finding the maximum or minimum of a function on an interval; you may want to allow students to use those routines after they have shown they understand the process given in the text.

To introduce the investigation, you can tell students that they will be solving some problems using functions. You may want to read the introductory text to Problem Set H as a group, or just let students get into pairs and read it on their own.

 Problem Set H Suggested Grouping: **Pairs**
In this problem set, students are given a function that describes the height of a stone above the water after it is thrown straight up. They use the graph to answer questions about the situation and about the maximum height the stone reaches.

 ## Access
for all Learners

Language Diversity Visualizing the situation is important for understanding these problems, and it might be helpful if you actually throw a wad of paper or the like straight up into the air. Help students see the relationship between the pier, the water, and the distance the stone travels. Some students may need help with the word *pier*.

In **Problem 1,** students need to make the connection that the stone leaves Tala's hand when $t = 0$. This may not be obvious to some.

 In **Problem 2,** students need to estimate how tall Tala is and the height from which the stone is thrown. If they seem stumped, encourage them to look at the illustration, which shows the stone being released at approximately shoulder level. You might have them demonstrate by throwing a wad of paper in the air, and ask them how far from the floor the paper is when they first let go. Have them connect this to the stone's height at $t = 0$, and let them consider why the stone is so much higher.

You may need to remind students how to use the calculator's Trace and Zoom features to answer **Problem 7.** See Investigation 1 of Lesson 4.3 or Master 14, which describes how to use the Zoom and Trace features for the Texas Instruments T1–83 Plus graphing calculator.

 Problem Set Wrap-Up You might want to review students' answers and methods, especially for Problem 7.

Investigation ▶3 Finding Maximum Values of Functions

Graphs are very useful for finding approximate maximum and minimum values of functions. For example, in Chapter 4, you considered the maximum height a thrown or bounced ball might reach. A manufacturer might use a function to predict the price that will give the maximum profit for a product.

Problem Set H

Tala threw a stone vertically up from the edge of a pier. The height of the stone above the water level is a function of t, where t is the number of seconds after the stone is thrown. The function, which measures height in meters, is

$$h(t) = 15t - 4.9t^2 + 6$$

At right is a graph of this relationship.

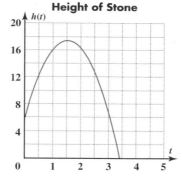

Height of Stone

1. When the stone first leaves Tala's hand, about how high is it above the water? Explain how you can find the answer from the equation or the graph.

2. About how high is the pier? Explain why your answer is reasonable.

3. When is the stone at a height of 15 meters?

4. Between what times is the stone more than 15 meters above the water?   between about 0.8 s and about 2.2 s

5. To the nearest meter, what is the maximum height the stone reaches?

6. About how long after it is thrown does the stone reach its maximum height?   about 1.5 s

7. Use your calculator's Trace and Zoom features to better approximate the stone's maximum height. Find the maximum height to the nearest hundredth of a meter.   17.48 m

LESSON 8.1   Functions   **497**

Problem Set I Suggested Grouping: Pairs

In this problem set, students use the graph of

$$C(t) = \frac{21t}{t^2 + 1.3t + 2.9}$$

to answer questions about the relationship between the number of minutes, t, after an anesthetic is administered and the concentration of the anesthetic, C(t), in grams per liter. Students may not have seen this kind of graph before, and it is reasonable for them to wonder whether there is only one maximum for this function. If they ask, encourage them to look at an expanded window to get a feeling for the behavior of this function for very large positive values of t. In fact, putting aside the issue of domain restrictions due to the context, they may be interested in what the graph looks like in all four quadrants.

Access
for all Learners

Language Diversity Some students may need help with the terms *local anesthetic* and *concentration*. You may want to discuss these ideas before letting students begin the problems:

Who knows what *concentration* means in this context?

Can you give another example of when you would want to measure the concentration of something?

In **Problem 1,** it is important that students be able to articulate clearly the meanings of C(1), C(6), and C(10). Have them explain the meanings to their partners. Not only does this reinforce the function notation, but it also puts the function in a context that relates the two variables.

Students could answer **Problem 5** using the Table feature on the calculator as well as the graph. You might want to point this out to students who would like an alternative approach.

In **Problem 6,** you might ask students whether they have ever experienced getting a tooth filled, where a local anesthesia is applied. Ask them if the dentist waited a bit before drilling.

Problem Set I

A company that manufactures medicine has researched the concentration of a local anesthetic in a patient's bloodstream. They found that the concentration can be approximately calculated with the function

$$C(t) = \frac{21t}{t^2 + 1.3t + 2.9}$$

where t is the number of minutes after the anesthetic is administered and $C(t)$ is the concentration of the anesthetic, measured in grams per liter. A higher concentration means the patient is less likely to feel pain.

1. Find $C(1)$, $C(6)$, and $C(10)$. What does each of these values represent in terms of this situation?   See below.

2. The graph shows the relationship between $C(t)$ and t. Use it to estimate the maximum concentration reached by the anesthetic.
about 4.5 g/L

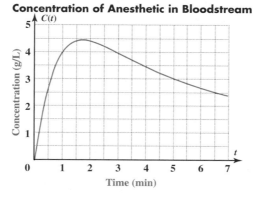

Concentration of Anesthetic in Bloodstream

3. About how long does it take the anesthetic to reach the maximum concentration?   about 1.7 min

4. Using the equation, draw your own graph on your calculator. Use Zoom and Trace to find the answers to Problems 2 and 3 to the nearest hundredth of the given units (g/L and min).   See below.

5. Tests have shown that when the concentration reaches 2 g/L, patients report feeling numbness. About how long after the injection does this happen?   about 20 s

6. A doctor wants to stitch a cut in Jemma's hand. She expects the stitching to take about 3 minutes. How long after she injects Jemma with anesthetic should she wait before she starts? Explain.
Possible answer: about 40 s, since the concentration will stay high for at least 3 min after that

1. $C(1) \approx 4.04$ g/L, $C(6) \approx 2.70$ g/L, $C(10) \approx 1.81$ g/L. These represent the concentration of the anesthetic 1 min, 6 min, and 10 min after it is administered.

4. 4.46 g/L at 1.70 min

Share & Summarize

Let students know that they can approximate their answers when reading these graphs. Students who completed Course 2 have seen graphs like the one in **Question 4,** but others may never have seen such a graph. In fact, this function reaches a maximum of 1 at two points in the interval shown, when x is -270 and when x is 90. Some students may speculate that if the pattern repeats, there will be other inputs that give the maximum; however, it is not expected that they extend the graph. (Notice that unlike the others, there are no arrows on the ends of the graph.) In future mathematics courses, students will learn that this is the graph of the sine curve, which in fact reaches the maximum of 1 at an infinite number of points.

Troubleshooting Even if students are having difficulty determining the maximum value of functions, you can move on to the next investigation. They will be looking at this topic again, from a different perspective, both in Investigation 4 and in the Lab Investigation.

On Your Own Exercises

Practice & Apply: 17–20, pp. 507–508
Connect & Extend: 31–33, p. 511
Mixed Review: 36–50, pp. 512–513

Investigation 4

Here students investigate rectangles to find maximum area for a fixed perimeter and minimum perimeter for a fixed area. These situations are similar to the Course 2 lab investigation in which students minimized surface area for a given volume.

There are many variations on this theme of maximizing one quantity in relation to another given quantity. If students show interest in pursuing this topic further, you might want to have them pose their own questions.

You might introduce the investigation by pointing out that the shapes at the bottom of page 499 all have the same perimeter. Ask students:

Do they all have the same area?

Which shape seems to have the least area?

Which shape seems to have the greatest area?

You can also ask students whether they remember doing a lab investigation to find the least amount of metal needed to make a soda can; you might let some of them tell you what they remember of that lab. Let them know they will be working with a similar activity in this investigation.

Share & Summarize

Decide whether each of these functions has a maximum value. If so, approximate the maximum value and the input that produces it.

1. Maximum value is 5 when $x = 0$.
2. Maximum value is 14 when $x = 2$.

1.

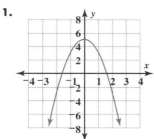

2.

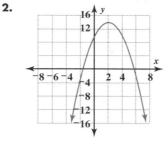

3. no maximum value
4. Maximum value is 1 when $x = {}^-270$ and 90.

3.

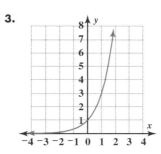

4.

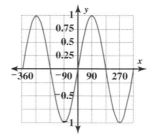

1 Point out that students can approximate maximums using the graphs.

Investigation 4 ▶ Maximum Areas, Minimum Lengths

These shapes have the same perimeter but different areas.

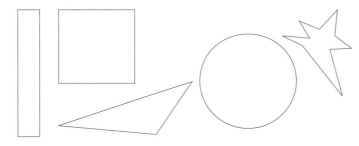

2 Introduce this investigation by talking about these shapes with students.

Just the facts

Geometers are mathematicians who specialize in geometry.

Farmers, builders, and geometers often want to maximize the area of a shape for a given perimeter. In this investigation, you will consider the maximum area for rectangular shapes with a given perimeter. You will also consider the minimum perimeter for a given area.

LESSON 8.1 Functions **499**

Problem Set J Suggested Grouping: Pairs

In this problem set, students explore different dimensions for a fenced pen of perimeter 6 meters. They first construct a table of possible widths and lengths, then graph the area as a function of the length, and finally determine the rectangle with the greatest area.

In **Problem 5,** students are asked to write a function A giving the area for length L. Some students may write $A = L(3 - L)$ rather than $A(L) = L(3 - L)$. Both are correct, but the second stresses the fact that this is a function (for each length, there is a unique area).

On the **Spot Assessment**

In **Problem 6,** many students will think the x *and* y values of points on the graphs represents the dimensions of the rectangle. It is important to stress that the y-coordinate is the *area* in this case.

About the **Mathematics**

Problem 7 leads to an interesting generalization: of all the rectangles with a given perimeter, the square is the shape that maximizes the area.

Access for all **Learners**

Early Finishers Extend this explanation by asking students to find the maximum area the pen could enclose if its perimeter were 8 meters. 4 m^2

Problem Set J

Keisha and her twin sister Monifa have bought some guinea pigs. They are building a fenced pen for the animals. They have 6 meters of fencing, and they want to give their pets as much space as possible.

Keisha drew some possible rectangular shapes for the pen.

2 m
1 m

2.6 m
0.4 m

1.2 m
1.8 m

3. Possible equation:
$W = 3 - L$

5. $A(L) = L(3 - L)$ or
$A(L) = 3L - L^2$

6.

1. The twins need to consider two dimensions for a rectangular pen: length and width. Copy and complete the table, which relates possible lengths and widths, both measured in meters. The total perimeter must be 6 meters in each case.

Length	0.5	1	1.5	2	2.5	3
Width	2.5	2	1.5	1	0.5	0
Perimeter	6	6	6	6	6	6

2. If the length of the rectangle increases by a certain amount, what happens to its width? It decreases by the same amount.

3. Write an equation that gives the width W for any length L.

Your equation shows the relationship between one dimension of the rectangular pen and the other. However, because Keisha and Monifa want to find the greatest rectangular area they can enclose using 6 meters of fencing, the mathematical relationship they need is between one of the dimensions, such as length, and the area.

4. Complete this table, showing dimensions and area of some possible rectangles. All measurements are in meters.

Length	0.5	1	1.5	2	2.5	3
Width	2.5	2	1.5	1	0.5	0
Area	1.25	2	2.25	2	1.25	0

5. Write an equation for the function A giving the area for length L.

6. Use your calculator to graph the length of the pen versus its area, using your function from Problem 5. Sketch your graph. Remember to label the minimum and maximum values on each axis.

7. What length and width should the pen be to produce the greatest area from 6 meters of fencing? Use the graph you drew to approximate your answer. 1.5 m each

Just the facts

Guinea pigs are native to South America and live an average of eight years.

You may have students work in pairs.

Stress that the y-coordinate represents the *area*, not the width.

Develop

Problem Set K Suggested Grouping: Pairs

In this problem set, students find the dimensions that will produce a minimum perimeter for a given area. You might want to have students discuss the following with a partner:

Why would the family want a pen of a certain size, such as 40 m²? *Possible answer: Health requirements may demand a certain amount of space for each chicken.*

Why would they want a fence of minimum length? *A shorter fence is cheaper.*

Why use an existing wall? *The wall may save money or act as a weather shield.*

In **Problem 3,** students are asked to write a function for the amount of fencing in terms of the width. Note that since we're using an existing wall, the length is not multiplied by 2, but the width is.

If you have students working in pairs, have partners use different methods in **Problem 4** and then compare answers. If there is time, or for students who typically finish early, some students may want to use a spreadsheet for this problem.

Students may find it interesting that the rectangle that has the minimum perimeter is half a square. Reflecting the fenced walls over the stone wall gives the other half of the square.

Problem Set K

A family wants to build a rectangular pen for their chickens, using an existing stone wall as one side and fencing for the other three sides. They decide on an area of 40 m². They want to know what shape rectangle will give this area using a minimum length of fencing. Here are some shapes they are considering.

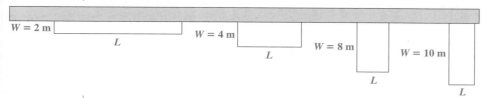

1. Copy and complete the table. Try additional width values, if necessary, to determine the least amount of fencing needed. All measurements are in meters.

Width, W	2	4	8	10
Length, L	20	10	5	4
Amount of Fencing	24	18	21	24

2. Express the length of the pen in terms of W. $L = \frac{40}{W}$

3. Use your expression from Problem 2 to write the amount of fencing as a function of W. Name your function F.

$$F(W) = \underline{2W + \frac{40}{W}}$$

4. Use one of the following methods to find the width that requires the least amount of fencing:

- Use your calculator to graph the amount of fencing versus width, using your function from Problem 3. Approximate the least value for the length.

- Use a calculator to guess-check-and-improve.
  The amount of fencing is a minimum (about 17.9 m) when the width is about 4.5 m, but there is not much practical difference in the amount of fencing for widths between 4 m and 5 m.

1 You may have students work in pairs.

2 Have partners use different methods and compare answers.

Share & Summarize

This Share & Summarize is a nice exploration. As an extension, you might have students find the minimum total algebraically. First, have them solve the equation $s = x + \frac{1}{x}$ for x:

$$sx = x^2 + 1$$

$$x^2 - sx + 1 = 0$$

$$x = \frac{s \pm \sqrt{s^2 - 4}}{2}$$

Using an idea presented in Chapter 7, they should see that, in order for solutions to exist, s must be at least 2—in other words, 2 is the lowest possible sum. This final leap in reasoning might be difficult for many students. If so, ask them to consider the number of solutions possible for different values of s, and then give them a day to consider what that might mean for the minimum total.

Troubleshooting If students are having difficulty with finding maximum and minimum values, give them additional problems, or have them go on to the lab investigation, which provides another context for this topic.

On Your Own Exercises

Practice & Apply: 21–22, pp. 508–509
Connect & Extend: 34, 35, pp. 511–512
Mixed Review: 36–50, pp. 512–513

Suggested Grouping: Pairs

In this lab, students examine different-size boxes, given a fixed surface area. They begin with 5-inch-by-8-inch cards, cut different-size squares from the corners, and then determine which box has the maximum volume.

This problem has become a classic in mathematics courses, and its beauty is that students at many different levels can find ways of solving it. They will see this problem again if they study calculus, where they will have an additional tool (the use of the derivative) for finding maxima and minima.

Materials and Preparation

Each pair of students will need 5-inch-by-8-inch cards, a ruler, scissors, a graphing calculator, and tape. If students work on the lab in small groups, each group should have these materials. You may want to substitute 3-inch-by-5-inch cards, but the larger size is easier for students to work with.

In introducing this lab, explain to students that they will be trying to find the box with the greatest volume by cutting squares from the four corners of index cards and measuring the resulting boxes.

Tips from Teachers

"I tell my students beforehand that I will fill their boxes with a treat (popcorn, small candies, or something similar) after they have built them. This adds motivation to build a big box, and allows for a preliminary comparison of boxes: 'How many candies did your box hold?' Be careful, though, about students with special dietary concerns."

Try It Out

There are many ways for students to estimate the volume of their boxes without calculating. They can fill them with marbles, or popcorn or candies as suggested above. When answering **Question 2,** however, it is important that all students use the same method of measuring volume. You may want to do this as a whole class, making a table on the board:

Group Number	Side Length of Cut Square	Volume of Box
1		
2		
. . .		

If you use 3-inch-by-5-inch cards instead of the larger size, the maximum volume is for a side length of about 0.6 inch, with a volume of about 4.1 cubic inches.

1. By graphing the
function $f(x) =$
$x + \frac{1}{x}$, you see that
the minimum total is
2 when $x = 1$.

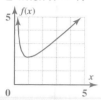

Share & Summarize

Héctor was experimenting with his calculator, adding positive numbers and their reciprocals. Here are some examples.

$$5 + \frac{1}{5} = 5.2 \qquad 0.1 + \frac{1}{0.1} = 10.1 \qquad 1.25 + \frac{1}{1.25} = 2.05$$

1. Do you think there is a minimum total he can produce doing this? If so, what is it? If not, explain why not. (Hint: Let x stand for the number, and write an equation to express what Héctor is doing.)

2. Do you think there is a maximum total he can produce? If so, what is it? If not, explain why not.
There doesn't appear to be a maximum. Possible explanation: The value of $f(x)$ is always a little greater than the value of the input x, because you add the positive value of $\frac{1}{x}$ to it. Since x has no maximum value, neither does $f(x)$.

1 Let students explore a little with this problem.

Lab Investigation ▶ The Biggest Box

2 You may have students work in pairs.

3 Distribute materials to students.

MATERIALS

• 5-inch-by-8-inch cards
• ruler
• scissors
• graphing calculator
• tape

Your teacher will give you 5-inch-by-8-inch cards. You can cut squares out of the corners of a card and then fold the sides to make an open box (a box without a top).

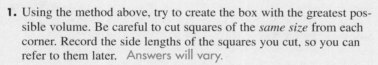

Your challenge is to create the box with the greatest possible volume.

Try It Out

The volume of your box will depend on the side length of the squares you cut from it.

1. Using the method above, try to create the box with the greatest possible volume. Be careful to cut squares of the *same size* from each corner. Record the side lengths of the squares you cut, so you can refer to them later.   Answers will vary.

Remember

For a rectangular prism such as a box, volume is area of base times height.

2. Compare the greatest volume you found with the greatest volume found by others in the class. Record the side length of the cutout squares for the boxes with the greatest volume.
Answers will vary. The actual maximum is for a side length of 1 in., giving a volume of 18 in.^{3}. It's possible that no student in class created this box; students should find the best approximation in the class.

4 You may want to do Question 2 as a class.

Analyze the Situation

1 In **Questions 3 and 4,** students create a table for given side lengths of squares and the resulting dimensions. If students are using 3-inch-by-5-inch cards, you may want to have them change the last two side lengths to values such as 0.25, 0.75, or $\frac{1}{3}$.

The values in the table are only a subset of all possible side lengths, so **Questions 5 and 6** ask students to find a function that relates the box's volume to the side length of the cut square. They then use their graphing calculators in **Question 7** to estimate the value that gives the maximum volume. For 3-inch-by-5-inch cards, the function is $v(x) = x(5 - 2x)(3 - 2x)$.

2 Students may need help making sense of what happens with the function for x values greater than $x = 2.5$ (where the graph crosses the x-axis). These represent "nonboxes"; that is, if the side length of the cutout is greater than 2.5 inches, you have completely cut away one dimension of the box. So the only logical inputs to the function (for this box problem) are x values between 0 and 2.5.

About the Mathematics

If you consider the graph of the function from Question 6, using all real numbers as the domain, you can see that it has no maximum value. For $x > \frac{10}{3}$, the graph increases again, without a bound on how great $v(x)$ can be.

When a graph increases and then decreases, as this one does for $x < \frac{10}{3}$, it has a *local maximum* at the point where it changes from increasing to decreasing. A local maximum that is also the greatest value the function reaches over its entire domain is called the *absolute maximum*.

Since students are working with a function that has practical restrictions on its domain, the entire domain of the function is not the real numbers, but values of x between 0 and 2.5. That means the local maximum at $x = 1$ is the absolute maximum as well.

If you wish, you can explain to students that when they take calculus, they will be able to find exact maximum and minimum values of a function without estimating.

What Have You Learned?

3 In **Questions 8 and 9,** students repeat the process for a sheet of paper, 8.5 inches by 11 inches. If students don't write a function (in function notation) for the volume of this box, it might be useful for you to prompt them to do so, giving them practice in making sense out of this form.

Analyze the Situation

3. Each dimension of your box depends on the side length of the squares you cut out. Copy and complete the table for squares of different side lengths. All measurements are in inches.

Side Length of Square	0	0.5	1	1.5	2	2.5
Height of Box	0	0.5	1	1.5	2	2.5
Length of Box	8	7	6	5	4	3
Width of Box	5	4	3	2	1	0
Volume of Box	0	14	18	15	8	0

4. the one with a square of side length 1 in.

5c. $5 - 2x$

5d. $x(8 - 2x)(5 - 2x)$

7. $x = 1$ in. appears to give the maximum volume.

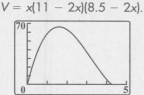

8a. about 1.59 in. or 1.6 in.; Possible explanation: I looked at the graph of $V = x(11 - 2x)(8.5 - 2x)$.

4. Add a row to your table, calculating the volume of the box for each side length of the square. Of those boxes listed in the table, which has the greatest volume?

Of course, there are more possible square sizes than the six listed in the table above. You can use functions and graphs to help you check *all* the possibilities.

5. If the side length of the square you cut out is x, find each of the following in terms of x.

  a. the height of the box $\quad x$
  b. the length of the box $\quad 8 - 2x$
  c. the width of the box
  d. the volume of the box

6. Based on your answer to Part d of Question 5, write an equation for the function relating the box's volume to the side length of the square you cut out. Name your function v. $\quad v(x) = x(8 - 2x)(5 - 2x)$

7. Use your calculator to graph the volume function, and sketch the graph. Then use Zoom and Trace to estimate the value of x that gives the maximum volume.

What Have You Learned?

You estimated the maximum volume of the open box you can make from a 5-inch-by-8-inch card. Suppose you start with a standard sheet of paper, 8.5 inches by 11 inches, instead.

8. Use what you learned in this lab investigation to answer these questions. Show your work, including sketches of any graphs you make.

  a. What cutout size will maximize the volume for an open box made from a standard sheet of paper?

  b. What is the greatest possible volume? $\quad$ about 66 in.^{3}

9. Use an ordinary sheet of paper and your answers to Question 8 to create the box you think has the greatest volume. Tape the corners to make it strong. $\quad$ See student work.

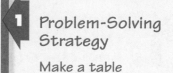
LESSON 8.1 Functions **503**

On Your Own Exercises

Exercise 2d:
Students are asked to find a machine that will undo a squaring machine. You may need to prompt students to explain why there is no such machine.

Practice & Apply

1. Consider this function machine.

   a. If the input is 10, what is the output? 5

   b. If the input is $-\frac{2}{3}$, what is the output? $-\frac{1}{3}$

   c. If the input is 1.5, what is the output? 0.75

   d. If the input is some number x, what is the output? $\frac{x}{2}$

   e. If the output is $^-9$, what was the input? $^-18$

   f. Suppose you want a function machine that will undo this machine. That is, if you put a number first through the "÷ 2" machine and then through your new machine, it *always* returns your original number. What function machine would accomplish this? a "× 2" machine

2. Consider this function machine, which squares the input.

   a. If the input is $\frac{4}{3}$, what is the output? $\frac{16}{9}$

   b. If the input is $-\frac{4}{3}$, what is the output? $\frac{16}{9}$

   c. If the output is 9, what was the input? 3 or $^-3$

   d. Suppose you want a function machine that will undo this machine. That is, if you put a number first through the "Square" machine and then through your new machine, it always returns your original number. What function machine would accomplish this?
   There is no such function machine. A machine that finds square roots will give two values, $\pm\sqrt{x}$, for every input x, and one that finds only the positive square root will give an incorrect response when the input to the "Square" machine is negative.

 impactmath.com/self_check_quiz

3. Consider this hookup, Function F.

Function F

a. If the input is 1.5, what is the output? 0.25

b. If the input is ⁻3, what is the output? ⁻2

c. If the input is 11, what is the output? 5

d. If the input is some number *x*, what is the output? $\frac{x-1}{2}$

e. If the output is ⁻8, what was the input? ⁻15

f. Suppose you want a function machine that will undo this machine. That is, if you put a number through the Function F machine and then through your new hookup, it will always return your original number. What function machine would accomplish this?

Tell whether each example below is a function, and explain how you decided.

4. Input: a circle
Output: the ratio of the circumference to the diameter

5. Input: a rugby team
Output: a member of the team

6. Input: a CD
Output: a song from the CD

3f. Possible answer:

4. A function; there is one such ratio (always equal to π) for every circle.

5. Not a function; each team has more than one member.

6. Not a function; CDs usually have more than one song.

Just the facts

Rugby is played in more than 100 countries by several million people.

Exercise 3f:
Students may answer that the machine that undoes "subtract 1, multiply by $\frac{1}{2}$," is the machine that "adds 1, multiplies by 2," giving the hookup in the reverse order. If so, ask them to test their machine with numbers to see whether it undoes the original machine.

Exercise 4:
It may be helpful to point out to students that this is another example of a constant function: this ratio is always equal to π.

Determine if the relationship represented by each input/output table could be a function.

7.

Input	Output
−3	4
−2	3
−1	2
0	1
1	0
2	−1
3	−2

7. function

8.

Input	Output
−3	0
−2	−2.828 and 2.828
−1	−2.236 and 2.236
0	−3 and 3
1	−2.236 and 2.236
2	−2.828 and 2.828
3	0

8. not a function

9.

Input	Output
−3	$\frac{1}{3}$
−2	$\frac{1}{2}$
−1	1
0	undefined
1	1
2	$\frac{1}{2}$
3	$\frac{1}{3}$

9. function

10b.

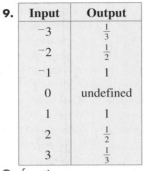

10. Consider this rule: *Square a number, subtract 2, and then divide by 2.*

a. Copy and complete the table using this rule.

b. Sketch a graph of the relationship shown in your table.

c. Is this rule a function? How do you know? Yes; each input has only one output.

Input, I	Output, O
−3	7/2
−2	1
−1	−1/2
0	−1
1	−1/2
2	1
3	7/2

11. When Kai entered math class, the table and functions below were on the board. Kai thought the values in the first column of the table were function inputs and the values in the second column were outputs.

1	3
2	7
3	13
4	21
5	31
6	43
7	57
8	
9	91
10	
11	

$g(t) = 1 + t + t^2$
$f(x) = x^2 + 2x$
$h(z) = z^2 + z + 1$
$b = a^2 + a + 1$
$K(d) = d^2 + d - 1$
$Y = 2x + 1$
$B(x) = 4x - 1$
$F(X) = (x + 1)^2 - x$

11b. 73, 111, and 133 are missing, associated with 8, 10, and 11, respectively.

a. Which of the functions, if any, might be shown in the table? Explain. See Additional Answers.

b. Complete the table by finding the missing values of the function.

Additional Answers
11a. $g(t)$, $h(z)$, $b = a^2 + a + 1$, and $F(X)$; they all produce the appropriate outputs.

12. Physical Science A rock falls over the edge of a cliff 600 meters high. The distance in meters the rock falls is a function of time in seconds and can be approximated by the function $s(t) = 4.9t^2$.

    a. Find the value of $s(8)$. In this situation, what does $s(8)$ represent?

    b. How far has the rock fallen after 9 seconds? After 10 seconds?

    c. When does the rock hit the ground? after about 11.066 s

    d. What is the domain of the function $s(t) = 4.9t^2$ in this context?

Describe the domain of each function.

13. $f(x) = 2^x$ all real numbers

14. $g(x) = \frac{1}{x+1}$ all real numbers except $^-1$

15. $h(x) = \frac{1}{x+1} + \frac{1}{x-1}$ all real numbers except $^-1$ and 1

16. Which of the following are not graphs of functions? Explain how you know.

a.   **b.**

c.   **d.**

12a. 313.6 m, the distance the rock falls in 8 s

12b. 396.9 m, 490 m

12d. t is between 0 (including 0) and about 11.066.

16. Graphs c and d; they have values of x that are associated with two or more values of y.

17a. 7.6 m, the height of the stone after 4 s

17c.

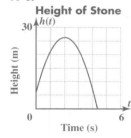

17. Suppose a person throws a stone straight upward so that its height h in meters is given by the function $h(t) = 6 + 20t - 4.9t^2$, where t represents the time in seconds since the stone was released.

    a. Find $h(4)$. What does it represent in this situation?

    b. Find the height of the stone after 3 seconds. 21.9 m

    c. Sketch a graph of the stone's height over time.

    d. Use your graph to approximate the stone's maximum height. How long does it take the stone to reach this height?
about 26.5 m, about 2 s

Exercise 16:
Students may need to be reminded of the significance of an open circle in the graph of **Part b.**

Exercise 17:
This exercise may take students a while since they may not have access to graphing calculators at home.

LESSON 8.1 Functions **507**

18. Economics ABC Deli sells several kinds of sandwiches, all at the same price. The weekly profit of this small business is a function of the price of its sandwiches. This relationship between profit, *P*, in hundreds of dollars and the price per sandwich, *s*, in dollars is given by the equation

$$P(s) = {}^-s(s - 7)$$

a. Complete the table for this function.

b. Explain the meaning of (7, 0) in terms of the deli's profit.

18b. Possible answer: If the deli sets its sandwich price at $7.00, it will not sell enough to make a profit.

c. Extend your table to search for the sandwich price that will yield the maximum profit. $3.50

d. What is the maximum profit this business can expect in a week? $1,225

s	P(s)
0	0
1	6
2	10
3	12
4	12
5	10
6	6
7	0

Find the maximum value of each function, and then determine the input value that yields that maximum value.

19. $f(t) = 200t - 5t^2$ 2,000; 20   **20.** $k(t) = 4 + 4t - 4t^2$ 5; 0.5

21. Marcus gave his little brother an 8-meter strip of cardboard for making a rectangular fort for his toy soldiers.

a. Copy and complete the table, which relates possible lengths and widths for the fort.

Length (m)	0.5	1	1.5	2	2.5	3	3.5
Width (m)	3.5	3	2.5	2	1.5	1	0.5
Perimeter (m)	8	8	8	8	8	8	8
Area (m²)	1.75	3	3.75	4	3.75	3	1.75

b. Write an equation for the function that gives the width for any length *L*. Name the function *W*. Possible function: $W(L) = 4 - L$

c. Now add a row to your table showing the area of some possible rectangles. See table.

21d. $A(L) = L(4 - L)$ or $A(L) = 4L - L^2$

21e.
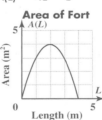

Area of Fort

Area (m²) vs Length (m)

d. Write an equation for the function *A* giving the area for length *L*.

e. Use your function from Part d to sketch a graph of the fort's area in terms of its length.

f. What dimensions give the greatest area for the fort? 2 m by 2 m

508 CHAPTER 8 Functions and Their Graphs

22. Geometry Roof gutters are designed to channel rainwater away from the roof of a house, protecting the house from excess moisture.

If you cut through a gutter and look at its side view, you see a *cross section.* Here are some cross sections of gutters.

Nicky's Metalworks wants to produce some gutters from a roll of metal that is 39 cm wide. They want the gutters to have vertical sides. Nicky has drawn some possible cross sections.

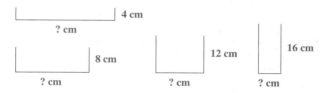

a. To keep the gutters from overflowing during heavy rainfall, the company wants them to have the greatest cross-sectional area possible. Copy and complete the table to show the widths and areas for gutters of various heights.

Height (cm), h	4	8	12	16
Width (cm), w	31	23	15	7
Area (cm²), A	124	184	180	112

b. Find a formula for width w in terms of height h. $w = 39 - 2h$

c. Write an equation for the cross-sectional area A as a function of h. What sort of function is it? $A(h) = h(39 - 2h) = 39h - 2h^2$, quadratic

d. Sketch a graph of the area function.

e. Estimate the gutter height that gives the greatest area.

22d. Roof Gutters

Area (cm²) vs Height (cm)

200, $A(h)$, 0, 25, h

22e. about 10 cm (9.75 cm exactly)

Exercises 23–25:
Students may describe, rather than draw, their machines.

Exercise 27:
Students are given several examples for the relationship between the sum of the interior angles of a polygon and the number of sides the polygon has, although they have to work a little to identify the numbers involved. You may need to prompt them to make a table, using the introductory paragraph:

Number of Sides	Angle Sum
3	180
4	360
5	540
6	720

This is a linear function. Students should be able to see the constant difference and either continue the table or write the function.

Connect & Extend

23. Possible answer:

24. Possible answer:

25. Possible answer:

26a. Possible graph:

26b. Yes; there is just one temperature for any given time.

27c. Whole numbers greater than or equal to 3; the number of sides must be a whole number, and 3 is the smallest such input since a triangle is the polygon with the least number of sides.

23. Create a function machine that produces 3 more than twice every input as an output.

24. Create a function machine that produces 1 less than one-third every input as an output.

25. Create a function machine that returns an odd number for any whole-number input.

26. Physical Science Think about the relationship between the temperature of a hot cup of coffee and the time (in minutes) since the coffee was poured.

a. Sketch a graph of how you think the relationship between temperature and time might look. (Hint: Think about the rate at which the coffee cools. Does it cool more quickly at first?)

b. Is this relationship a function? If so, explain why.

27. Geometry The sum of the interior angles of a polygon is a function of the number of sides the polygon has. For example, the sum of the interior angles of a triangle is 180°, of a square is 360°, of a pentagon is 540°, and of a hexagon is 720°.

a. What is the sum of the interior angles of a polygon with 12 sides (a dodecagon)? Use the pattern in the angle sums for the polygons mentioned above. 1,800°

b. Write an equation for the function relating the number of sides to the angle sum. Name the function g, and use s to represent the number of sides. $g(s) = 180(s - 2)$

c. What is the domain of this function? Explain your answer.

510 CHAPTER 8 Functions and Their Graphs

Challenge In Exercises 28–30, write an equation for a function f that does *not* have the given numbers in its domain.

28. 3 and $^-3$ Possible function: $f(x) = \frac{1}{x^2 - 9}$

29. negative numbers Possible function: $f(x) = \sqrt{x}$

30. positive numbers Possible function: $f(x) = \sqrt{-x}$

Use the given graph and a table of values, if necessary, to find the minimum value of each function and the input that produces it.

31. $f(x) = x + x^2$ $(^-0.25; ^-0.5)$ **32.** $f(x) = 1 - x + x^2$ $(0.75; 0.5)$

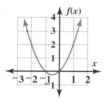 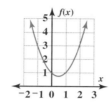

33. You can think of a *sequence* as a function for which the input variables are the counting numbers $(1, 2, 3, 4, \ldots)$. For example, the sequence of even whole numbers greater than zero—2, 4, 6, 8, . . .— can be given by the function $f(n) = 2n$, where $1, 2, 3, 4, \ldots$ are the inputs.

   a. List the first seven terms of the sequence described by the function $g(n) = \frac{1}{2^n}$, for n starting at 1. $\frac{1}{2}, \frac{1}{4}, \frac{1}{8}, \frac{1}{16}, \frac{1}{32}, \frac{1}{64}, \frac{1}{128}$

   b. Add the first five terms of this sequence. $\frac{31}{32}$

   c. Add the first six terms of this sequence. $\frac{63}{64}$

   d. Add the first seven terms of this sequence. $\frac{127}{128}$

   e. Suppose you were to add *all* the terms of this sequence for some large value of n—such as 100 terms. Do you think the sum of this sequence approaches a particular value, or do you think it increases indefinitely? The sum approaches 1.

34. Two numbers add to 1. What is the maximum value of their *product*? Explain.
0.25; If one number is x, the other is $1 - x$, so the product is $x(1 - x)$. Using a table of values, the maximum value of $x(1 - x)$ is 0.25 (when $x = 0.5$).

In your
own
words

Give one example of a function that can be described by an algebraic equation and one example of a function that can't. Explain how you know that both of your examples are functions.

Exercises 28–30:
These exercises are challenges because they require a different kind of thinking from what students have used in the investigation. Some students may find it difficult to switch gears in this way.

Exercise 33:
This is an example of a geometric sequence: each term is multiplied by a constant to get the next term. In second-year algebra, students will learn how to sum these sequences using a formula.

Exercise 34:
It may be interesting to bring up the similarity of this exercise to the work students did maximizing area of a rectangle for a given perimeter. In that case, the values that produce the maximum are the values that make the sides a square—that is, making the two values multiplied together equal, as is the case here as well.

Quick Check

Informal Assessment

Students should be able to:

- ✔ understand the definition of a function
- ✔ understand different ways of representing functions
- ✔ identify functions in a variety of contexts and representations
- ✔ describe the domain of a given function
- ✔ find the maximum or minimum value of a function from its graph

Quick Quiz

1. What is a *function*? **a relationship between two variables in which there is only one output for each input**

2. Determine whether each relationship defines a function. If it does not, state why not.

   a. Input: a number
      Output: 1 less than the number **function**

   b. Input: a street name
      Output: a town in which that street can be found **Not a function; there can be more than one town with the same street name.**

★ indicates multi-step problem

35a. 0.5 in.³, 6 in.³

35c. $y = \frac{6}{8x}$ or $y = \frac{3}{4x}$

35d. Possible formulas:
$$S = 2(8x) + 2(8)\left(\frac{3}{4x}\right) + 2x\left(\frac{3}{4x}\right) \text{ or}$$
$$S = 16x + \frac{12}{x} + \frac{3}{2}$$

Mixed Review

512 CHAPTER 8 Functions and Their Graphs

35. Economics A company that manufactures charcoal pencils for artists has decided to redesign the shipping boxes for the pencils. The pencils are in the shape of rectangular prisms, with a 0.25-inch-by-0.25-inch base and a length of 8 inches. The manufacturer plans to package a dozen pencils in each box.

  a. Calculate the volume of a single pencil. Then find the volume each box must contain—that is, find the volume of 12 pencils.

  b. One dimension of the box must be the length of the pencils, 8 in. Using *x, y,* and 8 for the dimensions of the box, write a formula for the volume a box can hold. $V = 8xy$

  c. Use the total volume of the 12 pencils, along with your formula from Part b, to write an equation for *y* in terms of *x.*

The company wants to use as little cardboard as possible in making the boxes.

  ★ **d.** Write a formula for the surface area *S* of the box, using only *x* as the input variable. Ignore the area of the flaps that hold the box together. (Hint: You may want to write it using *x* and *y* first, and then replace *y* with an expression in terms of *x.*)

  e. Make a table of values giving the surface area of the box for different values of *x.* Since the pencils are 0.25 in. wide, the dimensions of the box must be multiples of 0.25 in.—for example, 0.25 in., 0.5 in., and 0.75 in.   See Additional Answers.

  f. What dimensions should the box be so that it uses the least amount of cardboard?   0.75 in. by 1 in. by 8 in.

Set up and solve a proportion to answer each question.

36. 32.2 is 92% of what number? $\frac{32.2}{x} = \frac{92}{100}$, $x = 35$

37. What percent of 125 is 90? $\frac{90}{125} = \frac{n}{100}$, $n = 72$, 72%

38. What is 81% of 36? $\frac{x}{36} = \frac{81}{100}$, $x = 29.16$

Write each expression in the form 7^b.

39. $\frac{7^{23}}{7^{15}}$ 7^8 **40.** $(7^3)^{10}$ 7^{30} **41.** $\left(\frac{1}{7}\right)^{11}$ 7^{-11}

42. A rule for translating a figure on a coordinate grid changes the original coordinates (x, y) to the image coordinates $(x - 2, y + 3)$. On a coordinate grid, show the translation vector for this rule.
Possible answer:

512 CHAPTER 8 Functions and Their Graphs

35e.

x	s
0.25 in.	53.5 in²
0.5 in.	33.5 in²
0.75 in.	29.5 in²
1 in.	29.5 in²
1.5 in.	33.5 in²
3 in.	53.5 in²

Match each equation with one of the graphs.

43. $y = x^2 - 3$ Graph b

44. $y = {}^-x^2$ Graph d

45. $y = x^2$ Graph a

46. $y = x^2 - 5x + 4$ Graph c

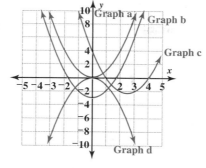

Rewrite each expression as a square with a constant added or subtracted.

47. $x^2 + 12x + 17 = x^2 + 12x + 36 - \underline{19} = (x + 6)^2 - \underline{19}$

48. $k^2 - 14k + 70$ $(k - 7)^2 + 21$

49. $b^2 + 5b - \frac{3}{4}$ $\left(b + \frac{5}{2}\right)^2 - 7$

50. Geometry This is a map of Golden Gate Park in San Francisco.

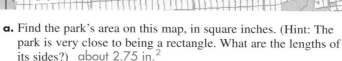

Remember
There are 5,280 feet in
1 mile and 12 inches in
1 foot.

a. Find the park's area on this map, in square inches. (Hint: The park is very close to being a rectangle. What are the lengths of its sides?)   about 2.75 in.²

★ **b.** The area of Golden Gate Park is about 1,017 acres, or about 1.59 square miles. Find the scale factor from this map to the actual park. (Hint: A scale factor is a comparison of the same linear, not square, units.)   about 48,200

c. About how many miles long is the northern (top) border of Golden Gate Park, along Fulton Street?   about 3 mi

LESSON 8.1 Functions **513**

3. Consider a function that takes a number, subtracts 1, and then squares the result.

a. Which of the following describe this function? ii and iii

    i. $y = x^2 - 1$
    ii. $f(x) = (x - 1)^2$
    iii. $p = (r - 1)^2$
    iv. $t(s) = s^2 - 1$

b. Is there a function that will undo this one? If so, state the function. If not, explain why not. No; to undo squaring would require taking the square root, which has two possibilities (positive and negative roots).

4. Draw a graph that does not represent a function. Possible graph:

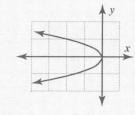

5. Describe the domain of $f(x) = \frac{3}{x^2 - 4}$. all real numbers except ± 2

6. Mr. D'Orazio has 50 feet of fencing. He wants to create a rectangular pen with the maximum area possible. What should be the dimensions of the rectangle? 12.5 ft by 12.5 ft

Teacher Notes

Graphs of Functions

Objectives

▶ To understand how horizontal and vertical translations of a graph are related to the equation of the function

▶ To specify the range of a function and understand the relationship between the range of a function and its maximum or minimum point

▶ To use x-intercepts and completing the square to find the line of symmetry and vertex of a parabola

▶ To use graphs to find approximate solutions to equations

Overview (pacing: about 5 class periods)

As one representation of a function, graphs provide easily accessible information about the nature of a function. In this lesson, students use graphs to compare families of functions, explore the range of a function, identify characteristics of parabolas, and find approximate solutions of equations.

In the case of parabolas, students extend their knowledge of lines of symmetry and vertices to explore how the equation of a parabola and its graphical representation are related. Throughout the lesson, students use graphing calculators to estimate x-intercepts and approximate solutions to equations they cannot solve by the algebraic methods they have learned thus far.

Advance Preparation

Students will need tracing paper for the introductory Think & Discuss activity. For Investigation 2, you may want to give students copies of Master 50, which reproduces the graphs for Problem Set E. They will also need GeoMirrors in Investigation 3.

	Summary	Materials	On Your Own Exercises	Assessment Opportunities
Investigation 1 page T515	Students compare families of functions to see how horizontal and vertical translations occur in both graphs and equations.	• Tracing paper • Graphing calculators • Overhead graphing calculator (optional)	Practice & Apply: 1–6, pp. 528–529 Connect & Extend: 30–35, pp. 532–533 Mixed Review: 47–60, pp. 536–537	On the Spot Assessment, page T517 Share & Summarize, pages T517, 517 Troubleshooting, page T517
Investigation 2 page T518	Students explore the connection between a function and its range. They give particular attention to quadratic functions and how the range can help them graph the function.	• Graphing calculators • Master 50 (optional)	Practice & Apply: 7–18, pp. 529–530 Connect & Extend: 36–40, pp. 533–534 Mixed Review: 47–60, pp. 536–537	Share & Summarize, pages T522, 522 Troubleshooting, page T522
Investigation 3 page A665	Students use the x-intercepts of graphs of quadratics to determine a parabola's line of symmetry and vertex.	*• GeoMirrors	Practice & Apply: 19–23, pp. 530–532 Connect & Extend: 41, 42, p. 534 Mixed Review: 47–60, pp. 536–537	Share & Summarize, pages T524, 524 Troubleshooting, page T524
Investigation 4 page T525	Students explore ways to approximate solutions to equations using the intersection of graphs.	• Overhead graphing calculator (optional) • Graphing calculators	Practice & Apply: 24–29, p. 532 Connect & Extend: 43–46, pp. 534–535 Mixed Review: 47–60, pp. 536–537	Share & Summarize, pages T527, 527 Troubleshooting, page T527 Informal Assessment, page 536 Quick Quiz, page 537

* Included in Impact Mathematics Manipulative Kit

Introduce

 To begin this lesson, you might remind students about the work they did in Chapter 5 with translations and dilation. Explain that in this lesson they will be looking at the graphs of some functions they have studied previously (quadratic, reciprocal, exponential) to study the effects of translations and dilation on functions.

 Have the class read the text before the cartoon and the cartoon itself. Then move right into the Think & Discuss on page 515.

8.2 Graphs of Functions

Ms. Torres drew the graphs and table below to show his class that the graphs of $f(x) = x^2$ and $g(x) = (x - 3)^2$ are related.

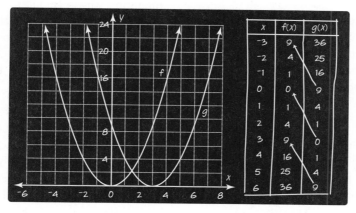

Ms. Torres then asked the class why the graphs look as they do.

Think & Discuss

This Think & Discuss illustrates ways students might think about the effects of adding or subtracting a constant in the rule for a function. Some of these questions are a review of earlier work. However, it is important for students to understand that Marcus, Bharati, Jesse, and Kai are thinking about different representations of functions (the rules, the description in words, the table). Each representation helps the students make sense of how the graphs are related, and why one graph is 3 units to the right of the other, in a different way.

Often students think the graph of $g(x) = (x - 3)^2$ is a translation to the left, rather than to the right, of $f(x) = x^2$, since they see a subtraction sign and connect subtraction with moving left on a number line. If this confusion occurs, you might ask students what the least possible value of $g(x)$ is. When students realize that this value is 0, they can then figure out that this occurs when $x = 3$.

You may find it useful to have an overhead graphing calculator to test students' predictions of what the graph of $h(x) = (x + 4)^2$ looks like.

For the last question, students may need to be reminded what a translation is.

Investigation 1

In this investigation, students explore families of functions, including quadratic, reciprocal, and exponential functions. These families are related by horizontal and vertical translations, and students are expected to describe the translations by looking at the equation and the graph.

You may want to have students graph the functions in this investigation by hand; the functions are accessible, and the practice will reinforce students' understanding of graphing: which numbers to choose for x, how to estimate the domain of x, and so on. If students graph by hand, you may want to complete this investigation over two days, stopping after Problem Set B on the first day. The student text specifically refers to graphing calculators; if you choose to have students graph by hand, the only difference in the directions would be in the creation of the graphs.

Problem Set A Grouping: Pairs or Groups of Four
If students work in pairs, one should graph the set of graphs in **Problem 1,** and the other should graph the set of graphs in **Problem 2.** Make sure students understand that they should keep these graphs for answering **Problem 3.**

When describing how the graphs are alike and different in **Part b,** let students know that it is helpful if they begin with a "parent" graph for the basis of comparison. Such a graph would be the most basic example of that type of graph. For Problem 1, the parent graph is $y = x^2$. For Problem 2, the parent graph is $y = \frac{1}{x}$. If you think it would be useful, encourage students to use the terms *quadratic* and *reciprocal functions* when referring to these two sets of graphs.

Functions other than quadratic functions are introduced to ensure that students don't develop the misconception that the relationships between functions and their graphs involving translations apply only to quadratics.

Problem Set Wrap-Up You may want to bring the class together to discuss answers to Problem 3.

Think & Discuss

Which of the four students' comments do you find the most helpful in understanding why the graphs look as they do? Explain. **Answers will vary.**

Describe in your own words why it seems reasonable for the graph of $g(x) = (x - 3)^2$ to be 3 units to the right of the graph of $f(x) = x^2$. **See ① below.**

Trace the graph of $f(x) = x^2$. Place your tracing on top of the graph of $g(x) = (x - 3)^2$, lining up the parabolas. Are the parabolas congruent? **yes**

The graph of $g(x) = (x - 3)^2$ is related to that of $f(x) = x^2$ by a translation. What are the direction and distance of the translation? **right 3 units**

Predict what the graph of $h(x) = (x + 4)^2$ looks like. Test your prediction by graphing with your calculator. **the same shape as the graph of f and 4 units to the left**

Is the graph of h related to the graph of f by a translation? If so, specify the direction and the distance of the translation. **yes, left 4 units**

---

① Possible answer: If we add 3 to each value of x in g, we'll have the graph of f. Adding 3 is the same as shifting x to the right.

Investigation ▶ 1 Comparing Graphs of Functions

In this investigation, you will explore sets of related functions.

Problem Set A   See Additional Answers.

For Problems 1 and 2, do Parts a–c. Work in pairs or groups of four. Your group will need two graphing calculators, one for each problem.

a. Graph the four equations in the same window, and make a quick sketch of the graphs. Don't erase your graphs for Problem 1 when you go on to Problem 2; you will need both sets for Problem 3.

b. Describe how the four graphs in the set are alike and different. Use the concept of translation in your comparisons.

c. Write equations for two more functions that belong in the set.

1. $j(x) = (x + 1)^2$
$f(x) = x^2$
$g(x) = (x - 1)^2$
$h(x) = (x - 2)^2$

2. $j(x) = \frac{1}{x + 1}$
$f(x) = \frac{1}{x}$
$g(x) = \frac{1}{x - 1}$
$h(x) = \frac{1}{x - 2}$

3. Describe how the two sets of graphs are alike and different.

4. On which graph would you find the point $(4, 9)$? Explain.

LESSON 8.2 Graphs of Functions **515**

Additional Answers
Problem Set A

1a.

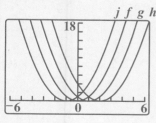

1b. All four graphs have the same shape. Each is a translation of f: g, 1 unit to the right; h, 2 units to the right; and j, 1 unit to the left.

1c. Possible answer: $m(x) = (x + 3)^2$, $k(x) = (x - 4)^2$

- **Additional Answers continued on page A686**

Problem Set B Grouping: Pairs or Groups of Four

In this problem set, students focus on two more functions and consider the effects of horizontal translations on the equations and the graphs. Students are expected to generalize from their experience with quadratic and reciprocal functions in Problem Set A.

This section is included to help students develop some fluency with the approaches to graphing functions and to recognizing patterns in translations.

In **Problem 2,** when considering the function $f(x) = 2x^2$, students need to recognize that the coefficient of x^2 has no effect on the translation.

 Problem Set C Grouping: Pairs or Groups of Four

In this problem set, students again need to use two calculators to graph the first two sets of functions (unless you prefer they graph by hand). These families represent different *vertical* translations of the parent functions $y = 2^x$ and $y = \frac{1}{x}$. Some of this will be review of past material, but not from a functional point of view.

1b.

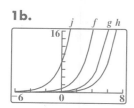

2b.

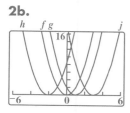

3. $j(x) = 2^{x+3}$.
Possible explanation:
For $j(x) = 2^{x+3}$, the output is 1 for an input of -3, so $(-3, 1)$ is on the graph of this function.

1a.

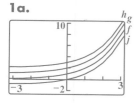

1b. All four graphs have the same shape. Each is a translation of f: g, 1 unit up; h, 2 units up; and j, 1 unit down.

1c. Possible answer:
$m(x) = 2^x - 4$,
$k(x) = 2^x + 5$

Problem Set B

Work in pairs or groups of four on this problem set.

1. Consider the function $f(x) = 2^x$.

  a. Write equations for three functions, *g*, *h*, and *j*, so that their graphs have the same shape as the graph of *f*, but

    i. *g* is translated 2 units to the right of *f*. $g(x) = 2^{x-2}$

    ii. *h* is translated 3 units to the right of *f*. $h(x) = 2^{x-3}$

    iii. *j* is translated 3 units to the left of *f*. $j(x) = 2^{x+3}$

  b. Graph the four functions in the same window, and make a quick sketch of the graphs.

2. Consider the function $f(x) = 2x^2$.

  a. Write equations for three functions, *g*, *h*, and *j*, so that their graphs have the same shape as the graph of *f*, but

    i. *g* is translated 1 unit to the right of *f*. $g(x) = 2(x - 1)^2$

    ii. *h* is translated 2 units to the left of *f*. $h(x) = 2(x + 2)^2$

    iii. *j* is translated 3 units to the right of *f*. $j(x) = 2(x - 3)^2$

  b. Graph the four functions in the same window, and make a quick sketch of the graphs.

3. On which graph from Problems 1 and 2 would you find the point $(-3, 1)$? Explain how you found your answer.

Problem Set C

Work in pairs or groups of four again. Your group will need two graphing calculators. For Problems 1 and 2, do Parts a–c.

  a. Graph the four equations in the same window, and make a quick sketch of the graphs, remembering to label them. Don't erase your graphs for Problem 1 when you go on to Problem 2.

  b. Describe how the four graphs in the set are alike and different. Use the concept of translation in your comparisons.

  c. Write two more functions that belong in the set.

1. $j(x) = 2^x - 1$

    $f(x) = 2^x$

    $g(x) = 2^x + 1$

    $h(x) = 2^x + 2$

1 You may have students work in pairs or groups of four.

2 You may have students work in pairs or groups of four, with two graphing calculators per group.

On the Spot Assessment

In **Problem 2,** watch for students who do not enter the functions properly on their calculators: $\frac{1}{x+1}$ as opposed to $\frac{1}{x} + 1$, for example. This might be a good opportunity to discuss the use of parentheses and order of operations.

Share & Summarize

These questions generalize the results of the translations students have been doing in the investigation. In essence, replacing x with $x + h$ translates the graph left or right, when h is positive or negative, respectively. Also, adding a constant h to a function translates the graph up or down, again if h is positive or negative, respectively.

As an extension to these questions, you might give students the function $f(x) = x^4 - 3x^3 + x^2 + x - 5$ and ask them to write a function that translates its graph 2 units to the right.

Troubleshooting If students are having difficulty with these translations, you may want to have them create their own families of functions. For example, ask them to take the parent function $f(x) = x^2$ and create a family that moves this function up and down, or right and left. Then have them use their graphing calculators to experiment with different equations to produce these translations. Be careful with linear functions, though; translating up is identical to translating left, although not necessarily by the same number of units.

On Your Own Exercises

Practice & Apply: 1–6, pp. 528–529
Connect & Extend: 30–35, pp. 532–533
Mixed Review: 47–60, pp. 536–537

2a.

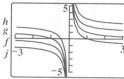

2b. All four graphs have the same shape. Each is a translation of f: g, 1 unit up; h, 2 units up; and j, 1 unit down.

2c. Possible answer: $m(x) = \frac{1}{x} + 4$, $k(x) = \frac{1}{x} - 5$

4. $g(x) = \frac{1}{x} + 1$; Possible explanation: For $g(x) = \frac{1}{x} + 1$, the output is $\frac{4}{3}$ for an input of 3, so $\left(3, \frac{4}{3}\right)$ is on the graph of this function.

Share & Summarize Answer

2. Possible answer: No matter what type of function f and g are, they will have the same shape, but g will be translated h units above (if h is positive) or below (if h is negative) f.

2. $j(x) = \frac{1}{x} - 1$

$f(x) = \frac{1}{x}$

$g(x) = \frac{1}{x} + 1$

$h(x) = \frac{1}{x} + 2$

3. Describe how the two sets of graphs are alike and how they are different.   See Additional Answers.

4. On which graph would you find the point $\left(3, \frac{4}{3}\right)$? Explain.

Share & Summarize

1. Possible answer: No matter what type of function f and g are, they will have the same shape, but g will be translated h units to the left (if h is positive) or right (if h is negative) of f.

1. Suppose you have the graph of a function f. You create a new function g by using the rule for f but replacing the variable x by the expression $x + h$, for some constant h. If $f(x) = 2x$, for example, you might replace x with $x + 3$ to get $g(x) = 2(x + 3)$. If $f(x) = 3x^2 - 2$, you might replace x with $x - 5$ to get $g(x) = 3(x - 5)^2 - 2$.

Write a sentence or two describing the differences and similarities between the graphs of f and g. You may want to draw sketches to help you explain.

2. Suppose you create a function g by adding a constant h to f—for example, $f(x) = 2x$ and $g(x) = 2x + 3$, or $f(x) = 3x^2 - 2$ and $g(x) = 3x^2 - 7$. Describe the differences and similarities between the graphs of f and g. You may want to include sketches.

3. Suppose you want to know whether the point (a, b) is on the graph of a function. How could you find out?
Treat a as the input of the function and calculate the output. If the output is b, the point (a, b) is on the graph.

1 Watch for students who do not enter these functions properly.

2 Discuss students' generalizations of the effects of translations.

Additional Answers
Problem Set C

3. They are similar in that the graph of each function in a set is translated 1 unit up from the graph of the previous function. They are different in that the functions in each set are of different types: Problem 1 has exponential functions, and Problem 2 has inverse variations.

Investigation 2

In this investigation, students are introduced to the concept of *range*. For quadratic functions, they also consider the relation between range and the maximum or minimum point (vertex) of a parabola.

The investigation formalizes what students may have already noticed: that graphs of quadratic functions are parabolas, that parabolas have a vertical line of symmetry, and that the turning point of a parabola lies on the line of symmetry. These observations, together with the relationship between the equation of the line of symmetry and the form of the function rule $f(x) = (x + h)^2 + k$, allow students to readily visualize the graph of a quadratic function.

You might introduce the investigation by reminding students that parabolas—that is, the graphs of quadratic functions—are symmetric. Point out that, for most y values, there are two points on a parabola that have that y value. Then go into the Think & Discuss.

Think & Discuss

These questions allow students to begin thinking about the concept of range, which is defined in the text following the Think & Discuss. Students should be able to understand that $f(x)$ cannot take values less than 1. These questions also give students practice in using function notation. Make sure they understand that in the first two questions, they are given output values (values of $f(x)$) and are asked to find the corresponding input values (x).

Define the *range* of a function for students: all possible output values of the function. Refer to the function they looked at in the Think & Discuss as an example: for $f(x) = (x - 2)^2 + 1$, the range is all numbers greater than or equal to 1.

Investigation 2 ▶ Working with Graphs

Earlier you saw that the maximum or minimum value of a quadratic function can be found by looking at the vertex of its graph, which is a parabola. You also learned that parabolas are *symmetric*—they can be folded on a line of symmetry so that the two sides match.

You will now examine connections between the graph and the equation of a quadratic function. You'll also learn what the range of a function is and how it relates to the maximum or minimum point.

1 Remind students that parabolas are symmetric.

2 Help students begin thinking about the range of a function.

3 Define range.

Think & Discuss

Look at this graph of $f(x) = (x - 2)^2 + 1$. Find the values of x for which

$f(x) = 1$ **2** $f(x) = 2$ **1 or 3** $f(x) = 5$ **0 or 4**

Now find values of x for which

No such values exist.

$f(x) = 0$ $f(x) = {}^-1$ $f(x) = {}^-5$

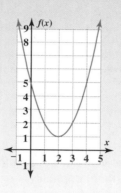

Describe all possible values for $f(x)$.   See ①.

Describe all values $f(x)$ can never be.   See ②.

① all numbers greater than or equal to 1

② all numbers less than 1

VOCABULARY
range

Just the facts

A biologist might need to know the range of a function modeling the temperature of a body of water over time to study how water temperature affects an organism living there.

All the possible *output* values of a function f are the **range** of the function. For the function graphed above, the range is $f(x) \geq 1$. No matter what you substitute for x, the value of $f(x)$ will always be greater than or equal to 1—and every value greater than or equal to 1 has an input value. Numbers less than 1 are not in the range of $f(x) = (x - 2)^2 + 1$.

Develop

 Problem Set D Suggested Grouping: Pairs
In this problem set, students are asked to specify the domain and range of a variety of functions. Note that use of a graphing calculator is optional; depending on your students, you may want to let them graph the functions so they can see what values are possible.

 Problem 1 may need some discussion as a class, since it requires students to understand that if a positive number is raised to any power, it will always be positive. Since students sometimes mistakenly think that a number raised to a negative power produces a negative result, this may be a good time to review negative exponents.

In **Problem 2,** students need to understand that $h(s)$ can never be 0. Again, they may need to be reminded that $\frac{1}{0}$ does not equal 0.

 For **Problem 5,** some students may be unsure what to do about irrational numbers such as $\sqrt{5}$. You might ask them for another way to write the number or for an estimate of the number. Try to get them to think of decimal equivalents, or suggest the idea to them explicitly. For example, $\sqrt{5}$ is approximately 2.2, so the integer part of $\sqrt{5}$ is 2.

About the Mathematics

There is a difference between a *number* and a *numeral*. A number is a quantity; for example, the typical *number* of fingers on a hand is a quantity called "five." A *numeral* is a symbol by which a number may be represented; 5 and V are both numerals for the number "five." So, one can talk about the integer part of a number regardless of how it's represented.

Problem Set Wrap-Up Review the answers to these problems briefly to be sure students understand what the range is (especially in conjunction with the domain).

 Example
Preface the Example by telling students that it's not always easy to determine the range of a function. Explain that with a quadratic function, it is often helpful to look at the graph and examine the vertex. Then refer students to the graph in the Example. Point out that the line of symmetry is $x = 2$, and the turning point, or vertex, is at the point where $x = 2$. Have students substitute 2 for x in the function to find that $f(2) = 1$, so the vertex is at (2, 1).

Students need to understand that the line of symmetry always passes through the vertex of the parabola.

Problem Set D

For each function, specify the domain (possible inputs) and range (possible outputs). For some functions, it may help to make a graph with a calculator.

1. $g(x) = 4^{x+2}$ (Hint: Can $g(x)$ be negative? Zero?)

2. $h(s) = \frac{1}{s+3}$ domain: all real numbers except $s = {}^-3$;
                                 range: all real numbers except 0

3. $c(x) = {}^-3x + 4$

4. Input: a state   domain: the 50 states; range: the 50 state capitals
    Output: the capital of that state

5. Input: a number   domain: all real numbers; range: all integers
    Output: the integer part of that number (For example, if the input is 4.5, the output is 4; if the input is $^-3.2$, the output is $^-3$.)

1. domain: all real
numbers; range:
$f(x) > 0$

3. domain: all real
numbers; range: all
real numbers

It's not always easy to determine the range of a function. You can test a few logical input values and draw some conclusions from the outputs, or you can graph the function. In Problem Set E, you will see how the range of a quadratic function is related to its vertex. To begin, consider how to find the vertex.

Remember

A parabola has its maximum or minimum value at the vertex.

EXAMPLE

This graph is of the function $f(x) = (x - 2)^2 + 1$.

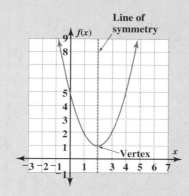

For this parabola, the line of symmetry is the line $x = 2$.

The turning point, or *vertex*, is the point on the graph where $x = 2$. When $x = 2$, $f(x) = (2 - 2)^2 + 1 = 1$, so the vertex has coordinates $(2, 1)$.

1 You may have students work in pairs.

2 Some students may need help understanding that a positive number raised to any power is always positive.

3 Students may need help interpreting this function for irrational inputs.

4 Discuss how to find the vertex of a parabola.

1 **Problem Set E** Suggested Grouping: Pairs

In this problem set, students examine how the range of a quadratic function is related to its vertex. At the end of the problem set, students are expected to generalize the effects of h and k on the parabola $f(x) = (x - h)^2 + k$. Students should develop an awareness that this form of a quadratic function gives more information about the graph of the parabola than the form $f(x) = ax^2 + bx + c$.

2 You may want to ask students how they arrived at their answers to **Problem 1a;** in particular, you might ask whether they checked points on the graph to see if they satisfied either equation. You may want to distribute Master 50, which reproduces the graphs from Problem 1 so students need not sketch them in **Part b.**

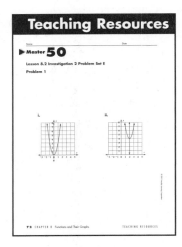

3 It is important that students understand **Problem 1e** before they continue. You may want to go over their answers to this question before they go to **Problem 2.**

In **Problem 2d,** students need to realize that if a function has a maximum point, that is, if the parabola opens down, then the range will be all values less than or equal to the y value at the vertex.

Problem Set E

1. Below are the graphs of these functions.

$$f(x) = 3x^2 \qquad g(x) = 3(x - 2)^2 + 4$$

i.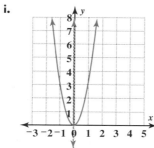

ii.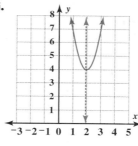

a. Without using your calculator, decide which graph represents which function.   Graph i: Function *f*; Graph ii: Function *g*

b. Sketch the graphs, and draw the line of symmetry for each.   See above.

c. What is the vertex of each graph?

d. Specify the range of each function. $f(x) \geq 0$, $g(x) \geq 4$

e. How is the range of a function related to the vertex?

2. Consider this graph.

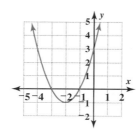

a. What is the graph's line of symmetry? What is its vertex?

b. Which of these functions does the graph represent? Explain how you know.

$$f(x) = (x + 2)^2 + 1 \qquad g(x) = (x + 2)^2 - 1$$
$$h(x) = -(x - 2)^2 + 1 \qquad i(x) = (x - 2)^2 - 1$$

c. For each function in Part b, specify the range and the vertex.

d. How is the range related to the maximum or minimum point of a function?   The range is greater than or equal to the *y*-coordinate of the minimum point, or less than or equal to the *y*-coordinate of the maximum point.

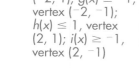

Remember

The range is the set of all possible outputs for a function.

1c. Function *f*: (0, 0); Function *g*: (2, 4)

1e. The range starts at the *y* value of the vertex (the minimum).

2a. $x = {}^-2$; $({}^-2, {}^-1)$

2b. *g;* Possible explanation: It's the only one with vertex $({}^-2, {}^-1)$.

2c. $f(x) \geq 1$, vertex $({}^-2, 1)$; $g(x) \geq {}^-1$, vertex $({}^-2, {}^-1)$; $h(x) \leq 1$, vertex $(2, 1)$; $i(x) \geq {}^-1$, vertex $(2, {}^-1)$

1 You may have students work in pairs.

2 You might ask students how they found their answers.

3 Be sure students understand this relationship before they continue.

By the time students get to **Problem 3,** they should be generalizing what they know about the form of the equation and its relation to the line of symmetry and the vertex.

In **Problem 4,** students should realize that there are an infinite number of parabolas with vertex (3, 4). You might ask them to sketch a few quickly.

Access
for all Learners

Extra Challenge You can point out that there are an infinite number of parabolas with vertex (3, 4), and then ask what other piece of information could be given to make the parabola with this vertex unique (that is, to make it the only possible parabola). **The coordinates of an additional point on the parabola will be enough.**

1 Ask students the following question:

> If you had the choice of graphing $f(x)$ from one of these two forms, which would you choose?
>
> $f(x) = 3(x + 1)^2 - 2$ or $f(x) = 3x^2 + 6x + 1$

Remind them they can rewrite all quadratic equations in the first form; to do so with an equation given in the second form, they can use a method they know from Chapter 7: completing the square.

3. Answer these questions about the function $f(x) = (x - 3)^2 - 1$ without drawing the graph.

   a. What is the line of symmetry? $x = 3$

   b. What is the vertex? $(3, {}^-1)$

4. A parabola has a vertex at the point (3, 4).

   a. Write an equation for a quadratic function whose graph has this vertex. Check your answer by graphing.

   b. Are there other parabolas with this vertex? If so, state two more. How many are there?

5. Suppose you have graphs of these quadratic functions.

$$f(x) = (x - h)^2 + k \qquad g(x) = x^2$$

   a. How is the graph of f related to the graph of g?

   b. What is the vertex of g? What is the vertex of f? $(0, 0); (h, k)$

When a quadratic function is written in a form like

$$f(x) = 2(x - 3)^2 + 1$$

you can predict the line of symmetry and the vertex of the parabola without drawing a graph.

It is much harder to visualize the graph when a quadratic function is written in a form like

$$f(x) = 2x^2 - 12x + 19$$

In this case, it is helpful to rewrite the function by completing the square, as you did in Chapter 7.

Just the facts

The sparks from a welder's torch travel in paths shaped like parabolas (ignoring the effect of wind and other factors).

4a. Possible functions: $f(x) = (x - 3)^2 + 4$ or $f(x) = {}^-2(x - 3)^2 + 4$

4b. yes; Possible functions: $f(x) = 3(x - 3)^2 + 4$ and $f(x) = {}^-4(x - 3)^2 + 4$; there are an infinite number.

5a. f is a translation of g, h units horizontally and k units vertically.

1 Discuss which of these two forms would be easier to graph and how to rewrite the harder one to look like the other.

1 **Problem Set F** Suggested Grouping: Pairs

In Chapter 7, students studied the method of completing the square by adding and subtracting the same quantity from each side of an equation. An alternative method is to add the same quantity to both sides of an equation. When working with equations in which $f(x)$ is a quantity on one side, the former method is better, since the goal is to isolate $f(x)$ on one side.

It would be helpful to do **Problem 1** with the whole class to make sure students remember the method accurately. Once students identify the vertex from the equation, ask how they would go about choosing additional points to sketch the graph in **Part d.** Encourage them to use what they know about the symmetry of parabolas when selecting these points. In **Problem 1,** for example, once they identify the vertex at $(^-4, ^-9)$, they might think about selecting points on either side of this vertex. Suggest that x values of $^-3$ and $^-5$ might be good choices. They should understand that the $f(x)$ values at these points should be the same, and this fact is a good check of whether their calculations are correct.

2 **Problem 2** can be tricky, since students need to factor $^-1$ out of some terms before they complete the square. You may want to go over this problem as an entire class if it seems to be confusing students.

Problem-Solving Strategies

- Some students might find it easier if they do *not* factor $^-1$ out of the last term, since it is not part of completing the square. If they do this, they have to be very careful about whether they should add or subtract *outside* the parentheses to keep the function equivalent:

$$f(x) = ^-(x^2 - 4x) + 1$$
$$= ^-(x^2 - 4x + 4) + 1 \ \underline{\ \ } \ 4$$

Without the complication of the $^-1$ coefficient for x^2, the 4 would be subtracted. Because of the $^-1$, though, it must be added. This keeps the function equivalent to its original form:

$$f(x) = ^-(x^2 - 4x + 4) + 1 + 4$$
$$= ^-x^2 + 4x - 4 + 1 + 4$$
$$= ^-x^2 + 4x + 1$$

- Some students may find it easier to factor $^-1$ out of all terms, complete the square as usual on the expression inside the parentheses, and then redistribute the $^-1$:

$$f(x) = ^-(x^2 - 4x - 1)$$
$$= ^-(x^2 - 4x + 4 - 1 - 4)$$
$$= ^-[(x^2 - 4x + 4) - 5]$$
$$= ^-(x^2 - 4x + 4) + 5$$

This option may be easier, particularly for students who are less comfortable with completing the square.

You may find it helpful to give students more practice with problems like Problem 2.

> **Additional Examples** Find the coordinates of the vertex by completing the square, and then graph.
>
> - $f(x) = ^-x^2 - 6x + 3 \ (^-3, 6)$
> - $g(x) = ^-2x^2 + 8x - 4 \ (2, 4)$

Share & Summarize

3 This question reviews the main point of what students have been working on in the investigation: the relationship between the range of a quadratic function and the vertex of the associated parabola. Make sure students consider the two possibilities for the vertex: when it is a maximum and when it is a minimum.

Troubleshooting If students are having difficulty with the concept of range, you may want to return to simple input/output tables and discuss the relationship of the output values to range. If they are having difficulty getting quadratic equations into the form $f(x) = a(x - h)^2 + k$ by completing the square, you may need to review the process more closely, or provide additional examples for them to work on. Also, you may want to give them a function in vertex form (such as $f(x) = 3(x - 4)^2 + 1$) and ask them to write it in $f(x) = ax^2 + bx + c$ form, to give them experience moving from one form to the other.

On Your Own Exercises

- *Teaching notes continued on page A687*

1a. $f(x) = (x + 4)^2 - 9$

1b. $x = {}^-4$

1c. $({}^-4, {}^-9)$

1d.

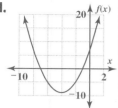

2b. $x = 2$

2c. $(2, 5)$

2d.

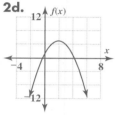

Problem Set F

For each function, do Parts a–d.

a. Complete the square to rewrite $f(x) = ax^2 + bx + c$ in the form $f(x) = a(x - h)^2 + k$.

b. Find the line of symmetry of the graph of f.

c. Find the coordinates of the vertex of the parabola.

d. Use the rewritten form of the function to sketch its graph. Check with a graphing calculator.

1. $f(x) = x^2 + 8x + 7$ **2a.** $f(x) = {}^-(x - 2)^2 + 5$

2. $f(x) = {}^-x^2 + 4x + 1$ (Hint: Factor out a $^-1$ first.)

3. $f(x) = x^2 - 6x - 3$ **3a.** $(x - 3)^2 - 12$

                              3b. $x = 3$

                              3c. $(3, {}^-12)$

Share & Summarize

Describe the relationship between a range of a quadratic function and the vertex of the related parabola.

The end value of the range is the y value of the vertex.

Investigation ▶ 3 Using x-intercepts

Recall that the y value at which a graph crosses the y-axis is called the y-intercept. In the same way, the x values at which a graph crosses the x-axis are called the **x-intercepts.**

3d.

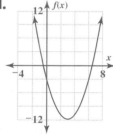

① The x-intercept is the solution of the equation.

Think & Discuss

How are the x-intercepts of the graph of a function f related to the solutions of $f(x) = 0$? For example, how is the x-intercept of $f(x) = 3x + 7$ related to the solution of $3x + 7 = 0$? See ①.

Without making a graph, find the x-intercepts of these functions:

$h(x) = (3x + 1)(x - 4)$ ${}^-\frac{1}{3}, 4$ $j(x) = x^2 - 7x - 18$ $9, {}^-2$

You will now explore how the x-intercepts of a quadratic function are related to each other and to a parabola's line of symmetry.

1 After completing Problem 1 with the class, you may have students work in pairs.

2 You may need to discuss Problem 2 with the class also.

3 Be sure students consider when the vertex is a minimum and when it is a maximum.

4 Introduce x-intercepts.

5 Help students connect the y value to the value of f(x).

Develop

1 **Problem Set G** Suggested Grouping: Pairs
In these problems, students notice that the *x*-intercepts are reflections of each other over the line of symmetry. They use their GeoMirrors to demonstrate this.

2 **Problem 5** asks students to solve the quadratic equation associated with the quadratic function *f*. It is important that students be able to articulate the difference between the quadratic function, $f(x) = 3x^2 - 3x - 6$, and the quadratic equation, $0 = 3x^2 - 3x - 6$. You may want to ask them how many points satisfy the first (an infinite number) and how many points satisfy the second (two). Or, you might ask where the solutions to the equation lie on the graph of $y = f(x)$. (They are the *x*-intercepts of $f(x)$, or the places where $f(x) = 0$.)

Problem 6 asks students to check their estimates in Problem 4 with the solutions they found in Problem 5. Both answers should be $\frac{3}{2}$. This is to help them see that the line of symmetry is halfway between the two solutions. The Example will make use of this fact.

3 **Problem Set Wrap-Up** You may want to go over students' answers to Problems 4 and 6 before moving on to the Example. It may help students connect the work they just did with the process presented in the Example if you ask for suggestions about how what they did in Problem Set G might help them sketch a graph of the function.

4 ## Example
In this example, students learn how to use the intercepts of the graph of a quadratic function to make a quick sketch of the graph. They need to understand that the *x*-coordinate of the vertex must be halfway between the values of the *x*-intercepts. Once they find the *x*-coordinate of the vertex, they can find the second coordinate by evaluating the function at that *x* value. Before students go on to Problem Set H, make sure they can articulate the process they will use to sketch these graphs from factored forms.

MATERIALS

GeoMirror

Problem Set G

The graph shows the function
$f(x) = 3x^2 - 3x - 6$.

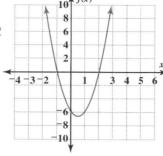

1. Estimate the x-intercepts of f. $^-1$, 2

2. Find the line of symmetry. $x = \frac{1}{2}$

3. The reflection of the left x-intercept is the right x-intercept.

3. On each side of the line of symmetry is an x-intercept. Use your GeoMirror to find a reflection of the x-intercept on the left side over the line of symmetry. What do you notice?

4. $\frac{3}{2}$ units

4. Find the distance between each estimated x-intercept and the line of symmetry.

5. Find the exact values of the x-intercepts by solving the equation $3x^2 - 3x - 6 = 0$. $^-1$, 2

6. Check that the distance between each x-intercept you found in Problem 5 and the line of symmetry is equal to your answer from Problem 4. $\frac{1}{2} - ^-1 = \frac{3}{2}$ and $2 - \frac{1}{2} = \frac{3}{2}$

You can find the x-intercepts and the vertex of the graph of a quadratic function and use them to make a quick sketch of the graph.

EXAMPLE

Sketch a graph of the function $g(x) = (3x - 7)(x + 1)$ without using a calculator.

The x-intercepts of g are the solutions of $(3x - 7)(x + 1) = 0$. Since one factor must be 0, the solutions are $\frac{7}{3}$ and $^-1$.

The vertex must be halfway between these x-intercepts, so its x value is the mean of the solutions: $\frac{\frac{7}{3} + ^-1}{2} = \frac{2}{3}$. Since $g\left(\frac{2}{3}\right) = -\frac{25}{3}$, the vertex is $\left(\frac{2}{3}, -\frac{25}{3}\right)$.

Now plot the vertex and the points where the graph of g crosses the x-axis, $\left(\frac{7}{3}, 0\right)$ and $(^-1, 0)$, and then draw a parabola through the three points.

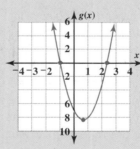

You may have students work in pairs.

Help students see the difference between the function and the equation.

Discuss answers to Problems 4 and 6.

Show students how to use the intercepts to make a quick sketch.

LESSON 8.2   Graphs of Functions   **523**

Problem Set H Suggested Grouping: Pairs

In this problem set, students are given quadratic functions and asked to find the x-intercepts, to use those values to find the vertex, and then to sketch the graph of the function.

In **Problem 3,** students need to factor the expression first. It might be interesting to ask students whether they think this method is simpler than completing the square to find the vertex. Of course, it is not always possible to factor quadratic expressions, and in the situations for which they cannot be factored, completing the square can always be used to rewrite the function.

In **Problem 4,** students reverse the process, using a given graph to determine the x-intercepts and the function. You can use this problem to make the distinction between the quadratic expression set equal to 0, and the quadratic expression set equal to $f(t)$, which is the function definition.

Share & Summarize

In this question, students need not solve the equation, but instead need to explain how they would go about finding the x-intercepts and the vertex. You can extend this by asking how to use that information to sketch the graph.

You might also ask students to explain the method they would use to find the solutions to this equation (factoring, completing the square, or the quadratic formula).

Troubleshooting If students are having difficulty, you may want to have them do more work finding x-intercepts and axes of symmetry for given parabolas and looking at the visual connections, as in Problem Set G. You might also have them draw a line of symmetry and plot a vertex, and then *carefully* draw several parabolas with these features. Then ask them to identify what is true about the x-intercepts of each parabola: they are reflections of each other over the line of symmetry.

On Your Own Exercises

Practice & Apply: 19–23, pp. 530–532
Connect & Extend: 41, 42, p. 534
Mixed Review: 47–60, pp. 536–537

1a. (2, 0) and (⁻3, 0)

1b. (⁻0.5, ⁻6.25)

1c.

2a. (5, 0) and $\left(-\frac{1}{2}, 0\right)$

2b. (2.25, 15.125)

2c. See below.

3a. (8, 0) and (⁻5, 0)

3b. (1.5, ⁻42.25)

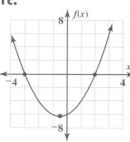

2c.

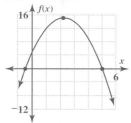

Problem Set H

For the quadratic equations given in Problems 1–3, do Parts a–c.

    a. Find the *x*-intercepts of *f*.

    b. Use the *x*-intercepts to find the vertex of the parabola.

    c. Plot the three points from Parts a and b, and then draw a parabola.

1. $f(x) = (x - 2)(x + 3)$

2. $f(x) = {}^-(x - 5)(2x + 1)$

3. $f(x) = x^2 - 3x - 40$

4. Angelo drew this parabola on a graphing calculator and made a sketch of it to take home for homework. By the time he got home, he had forgotten what function had generated the parabola. He did remember that he was trying to solve an equation like $(t + \underline{})(t - \underline{}) = 0$.

What function had he used, and what are the solutions of Angelo's equation? $f(t) = (t + 4)(t - 3)$, ⁻4 and 3

3c.

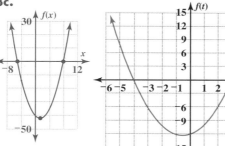

Share & Summarize

Explain how to find the *x*-intercepts and the vertex of the graph of this function.

$$f(x) = 3x^2 - 44x - 15$$

Possible answer: Find the mean of the solutions, *m*. The vertex is (*m*, *f*(*m*)).

1 You may have students work in pairs.

2 You might have students compare this method for finding the vertex to completing the square.

3 Point out that students are not asked to solve an equation but to explain a process.

Investigation 4

In this investigation, students explore ways to approximate solutions of equations using the intersection of graphs. The payoff for this work is the treatment of equations for which exact solutions are not possible. In addition, thinking of each side of an equation as a function, graphing the functions, and then observing where they intersect allows students to find immediately how many solutions an equation has or to determine whether it has any solutions at all.

A critical aspect of this graphing technique for solving equations is understanding that the solution to the equation is the x value of the point of intersection and not the pair of coordinates of the point.

 You might begin this investigation by reading the introductory text with the class. You can use the Example simultaneously to illustrate the method described.

Example

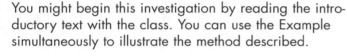 Go over this example in a class discussion. You can either graph the functions on an overhead graphing calculator or have students create graphs in pairs on their own graphing calculators.

 Some students may wonder whether the graphs, when continued outside of the calculator window, might intersect again. This is a very good question and deserves some careful thought. In fact, one can't be absolutely certain that they will never intersect again just by looking at the graph in the given window, unless one is familiar with the behavior of these classes of functions over the entire domain. For this reason, the graphical approach to solving equations does not always produce the whole picture and therefore all of the solutions. But in this case, students should agree that the line will continue in the same directions. They have also worked some with cubic equations, and they should recognize that the cubic equation will not "turn" when extended in either direction, so it clearly won't cross the line outside this window.

Investigation Intersections of Functions

Suppose you encounter an equation you don't know how to solve exactly. There *are* ways to find approximate solutions.

One nice method for finding an approximate solution is as follows:

- Think of each side of the equation as a function.
- Graph the two functions.
- Find the point or points where the functions intersect.
- Check that the x value (input) at each intersection point gives you approximately the same y value (output) for both functions. That is, check that the two sides of the original equation are approximately equal at that input.

EXAMPLE

Solve $x^3 = 5x + 10$.

- First, think of each side of the equation as a function: $f(x) = x^3$ and $g(x) = 5x + 10$.

- Graph the two functions.

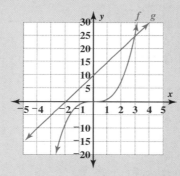

- Find the point or points where the functions intersect. In this case, there is only one point, near $x = 2.9$.

- Check: At $x = 2.9$, $f(x) = 24.389$ and $g(x) = 24.5$, so the two sides of the original equation are approximately equal.

1 Estimation

Discuss this method for approximating solutions, perhaps using the Example to illustrate.

2 Use an overhead graphing calculator, or have students use their own calculators.

3 You may want to discuss how you know the graphing window shows all intersections.

Develop

1 **Problem Set I** Suggested Grouping: **Pairs**

In this problem set, students are asked to find the intersection of the graphs of a linear equation, $L(h) = 10h$, and an exponential equation, $D(h) = 2^h$.

2 For **Problem 2,** students may need to create a table of values like the one shown below to help them write the correct equation.

Hours Worked	Baby-sitting Earnings
1	2
2	4
3	8
4	16

3 In **Problem 4,** note that the second solution appears off the screen in the standard window. This is a good time to discuss the limitations of the graphing method. Some students may assume there is only one solution here. In fact, since the first solution is for $x < 1$, only the second solution ($x = 5.9$) makes sense for the problem's context.

4 **Problem Set J** Suggested Grouping: **Pairs**

In this problem set, students work with the function $p(x) = 1,000(1.1^x)$, an exponential function describing the number of bacteria in a certain population after x hours. Although students studied this kind of function in Chapter 3, they may need some reminders about constructing exponential functions.

Access
for all **Learners**

Language Diversity Some students may need help with the term *culture dish*. You might mention medical tests in which a sample is taken and then rubbed on a culture dish, such as testing for strep throat.

Problem Set I

Suppose you are given two options for getting paid at a baby-sitting job:

- You can earn $10 per hour for each hour worked.

- You can earn $2 if you stay 1 hour, $4 if you stay 2 hours, $8 if you stay 3 hours, and so on. The amount you earn doubles for each additional hour you stay.

Is there some number of hours for which you would earn the same amount using either payment plan? In this problem set, you will explore this question.

1. Write an equation for a function L that describes earning $10 per hour. Use h for the input variable. $L(h) = 10h$

2. Write an equation for a function D that describes doubling the amount you earn for each hour you stay. Use h for the input variable. $D(h) = 2^h$

3.

4. two, approximately 0.11 and 5.9

3. Graph your two functions in a single window. Sketch the graphs, and label which graph matches which function.

4. How many solutions can you find to $L(h) = D(h)$? Use Zoom and Trace to approximate the solutions.

5. If you had a baby-sitting job, how would you decide which payment plan to choose? Explain. For more than about 5.9 h, you earn more money with the doubling plan. For less than this amount of time, you earn more money at $10 per hour.

Problem Set J

1.

Hour	Bacteria
1	1,100
2	1,210
3	1,331

In a culture dish, a population of bacteria is growing at a rate of 10% each hour. There were 1,000 bacteria in the dish at the beginning of the experiment. An hour later, there will be 10% of 1,000, or 100, more bacteria, for a total of 1,100 bacteria in the dish.

1. Make a table to show the bacteria population after 1 hour, 2 hours, and 3 hours.

2. Write an equation for a function that represents how many bacteria there will be after x hours. Name the function p. $p(x) = 1,000(1.1^x)$

Just the **facts**

Although you have evaluated exponential expressions for integer powers only, it is possible for exponents to be fractions or decimals.

526 CHAPTER 8 Functions and Their Graphs

① You may have students work in pairs.

② Problem-Solving Strategy

Make a table

③ If students assume there is only one solution, discuss limitations of this graphing method.

④ You may have students work in pairs.

In **Problem 3,** students might graph $p(x) = 1,000(1.1^x)$ and $y = 2,000$ to see where the graphs intersect. Likewise, in **Problem 5,** they might graph to see where $y = p(x)$ intersects $y = 3,000$. An alternative method is to use the trace function on $y = p(x)$ and determine what values of x give $p(x)$ values of 2,000 and 3,000.

Access
for all Learners

Extra Challenge The following situation involves equating two functions but is impossible to graph. Students who enjoy playing with numbers may like this puzzle.

Consider the function F, which takes an integer greater than 1 as an input and outputs the sum of the integer's factors (except the number itself). For example, the factors of 8 are 1, 2, 4, and 8, so $F(8) = 1 + 2 + 4 = 7$. Another function, G, takes a number as an input and outputs that number. That is, $G(x) = x$ for any number x.

An integer n greater than 1 for which $F(n) = G(n)$ is called a *perfect number*. For example, $F(6) = 1 + 2 + 3 = 6$, and $G(6) = 6$, so 6 is a perfect number. Can you find the next greater perfect number? **24**

Problem Set Wrap-Up You may want to review student answers to both Problem Sets I and J at this time, to be sure students understand that graphing two functions f and g to find their intersection allows them to solve the equation $f(x) = g(x)$. Problem Set K adds a small complication to this idea.

Problem Set K Suggested Grouping: **Pairs**

In this problem set, students explore the solutions to the cubic equation $x^3 = 2x - 0.5$ by graphing both sides of the equation as separate functions and then setting the equation equal to 0 and looking at the x-intercepts of the associated parabola, $h(x) = x^3 - 2x + 0.5$. You might ask students if they know any general methods for solving cubic equations. In fact, they do not know a "cubic formula" (although there is a complicated one), and at this point they need to rely on estimates using a graph.

In **Problem 3,** the answers to the nearest hundredth are $^-1.53$, 0.26, and 1.27.

In **Problem 4,** students need to graph just one equation and look for the points at which it crosses the x-axis. They may be surprised that they get the same answer as they did before. Students could also rewrite this equation as $x^3 - 2x = ^-0.5$ and look for the intersections of the two related functions. In fact, there are many ways to rearrange an equation so that a graphical solution is possible. It would be useful to point this out to students so that they have some awareness that they are really solving the same equation in different ways.

Share & Summarize

In these questions, students determine whether they can solve given equations exactly or whether they would have to try to approximate solutions using a graph. Clearly, using a graph to solve **Question 1** would be less efficient than solving the equation exactly. For this reason, it is important for students to develop good judgment regarding which strategies or techniques to use in specific situations. Be aware of students who want to use a "one method for all" approach to solving equations, rather than stepping back to think about what makes sense and what is appropriate for the specific problem.

Troubleshooting If students are having difficulty with these problems, you can still move on to the next chapter. As they continue in their study of mathematics, they will grow more comfortable solving these types of equations.

On Your Own Exercises

Practice & Apply: 24–29, p. 532
Connect & Extend: 43–46, pp. 534–535
Mixed Review: 46–60, pp. 536–537

4. Possible answers:
I graphed p and
estimated when
$p(x) = 2,000$. *Or,*
I graphed p and
$y = 2,000$ and
looked at where
they crossed.

MATERIALS

graphing calculator

1. $f(x) = x^3$ and
$g(x) = 2x - 0.5$

4a. the x-axis (or the
x-intercepts)

4b. $^-1.53$, 0.25, 1.27

4c. Answers will vary.
Most students will
find it easier to
estimate the x
values using
Hakeem's method.

3. After some amount of time, the bacteria will double in number. That
is, $p(x) = 2,000$. After how many hours will this be? Use your
graphing calculator to find an approximate solution. about 7.3 h

4. Explain how you found your answer to Problem 3.

5. What equation would you solve to find how many hours are needed
for the number of bacteria in the dish to triple? Find an approximate
solution. $p(x) = 3,000$ or $1,000(1.1^x) = 3,000$; about 11.5 h

Problem Set K

Consider how you might solve the *cubic* equation $x^3 = 2x - 0.5$.

1. If you use the method of graphing two functions and finding their
intersections, what two functions would you graph?

2. Graph your functions. How many solutions does $x^3 = 2x - 0.5$
have? three

3. Approximate all the solutions of the equation. Check your solutions
by substituting. Possible answer: $^-1.53$, 0.26, 1.27

4. Hakeem suggested doing the same thing to both sides of the
equation to obtain $x^3 - 2x + 0.5 = 0$ and then graphing the
function $h(x) = x^3 - 2x + 0.5$.

a. Where would you look to find the solutions of $x^3 - 2x + 0.5 = 0$?

b. Graph the function, and estimate the solutions using your graph.

c. Which method did you prefer: Hakeem's method or graphing two
functions and finding their intersections?

Share & Summarize

For each equation, state whether you can solve it exactly or approximately. Then solve it the best way you can.

1. $400k + 10 = 500k$ exactly, 0.1

2. $3^G = 1.5G + 5$ approximately, about $^-3.32$ and about 1.87

3. $x^2 = \sqrt{x + 1}$ approximately, about $^-0.72$ and about 1.22

1 Discuss answers to
Problem Sets I and J.

2 You may have students
work in pairs.

3 If necessary, point out
that graphing would be
an inefficient way to
solve Question 1.

LESSON 8.2 Graphs of Functions **527**

On Your Own Exercises

Exercise 1:
Some complex issues arise when looking at the graphs of the families of equations in **Parts a and b.** Ignoring the equations, one could easily assume that the graphs are moving up (in Part a) or left (in Part b). To make the distinction, you must consider the form of the equation, not the final outcome. In Part a, the values are clearly being added to x as a first step, which indicates a translation along the x-axis (that is, horizontal). In Part b, the values are being added as a last step—in other words, they change the y values by exactly their own value, which is a vertical translation.

Practice & Apply

1b.

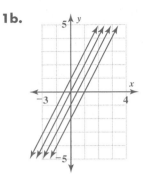

1c. Possible answer: All eight graphs are parallel lines.

1d. Possible answer: Each function in Part a is shifted horizontally 2 units to the left of the previous function; in Part b the shifts are vertical and occur 1 unit at a time.

1e. Answers will vary. Functions will be of the form $y = 2(x + a)$ for part a and $y = 2(x - 1) + a$ for part b.

1f. $y - 3 = 2(x - 1)$; Substitute $x = 3$ and $y = 7$ in the equations to find the correct one.

1. Sketch a graph of each function in Part a on a single set of axes. Using a different set of axes, do the same for the functions in Part b. Then answer the questions that follow.

1a.

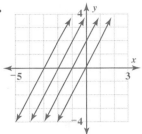

    a. $y = 2x$
       $y = 2(x + 1)$
       $y = 2(x + 2)$
       $y = 2(x + 3)$

    b. $y = 2(x - 1)$
       $y = 2(x - 1) + 1$
       $y = 2(x - 1) + 2$
       $y = 2(x - 1) + 3$

    c. Describe how the four graphs in Part a are like those in Part b.

    d. Describe how the four graphs in Part a are different from those in Part b.

    e. Find another function that belongs to the set of functions in Part a and another that belongs to the set in Part b.

    f. Which of the eight graphs contains the point (3, 7)? Explain how you found your answer.

2. Below is a graph of $f(x) = x^2 + 3x - 2$.

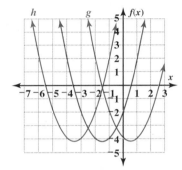

    a. Sketch a graph of $g(x) = (x - 2)^2 + 3(x - 2) - 2$ and one of $h(x) = (x + 2)^2 + 3(x + 2) - 2$. See graph.

    b. How are the graphs of g and h related to the graph of f?
    The graph of g is the same shape as the graph of f but shifted 2 units to the right. The graph of h is the same shape as the graph of f but shifted 2 units to the left.

 impactmath.com/self_check_quiz

6. $g(x) = (x + 5)^2$

7. domain: all real numbers; range: $f(x) \leq 4$

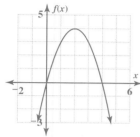

8. domain: all real numbers; range: all real numbers

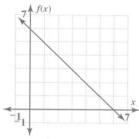

9. domain: all real numbers except 10; range: all real numbers except 0

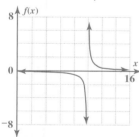

10b. Function f: $x = 0$; Function g: $x = 1$

11b. h; The graph has its vertex at (2, 3), as does the function h.

In Exercises 3–6, write an equation for the function g so that the graph of g has the same shape as the graph of f.

3. The graph of g is translated 5 units to the right of the graph of $f(x) = \frac{1}{x}$. $g(x) = \frac{1}{x - 5}$

4. The graph of g is translated 3 units up from the graph of $f(x) = x^2 + x - 2$. $g(x) = x^2 + x + 1$

5. The graph of g is translated 1 unit to the left of the graph of $f(x) = \frac{1}{x - 3}$. $g(x) = \frac{1}{x - 2}$

6. The graph of g is translated 4 units to the left of $f(x) = (x + 1)^2$.

Sketch a graph of each function, and state the domain and the range.

7. $f(x) = 4 - (x - 2)^2$

8. $g(x) = 5 - (x - 1)$

9. $f(x) = \frac{1}{x - 10}$

10. Consider these functions.

$$f(x) = 2x^2 + 1 \qquad g(x) = 2(x - 1)^2 + 2$$

   a. What are the coordinates of the vertices for the graphs of these two functions?   Function f: (0, 1); Function g: (1, 2)

   b. What is the line of symmetry for each?

   c. Sketch the graphs of both functions on one set of axes.

11. Consider this graph.

10c.

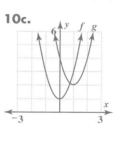

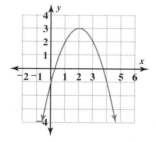

   a. Identify the line of symmetry and the vertex. $x = 2$; (2, 3)

   b. Which of these functions does the graph represent? Explain how you know.

$$f(x) = {}^-3 + (x - 2)^2 \qquad g(x) = 3 - (x + 2)^2 \qquad h(x) = 3 - (x - 2)^2$$

Exercise 12:
Some students may have difficulty interpreting the function because the constant term appears first on the right side. Rewriting the expression may help.

Exercise 17:
Students may need help factoring out $^-1$ before they complete the square. Check to see that they have done this correctly. See the sample strategies on page T522.

Identify the vertex, the line of symmetry, and the range of each function.

12. $f(x) = 4 - (x + 3)^2$ $(^-3, 4)$; $x = ^-3$; $f(x) \leq 4$

13. $g(p) = (p - 5)^2 - 9$ $(5, ^-9)$; $p = 5$; $g(p) \geq ^-9$

14. $h(x) = (x + 6)^2 - 3$ $(^-6, ^-3)$; $x = ^-6$; $h(x) \geq ^-3$

15. Consider a parabola with its vertex at $(^-2, 6)$.

15a. Possible function:
$f(x) = 6 + (x + 2)^2$

a. Write an equation for a quadratic function for a parabola with this vertex.

15b. yes; Possible functions:
$g(x) = 6 - (x + 2)^2$;
$h(x) = 6 + 2(x + 2)^2$;
there are an infinite number.

b. Are there other parabolas with this vertex? If so, state two more. How many more are there?

In Exercises 16–18, do Parts a–c.

a. Complete the square to rewrite $f(x) = ax^2 + bx + c$ in the form $f(x) = a(x - h)^2 + k$.

b. Find the line of symmetry of the graph of f.

c. Find the coordinates of the vertex of the parabola.

16b. $x = 1$
16c. $(1, ^-7)$
17b. $x = 2$
17c. $(2, 7)$
18b. $x = ^-4$
18c. $(^-4, ^-17)$

16. $f(x) = x^2 - 2x - 6$ **16a.** $f(x) = (x - 1)^2 - 7$

17. $f(x) = 3 + 4x - x^2$ **17a.** $f(x) = ^-(x - 2)^2 + 7$

18. $f(x) = x^2 + 8x - 1$ **18a.** $f(x) = (x + 4)^2 - 17$

19. Consider this graph of $f(x) = ^-x^2 + 2x + 5$.

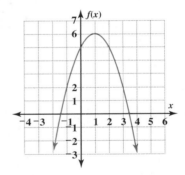

19a. $^-1.5, 3.5$; Possible explanation: The parabola appears to cross the x-axis about halfway between $^-1$ and $^-2$ and halfway between 3 and 4.

a. Use the graph to find approximate solutions of $f(x) = 0$. Explain how you found your answer.

b. Use the quadratic formula or complete the square to solve $f(x) = 0$ exactly. How close are your approximations?
$1 - \sqrt{6}, 1 + \sqrt{6}$; The approximations in the answer to Part a are very close.

530 CHAPTER 8 Functions and Their Graphs

c. Find the vertex of the graph of *f*. (1, 6)

d. What is the line of symmetry of the graph of *f*? *x* = 1

e. Find the distance between each solution of *f*(*x*) = 0 and the line of symmetry.

20. Consider this graph of $f(x) = x^2 - \frac{1}{2}x - \frac{3}{16}$.

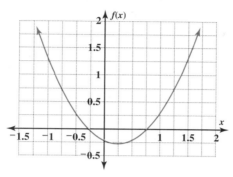

20a. Possible answer: ⁻0.25, 0.75

20b. ⁻0.25, 0.75; The approximations in Part a are accurate.

a. Use the graph to find approximate solutions of *f*(*x*) = 0.

b. Use the quadratic formula or complete the square to solve *f*(*x*) = 0 exactly. How close are your approximations?

c. Find the vertex of the graph of *f*. (0.25, ⁻0.25)

d. What is the line of symmetry of the graph of *f*? *x* = 0.25

e. Find the distance between each solution of *f*(*x*) = 0 and the line of symmetry. 0.5 unit

Exercise 23:
If students do not have access to graphing calculators when solving this problem, they can find the x-intercepts by factoring, completing the square, or using the quadratic formula.

Exercises 27–29:
These may take students some additional time if they do not have access to graphing calculators. Graphing these equations is not trivial. Note that the cubic expressions are identical, which should help save time.

In Exercises 21–23, the graph of the function is a parabola. Do Parts a–c for each exercise.

a. Find the x-intercepts of the parabola.

b. Use the x-intercepts to find the line of symmetry and the vertex.

c. Use the x-intercepts and the vertex to sketch the parabola.

21a. (3, 0) and (⁻0.5, 0)

21b. $x = 1.25$; (1.25, ⁻3.0625)

21c.

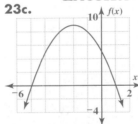

21. $g(x) = (x - 3)(x + 0.5)$

22. $h(x) = (2x + 3)(x - 1)$

23. $f(x) = {}^-x^2 - 4x + 5$

In Exercises 24–26, use graphs to determine how many solutions the equation has.

24. $x^2 - 2x = 4 - x - x^2$ **24–26.** See Additional Answers.

25. $x^2 - x - 2 = 1 - 2x - x^2$

26. $2 - x^2 = 1 - 2x^2$

Sketch graphs to find approximate solutions of each equation.

27. $x^3 - 4x - 1 = x - 1$ **27–29.** See Additional Answers.

28. $x^3 - 4x - 1 = x + 4$

29. $x^3 - 4x - 1 = 5 - x^2$

22a. (1, 0) and (⁻1.5, 0)

22b. $x = {}^-0.25$; (⁻0.25, ⁻3.125)

22c. See Additional Answers.

23a. (1, 0) and (⁻5, 0)

23b. $x = {}^-2$; (⁻2, 9)

Connect & **Extend**

23c.

30. Sketch a graph of each function in Part a on a single set of axes. Do the same for Part b, using a new set of axes. Then answer the questions that follow. (Hint: Sketch the graph of $y = \frac{1}{x^2}$ by plotting points, and use this graph to help sketch the others.)

a. $y = \frac{1}{x^2}$

$y = \frac{1}{(x - 2)^2}$

$y = \frac{1}{(x + 2)^2}$

b. $y = {}^-\frac{1}{x^2}$

$y = 3 - \frac{1}{x^2}$

$y = 3 - \frac{1}{(x + 2)^2}$

c. Describe how the graphs in Part a are like those in Part b.

d. Describe how the graphs in Part a are different from those in Part b.

e. Find another function that belongs to the set of functions in Part a and another that belongs to the set in Part b.
Answers will vary. Functions will be of the form $y = \frac{1}{(x + a)^2}$ for Part a and $y = \frac{-1}{(x + a)^2}$ or $y = 3 - \frac{1}{(x + a)^2}$ for Part b.

30a, b. See Additional Answers.

30c. Each of the six graphs consists of two curves that are mirror images.

30d. Possible answer: The second and third functions in Part a are horizontal shifts of the first; in Part b the curves have been shifted vertically and one has been shifted horizontally as well.

532 CHAPTER 8 Functions and Their Graphs

• *Additional Answers on page A687*

31. Physical Science A launcher positioned 6 feet above ground level fires a rubber ball vertically with an initial velocity of 60 feet per second. The equation relating the height of the ball over time t is

$$h(t) = 6 + 60t - 16t^2$$

where h is in feet and t is in seconds.

31a. Height of Ball

a. Sketch a graph of h.

Another rubber ball is launched 2 seconds later, with the same direction and initial velocity.

b. Suppose you graph the height of the second ball, with time since the *first* ball was launched on the horizontal axis. How will the second graph be related to the first?

c. Write an equation for the height of the second ball over time.

d. Will the second ball collide with the first ball when the first ball is on its way up or on its way down? Explain how you could tell from the graphs of the two functions.

31b. The graph will be the same shape but translated 2 units to the right.

31c. $h(t) = 6 + 60(t - 2) - 16(t - 2)^2$

31d. When the first ball is on its way down; the graphs would intersect after the first ball has reached its maximum height.

For each function f, write a new function g translated 2 units down and 4 units to the left of f.

32. $f(x) = 2^{x+1} - 1$ $g(x) = 2^{x+5} - 3$

33. $f(x) = 2(x - 3)^2 + 1$ $g(x) = 2(x + 1)^2 - 1$

34. $f(x) = (x - 1)^3 - x + 1$ $g(x) = (x + 3)^3 - (x + 4) - 1$

35. $f(x) = 1 + \frac{1}{x^2 + 1}$ $g(x) = {}^-1 + \frac{1}{(x + 4)^2 + 1}$

36. Geometry A piece of wire 20 cm long is used to make a rectangle.

a. Call the length of the rectangle L. Write a formula for the width W of the rectangle in terms of its length. $W = 10 - L$

b. Write a function for the area A of the rectangle in terms of the length L. $A(L) = L(10 - L)$ or $A(L) = 10L - L^2$

36c. $A(L) = {}^-(L - 5)^2 + 25$; vertex at (5, 25)

c. Complete the square of the quadratic expression you wrote for Part b. Use your rewritten expression to find the coordinates of the vertex of the graph of Function A.

d. What are the dimensions of the sides of the rectangle with the maximum area? What is the area of that rectangle?
5 cm by 5 cm, 25 cm^2

Exercise 37:

Students may find that identifying the range of the function is complicated; using a sketch may help. The function f is equivalent to the function $g(x) = x + 1$ for all x values except 2, for which f is not defined. For the sketch, students need to indicate that f is not defined at $x = 2$ by placing an open circle at the point $(2, 3)$.

Exercise 43:

For **Part b,** students need to realize that they have to rewrite the equation in the form $ax^2 + bx + c = 0$ before using the quadratic formula. Watch for students who apply the formula prematurely.

37. The domain is all real numbers except 2, and the range is all real numbers except 3.

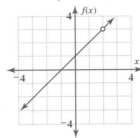

41. The graph of $y = 3^x + 2$ never gets below the line $y = 2$, so you can never have $3^x + 2 = 0$.

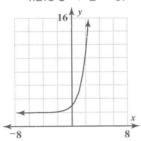

42c.

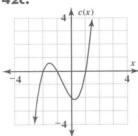

37. The expression $\frac{2x^2}{x}$ is equivalent to $2x$ for all x values except 0 ($\frac{2x^2}{x}$ is undefined for $x = 0$). The graph of $g(x) = \frac{2x^2}{x}$ looks like the graph of $h(x) = 2x$ with a hole at $x = 0$.

The domain of g is all real numbers except 0. The range of g is also all real numbers except 0.

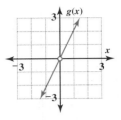

Now consider the function $f(x) = \frac{(x-2)(x+1)}{x-2}$. Sketch a graph of f, and give its domain and range.

In Exercises 38–40, do Parts a–c.

  a. Write the equation in the form $f(x) = ax^2 + bx + c$. Then complete the square to rewrite it in the form $f(x) = a(x - h)^2 + k$.

  b. Find the line of symmetry of the graph of f.

  c. Find the coordinates of the parabola's vertex.

38. $f(x) = 2x^2 - 8x + 2x^2 - 1$ **38–40.** See below.

39. $f(x) = 1 + 4x - 2x^2$

40. $f(x) = {}^-x^2 - x - 1 - x - (2 + x)$

41. Sketch a graph and use it to explain why the equation $3^x + 2 = 0$ has no solutions.

42. The cubic function $c(x) = x^3 + 2x^2 - x - 2$ can be rewritten as $c(x) = (x + 2)(x + 1)(x - 1)$.

  a. Find the x-intercepts of c. $^-2, {}^-1, 1$

  b. Find the y-intercept of c. $^-2$

  c. Use the intercepts to draw a rough sketch of c.

43. Consider the equation $(x + 2)^2 - 2 = {}^-x^2 + 4$.

  a. Use the method of graphing two functions to estimate solutions of the equation. See Additional Answers.

  b. Use the quadratic formula to find the exact solutions of this equation. How close were your estimates?

38a. $f(x) = 4x^2 - 8x - 1$, $f(x) = 4(x - 1)^2 - 5$ **38b.** $x = 1$ **38c.** $(1, {}^-5)$

39a. $f(x) = {}^-2x^2 + 4x + 1$, $f(x) = {}^-2(x - 1)^2 + 3$ **39b.** $x = 1$ **39c.** $(1, 3)$

40a. $f(x) = {}^-x^2 - 3x - 3$, $f(x) = {}^-(x + 1.5)^2 - 0.75$ **40b.** $x = {}^-1.5$ **40c.** $({}^-1.5, {}^-0.75)$

• **Additional Answers on page A688**

Explain how graphing can help you solve equations. How would you decide when to find approximate solutions with a graph and when to find exact solutions using algebra?

44. Sketch a graph of $y = \frac{1}{x}$. Use your sketch to think about these questions.

    a. How many solutions of $\frac{1}{x} = 5$ are there? one

    b. How many solutions of $\frac{1}{x-5} = 5$ are there? one

    c. How many solutions of $\frac{1}{x} = x$ are there? Of $\frac{1}{x} = {}^-x$? two, none

    d. How many solutions of $\frac{1}{x} = x^2$ are there? one

                                    See below.

    e. Use the method of graphing two functions to show the solutions of $\frac{1}{x} = (x-3)^2$. Use your graph to estimate those solutions.

45. Use the method of graphing two functions and locating the points of intersection to find at least four values of x for which each inequality is satisfied.

    a. $x^2 - 2x - 7 < 2x - 3$ Possible answer: 0, 1, 2, 3

    b. $x^2 - 2x - 7 > 2x - 3$ Possible answer: $^-5$, $^-4$, 7, 10

46. Geometry The radius of the cylindrical container is 1 unit less than the side length of the square base of the rectangular container.

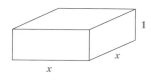
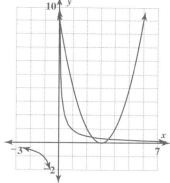

    a. For each container, write a function for the volume.

    b. Use the volume functions to make a graph comparing the volumes of the two containers. Keep in mind that the value of x must be greater than 1, or the cylindrical container would not exist.

    c. For what value of x do the containers hold the same amount?
       about 2.3   **44e.** Possible answer: 0.1, 2.3, 3.5

46a. rectangular: $R(x) = x^2$;
cylindrical: $C(x) = \pi(x-1)^2$

46b.

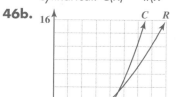
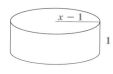

LESSON 8.2 Graphs of Functions **535**

Exercise 45:
In this exercise, students work with graphs to determine the solutions to inequalities. If they have difficulty with these, you might want to ask, "For what values of x is the parabola below the line? Above the line?"

Informal Assessment

Students should be able to:

✔ understand how horizontal and vertical translations of a graph are related to the equation of the function

✔ specify the range of a function and understand the relationship between the range of a function and its maximum or minimum point

✔ use x-intercepts and completing the square to find the line of symmetry and vertex of a parabola

✔ use graphs to find approximate solutions to equations

Mixed Review

47. Geometry Recall that a two-dimensional figure that can be folded into a closed three-dimensional figure is called a *net*. For example, this is a net for a cube.

Draw another net for a cube. Possible answer:

In Exercises 48–51, tell which of the following descriptions fits the relationship:

• a direct variation

• linear but not a direct variation

• nonlinear

48. $r = 25v + 32$ linear but not a direct variation

49. $a = -\frac{5}{6}j$ a direct variation

50. $k = \frac{3}{n}$ nonlinear

51.

x	2	4	6	8	10	12
y	25	36	47	58	69	80

linear but not a direct variation

Tell whether the points in each set are collinear.

52. $(3, 1); (8, 12); (-1, -10)$ no

53. $(-2, 9); (2, 2); (4, -1.5)$ yes

54. $(15, 22); (0, 1); (5, -6)$ no

Solve each equation.

55. $3 - \sqrt{7s + 2} = -7$ 14

56. $3 - \frac{1}{z + 7} = 2$ -6

57. $x^2 + 3x = 6$ $\frac{-3 \pm \sqrt{33}}{2}$

58. $16k^2 + 1 = -8k$ -0.25

59. Prove that this number trick always gives 3: *Choose any number except 0. Multiply the number by 9 and add 6. Then divide by 3 and subtract 2. Divide by the number you started with.*
Possible answer: If the chosen number is x, you get $\left(\frac{9x + 6}{3} - 2\right) \div x = 3x \div x$, which always equals 3.

60a, b. See Additional Answers.

60. Statistics Following are the areas of the 50 U.S. states, in square miles.*

1,545	2,489	5,543	8,721	9,350	9,614	10,555	10,931	12,407	24,230
32,020	35,385	36,418	40,409	42,143	42,774	44,825	46,055	48,430	51,840
52,419	53,179	53,819	54,556	56,272	57,914	59,425	65,498	65,755	69,704
69,898	70,700	71,300	77,116	77,354	82,277	83,570	84,899	86,939	96,716
97,814	98,381	104,094	110,561	113,998	121,589	147,042	163,696	268,581	663,267

The Washington Monument in Washington, D.C.

a. Create a histogram to display these data. Use intervals of 20,000 for the bars. Because two states are much larger than all the others, you may want to exclude them or make a special bar, such as "over 200,000."

b. Complete the stem-and-leaf plot, shown below, of these data. The "stems" in this plot represent ten-thousands.

Stem	Leaf
0	1545 2489 5543 8721
1	0555 0931 2407
2	4230 Key: 1|0555 = 10,555

c. Now create a box-and-whisker plot for these data. Recall that to create the plot, you need the maximum and minimum values along with the median and the first and third *quartiles*. The quartiles can be thought of as medians of the lower and upper halves of the data. For example, consider this data set:

$$2 \quad 3 \quad 4 \quad 5 \quad 6 \quad 7$$

The median is 4.5, the first quartile is 3, and the third quartile is 6. The box-and-whisker plot of this small data set is shown below.

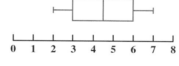

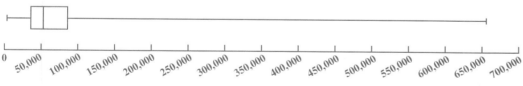

---

*Source: *World Almanac and Book of Facts 2003*.

LESSON 8.2   Graphs of Functions   **537**

Quick Quiz

1. Consider the function $f(x) = 3x$.

   a. Write an equation of a function g that has the same shape as f but is translated 4 units to the left of f. $g(x) = 3(x + 4)$

   b. Write an equation of a function h that has the same shape as f but is translated 2 units up from f. $h(x) = 3x + 2$

2. Describe how the graph of $g(x) = 3(x - 1)^2 + 2$ is related to the graph of $h(x) = 3x^2 + 2$. They're the same shape, but g is translated 1 unit to the right of h.

3. Specify the domain and range of each function.

   a. $h(x) = \frac{2}{x + 5}$ domain: all real numbers except $x = {}^-5$; range: all real numbers except $x = 0$

   b. $g(x) = 3x$ domain and range: all real numbers

• **Quick Quiz continued on page A688**

• **Additional Answers on page A689**

Chapter Summary
This summary helps students recall the major topics of the chapter.

Vocabulary
Students should be able to explain each of the terms listed in the vocabulary section.

Problem-Solving Strategies and Applications
The questions in this section help students review and apply the important mathematical ideas and problem-solving strategies developed in the chapter. The questions are organized by mathematical highlights. The highlights correspond to those in "The Big Picture" chart on page 485a.

Question 2:
Some students may find it difficult to find non-examples, but such questions help assess whether a student understands a concept or simply knows how to apply it.

Chapter Summary

▶ **VOCABULARY**
domain
function
range
x-intercepts

This chapter focused on a particular type of mathematical relationship called a *function*. A mathematical function produces a single output for each input and can be described with a graph or an equation.

You worked with graphs and equations to find the maximum and minimum values of functions. You used these extreme values to identify the range of a function and to solve problems involving maximum height or maximum area.

You studied in depth the graphs of quadratic functions. You found the line of symmetry and the coordinates of the vertex by inspecting graphs and by completing the square of quadratic expressions. You also solved equations of the form $f(x) = 0$ to find the x-intercepts of quadratic functions.

Finally, you solved equations of the form $f(x) = g(x)$ by locating the points where the graphs of f and g intersect.

Strategies and Applications

The questions in this section will help you review and apply the important ideas and strategies developed in this chapter.

Understanding functions and describing the domain and range of a function

1. The relationship could be a function if for every input there is only one output.

1. Explain how you can determine whether a relationship could be a function by examining a table of inputs and outputs.

2. Possible answers: $y^2 = x$; or $y = \pm\sqrt{x}$; or input: a state, output: a city in the state

2. Give an example of a relationship that is *not* a function.

3. A graph is not a function if for any x value there is more than one y value. Possible example:

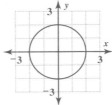

3. Explain how you can tell whether a relationship is a function by looking at its graph. Give an example of a graph that is not a function.

4. Give an example of a function in which negative numbers do not make sense as part of the domain.

4. Possible answer: the height over time of a stone tossed vertically into the air

5. Describe the range of the function $k(n) = 3n^2 - 4$. $k(n) \geq -4$

---

 impactmath.com/chapter_test

Finding the maximum and minimum values of quadratic functions

6. Possible answer: Graph the function or complete the square to help you find its vertex.

8. about 510 m, attained approximately 10 s after launch

9. The graph of g is the same shape as f, translated 10 units up and 2 units to the left. The graph of h is the same shape as f, translated 3 units down and 2 units to the right.

6. Explain two ways to find the maximum or minimum value of a quadratic function.

7. Consider all the possible rectangles with a perimeter of 22 centimeters.

a. If the length of one such rectangle is x cm, write an equation for a function A for the area of the rectangle. $A(x) = x(11 - x)$

b. Use your answer to Part a to find the maximum possible area of the rectangle. 30.25 cm^2

c. What dimensions give the maximum area? 5.5 cm by 5.5 cm

8. Assume the function $H(t) = 100t - 4.9t^2$ gives the height in meters of a rocket launched vertically from ground level, where t is time in seconds. Estimate the maximum height of the rocket, and tell how many seconds after its launch it attains this maximum height.

Understanding and using graphs of quadratic functions

9. Explain how the graphs of g and h are related to the graph of $f(t) = 2t^2$.

$$g(t) = 10 + 2(t + 2)^2 \qquad h(t) = 2(t - 2)^2 - 3$$

10. Which of these quadratic functions has its vertex at $(3, {}^-3)$?

$$g(t) = 3(t + 3)^2 - 3 \qquad h(t) = 4(t - 3)^2 - 3 \qquad k(t) = 3 - 3(t - 3)^2$$

11. Write the equation for a quadratic function with vertex $({}^-6, 1)$.

12. Explain how the range of a quadratic function is related to the vertex of its parabola.

13. Explain two methods for finding the vertex and the line of symmetry for the graph of $g(x) = (x + 2)(x + 4)$. Give the vertex and the line of symmetry. See Additional Answers.

14. Explain how you can use the x-intercepts of a quadratic function f to find its vertex. Possible answer: The line of symmetry lies halfway between the x-intercepts; this gives the x-coordinate of the vertex, which is $(x, f(x))$.

10. $h(t) = 4(t - 3)^2 - 3$

11. Possible function: $y = 2(x + 6)^2 + 1$

12. Possible answer: The y value of the vertex is an extreme value for the range of the function, so the range is either all values greater than or equal to that value, or all values less than or equal to that value.

Additional Answers

13. One method is setting $g(x) = 0$ to find the x-intercepts, $^-2$ and $^-4$. The line of symmetry is midway between the x-intercepts, at $x = {}^-3$. The vertex is thus $({}^-3, {}^-1)$. Another method is to find the product and rewrite the function, $g(x) = x^2 + 6x + 8$. Then complete the square to rewrite it again, giving $g(x) = (x + 3)^2 - 1$. Again, the vertex is $({}^-3, {}^-1)$ and the line of symmetry is $x = {}^-3$.

15. Graph $y = x^3$ and $y = 2x^2 + 1$ and find the x values of their points of intersection.

16. two solutions; Possible explanation: The function $f(x) = x^2 + 2x - 3$ is a parabola opening up with vertex $(^-1, ^-4)$ and $y = x - 2$ is a line with a positive slope that intersects the parabola twice.

Solving equations involving two functions

15. Explain how to use the method of graphing two functions to solve the equation $x^3 = 2x^2 - 1$.

16. Determine how many solutions this equation has, and explain how you found your answer.

$$x^2 + 2x - 3 = x - 2$$

Demonstrating Skills

Copy and complete each table for the given function.

17. $g(x) = x^2 + 3x - 1$

Input	Output
$^-2$	$^-3$
$^-1$	$^-3$
0	$^-1$
1	3
2	9

18. $h(x) = \frac{1}{4 - x}$

Input	Output
$^-4$	1/8
$^-2$	1/6
0	1/4
2	1/2
4	undefined

19. This is a graph of $f(x) = 2^x$.

   a. Sketch a graph of $g(x) = 2^{x-2}$.

   b. Sketch a graph of $h(x) = 2^{x+3}$.

   c. Sketch a graph of $j(x) = 2^x - 2$.

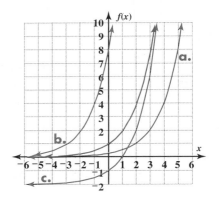

Tell whether each function has a minimum or maximum value, and give the coordinates of this point.

20. $f(x) = ^-x^2 + 2x - 2$ maximum; $(1, ^-1)$

21. $j(x) = ^-5 + x + x^2$ minimum; $(^-0.5, ^-5.25)$

22. $k(x) = 3 - 4(1 - x)^2$ maximum; $(1, 3)$

Write the equation for a function g that is the same shape as f but translated 2 units to the left and 1 unit down.

23. $f(x) = {}^{-}1 + \frac{1}{x^3 + 1}$ $g(x) = {}^{-}2 + \frac{1}{(x + 2)^3 + 1}$

24. $f(x) = 3^{x+1} - 2$ $g(x) = 3^{x+3} - 3$

25. $f(x) = x(x - 2)$ $g(x) = (x + 2)x - 1$

26. Determine the vertex and the line of symmetry of $f(x) = (x + 5)^2 + 9$ without graphing. $({}^{-}5, 9); x = {}^{-}5$

For each quadratic function, complete the square and find the vertex and the line of symmetry of its parabola without graphing.

27. $Q(x) = 2x^2 + 2x - 6$

28. $m(x) = {}^{-}x^2 + \frac{7}{2}x - 3$

29. $r(x) = x(x + 3)$

30. Consider the function $f(x) = {}^{-}x^2 + 8x - 7$.

a. Find the x-intercepts of the graph of f. $1, 7$

b. What is the line of symmetry and the vertex of the graph of f?

c. Use the x-intercepts and the vertex to sketch a graph of f.

31. Solve this equation by graphing.

$$x^2 + 1 = 0.5x + 2.5 \quad {}^{-}1, 1.5$$

32. Explain how to solve the equation $x^2 + x = {}^{-}x - 1$ without graphing. Solve for x.

Rewrite the equation as $x^2 + 2x + 1 = 0$ and solve by factoring or using the quadratic formula; $x = {}^{-}1$.

27. $q(x) = 2\left(x + \frac{1}{2}\right)^2 - \frac{13}{2}$; vertex: $\left(-\frac{1}{2}, -\frac{13}{2}\right)$; line of symmetry: $x = -\frac{1}{2}$

28. $m(x) = -\left(x - \frac{7}{4}\right)^2 + \frac{1}{16}$; vertex: $\left(\frac{7}{4}, \frac{1}{16}\right)$; line of symmetry: $x = \frac{7}{4}$

29. $r(x) = \left(x + \frac{3}{2}\right)^2 - \frac{9}{4}$; vertex: $\left(-\frac{3}{2}, -\frac{9}{4}\right)$; line of symmetry: $x = -\frac{3}{2}$

30b. $x = 4; (4, 9)$

30c.

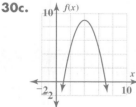

CHAPTER 9

Probability

Chapter Overview

In this chapter, students further their knowledge of and experience with probabilities. They learn different ways to find the size of the *sample space* for a probabilistic situation, including such systemic processes as listing outcomes using a tree diagram. They also learn basic combinatorial techniques, such as multiplying the number of outcomes in two independent trials. Students apply their new counting techniques to find probabilities and to make decisions based on probabilities.

the Big Picture

Chapter 9 Highlights	Links to the Past	Links to the Future
Making a systematic list of every possible outcome (9.1)	**Course 2:** Listing outcomes in simple situations	**High School:** Finding paths in digraphs and other vertex-edge graphs **High School:** Constructing algorithms
Using a pattern or shortcut to find the size of a sample space without listing every outcome (9.1)	**Courses 1 and 2:** Using the first few stages of a numeric or geometric pattern to make predictions about other stages	**High School:** Understanding and applying formulas for calculating permutations and combinations
Determining the probability of an event (9.1, 9.2, 9.3)	**Courses 1 and 2:** Calculating probabilities	**High School:** Understanding and calculating conditional probabilities
Using probability to determine whether a game is fair (9.2)	**Course 2:** Identifying whether a game is fair	**High School:** Understanding, calculating, and using the expected value of a probabilistic situation
Using probability to make decisions (9.2, 9.3)	**Course 2:** Using probability to make decisions and to create strategies	**Chapter 10, High School:** Using mathematics, including statistics, to make decisions

Lesson Objectives	Pacing	Materials	NCTM Standards	Hot Topics
9.1 Counting Strategies page 543b • To understand the concept of a sample space and its application to probability • To list the outcomes of sample spaces using strategies that guarantee no outcome will be left out • To use a pattern or shortcut to find the size of a sample space without listing every outcome	4 class periods	• 2 transparent spinners (optional) • Cubes in 5 colors • Master 51 or other circles to represent pizzas • 4 identical slips of paper (per pair) • Container (1 per pair)	2, 5, 6, 8, 10	pp. 232–238, 240–248
9.2 Probability Distributions page 564a • To create sample spaces with equally likely outcomes for a variety of games of chance involving dice • To apply calculated probabilities to create strategies for winning a game of chance	4 class periods	• 2 dice (per pair) • Graph paper • Master 52 * • Game markers (such as counters or small pieces of paper)	2, 5, 6, 8	pp. 232–238, 240–249
9.3 Probability Investigations page 581b • To analyze probabilities in real-world situations	3 class periods	• 6 identical slips of paper (per pair) • Container (1 per pair) • Master 53 (1 per group of 3) • 2 dice (per group of 3) • Master 54 (1 per group of 4) • Master 55 (1 per group of 4)	2, 5, 6, 8	pp. 232–238, 240–249

* Included in Impact Mathematics Manipulative Kit

Key to NCTM Curriculum and Evaluation Standards: 1=Number and Operations, 2=Algebra, 3=Geometry, 4=Measurement, 5=Data Analysis and Probability, 6=Problem Solving, 7=Reasoning and Proof, 8=Communication, 9=Connections, 10=Representation

Assessment Opportunities

Standard Assessment

Impact Mathematics offers three types of formal assessment. The Chapter 9 Review and Self-Assessment in the Student Edition serves as a self-assessment tool for students. In the Teacher's Guide, a Quick Quiz at the end of each lesson allows you to check students' understanding before moving to the next lesson. The Assessment Resources include blackline masters for chapter and quarterly tests.

- **Student Edition** Chapter 9 Review and Self-Assessment, pages 596–599
- **Teacher's Guide** Quick Quizzes, pages 564, 581, 595
- **Assessment Resources** Chapter 9 Test Form A, pages 230–232; Chapter 9 Test Form B, pages 233–235

Ongoing Assessment

Impact Mathematics provides numerous opportunities for you to assess your students informally as they work through the investigations. Share & Summarize questions help you determine whether students understand the important ideas of an investigation. If students are struggling, Troubleshooting tips provide suggestions for helping them. On the Spot Assessment notes appear throughout the teaching notes. They give you suggestions for preventing or remedying common student errors. Assessment Forms in the Assessment Resources provide convenient ways to record student progress.

- **Student Edition** Share & Summarize, pages 550, 554, 557, 568, 570, 572, 586, 589
- **Teacher's Guide** On the Spot Assessment, pages T545, T553, T566
  Troubleshooting, pages T550, T554, T557, T568, T570, T572, T586, T589
- **Assessment Resources** Chapter 9 Assessment Checklists, page 297

Alternative Assessment, Portfolios, and Journal Ideas

The alternative assessment items in *Impact Mathematics* are perfect for inclusion in student portfolios and journals. The In Your Own Words feature in the Student Edition gives students a chance to write about mathematical ideas. The Performance Assessment items in the Assessment Resources provide rich, open-ended problems, ideal for take-home or group assessment.

- **Student Edition** In Your Own Words, pages 563, 579, 592
- **Assessment Resources** Chapter 9 Performance Assessment, pages 236–237

Assessment Resources

The Assessment Resources provide a chapter test in two equivalent forms, along with additional performance items. The performance items can be used in a variety of ways. They are ideal for take-home assessment or in-class group assessment.

- Chapter 9 Test Form A, pages 230–232
- Chapter 9 Test Form B, pages 233–235
- Chapter 9 Performance Assessment, pages 236–237
- Chapter 9 Assessment Solutions, pages 238–241

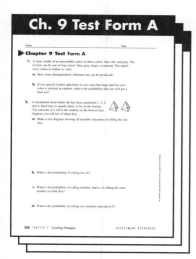

Ch. 9 Test Form A

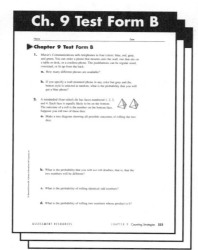

Ch. 9 Test Form B

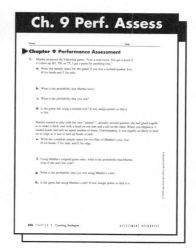

Ch. 9 Perf. Assess

Additional Resources

- **Math Skills Maintenance Workbook,** 2, 3, 6, 20, 22
- **Investigations for the Special Education Student in the Mathematics Classroom,** 17
- **Virtual Activities CD-ROM,** Experimental Probability
- **StudentWorks™ CD-ROM**
- **Reading and Writing in the Mathematics Classroom**
- **Using the Internet in the Mathematics Classroom**

ExamView® Pro

Use ExamView® Pro Testmaker CD-ROM to:

- Create Multiple versions of tests.
- Create Modified tests for Inclusion students with one mouse click.
- Edit existing questions and Add your own questions.
- Build tests aligned with state standards using built-in State Curriculum Correlations.
- Change English tests to Spanish with one mouse click and vice versa.

Probability

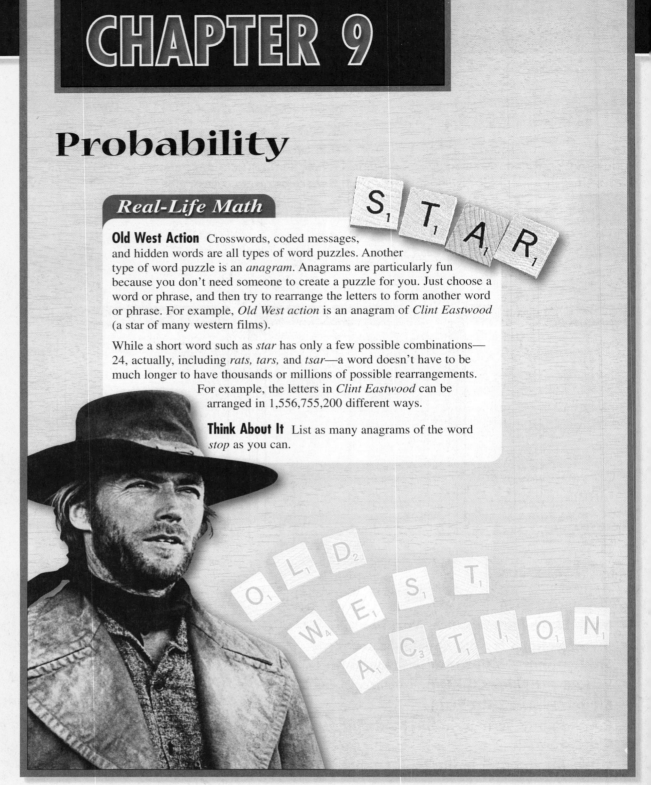

Real-Life Math

Old West Action Crosswords, coded messages, and hidden words are all types of word puzzles. Another type of word puzzle is an *anagram*. Anagrams are particularly fun because you don't need someone to create a puzzle for you. Just choose a word or phrase, and then try to rearrange the letters to form another word or phrase. For example, *Old West action* is an anagram of *Clint Eastwood* (a star of many western films).

While a short word such as *star* has only a few possible combinations—24, actually, including *rats, tars,* and *tsar*—a word doesn't have to be much longer to have thousands or millions of possible rearrangements. For example, the letters in *Clint Eastwood* can be arranged in 1,556,755,200 different ways.

Think About It List as many anagrams of the word *stop* as you can.

Family Letter

Dear Student and Family Members,

   In the next few weeks, we will be looking at many new situations that involve probability. In finding the probability that something will occur, you must first find all the *possible* outcomes. For example, if you are drawing blocks from a bag containing 3 blue, 2 green, and 5 white blocks, there are 10 possible outcomes: the 10 blocks. The probability of drawing a green block is the ratio of the number of green blocks, 2, to the number of possible outcomes: $\frac{2}{10}$.

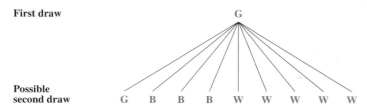

First draw

Possible second draw

   Our class will consider more complicated situations soon. For example, imagine that you draw a block and keep it, and then draw another block. We will learn how to calculate such probabilities as the probability of drawing a green block first and a blue block second, using methods from the mathematical field called *combinatorics*—which includes finding the possible combinations of items. One such method is to use a tree diagram, like the one below, to record all 10 possible first draws, and then for each first draw, the 9 possible second draws. This diagram shows the branches for a tree diagram when green is the result of the first draw:

   At the end of this chapter, we will apply what we have learned to analyze the fairness and probabilities of complicated games, such as sports playoffs and state lotteries. We will answer questions like these:

   • What are the chances of winning any of several lotteries?
   • Is one team favored by a particular playoff structure?
   • Which playoff structure is the fairest in a given situation?

Vocabulary There is only one new vocabulary term in this chapter—*sample space*. We'll find the sample space to determine the probability of various events.

What can you do at home?

   During the next few weeks, your student may show interest in the topic of probability. You might help him or her think about common occurrences of this topic such as lotteries, or play a game with your student that involves the use of dice or spinners and probability.

Another version of the Family Letter, available in English and Spanish, is found in the Teaching Resources. You may want to send a copy of this letter home with your students.

543

Mathematical Background

Chapter 9 extends the basic, random-drawing probability model to quite different situations by introducing the concept of a sample space. A *sample space* is the set of all possible outcomes for a particular situation. An *event* is a subset of the sample space. Depending on the situation, an event can be one outcome (such as getting the king of spades when drawing from a complete deck of playing cards), several outcomes together (drawing any king from the deck), or none of the possible outcomes (drawing an F from the deck).

Simple Events If a sample space is composed of S equally likely outcomes and the number of outcomes in an event is E, then the probability of the event is the ratio $\frac{E}{S}$. It follows that the probability of an event is a number between 0 and 1, inclusive. If an event is not included in the sample space, its probability is 0; if an event is the whole sample space, its probability is 1.

For example, in a single drawing from a bag containing 3 blue, 2 gray, and 5 white blocks, the sample space is just the set of 10 blocks: B1, B2, B3, G1, G2, W1, W2, W3, W4, W5. The probability of the event "drawing a blue block" is the ratio of the number of blue blocks to the number of blocks in the sample space, or $\frac{3}{10}$. The probability of drawing a purple block is $\frac{0}{10}$, or 0; the probability of drawing a block of any color is $\frac{10}{10}$, or 1.

Drawing without Replacement In a drawing from the bag above of two successive blocks without replacement, the sample space is more complicated. The sample space is all possible combinations of two blocks drawn without replacement and contains such pairs as (B1, G1), (B1, G2), and (B2, W3). The probability of drawing two white blocks can be determined by exhaustively listing and then counting all of the outcomes in the sample space, then counting those outcomes consisting of two white blocks, and finally making a ratio of these two numbers.

Thus the problem of calculating a probability, such as the probability of drawing a white block and a blue block, is primarily a problem of counting outcomes—all the possible combinations of block drawings. Students begin such calculations by listing and then counting all outcomes. In even simple cases, it rapidly becomes obvious that one needs a strategy for listing outcomes that guarantees no outcome will be left out or repeated.

Making Lists In the case of two successive drawings of blocks from the bag, one might construct the sample space by listing all drawings that begin with a blue block (there are 27), then all drawings that begin with a gray block (18), and finally all drawings that begin with a white block (45). Or one might construct a tree diagram, putting down all 10 possible first drawings and then listing for each first drawing the 9 possible second drawings. This diagram shows the branches for a tree diagram that begins with G1.

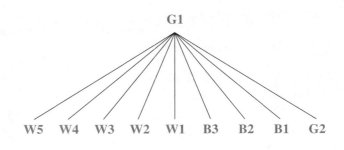

• *Teaching notes continued on page A690*

9.1

Counting Strategies

Objectives

▶ To understand the con-cept of a sample space and its application to probability

▶ To list the outcomes of sample spaces using strategies that guaran-tee no outcome will be left out

▶ To use a pattern or shortcut to find the size of a sample space without listing every out-come

Overview (pacing: about 4 class periods)

The first lesson of this chapter introduces the concept of a sample space and defines the probability of an event in terms of the ratio of outcomes in the event to the total possible outcomes. Students begin by developing strategies for listing and counting all outcomes in a sample space and extend these to strategies for calculating outcomes without listing them.

Advance Preparation

For the introductory Think & Discuss, it would be helpful (although not required) to have two transparent spinners, each divided into three sections colored (or labeled) orange, blue, and white. For the lab investigation, pairs of students will need circles to represent pizzas and colored cubes (in five colors) to represent toppings. You may want to distribute copies of Master 51, which has circles students can use as model pizzas. In Investigation 1, student pairs will need a container of some sort from which they can draw names written on paper and four identical pieces of paper on which they can write names.

	Summary	Materials	On Your Own Exercises	Assessment Opportunities
Lab Investigation page T545	Students list and count the number of different pizzas that can be made from four toppings.	• 2 transparent spinners (optional) • Cubes in 5 colors • Master 51 or other circles to represent pizzas		On the Spot Assessment, page T545
Investigation 1 page T547	Students develop a system for listing all outcomes in a sample space.	• 4 identical slips of paper (per pair) • Container (1 per pair)	Practice & Apply: 1, 2, pp. 558–559 Connect & Extend: 8–10, pp. 560–561 Mixed Review: 14–29, pp. 563–564	Share & Summarize, pages T550, 550 Troubleshooting, page T550
Investigation 2 page T550	Students calculate probabilities by using a tree dia-gram to list and count elements in sample spaces.		Practice & Apply: 3, 4, p. 559 Connect & Extend: 11, 12, p. 562 Mixed Review: 14–29, pp. 563–564	On the Spot Assessment, page T553 Share & Summarize, pages T554, 554 Troubleshooting, page T554
Investigation 3 page T554	Students extend listing strategies to count elements in sample spaces without actually listing them.		Practice & Apply: 5–7, p. 560 Connect & Extend: 13, p. 563 Mixed Review: 14–29, pp. 563–564	Share & Summarize, pages T557, 557 Troubleshooting, page T557 Informal Assessment, page 563 Quick Quiz, page 564

Introduce

1 Discuss the material in the introduction, including why the probability of an event must be 0, 1, or some number in between. This should be familiar information to most students.

2 ## Think & Discuss

Although this problem can be discussed without having spinners available, it is more fun to have something to spin. You can project two spinners using the overhead, pose a probability question, do a few experiments, and then formally list the outcomes at the board with the class. The concrete situation really helps to focus the questions, and for some students it may be a necessary first step to physically manipulate the spinners in order to list all the possible outcomes.

3 As you discuss the questions, remind students that probabilities stated as fractions or ratios can also be expressed in lowest terms. The probability of drawing a club from a standard deck of cards is $\frac{13}{52}$, but if you consider that there are four suits, one of which is clubs, the probability can also be expressed as $\frac{1}{4}$.

Counting Strategies

A *probability* is a number between 0 and 1 that indicates how likely something is to happen. Often the key to determining the probability that something will occur is to first find all the possible *outcomes*.

When you toss a coin, the two possible outcomes—heads and tails—are equally likely. So, the probability of getting heads is 1 out of 2, or $\frac{1}{2}$, or 0.5, or 50%.

Think & Discuss

Suppose you spin the two spinners below. Each spinner has an equal chance of landing on white, blue, or orange.

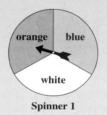 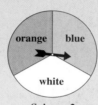

Spinner 1   **Spinner 2**

① WW, WB, WO, BW, BB, BO, OW, OB, OO

List all the possible outcomes. For example, one outcome is Spinner 1 landing on white and Spinner 2 landing on orange. You can use the notation white/orange, or WO, to represent this outcome. See ①.

How many possible outcomes are there? 9

In how many outcomes does Spinner 1 land on blue and Spinner 2 land on orange? What is the probability of this happening?

In how many outcomes does one spinner land on blue and the other land on orange? What is the probability of this happening?

In how many outcomes does Spinner 2 land on blue? What is the probability of this happening? 3; $\frac{3}{9}$, or $\frac{1}{3}$

In some situations, counting outcomes is not as easy as it sounds. In this lesson, you will investigate some counting strategies.

544 CHAPTER 9 Probability

1 Discuss why probabilities must be between 0 and 1, inclusive.

2 You may want to use actual spinners to help focus the questions.

3 Remind students that probabilities can be expressed as fractions in lowest terms.

Lab Investigation

1 **Suggested Grouping: Pairs**

In this lab, students use manipulatives to form all pizzas that can be made from any of four toppings. The lab provides a simple, concrete point of reference for the activities in the rest of the chapter, some of which are abstract and complex. It also helps students develop intuition about the large number of combinations that are possible from a small number of items. In lotteries and most other games of chance, the unexpectedly large sample space leads to the minute possibilities of actually winning; creating a sample space and counting or calculating the size of it is mysterious and difficult for many adults!

Materials and Preparation

Before beginning, have students draw circles at least 3 inches in diameter, if you don't already have these prepared. You can use Master 51 for this purpose. Each pair of students will need several cubes, or similar manipulative, in each of five colors.

Teaching Resources

▶ **Master 51**

Lesson 9.1 Lab Investigation

2 ### Make a Prediction

Some students may be willing to guess a number; others will start experimenting first. Encourage all to make a prediction first, which will help them later see their misconceptions about the size of a sample space.

3 ### Try It Out

Walk around and observe as students begin to explore the situation. When most pairs have finished, discuss answers and draw out the strategies students used for finding and counting the possibilities.

Problem-Solving Strategies Students may use a variety of counting strategies.

- Some students will build pizzas randomly using the model.
- Two students working together are likely to achieve a pattern for obtaining all pizzas.

On the Spot Assessment

Watch for students who use unsystematic counting strategies. Push them to see the value of a logical and systematic way to list the possibilities by asking:

Are you sure you have found them all? How do you know?

How can you tell when you have counted a combination more than once?

Before moving on, ask in a casual way whether there might be a method for calculating the number of possibilities without listing them. Accept, and perhaps list on the board, suggestions without comment or correction.

Lab Investigation ▶ Pizza Toppings

Paula's Pizza Place offers four toppings for its vegetarian cheese pizzas.

Customers can order a pizza with any combination of toppings, from no topping at all (just cheese) to all four toppings. However, a topping can be used only once—a customer can't order a pizza with two helpings of green peppers, for example.

MATERIALS

- cubes in 5 colors
- circles to represent pizzas

M, A, T, G, MA, MT, MG, AT, AG, TG, MAT, MAG, MTG, ATG, MATG, and cheese; 16

Make a Prediction

1. How many different pizzas do you think can be made using these four toppings? Predictions will vary.

Try It Out

You can explore this problem by making a model. Use colored cubes to represent the toppings, and circles to represent pizzas. Create a few pizzas by placing the cubes on the circles. Remember, use only one helping of a topping on any one pizza.

See whether you can make all the possible pizzas. Try to find a systematic way to organize the pizzas so you can be sure you found them all.

2. List all the different pizzas that are possible. How many possibilities are there?

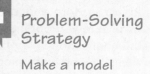

1 Problem-Solving Strategy

Make a model

2 Encourage students to predict before experimenting.

3 • Discuss strategies for finding and counting possibilities

• Ask if there might be a way to find the number of possibilities wihtout listing them.

LESSON 9.1 Counting Strategies **545**

Develop

Try It Again

In this section, students model similar situations that involve fewer toppings; the questions are simpler than the challenge in "Try It Out." The point here is for students to work with simple examples in order to find a pattern that can then be extended to similar but more complex problems.

Question 7 gets to the heart of the matter and is important to discuss, perhaps after most students have completed **Question 8** and before they continue to the "What Did You Learn?" section. Most students will see the pattern immediately and realize that the original challenge using four toppings fits the pattern. Push students to explain why the pattern is exponential.

About the Mathematics

With each topping considered, there are two options: put it on the pizza or don't. There are four different pizzas with two toppings; when you add the possibility of a third topping, there are four pizzas that don't include the third topping and four that do. So, with each new topping, the possibilities are doubled.

It is important to note that in this situation, the order in which the toppings are placed on the pizza doesn't matter—an artichoke and mushroom pizza is the same as a mushroom and artichoke pizza. This is not the case in all situations, including others in the chapter.

What Did You Learn?

Watch how students answer **Question 9,** in particular looking for those who seem to be listing combinations unsystematically or relying only on the paper-and-cube model. For those who answer the question by using the pattern and calculating, you will learn a good deal about their understanding by asking them to explain or to start listing the sample space for a given number of toppings. Even if the students do not list the entire sample space, it should be clear fairly quickly whether they are using a systematic strategy. Students who do use such a strategy have understood the concepts of the lab well.

Access for all Learners

Problem-Solving Strategies
- Make a table
- Look for a pattern

Extra Challenge Ask students to make a table listing the two-topping pizzas that can be created from different numbers of available toppings. For example, for five available toppings—mushroom, onion, peppers, garlic, and broccoli—the two-topping pizzas that could be made include mushroom-onion, mushroom-pepper, and garlic-broccoli.

Such a table might look like the following:

Available Toppings	2	3	4	5	$\cdots$	12
Number of 2-Topping Pizzas	1	3	6	10		66

You can also ask whether students see a pattern in the numbers and, if so, where they may have seen that pattern before. The pattern is $\frac{n^2 - n}{2}$; this is the sum of the first n integers (also known as the *triangular numbers*). Students may recall seeing this in an On Your Own Exercise (Exercise 45 of Lesson 7.2).

Try It Again

You will now solve the problem again, but with fewer toppings available to choose from. As you work, look for a pattern in your results that may confirm your answer to the four-topping pizza problem.

3. How many different pizzas can you make if only one topping is available? 2

4. How many different pizzas can you make if only two toppings are available? 4

5. How many different pizzas can you make if only three toppings are available? 8

6. Organize your results from Questions 3–5 in a table.

Toppings	1	2	3
Different Pizzas	2	4	8

7. Do you see a pattern in your results? If so, does the number of different pizzas you made from four toppings fit the pattern? If not, check your work for Questions 2–5.

8. Suppose Paula adds pineapple to the list of toppings. How many combinations do you predict are now possible? Use a fifth color of cube to represent pineapple, and make enough pizzas to see a pattern and check your prediction. 32

What Did You Learn?

Review your results for all the pizza problems. You should see a pattern in them. If you don't, check your work.

9. Use the pattern in your results to extend your table up to at least 12 toppings. You may use a calculator, but try to complete the table without using paper-and-cube pizza models. See below.

10. Make a list of all the pizza toppings you have ever heard of. In a short report, explain how to determine the number of combinations that can be made from your list of toppings. In your report, also answer this question:

If you order a different type of pizza every day, how many days, weeks, or months will pass before you will have ordered all the possibilities? Reports will vary.

Discuss Question 7, perhaps after most students have finished Question 8.

Problem-Solving Strategy

Make an organized list

7. Possible answer: The number of different pizzas doubles with each topping added. Eight different pizzas can be made from 3 toppings, so there should be 16 different pizzas from 4 toppings. This is what I found in Question 2.

9.

Toppings	1	2	3	4	5	6	7	8	9	10	11	12
Different Pizzas	2	4	8	16	32	64	128	256	512	1,024	2,048	4,096

Investigation 1

If students have done the lab investigation, many of the ideas in this investigation will be familiar, although the contexts are slightly more complex. You may find that students can move through this investigation quickly. If students haven't done the lab, this investigation extends the work in the Think & Discuss on page 544 to more situations with larger sample spaces.

 If you haven't introduced the term *sample space,* do so now.

 Problem Set A Suggested Grouping: Pairs
This problem set gets students to start looking at the sample space they will use throughout the investigation. **Problems 1–3** ask students to list possible combinations so that, in **Problem 4**, they should have all outcomes in the sample space listed.

 Problem Set Wrap-Up As students finish the problem set, discuss their answers to **Problem 5b.** You may want to ask students to give their answers as you list them for all to see without commenting. If any students give an incorrect answer, you may want to go back to the answer for Problem 4b and review that one as well, focusing not only on *whether* a particular pairing might have been missed or listed more than once but also on *why* this may have happened. Understanding the listing process is the important idea here.

You can use this discussion to lead into the paragraphs at the top of page 548.

Investigation One-on-One Basketball

Ally, Brevin, Carol, and Doug are playing one-on-one basketball. To decide the two players for each game, they put their names into a hat and pull out two at random.

To find the probability that Brevin and Carol will play the next one-on-one game, you might start by first listing all the possible pairs of the four friends. Each pair is an *outcome* in this situation. The set of all possible outcomes—in this case, the set of all possible pairs—is called the **sample space.**

1 Introduce the term *sample space.*

VOCABULARY
sample space

There are many ways to find the sample space for a particular situation, but you need to be careful. If there are lots of possible outcomes, it can be difficult to determine whether you have listed them all or have listed an outcome more than once.

Problem Set A

2 You may have students work in pairs.

You will now use a systematic method to find the sample space for drawing pairs of names for the one-on-one basketball situation.

1. List all the possible pairs of names that include Ally.

1. Ally/Brevin, Ally/Carol, Ally/Doug

2. List all the possible pairs that include Brevin but *not* Ally (since you already listed that pair in Problem 1).   Brevin/Carol, Brevin/Doug

3. Now list all the pairs that include Carol but *not* Ally or Brevin.
Carol/Doug

4. Review your answers to Problems 1–3.

4a. If students did Problems 1–3 correctly, they will have listed each pair exactly once.

    a. Are there any pairs you have listed more than once or that you have overlooked? If so, correct your errors.

    b. How many pairs are there in all? List them.

4b. 6 pairs; Ally/Brevin, Ally/Carol, Ally/Doug, Brevin/Carol, Brevin/Doug, Carol/Doug

5. Brevin wants to play Carol in the next game.

    a. How many pairs match Brevin with Carol?   1

    b. What is the probability that Brevin will play Carol in the next game? $\frac{1}{6}$

3
• Discuss Problem 5b, focusing on the listing process.

• Use the discussion to lead into the text on page 548.

Develop

1 Make sure to discuss these explanatory paragraphs before students begin Problem Set B: calculated probabilities don't determine whether an event will occur but, rather, describe how likely an event is to occur. You might ask students what's meant by the phrase *over the long run* that is used in the text.

2 **Problem Set B** Suggested Grouping: Pairs
In this problem set, students experiment to see whether a probability they calculate from their sample space gives a reasonable prediction about what actually happens.

Before students begin, have them write the four names on identical slips of paper. You may want to ask:

> Why should these pieces of paper be identical? Any differences, such as size, color, or whether the slip is folded, can influence the person drawing slips from the container and make the results not random.

Students may want to use the letters A, B, C, and D rather than writing the whole names.

3 **Problems 3 and 4** ask students to compile the results of all the draws in the class. You may want to designate a student to record the results on the board, or do so yourself.

4 **Problem Set Wrap-Up** You can use the class results at the end of the problem set to extend the meaning of *over the long run* in this example. For example, although some pairs may have results that were not close to $\frac{1}{6}$, the combined results should be.

In some cases, a pair might get exactly $\frac{1}{6}$ while the class result is not. You can point this out, too, but emphasize the fact that *most* of the groups did not get that exact result.

In Problem Set A, you calculated that the probability that Brevin and Carol will play in the next game is $\frac{1}{6}$. This does not necessarily mean that in the next six draws, the pair Brevin/Carol will be chosen exactly once. It's possible—though not likely—that the pair will be drawn all six times or that Carol's name won't be drawn even once.

Probabilities do not tell you what will definitely happen. They tell you what you can expect to happen *over the long run.*

1 Discuss the difference betwen a calculated probability and what actually occurs.

2 • You may have students work in pairs.

• Have students write names on identical slips of paper and discuss why the slips should be identical.

3 You may want to have students compile results, or do it yourself.

4 Use class results to discuss *over the long run* and to emphasize that most groups did not draw the pair exactly $\frac{1}{6}$ of the time.

MATERIALS
• 4 identical slips of paper
• container

Problem Set B

Write the four names—*Ally, Brevin, Carol,* and *Doug*—on identical slips of paper and put them into a container.

1. Suppose you randomly—that is, without looking or trying to choose one name over another—draw 12 pairs of names from the container, putting the pair back after each draw. Based on the probability you found in Problem Set A, how many times would you expect to draw the pair Brevin/Carol?   2

Draw two names at random and record the results. Return the names to the container. Repeat this process until you have drawn 12 pairs.

2. Answers will vary.

2. How many times was the pair Brevin/Carol drawn? How do these experimental results compare with your answer to Problem 1?

3. Total draws will vary; $\frac{1}{6}$ of the total.

3. Each group in your class drew 12 pairs of names. How many total draws occurred in your class? In this number of draws, how many times would you expect the pair Brevin/Carol to be drawn?

4. Each group in your class should now record how many times they drew the pair Brevin/Carol. How many times in all was the pair Brevin/Carol drawn? How does this compare with your answer to Problem 3?   Answers will vary.

Next you will investigate what happens when a fifth player is added to the one-on-one basketball situation.

Problem Set C Suggested Grouping: Pairs
Here students extend their previous listing to include a new name. The ease with which students achieve this should indicate how well they understand the strategy developed in Problem Set A.

Problem Set Wrap-Up Read and discuss the first paragraph after the problem set. Be sure students either found the correct answer for **Problem 2b** or understand what they did wrong. ■

About the Mathematics

The mathematical definition of *event* is a subset of the sample space, that is, any collection of outcomes from size 0 to the size of the sample space itself. This definition is a little more complicated than most students need at this point, so the student text presents an informal definition by example.

If a student has trouble differentiating between *outcome, event,* and *sample space,* you may want to explain that an outcome is a single thing that could occur; an event can include any number of things that might (or might not) occur; and the sample space is all the things that can occur.

Read through the paragraph before the Example with the class before considering the Example.

Example

You may need to review the use of the word *or* here. Emphasize that the events must be equally likely for the counting principles to apply; otherwise, some students may think they can always find the probability by dividing favorable outcomes by total possible outcomes. You can elaborate on this by giving examples of outcomes that are not equally likely, such as a spinner with different-sized sections or a number cube with the numbers 1, 2, 2, 3, 4, and 5.

Problem Set C

1. Suppose Evan joins Ally, Brevin, Carol, and Doug.

   a. How many new pairs can now be made that could not be made before Evan joined? 4

   b. What is the size of the new sample space? 10

   c. To verify the size of the new sample space, systematically write down all the possible pairs. (Rather than writing out the entire names, just use each player's first initial.)

2. Look at the new sample space you listed in Problem 1.

   a. How many of the pairs involve Evan? Which are they?

   b. What is the probability that Evan will be involved in the next game? $\frac{4}{10}$, or $\frac{2}{5}$

1c. AB, AC, AD, AE, BC, BD, BE, CD, CE, DE

2a. 4 pairs; AE, BE, CE, DE

In Problem Set C, you found the probability that the following event would occur: *Evan is in the pair.* This particular event has four outcomes in the sample space: Evan/Ally, Evan/Brevin, Evan/Carol, and Evan/Doug.

If you know that the outcomes in a sample space are *equally likely*—that is, that each outcome has the same chance of occurring—it is easy to calculate the probability of a particular event.

EXAMPLE

The names *Ally, Brevin, Carol, Doug,* and *Evan* are put into a hat, and one pair of names is pulled out at random. What is the probability that the pair will include either Ally or Brevin (or both)?

The sample space consists of 10 outcomes:

Ally/Brevin	Ally/Carol	Ally/Doug	Ally/Evan
Brevin/Carol	Brevin/Doug	Brevin/Evan	Carol/Doug
Carol/Evan	Doug/Evan		

Of these 10 outcomes, 7 include Ally or Brevin:

Ally/Brevin	Ally/Carol	Ally/Doug	Ally/Evan
Brevin/Carol	Brevin/Doug	Brevin/Evan	

Since each pair has the same chance of being drawn, the probability that the pair will include either Ally or Brevin is $\frac{7}{10}$.

---

1 You may have students work in pairs.

2 Wrap up Problem Set C by discussing this paragraph and Problem 2b.

3 Discuss the meaning of *equally likely*.

4 • You may need to review the use of the word *or*.

• Emphasize that each outcome must be equally likely to calculate probabilities by counting in this way.

Problem Set D Suggested Grouping: Pairs
This problem set emphasizes the fact that an event can involve more than one outcome. The problems are varied in terms of the outcomes and the number of outcomes in an event.

Problems 1–6 are fairly straightforward, but some students may have trouble with the language describing the various subsets of the sample space. Pairing students will help, especially with **Problems 7 and 8.**

Students should be comfortable with the idea that an event can include more than one outcome. If they are not, you might have the class form small groups and have group members pose the problems they created in Problem 8 for one another.

Share & Summarize
Make sure everyone is comfortable with the notion of a sample space and with making a ratio that describes the probability of an event in terms of a subset of a sample space. Push students to explain just how they will count the number of outcomes in the sample space.

Troubleshooting It is important that students be able to invoke a strategy for listing outcomes in a simple sample space. If some are having trouble, work with more concrete situations like those in the problem sets.

Additional Example List all the sets of three class officers that can be picked from candidates A, B, C, D, and E.

ABC	BCD	CDE
ABD	BCE	
ABE	BDE	
ACD		
ACE		
ADE		

On Your Own Exercises
Practice & Apply: 1, 2, pp. 558–559
Connect & Extend: 8–10, pp. 560–561
Mixed Review: 14–29, pp. 563–564

Investigation 2

The investigation begins with a situation in which five CDs can be played in any order. Students learn to use a tree diagram as an alternative to the systematic listing strategy of Investigation 1.

Have students read the introductory paragraph and then continue to the Think & Discuss on page 551.

Problem Set D

The names *Ally, Brevin, Carol, Doug,* and *Evan* are put into a hat, and one pair of names is pulled out at random.

1. What is the probability that the pair includes Doug? $\frac{4}{10}$

2. What is the probability that the pair includes Carol or Evan (or both)? $\frac{7}{10}$

3. What is the probability that the pair does not include Brevin? $\frac{6}{10}$

4. What is the probability that the pair includes Ally or Brevin or Doug? $\frac{9}{10}$

5. What is the probability that the pair includes Carol but not Doug? $\frac{3}{10}$

6. What is the probability that the pair includes Ally and Evan? $\frac{1}{10}$

7. Make up a question like those in Problems 1–6 that involves an event with a 2-in-10 chance of occurring.

8. Make up another question like those in Problems 1–6, and give the answer to your question. *Answers will vary.*

7. Possible question: What is the probability that the next game involves Carol and either Ally or Doug?

Share & Summarize

If all the outcomes in a sample space are equally likely, how can you find the probability that a particular event will occur?

Count all the outcomes that produce the event and divide by the total number of outcomes in the sample space.

Investigation More Counting Strategies

You have seen that to find the probability of an event, you must find the size of the sample space. In Investigation 1, you used a systematic strategy to list all the possible pairs for a one-on-one matchup. In this investigation, you will discover some other useful counting strategies.

1
- You may have students work in pairs.
- Watch for students having trouble with the language used.

2 You might have students pose their questions to each other.

3 Be sure students understand the idea of a sample space and how to count outcomes using a listing strategy.

4 Let students know they will learn counting strategies other than listing.

Think & Discuss

If students completed the lab investigation, they predicted the number of combinations of a given number of pizza toppings and then found the sample space. This activity is similar in some respects. You may find that students' predictions in this activity are more on target than those for the pizza toppings; in any case, it is helpful to remind students of the pizza-toppings predictions. You might ask them:

> In what ways is this situation different? *We're using five CDs instead of four toppings; we have to use them all this time; we have to use them in order.*

> Can you use a process similar to one you used in the lab?

Have students discuss their predictions and how they found them. ■

As a class, start a listing for two and then three CDs, as described in the text. This is a good time to explain to students that this is a general problem-solving strategy: break a large or complicated problem into smaller steps; as you work through the smaller steps, look for patterns you can extend to the larger problem.

Follow this by introducing the tree diagram as a much simpler way for keeping track of outcomes in these sample spaces. For creating orderly tree diagrams quickly, an overhead projector may be preferable to a chalkboard; on the smaller writing area, it's easier to plan your tree diagram and not run out of space.

If students completed the lab investigation, you might want to have them compare the number of orders of three CDs to the number of pizzas from three toppings, after you have discussed the listing methods. The class can then discuss why the results are not the same.

You may also wish to point out the Just the Facts on this page, which alerts students to a probability term they will encounter in future mathematics courses— *permutation.*

Think & Discuss

Jesse and Marcus have the five CDs by their favorite band, X Squared:

- *Algebraic Angst*

- *Binary Breakdown*

- *Chalkboard Blues*

- *Dog Ate My Homework*

- *Everyday Problems*

The friends want to listen to all five CDs. Predict the number of different orders in which they can play the five CDs.

Just the facts

The table and tree diagram show the ways these CDs can be arranged or listed. A listing in which order is important is called a permutation.

Predictions will vary. There are 120 orders.

To find how many ways a group of CDs can be ordered, you can list all the possibilities. With only one CD, there is obviously only one order. With two CDs—call them A and B—there are two possible orders: AB and BA. With three CDs, there are six orders:

$$\text{ABC} \quad \text{ACB} \quad \text{BAC} \quad \text{BCA} \quad \text{CAB} \quad \text{CBA}$$

To be certain you haven't missed any possibilities, you need a systematic method of counting and recording. You could list the possibilities for three CDs in a table.

A First	B First	C First
ABC	BAC	CAB
ACB	BCA	CBA

Or you could organize them using a *tree diagram*.

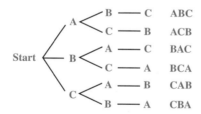

The tree diagram works in much the same way as the table. It shows that there are three ways to start: A, B, or C. Then there are two choices for the second CD and one choice for the third.

1 You might remind students of the lab investigation, if they completed it.

2 Discuss predictions and how students found them.

3 **Problem-Solving Strategies**

- Solve a simpler problem
- Look for a pattern

4 Introduce tree diagrams.

Problem Set E Suggested Grouping: Pairs
The text following the Think & Discuss on page 551
showed students the possible ways to order two and
then three CDs; in this problem set, students extend that
to find the ways to order four and then five CDs.

 Some students may prefer the more familiar systematic
listing. This will produce the same answer as a tree diagram, but you should encourage them to try the tree diagram so that they gain it as a tool for future work. Have
each pair of students work together to create a single
diagram, so they can catch each other's mistakes.

Problem Set Wrap-Up Students can compare their
answers for **Problem 8** to their predictions in the Think
& Discuss at the beginning of the investigation. This
problem is particularly important because it asks students to figure out the sample space *without* listing all
the possibilities. Discuss solutions as a class, focusing on
students' explanations of their work.

Additional Examples You may want to introduce
another example for students to consider.

- In one middle school, students take six classes: math,
  English, science, social studies, music, and physical
  education. How many different daily schedules are
  possible? *720*

- An amusement park sells tickets that allow the holder
  to ride *twice* on any of the four most popular rides:
  water slide, roller coaster, haunted house, and octo-
  pus. How many ways are there to use the ticket for
  two rides without going on the same ride twice? Let
  order count; for example, water slide then haunted
  house is different from haunted house then water
  slide. 12

Be sure all students have the correct sample space of the
four-CD situation, as the next problem set makes use of it.

Problem Set E

Consider the case of four CDs: A, B, C, and D.

1. **Predictions will vary.**

    1. Predict the number of ways these four CDs can be ordered.

    2. Make an organized list of all the possibilities in which A is played first. To do this, you may want to make a tree diagram like the one started at right. ABCD, ABDC, ACBD, ACDB, ADBC, ADCB

A First
ABCD
ABDC
ACBD
⋮

3. **After deciding that A is first, all that is being rearranged are the other three CDs.**

    3. The number of orders of four CDs in which A is first is the same as the total number of ways three CDs can be ordered. Explain why.

    4. Why is the number of orders of four CDs in which B is first the same as the number of orders of four CDs in which A is first?

4. **It doesn't matter which CD is first; there are still exactly three other CDs being rearranged.**

    5. List all the orders in which B is first. Then list all the orders in which C is first. Finally, list all the orders in which D is first. Use your answer to Problem 4 to verify that you have listed all the possibilities. See below.

6. **24 orders; multiply the number of lists by the total number of lists.**

    6. How many possible orders are there altogether? If you know how many entries are in each list, how can you determine the total number of entries without counting them all?

    7. Is your estimate from Problem 1 greater than or less than the actual number of orders? Answers will vary.

    8. Now return to the problem presented in the Think & Discuss on page 551: In how many different orders can Jesse and Marcus play their five CDs? Try to find your answer *without* listing all the possibilities. Show how you found it. 5 lists of 24 = 120

5.

B First	C First	D First
BACD	CABD	DABC
BADC	CADB	DACB
BCAD	CBAD	DBAC
BCDA	CBDA	DBCA
BDAC	CDAB	DCAB
BDCA	CDBA	DCBA

Example

Have students study this Example in pairs, and discuss any questions they have. Make sure everyone understands the point before moving on to Problem Set F.

On the Spot Assessment

Watch for students who seem uncertain about the Example. By this time, calculating probabilities from the sample space should be fairly straightforward. If you find students who need additional help, you might have them think back to the spinners problem in the lesson introduction. There were two spinners, each with three outcomes, blue, white, and orange. Ask students:

What's the probability that the second spinner lands on white? $\frac{1}{3}$

Now list the sample space if you spin both spinners. BB, BW, BO, WB, WW, WO, OB, OW, OO

In how many outcomes is the second spinner white? 3

Now point out that in three of the nine outcomes, the second spinner lands on white, which means the probability is $\frac{3}{9}$, or $\frac{1}{3}$. That should agree with the probability students stated for the second spinner landing on white.

Problem Set F Suggested Grouping: Pairs

In this problem set, students use the sample space of the four-CD situation to find probabilities. Pairs are particularly useful for Problems 13–16 on page 554.

Problems 1–7 are fairly straightforward.

Problems 8 and 9 are a little more difficult. In each, students are asked to consider why two probabilities are the same. If students are having trouble with Problem 8, you might ask:

Suppose you give A to me, then order the remaining CDs, and I just add A to the end of each ordering. How many orderings would you have? 6

The important information you needed to answer the question wasn't the letter of the CD you gave me. What was it? the number of CDs I had left

For Problem 9, you can ask a similar first question, and then follow up with:

How is the situation the same if I add A to the beginning of each ordering rather than to the end? The other CDs still have the same orderings and so the same number of orderings.

Problems 10–12 focus on the *complement* of an event, that is, when an event *doesn't* happen. Students may have already considered this in On Your Own Exercise 1. It may help students who are having trouble with this if you ask:

In Problem 3, you considered when C was not played first, and Problem 10 asks about when C *is* played first. Are there any orderings that wouldn't fall into at least one of these events? no Are there any that would fall into both of these events? no

What does that tell you about the number of orderings in the two events together? That's the entire sample space.

If students are still unable to make the connection, you might give one last hint to look at the sum and the difference of the number of outcomes in the two events and compare each of them to the size of the sample space.

If you consider the orders of the CDs as the outcomes in a sample space, you can calculate probabilities of specific events.

EXAMPLE

Consider all the orders of four CDs: A, B, C, and D. If one of these orders is selected at random, what is the probability that B will be before D?

In Problem Set E, you found that there are 24 outcomes in the sample space for this situation. B appears before D in 12 of these 24 outcomes.

ABCD	BACD	CABD
ABDC	BADC	CBAD
ACBD	BCAD	CBDA
	BCDA	
	BDAC	
	BDCA	

So, the probability that B will be played before D is $\frac{12}{24}$, or 50%.

In Problem Set F, you will find the probability of other events that involve the order in which four CDs are played.

Problem Set F

In Problems 1–7, determine the probability that the given event will occur. Before you begin, be sure you have a complete list of the 24 outcomes in the sample space for this situation.

1. C immediately follows B.   **2.** A is played last. $\frac{6}{24}$, or $\frac{1}{4}$

3. C is not played first. $\frac{18}{24}$, or $\frac{3}{4}$ **4.** B is played before A. $\frac{12}{24}$, or $\frac{1}{2}$

5. D is played first *and* A is played last. $\frac{2}{24}$, or $\frac{1}{12}$

6. The CDs are played in the order CBAD. $\frac{1}{24}$

7. A is played first *and* C is not played last. $\frac{4}{24}$, or $\frac{1}{6}$

8. The probability of A being played last is the same as the probability of B being played last. Explain why.

9. Why are the chances of A being played last the same as the chances of A being played first?

10. How can you use the chances that C is played first to check your answer to Problem 3?
   C has 6 out of 24 chances of being played first. So, it must have 24 − 6 = 18 chances out of 24 of *not* being played first.

1. $\frac{6}{24}$, or $\frac{1}{4}$

8. No matter which CD is last, there are exactly 6 ways of arranging the other three CDs.

9. No matter whether A is first or last— or, for that matter, second or third— there are exactly 6 ways of arranging the other three CDs.

In **Problem 12,** students are asked to generalize the results of Problems 10 and 11.

Problems 13–16 can be difficult for some students, but by working in pairs most will be able to think of a possible answer. Don't insist on mastery of these problems, however.

Share & Summarize

This Share & Summarize is worth a fair amount of discussion, because it focuses on using numeric patterns to calculate the size of a sample space without listing or making a tree diagram for all the possibilities.

In **Question 1c,** you might find it helpful to ask for connections between creating a tree diagram and Kai's method; some students may be able to construct a tree diagram in a mechanical way without considering how a stage in its construction depends on the previous stage.

Question 1d asks students to find the number of orders for a specific number of CDs without building up to it. Students may want to continue their work in Questions 1a and b, finding the number of orders for five and six CDs as well. You may want to let them do this, then ask whether anyone sees a way to do it without actually calculating each number. If no student suggests it, you might ask them to start with seven and use Kai's method. Write on the board or overhead projector:

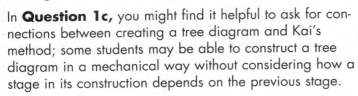

$$\text{Number of orders for 7 CDs} = 7 \cdot \text{Number of orders for 6 CDs}$$

Then ask how to find the number of orders for six CDs. Erase the words "Number of orders for 6 CDs" and replace them with "6 · Number of orders for 5 CDs." Continue this until students see that the number of orders is

$$7 \cdot 6 \cdot 5 \cdot 4 \cdot 3 \cdot 2 \cdot 1$$

You may wish to point out that the product $7 \cdot 6 \cdot 5 \cdot 4 \cdot 3 \cdot 2 \cdot 1$ is called *7 factorial* or 7! This terminology and notation will be important in future mathematics courses.

Question 2 asks students to use the strategy from Problem Set E, that is, making a tree diagram or a list, to find the different possible orders of a set of items. If students need prompting, you might want to ask:

How is the CD situation different from the name-drawing situation? In the name-drawing situation, order is not important.

Troubleshooting The next investigation focuses on using patterns, so you can go on even if students don't fully understand these ideas yet. Some students may have developed their own strategies for using numeric patterns to find the size of a sample space; if so, you might have them explain their approaches and why they work to the whole class.

On Your Own Exercises

Practice & Apply: 3, 4, p. 559
Connect & Extend: 11, 12, p. 562
Mixed Review: 14–29, pp. 563–564

Investigation 3

This investigation emphasizes the use of numeric patterns to calculate the size of a sample space without naming each possible outcome. This is particularly important in situations for which naming all outcomes is an overwhelmingly large task (for example, finding the number of possible combinations in a lottery that chooses 6 of 40 numbers).

Have students read the introductory paragraph, and then move on to the Think & Discuss on page 555.

11. $\frac{3}{4}$; Possible explanation: I subtracted from 1.

13. Possible answer: A is played first.

14. Possible answer: A is not played first and D is not played last.

15. Possible answer: A is played.

16. Possible answer: B is played immediately after A, A is not played first, and C is not played last.

Share & Summarize Answers

1a. $2 \cdot 1 = 2$ ways; yes

1b. $3 \cdot 2 = 6$ ways, $4 \cdot 6 = 24$ ways; yes

1c. For n CDs, there are n choices for the first disc. After that, you must arrange the remaining $n - 1$ CDs, so there are $n \times$ (the number of ways to put $n - 1$ in order) ways to do it.

---

11. If the probability of an event is $\frac{1}{4}$, what is the probability that the event will *not* happen? Explain how you found your answer.

12. If the probability of an event is p, where p is between 0 and 1, what is the probability that the event will not happen? $1 - p$

Describe an event related to the CD problem with the given probability.

13. $\frac{6}{24}$ **14.** $\frac{22}{24}$ **15.** $\frac{24}{24}$ **16.** $\frac{3}{24}$

Share & Summarize

1. Kai found a shortcut for determining the number of ways to put CDs in order. He said, "For five CDs, multiply 5 by the number of ways to put four CDs in order. In fact, for n CDs, just multiply n by the number of ways to put $n - 1$ CDs in order."

   a. There is only one way to order one CD. Use Kai's method to find the number of ways to order two CDs. Did it work?

   b. Use Kai's method and your answer to Part a to find the number of ways to order three and four CDs. Did it work?

   c. Explain why Kai's method makes sense.

   d. How many ways are there to order seven CDs?   5,040

2. Lucita thought she could use the strategy from Problem Set E to find the number of one-on-one pairs of Ally, Brevin, Carol, and Doug. She started listing the possibilities.

Ally First
Ally/Brevin
Ally/Carol
Ally/Doug

   Lucita said, "There are three outcomes on this list, and there will be four lists—one for each friend—so there are 12 pairs in all." Is she correct? Explain.

   no; Possible explanation: She is counting each outcome twice. In this situation, order is not important; for example, Ally/Carol is the same as Carol/Ally. Lucita's method counts these outcomes separately.

Investigation ▶3 Counting Strategies Using Patterns

In Investigation 1, you found the size of a sample space by listing all the possibilities (all the one-on-one pairs). In Investigation 2, you saw that you can sometimes discover a pattern that allows you to find the total number of outcomes without listing them all. In this investigation, you will explore other counting strategies.

1 Take some time to discuss these with the class.

2 You might ask for connections between tree diagrams and Kai's shortcut.

3 Briefly review what students learned the past few days.

Develop

Think & Discuss

Ask students for possible answers to the first question and write them where everyone can see them. After a few answers have been recorded, you might ask whether the responses are being given in a systematic way and, if not, whether there is a way to list all the possible answers systematically.

Once you have listed the possible answers using a method the students suggest, give them a minute to think about how many whole-number pairs have a sum of 100. Record their predictions without judgment or comment. The question poses a challenge for the rest of the investigation, and the next two problem sets help students work this problem in a systematic way. Some students may recognize that for every number from 1 to 50, there is another number that can be added to it to make 100. That gives 50 pairs; the pair 0 + 100 makes 51 pairs.

Problem Set G Suggested Grouping: Individuals

This problem set approaches the large problem of sums adding to 100 by looking at simpler cases first. This is not exactly the same as the strategy students used to count orders of CDs, in which they broke the problem into smaller problems, although they look similar. There will be an opportunity between Problem Sets H and I to clarify the difference to students, but you may want to describe this new strategy before students start working with it.

If students follow the directions, they should have no trouble finding the pattern they will use to answer the probability questions in Problem Set H.

Some students may find it hard in **Problem 6b** to explain why there is a difference in the patterns. Encourage them to think past the simple answer that since an even number and the number 1 greater have the same number of pairs, the expressions must be different. While this is a valid point, it doesn't really explain why that pattern exists. You may want to discuss the answers with the entire class.

A slightly different explanation from the one given on page 555 is to again consider the number pairs such as 1-100 and 2-99 for the odd number 101. In this case, there are 102 different numbers involved, 0–101. So there are $\frac{101+1}{2}$ pairs, or more generally, $\frac{S+1}{2}$ pairs. For an even number, such as 100, there are only 101 different numbers involved, 0–100. One number, namely 50, has to be used twice, to give 102 numbers. So there are $\frac{100+2}{2}$ pairs, or more generally, $\frac{S+2}{2}$, or $\frac{S}{2}+1$, pairs.

Problem Set Wrap-Up Students will use the patterns and answers from Problem Set G in the next problem set, so a quick review of their answers would be helpful. Be sure they know correct formulas for the number of pairs giving even and odd sums.

Remember

Whole numbers are nonnegative integers, or the numbers 0, 1, 2, 3, ...

① 0-12, 1-11, 2-10, 3-9, 4-8, 5-7, 6-6; 7 pairs

6a. even sums: $\frac{S}{2} + 1$ or $\frac{S+2}{2}$; odd sums: $\frac{S}{2} + \frac{1}{2}$, or $\frac{S+1}{2}$

6b. Possible answer: For even totals— for example, $S = 100$—you start writing the pairs 1-99, 2-98, 3-97, until 50-50, which is 50 pairs, half of 100. Then there is one extra pair, 0-100, so the number of pairs is $1 + \frac{S}{2}$.

For odd totals, like 101, you start the same way—1-100, 2-99, 3-98, until 50-51—but because half of 101 is 50.5, which isn't a whole number, the counting stops at 50, which is $\frac{S}{2} - \frac{1}{2}$, or $\frac{S-1}{2}$. There is one extra pair, 0-101, so you add a pair, giving $\frac{S}{2} + \frac{1}{2}$, or $\frac{S+1}{2}$.

Think & Discuss

Two whole numbers add to 12. What might the numbers be?
Answers will vary.

List every pair of whole numbers with a sum of 12. Make sure you've listed all the possibilities. How many pairs are there? (In this situation, order does not matter. The pair 3-9 is the same as the pair 9-3.)
See ①.

Predict how many whole-number pairs have a sum of 100.
Predictions will vary. The answer is 51.

One strategy for finding the number of whole-number pairs with a sum of 100 is to first consider some simpler problems and look for a pattern.

Problem Set G

1. The sum of two whole numbers is 10. Three possible pairs are 0-10, 1-9, and 2-8. What are the other pairs? How many pairs are there in all? *3-7, 4-6, 5-5; 6 pairs*

2. Now write down all the whole-number pairs with a sum of 11. How many pairs are there? *0-11, 1-10, 2-9, 3-8, 4-7, 5-6; 6 pairs*

3. Look back at the Think & Discuss above. How many whole-number pairs have a sum of 12? *7*

4. Copy and complete the table to show the number of whole-number pairs with each sum.

Sum	10	11	12	13	14	15	16
Number of Pairs	6	6	7	7	8	8	9

5. Copy this table, and use any patterns you have observed to find the number of whole-number pairs with each given sum.

Sum	20	27	40	80	100	275
Number of Pairs	11	14	21	41	51	138

6. Look at the even and odd sums and the number of pairs that produce them.

    a. Write two expressions—one for even sums and one for odd sums—that describe the relationship between the sum S and the number of whole-number pairs that produce that sum.

    b. Explain why the expressions for even sums and odd sums are different.

1 Record a few responses, then prompt students to list answers systematically.

2 Record predictions without comment.

3 Problem-Solving Strategy

Solve a simpler problem

4 Encourage students to explain why an even number and the next greater odd number have the same number of pairs.

5 Go over answers to Problem Set G.

Problem Set H Suggested Grouping: Individuals
This problem set asks students to find probabilities of different events in the situation from Problem Set G.

The problems are fairly straightforward, but some students may be unsure how to begin **Problem 1b.** Prompt them to start a list of the number pairs. ■

Review the strategy summary that follows Problem Set H with the class. Some students may not be clear how the second strategy (breaking a problem into smaller parts) is different from the third (beginning with simpler cases), and in fact the difference is subtle. When you break a problem into smaller parts, each part is often just a smaller case of the larger problem, as in the ordering-of-CDs problem.

It may help if you point out that in the CD problem, students were able to build on the smaller problems as they added a new CD into the problem. With the number sums, students might have used the process by which they found the answer to the smaller problem as they continued to a greater sum, but they were not simply adding to the previous result.

Once you know the size of the sample space, you can calculate the probability of an event occurring.

Problem Set H

Use the patterns and answers you found in Problem Set G to determine these probabilities.

1. All the whole-number pairs with a sum of 20 are put into a hat, and one is drawn at random.

a. What is the size of the sample space in this situation? 11

b. What is the probability that one of the numbers in the pair selected is greater than 14? Explain how you found your answer.

2. All the whole-number pairs with a sum of 100 are put into a hat, and one is drawn at random.

a. What is the size of the sample space in this situation? 51

b. In how many pairs are both numbers less than 60? List them.

c. What is the probability that both of the numbers in the selected pair are less than 60? $\frac{10}{51}$

3. All the whole-number pairs with a sum of 55 are put into a hat, and one is drawn at random.

a. What is the size of the sample space in this situation? 28

b. How many pairs include a number greater than 48? List them.

c. What is the probability of choosing a pair in which neither number is greater than 48? $\frac{21}{28}$, or $\frac{3}{4}$

So far, you have used three strategies to find the size of a sample space:

• Systematically list all the possibilities.

• Begin a systematic list of possibilities, and look for a pattern that will help you find the total number without completing the list.

• Start with simpler cases and look for a logical pattern that you can extend to the more complicated cases.

In Problem Set I, you will find the size of a sample space by breaking it into manageable parts. The problem you will work on is similar to those in Problem Set G, but a bit more complicated.

1b. $\frac{6}{11}$; Of the 11 pairs, 6 include a number greater than 14: 0-20, 1-19, 2-18, 3-17, 4-16, and 5-15.

2b. 10 pairs: 41-59, 42-58, 43-57, 44-56, 45-55, 46-54, 47-53, 48-52, 49-51, 50-50

3b. 7 pairs: 0-55, 1-54, 2-53, 3-52, 4-51, 5-50, 6-49

1 You may have students work on their own.

2 Discuss these problem-solving strategies, clarifying the difference between the last two.

Problem Set I Suggested Grouping: Pairs

This problem set offers an opportunity to practice finding the sample space by using numeric patterns. You may need to review the mean of a set of numbers before starting this problem set.

Work through **Problems 1–3** as a class, and then let students work together in pairs on the remaining problems. Explanations are likely to be better when constructed as a team.

2 If students have trouble with **Problem 4,** you may want to help them start their lists:

> Since we want triples that contain at least one 1, let's start each triple by writing a 1. We can't use 0, so what should we use for the next number? *any number from 1 to 7* Then what must the last number in the triple be? *8 minus the number chosen for the second one*

> Now let's see if we can get another triple. Start with 1 again. We still can't use 0, and we can't use the number we used last time because that would give the same triple. What *can* we use?

Note that some students may not want to use 1 the second time. If they suggest 2, then 3, recognize that they are trying a systematic approach but ask why they didn't use 1. Remind them that there should be at least one 1, which does not exclude the possibility of two 1s.

3 **Share & Summarize**

Have students work in their pairs from Problem Set I to answer this question. You may want to select pairs to present their responses to the class. Encourage students to give detailed explanations of their processes.

Some students may have difficulty with the general *m.* You might ask them to consider a particular sum instead. For example, you could say:

> Suppose the set of four numbers has a mean of 5. Now explain how to find the number of whole-number sets this describes. Can you find the places where your explanation relies on the mean of 5? How can you make those places more general, for a mean of *m?*

Troubleshooting If students continue to have trouble, offer some examples requiring constructing an orderly list. The process of listing can be made more obvious by constructing a series of tree diagrams. For example, this tree diagram reflects a triple having at least one 0:

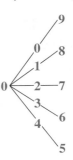

 ## On Your Own Exercises

Practice & Apply: 5–7, p. 560
Connect & Extend: 13, p. 563
Mixed Review: 14–29, pp. 563–564

Problem Set I

Consider this problem: *Three whole numbers have a mean of 3. How many such whole-number triples exist? How can you be sure you've found them all?* Here's one way to think through this problem.

1. If the mean of three whole numbers is 3, what is their sum? Why?

Now you can think about the problem as finding all the combinations of three numbers with a sum of 9.

2. When you list combinations of three whole numbers with a sum of 9, does the *order* of the numbers matter? For example, is the triple 1-2-6 considered the same as or different from the triple 6-2-1?

3. One way to break the problem into manageable parts is to start by thinking about all the whole-number triples in which at least one number is 0. List all such triples with a sum of 9. How many are there?

4. To continue listing the combinations, you might next decide to find all those that contain at least one 1 but no 0s.

a. Why would you exclude 0s from your triples at this stage?

b. List the triples that contain at least one 1 but no 0s. How many are there?   1-1-7, 1-2-6, 1-3-5, 1-4-4; 4 triples

5. Continue this process. List all the triples that contain at least one 2 but not 0 or 1, and then all the triples that include at least one 3 but not 0, 1, or 2. Complete the table.

Smallest Number in Triple	0	1	2	3
Number of Triples	5	4	2	1

6. Why are no more columns needed in this table? In other words, explain why you don't need to consider triples in which the smallest number is 4, 5, or any greater number.

7. How many different triples are there in all?   12

8. If all the triples are put into a hat, what is the probability of drawing a combination whose smallest number is 0? Whose smallest number is 4? $\frac{5}{12}$; $\frac{0}{12}$, or 0

9. Use the strategy of breaking the problem into smaller parts to find the number of whole-number triples with a mean of 4.   19

Share & Summarize

A set of four numbers has a mean of *m*. Explain how you would find the number of whole-number sets that this could describe.

---

1. 9; $\frac{x}{3} = 3$ only when $x = 9$.

2. No; 1-2-6 is considered the same as 6-2-1.

3. 0-0-9, 0-1-8, 0-2-7, 0-3-6, 0-4-5; 5 triples

4a. If it has a 0, it would have been listed in Problem 3. If I listed it here, it would be counted twice.

6. The higher numbers have been used in the triples already counted.

Share & Summarize Answer

Possible answer: The sum of the four numbers would have to be *4m*, so I would start by finding all the sets that include two or more 0s, then one 0 and at least one 1, then one 0 and at least one 2 but no 1s, then one 0 and at least one 3 but no 1s or 2s, and so on. I would then do the same with 1s instead of 0s, and exclude 0 from the triples. Then I would do the same with 2s, excluding 0s and 1s, and so on.

1 Work Problems 1–3 with the class, then you may have students continue in pairs.

2 You may want to help students start their lists.

3 Encourage detailed explanations.

On Your Own Exercises

Investigation 1,
  pp. 547–550
Practice & Apply: 1, 2
Connect & Extend: 8–10

Investigation 2,
  pp. 550–554
Practice & Apply: 3, 4
Connect & Extend: 11, 12

Investigation 3,
  pp. 554–557
Practice & Apply: 5–7
Connect & Extend: 13

Assign Anytime
Mixed Review: 14–29

Exercise 1e:
It is worth being explicit about the relationship between the probability that an event happens and the probability that the event does not happen. If $P(E)$ is the probability that event E occurs, then $P(\text{not } E) = 1 - P(E)$. To calculate the probability that the next match will *not* involve Batai, students can either count the appropriate outcomes directly or calculate the probability that the next match *will* involve Batai and subtract this from 1.

Students will work on this concept again in the class work for Investigation 2, so if any are having trouble, you might assure them that they will have another opportunity to think about it.

Exercise 2:
Students will probably start to list possibilities to answer **Parts b and c.** The intent of these parts is to have them make quick guesses and then, in **Part d,** check the results by listing. For some classes, you might want to eliminate the "guess" component from this question by having students skip Parts b and c and just make the list for Part d.

Practice & Apply

1c. 15 pairs; AB, AC, AD, AE, AF, BC, BD, BE, BF, CD, CE, CF, DE, DF, EF

1e. $\frac{10}{15}$, or $\frac{2}{3}$

1. Three friends—Avery, Batai, and Chelsea—get together to play chess. To determine who will play whom, they put their names into a hat and draw out two at random.

   a. List all the possible pairs of names. AB, AC, BC

   b. What is the probability that Batai and Chelsea will play the next game? $\frac{1}{3}$

   c. Three more friends—Donae, Eric, and Fran—join the group. Now how many possible pairs are there? List them.

   d. What is the probability that the next match will involve Avery or Eric (or both)? $\frac{9}{15}$, or $\frac{3}{5}$

   e. What is the probability that the next match will *not* involve Batai?

2. **Sports** You have been asked to organize the matches for the singles competition at your local tennis club. There are seven players in the competition, and each must play every other player once.

   a. The matches Player A must play are listed below. Notice that this list already includes the match of Player A against Player B. Copy the table, and in the row for Player B, list all the other matches Player B must play. (In other words, list all the matches that include Player B but *do not* include Player A.)

Player	Matches to Play	Number of Matches
A	AB, AC, AD, AE, AF, AG	6
B	BC, BD, BE, BF, BG	5
C	CD, CE, CF, CG	4
D	DE, DF, DG	3
E	EF, EG	2
F	FG	1
G		0

   b. Predict the number of matches Player C must play that *do not* include Players A or B. Write your prediction in the "Number of Matches" column. Predictions will vary.

   c. Predict the number of matches for the remaining players. In each case, consider only those matches that *do not* include the players listed above that player. Predictions will vary.

 impactmath.com/self_check_quiz

Quick Review
Math Handbook

hot words
hot topics

Hot Topics
pp. 232–238,
240–248

2d. See the table in Part a.

2g. 28; add all the numbers from 1 to 7.

4c. $\frac{18}{24}$, or $\frac{3}{4}$

d. Check your predictions by listing the matches for each player.

e. Describe the pattern in the "Number of Matches" column. Why do you think this pattern occurs?   See below.

f. Find the total number of matches that will be played in the singles competition.   21

g. Use what you have discovered in this problem to predict the total number of matches in a singles competition involving eight players. Explain how you found your answer.

3. Petra wants to make a withdrawal from an automated teller machine, but she can't remember her personal identification number. She knows that it includes the digits 2, 3, 5, and 7, but she can't recall their order. She decides to try all the possible orders until she finds the right one.

a. How many orders are possible?   24

b. Petra remembers that the first digit is an odd number. Now how many orders are possible?   18

c. Petra then remembers that the first digit is 5. How many orders are possible now?   6

4. The "Shuffle" button on Tamika's CD player plays the songs in a random order. Tamika puts a four-song CD into the player and presses "Shuffle."

a. How many ways can the four songs be ordered?   24

b. What is the probability that Song 1 will be played first? $\frac{6}{24}$, or $\frac{1}{4}$

c. What is the probability that Song 1 will *not* be played first?

d. Songs 2 and 3 are Tamika's favorites. What is the probability that *one* of these two songs will be played first? $\frac{12}{24}$, or $\frac{1}{2}$

e. What is the probability that Songs 2 and 3 will be the first two songs played (in either order)? $\frac{4}{24}$, or $\frac{1}{6}$

2e. The numbers decrease by 1. Possible explanation: Since the person for a particular row must play everyone else, the number of matches is equal to the number of remaining players—but for each row, you are reducing the number of players being considered by 1.

Exercises 2e and 2g:
These can be profitably discussed in class so that all students get a chance to evaluate the reasonableness of a particular student's explanation.

Exercise 3:
Assess whether students have the basic "tree" counting principle. It is important that they realize that **Part b** restricts the first choice to three numbers while **Part c** provides only one first-digit possibility.

If a student suggests that the PIN could conceivably allow for repetitions—that is, it might consist of five or more digits—point out the increased complexity of the problem, not just in how many digits are involved but also in the issue of duplicate combinations.

For example, if you approach this problem as if the PIN consisted of five different digits, say 2, 3, 5, 6, and 7, there are 120 possibilities, including 23567 and 26537. If there were only four digits to choose from, but you still needed to choose a five-digit combination, you might start by replacing all 6s by 3s. Then you would get 23537 twice.

You may want to tell students that if they continue studying mathematics, they will probably learn how to take such duplicates into account.

Exercise 4c:
You might point out that it is easier to count the number of times Song 1 *will* be played first: $\frac{6}{24}$. Hence the answer is $1 - \frac{6}{24}$, or $\frac{18}{24}$.

5a. 0-26, 1-25, 2-24, 3-23, 4-22, 5-21, 6-20, 7-19, 8-18, 9-17, 10-16, 11-15, 12-14, 13-13

5c. $\frac{12}{14}$, or $\frac{6}{7}$; In 2 of the 14 pairs listed, both number are less than 15.

5d. $\frac{2}{14}$, or $\frac{1}{7}$; In 2 of the 14 pairs listed, both numbers are less than 15.

Connect & Extend

6b. 180; Possible explanation: For one number to be greater than 300, the other must be between 0 and 179. There are 180 such pairs.

8a. 20 teams; ABC, ABD, ABE, ABF, ACD, ACE, ACF, ADE, ADF, AEF, BCD, BCE, BCF, BDE, BDF, BEF, CDE, CDF, CEF, DEF

5. All the whole-number pairs with a sum of 26 are put into a hat, and one is drawn at random.

   a. List all the possible whole-number pairs with a sum of 26.

   b. What is the size of the sample space in this situation? 14

   c. What is the probability that at least one of the numbers in the pair selected is greater than or equal to 15? Explain how you found your answer.

   d. What is the probability that both numbers in the pair selected are less than 15? Explain.

6. **Challenge** All the whole-number pairs with a sum of 480 are put into a hat, and one is drawn at random.

   a. What is the size of the sample space in this situation? 241

   b. What is the probability that one of the numbers in the pair selected is greater than 300? Explain how you know.

7. Three whole numbers have a mean of 5.

   a. List all the whole-number triples with a mean of 5, and explain how you know you have found them all. See Additional Answers.

   b. How many such whole-number triples exist? 27

   c. Suppose all the whole-number triples with a mean of 5 are put into a hat, and one is drawn at random. What is the probability that at least two of the numbers in the triple are the same? $\frac{8}{27}$

8. The Alvarez family—Amelia, Bernie, Carlos, Dina, Eduardo, and Flora—want to form two teams of three to play charades. They put their names into a hat and choose three names to form one team. The remaining three players will form the other team.

   a. How many teams are possible? List them all.

   b. What is the probability that the three names drawn will include Amelia or Eduardo (or both)? $\frac{16}{20}$, or $\frac{4}{5}$

   c. What is the probability that the three names drawn will include both Amelia and Eduardo? $\frac{4}{20}$, or $\frac{1}{5}$

   d. What is the probability that the three names drawn will include neither Amelia or Eduardo? $\frac{4}{20}$, or $\frac{1}{5}$

   e. What is the probability that Amelia and Eduardo will be on the same team? Explain how you found your answer.
   $\frac{8}{20}$, or $\frac{2}{5}$; Amelia and Eduardo will be on the same team if both names are drawn or if neither name is drawn. So, we can add probabilities from Parts b and c.

Additional Answers

7a. 0-0-15, 0-1-14, 0-2-13, 0-3-12, 0-4-11, 0-5-10, 0-6-9, 0-7-8, 1-1-13, 1-2-12, 1-3-11, 1-4-10, 1-5-9, 1-6-8, 1-7-7, 2-2-11, 2-3-10, 2-4-9, 2-5-8, 2-6-7, 3-3-9, 3-4-8, 3-5-7, 3-6-6, 4-4-7, 4-5-6, 5-5-5; Possible explanation: I know I found them all because I systematically listed all the triples that included 0, then all that included 1 but not 0, and so on.

9a. 25; Possible explanation: There are 5 possibilities for the seventh grader, and for each of these, there are 5 possibilities for the eighth grader. So, there are 5 · 5 = 25 pairs in all.

9. Five seventh grade friends—Anya, Ben, Calvin, Dan, and Ezra— challenged five eighth grade friends—Vic, Wendi, Xavier, Yvonne, and Zac—to a backgammon tournament. They put the names of the seventh graders into one hat and the names of the eighth graders into another. To determine the two players for each match, they pulled one name from each hat.

   a. What is the size of the sample space in this situation? That is, how many different pairs of names are possible? Explain.

   b. What is the probability that the next match will involve Anya and either Xavier or Yvonne? $\frac{2}{25}$

   c. What is the probability that the next pair drawn will not involve Calvin? $\frac{20}{25}$, or $\frac{4}{5}$

   d. Suppose all 10 names are put into one hat, and two are drawn at random. What is the probability that the pair will include one seventh grader and one eighth grader? Explain.   See below.

10. Kai is helping to plan a school picnic. Each picnic lunch will include a sandwich, a side item, and a dessert. The possible choices for each are given below.

Sandwich	Side	Dessert
peanut butter	salad	fresh fruit
cheese	chips	cookie
egg salad		cheesecake
		pie

   a. How many different lunch combinations are possible?   24

   Kai and his co-workers make an equal number of each combination, but they forgot to mark the bags. Assume that when a person takes a bag, each combination is just as likely to be in the bag as any other combination.

   b. Bharati doesn't care what dessert she gets, but she really wants an egg sandwich and a salad. What is the probability that her lunch will include these two items? $\frac{4}{24}$, or $\frac{1}{6}$

   c. Evan doesn't like eggs. What is the probability that he will choose a bag that *does not* include an egg salad sandwich? $\frac{16}{24}$, or $\frac{2}{3}$

9d. $\frac{25}{45}$, or $\frac{5}{9}$; Possible explanation: There are 45 possible pairs—25 that include one seventh grader and one eighth grader, 10 that include two seventh graders, and 10 that include two eighth graders. So, the probability that the pair will include one seventh grader and one eighth grader is $\frac{25}{45}$, or $\frac{5}{9}$.

Exercise 9:
Part c is the type of problem for which it is easier to calculate the probability of the "opposite" event and subtract from 1 than to find the probability of the event directly.

It is easier to find the probability that Calvin's name *will* be drawn and subtract that probability from 1.

Part d changes the situation significantly; the answers to the preceding questions will not help a student's reasoning.

Exercise 10:
If students had trouble thinking through this exercise, you might have them start a tree diagram and then try to count possibilities. In **Part c,** some may calculate the probability that Evan's lunch *does* include an egg salad sandwich and subtract this from 1.

Exercise 11:

You may want to spend a little time discussing different orderings of elements in a circle. Two people can be ordered in a circle in only one way: A is always both to the right and left of B. For three people, either A can be to the right of B and C to the left of B, or A can be to the left of B and C to the right of B. The problem is to determine how many linear arrangements are really the same arrangement when placed in a circle. The linear arrangement (A, B, C) is the same order as (C, A, B) and (B, C, A) when placed in a circle (just keep moving the last element to the first of the list). Thus three row arrangements count as one circular arrangement, so for three people, divide the number of row arrangements by 3 to obtain the number of circular arrangements. In general, given *n* elements, determine the number of circle arrangements by dividing the number of row arrangements by *n*.

11a. 6 ways; ABC, ACB, BAC, BCA, CAB, CBA

11b. There are two ways.

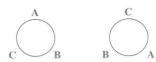

11d. Possible answer: The number of row arrangements divided by the number of people equals the number of circle arrangements. The number of circle arrangements for *n* people is the same as the number of row arrangements for *n* − 1 people.

11. In this exercise, you will think about the different ways a number of people can be seated along a bench and around a circular table.

a. How many ways can three people—call them A, B, and C—be seated along a bench? List all the possibilities.

b. If the three people are arranged around a circular table, there will be no starting or ending point. So, for example, these two arrangements are considered the same.

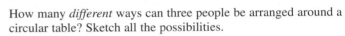

How many *different* ways can three people be arranged around a circular table? Sketch all the possibilities.

c. Copy and complete the table to show how many ways the given number of people can be arranged along a bench and around a circular table.

People	Row Arrangements	Circle Arrangements
1	1	1
2	2	1
3	6	2
4	24	6

d. Describe at least one pattern you see in your table.

e. Five people can be arranged along a bench in 120 ways. Use the patterns in your table to predict the number of ways five people can be seated around a circular table.   24

12. A programmer wrote some software that composes pieces of music by randomly combining musical segments. For each piece, the program randomly chooses 4 different segments from a group of 20 possible segments and combines them in a random order.

How many different musical pieces can be created in this way? (Hint: How many choices are there for the first segment? For each of those, how many choices are there for the second segment?)
$20 \cdot 19 \cdot 18 \cdot 17 = 116{,}280$

13. Ms. McDonald raises only chickens and pigs on her farm. If you know how many legs are in Ms. McDonald's barn, you can find all the possible combinations of pigs and chickens. For example, if there are 6 legs, there could be 3 chickens, or 1 chicken and 1 pig.

a. Copy and complete the table to show the possible combinations for different numbers of legs. The notation 3C-0P means 3 chickens and no pigs.

Legs	Combinations	Number of Combinations
2	1C-0P	1
4	2C-0P, 0C-1P	2
6	3C-0P, 1C-1P	2
8	4C-0P, 2C-1P, 0C-2P	3
10	5C-0P, 3C-1P, 1C-2P	3
12	6C-0P, 4C-1P, 2C-2P, 0C-3P	4
14	7C-0P, 5C-1P, 3C-2P, 1C-3P	4

13b. 5 combinations for each; for 16 legs: 8C-0P, 6C-1P, 4C-2P, 2C-3P, 0C-4P; for 18 legs: 9C-0P, 7C-1P, 5C-2P, 3C-3P, 1C-4P

b. Predict the number of combinations for 16 legs and for 18 legs. Check your predictions by listing all the possibilities.

c. Challenge Write two expressions that describe the number of chicken-pig combinations for L legs. One of your expressions should be for L values that are multiples of 4; the other should be for L values that are not multiples of 4.

13c. for multiples of 4: $\frac{L}{4} + 1$; for nonmultiples of 4: $\frac{L-2}{4} + 1$

14. Possible equation: $y = -\frac{7}{2}x$

d. There are 42 legs in the barn. Assuming each possible combination of pigs and chickens is equally likely, what is the probability that there are 8 pigs and 5 chickens in the barn? $\frac{1}{11}$

Mixed Review

15. Possible equation: $y = -x$

16. 2^{-3+2p}

17. 3^{18m}

Write an equation of a line that is parallel to the given line.

14. $2(y - 3) = -7x + 1$ **15.** $x = -2 - y$

Rewrite each expression using a single base and a single exponent.

16. $2^5 \cdot 2^{-8} \cdot 2^{2p}$ **17.** $(-3^{3m})^6$ **18.** $k^7 \cdot 2^7$ $(2k)^7$

Solve each inequality, and graph the solution on the number line.

19. $5(9 - x) \le 4(x + 18)$ **20.** $3x - 9 < -4.5x + 6$

Factor each expression.

21. $-3x^2 + 3x + 18$ **22.** $0.5a^2 - 2a - 16$
     $-3(x + 2)(x - 3)$ $0.5(a - 8)(a + 4)$

19. $x \ge -3$

(number line: $-4\ -3\ -2\ -1\ 0\ 1\ 2$)

20. $x < 2$

(number line: $-2\ -1\ 0\ 1\ 2\ 3\ 4$)

Quick Quiz

1. Samantha is conducting an ESP experiment with four cards labeled A, B, C, and D on one side. She shuffles them and then lays out three of them side by side. The subjects of Samantha's experiment will guess the three cards, in order.

a. Construct a tree diagram that lists all possible sequences of three cards.
(Note: The initial branches are not shown for reasons of space.)

b. What is the probability that a subject guessing at random will get the correct sequence of cards?
$\frac{1}{24}$

Samantha then decides to have the subjects guess the three cards *without* regarding the order.

Copy each expression, adding a constant to complete the square.

23. $a^2 + 0.4a + \underline{\ 0.04\ }$ **24.** $b^2 - 12b + \underline{\ 36\ }$

25. Suppose a certain type of cell divides into two cells every half hour.

     a. Make a table showing how many cells there will be at the end of every hour, starting with one cell, for a 4-hour period.

Time (h)	0	1	2	3	4	5
Cells	1	4	16	64	256	1,024

     b. Write an equation for the number of cells c at t hours. $c = 4^t$

     c. Graph the data from your table, showing times up to 4 hours on the horizontal axis.

25c.

Number of Cells Per Hour

26. Match these 12 expressions to create six pairs of expressions in which one expression is a simplified version of the other.

   a. $\frac{4}{9} - \frac{x+1}{9}$ **b.** $\frac{5}{6x} - \frac{1}{4x}$ **c.** $\frac{2}{9x} - \frac{5}{6x}$

   d. $\frac{4+x}{-2x-8}$ **e.** $\frac{-11}{18x}$ **f.** $\frac{x}{4x} - \frac{x}{3x}$

   g. $\frac{7}{12x}$ **h.** $\frac{-x+3}{9}$ **i.** $-\frac{1}{12}$

   j. $\frac{1}{(x-2)^2}$ **k.** $\frac{1}{x(x-4)+4}$ **l.** -0.5

26. a and h, b and g, c and e, d and l, f and i, j and k

Geometry The area of a sector of a circle is found by multiplying the ratio of the sector's angle measure to 360 by the circle's area:

$$\text{area of sector} = \frac{\text{sector's angle measure (in degrees)}}{360°} \cdot \pi r^2$$

Find the area of each sector.

27.

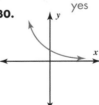

$4\pi \approx 12.6$

28.

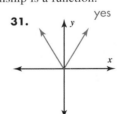

$\frac{20\pi}{3} \approx 20.9$

29.

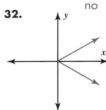

$\frac{400\pi}{9} \approx 139.6$

Tell whether each relationship is a function.

30. yes   **31.** yes   **32.** no

c. How many different three-card combinations are there, without regarding the order? Explain. four; Leaving out A, there is one three-card set, namely B, C, D. Similarly, leaving out each of the other cards, there is exactly one three-card set.

d. What is the probability that a subject guessing at random will get the three cards correct? $\frac{1}{4}$

• **Quick Quiz continued on page A690**

Probability Distributions

Objectives

▶ To create sample spaces with equally likely outcomes for a variety of games of chance involving dice

▶ To apply calculated probabilities to create strategies for winning a game of chance

Overview (pacing: about 4 class periods)

This lesson applies the counting principles of Lesson 9.1 to analyzing the likelihood of various outcomes in several games of chance.

Advance Preparation

For Investigation 3, you may want to prepare Master 52, which is a copy of the *Land Grab* game board shown in the text.

Lesson Planner

	Summary	Materials	On Your Own Exercises	Assessment Opportunities
Investigation 1 page T566	Students calculate the probability of outcomes in situations involving dice and spinners.	• 2 dice (per pair)	Practice & Apply: 1–5, pp. 573–574 Connect & Extend: 9, 10, p. 577 Mixed Review: 16–24, p. 581	On the Spot Assessment, page T566 Share & Summarize, pages T568, 568 Troubleshooting, page T568
Investigation 2 page T569	Students work with a more complicated sample space created by calculating the difference of two die rolls.	• 2 dice (per pair) • Graph paper	Practice & Apply: 6, 7, pp. 575–576 Connect & Extend: 11, 12, p. 578 Mixed Review: 16–24, p. 581	Share & Summarize, pages T570, 570 Troubleshooting, page T570
Investigation 3 page T571	Students play a game involving gridded cards and dice that lends itself to an experimental analysis of probable outcomes.	• Master 52 • 2 dice (per pair) *• Game markers (such as counters or small pieces of paper) • Graph paper	Practice & Apply: 8, pp. 576–577 Connect & Extend: 13–15, pp. 578–580 Mixed Review: 16–24, p. 581	Share & Summarize, pages T572, 572 Troubleshooting, page T572 Informal Assessment, page 580 Quick Quiz, page 581

* Included in Impact Mathematics Manipulative Kit

Introduce

1 Introduce the lesson by discussing situations in which understanding the probabilities is helpful for making decisions. In addition to board and dice games, weather prediction and games of skill involve probabilities. Students may argue that these situations do not depend on probability; however, you can explain that there are so many factors involved in the outcome that treating them as chance situations is often the best way to analyze or plan for them.

Think & Discuss

This Think & Discuss requires students to use what they have learned so far in the chapter: defining a sample space by listing possible outcomes, finding probabilities of events, recognizing when outcomes are equally likely, and using patterns to find probabilities. Work through this as a class, calling on students to supply the next number in the list and to answer the questions.

2 Save the list created in the first question so that students may refer to it during the investigation, if necessary.

Comparing the probabilities of rolling at least one 3 and rolling doubles is a situation in which it is more helpful not to express a probability in lowest terms: it is easier to compare $\frac{11}{36}$ to $\frac{6}{36}$ than to $\frac{1}{6}$. For students who are struggling, this might be a good hint. Even if all the students seem to work through the problem easily, it is worth pointing out casually.

3 The last question is a good one for an extended discussion, because students will be able to think of various approaches in addition to the one given in the sample answer on page 565. You may even want to let students work on this problem individually or in pairs before discussing it as a class, so all will have a chance to find their own approaches.

Probability Distributions

Suppose you are planning a camping trip. If you think it is likely to rain during the trip, you will probably decide to bring along a raincoat, boots, a tarp, or other rain gear.

Understanding how likely certain events are can help you make decisions and predictions. Sometimes you can use common sense or logic to decide whether one event is more likely than another.

In some situations, you can determine what is most likely to happen only after more careful analysis. In this lesson, you will analyze situations and games to determine how likely certain events are.

Think & Discuss

List all the possible outcomes from rolling two dice, one after the other. See ①.

Are these outcomes all equally likely? yes

What is the probability you will roll doubles (both dice having the same number)? $\frac{6}{36}$, or $\frac{1}{6}$

What is the probability that at least one die will show a 3? $\frac{11}{36}$

Which is more likely, rolling at least one 3 or rolling doubles? Could you have answered this question without counting all the combinations for each? Explain. See ②.

① 1-1, 1-2, 1-3, 1-4, 1-5, 1-6, 2-1, 2-2, 2-3, 2-4, 2-5, 2-6, 3-1, 3-2, 3-3, 3-4, 3-5, 3-6, 4-1, 4-2, 4-3, 4-4, 4-5, 4-6, 5-1, 5-2, 5-3, 5-4, 5-5, 5-6, 6-1, 6-2, 6-3, 6-4, 6-5, 6-6

② rolling at least one 3; yes; Possible explanation: To roll doubles, the numbers must be the same, and with 6 numbers, there are 6 ways to get doubles. To roll at least one 3, if the first die shows 3, there are 6 ways to roll the second die, so there are already as many ways as there are for doubles. But I can also roll something other than 3 on the first die and roll 3 on the second, so there are even more ways to get at least one 3.

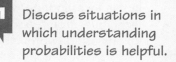

1 Discuss situations in which understanding probabilities is helpful.

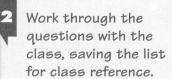

2 Work through the questions with the class, saving the list for class reference.

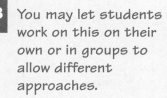

3 You may let students work on this on their own or in groups to allow different approaches.

Investigation 1

In this investigation, students practice their counting techniques from Lesson 9.1 in situations involving calculations using two numbers randomly generated.

Problem Set A Suggested Grouping: Pairs
This problem set asks students to find the probabilities involved with products of randomly generated numbers. The questions about even and odd products depend on unfamiliar sample spaces to avoid having students invoke automatic responses based on earlier work.

On the **Spot**
Assessment

If students are uncomfortable with the idea of the four-outcome, even-odd sample space, let them do the problems using the larger sample space, such as the one created in the Think & Discuss on page 565.

If students do try to create a larger space, be aware that some may be inclined to count how many *unique products* there are rather than how many *dice combinations* there are. In fact, only 18 different products can be produced by a pair of integers ranging from 1 to 6: these are 1, 2, 3, 4, 5, 6, 8, 9, 10, 12, 15, 16, 18, 20, 24, 25, 30, and 36. Some of these (1, 9, 16, 25, and 36) can occur in only one way. Others, like 4, 6, and 12, can be made in more than one way. To help students see that there are 36 outcomes, you might refer to the sample space from the Think & Discuss. Tell the students to imagine that the dice are different colors. A red 3 and a green 4 is distinct from a red 4 and a green 3, and different yet from a red 2 and a green 6, even though all products are 12.

Investigation 1 ▶ Comparing Probabilities of Events

You will now look at probabilities involving the roll of two dice and determine which of two events is more likely.

MATERIALS

2 dice

Problem Set A

Tamika rolled two dice 15 times. On each roll, she multiplied the two numbers. Based on her findings, she conjectured that rolling an even product is more likely than rolling an odd product.

1. Answers will vary.

1. Roll a pair of dice 15 times, and record whether each product is even or odd. Do your results support Tamika's conjecture?

To figure out whether an even product or an odd product is more likely, you could find the products for all 36 possible dice rolls and count how many are even and how many are odd.

An easier way to analyze Tamika's conjecture is to use what you know about multiplying even and odd factors. On each die, the probability of rolling an odd number is the same as the probability of rolling an even number, so you can simply figure whether each possible combination is odd or even:

even × even   even × odd   odd × even   odd × odd

2. Copy and complete the table to show whether the product of each combination of even and odd factors is even or odd.

Die 1

×	Even	Odd
Even	even	even
Odd	even	odd

Die 2

3. Which is more likely to occur: an even product or an odd product?

even

4. Complete these probability statements.

a. The probability that the product of two dice will be even is ___3___ out of 4.

b. The probability that the product of two dice will be odd is ___1___ out of 4.

1 You may have students work in pairs.

2 If students are uncomfortable with this approach, let them use the sample space from the Think & Discuss from page 565.

Problem Set Wrap-Up A class discussion of **Problem 5b** will help you assess students' understanding: students who see quickly how the answer to Problem 2 relates to the answer to Problem 5 have a good grasp on the concepts of the chapter so far. It may also help students who are uncomfortable with the four-outcome sample space in Problem 2 to contrast the two situations.

In Problem 2, rolling an odd number was just as likely as rolling an even number. Because of that, the six outcomes for a single roll could be considered two outcomes, even or odd. In Problem 5, however, spinning an odd number is more likely than spinning an even number, so students must consider the individual outcomes.

About the Mathematics

One way in which it is possible to use an even-odd strategy with the spinners in Problem 5 is to *weight* the outcomes. Each spinner has three odd and two even numbers, so a chart that assigns a weight of 3 to "odd" and 2 to "even" would give an accurate representation of this situation:

Spinner 1

	×	(Even (2)	Odd (3)
Spinner 2	Even (2)	Even (4)	Even (6)
	Odd (3)	Even (6)	Odd (9)

Notice that the weights of the spins (in parentheses) are multiplied to get the weights of the product. This is similar to the work students did in Lesson 9.1; listing outcomes or making a tree diagram will show that for each odd number on one spinner, there are three odd numbers that can be spun on the other, for a total of nine odd-odd combinations. (Students will work more with this *muliplication principle* in Lesson 9.3.)

Adding the weights of the products gives the weight of the total sample space, 25; similarly, adding the weights of the even products gives the total weight for spinning an even product, 16. The probability of getting an odd product is $\frac{9}{25}$, and the probability of getting an even product is $\frac{16}{25}$.

5. Suppose that, instead of rolling dice to determine the factors to multiply, Tamika spins these spinners.

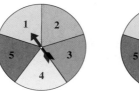

Spinner 1   **Spinner 2**

a. Predict whether an even product or an odd product is more likely.

b. Can you use your table from Problem 2 to determine whether an odd or an even product is more likely? Why or why not?

c. Systematically determine the probability of getting an even product and the probability of getting an odd product. You might find it helpful to complete a multiplication table like the one below.

Spinner 1

	×	1	2	3	4	5
	1	1	2	3	4	5
	2	2	4	6	8	10
Spinner 2	3	3	6	9	12	15
	4	4	8	12	16	20
	5	5	10	15	20	25

5a. Predictions will vary.

5b. No; with both spinners you are more likely to spin an odd number. The table would work only if spinning an odd and spinning an even were equally likely.

5c. probability of even: $\frac{16}{25}$; probability of odd: $\frac{9}{25}$

Some games are based entirely on skill, some entirely on chance, and some on a combination of the two.

1 Discuss Problem 5b to assess students' understanding and to help those still uncomfortable with the four-outcome space in Problem 2.

Develop

Problem Set B **Suggested Grouping: Pairs**
You may want to review bases and exponents before students begin work on this problem set.

In **Problem 1,** some students will see that even and odd products are equally likely without experimenting. Ask them to try the experiment anyway, to see how well the experimental results coincide with what they feel the probability should be.

Share & Summarize
Have students work in pairs on this section. Two students are far more likely to describe methods successfully than one student acting alone.

Troubleshooting Some students still may not be comfortable with the 4-outcome sample space. This is OK, as long as they are able to use the larger 16-outcome sample space properly.

However, if you have time, you might help them understand how to simplify the problem to the 4-outcome sample space. Ask what the outcomes would be like if the 3s were 1s and the 4s were 2s, so 1 and 2 are the only possible outcomes on a single spinner. Ask them:

> Are the probabilities for even and odd sums the same in this case as they were for the spinners given in the text? Why? *Yes, because it doesn't matter what the even and odd numbers are; it only matters if they're even or odd.*

> How many outcomes are possible on the spinners with only 1 and 2? *4* Are the outcomes equally likely? *yes*

Then ask students to explain what's wrong with this reasoning:

> Suppose I flip two coins. Either they come up both tails or they don't. The sample space consists of two possible outcomes: both tails or not both tails. Therefore the probability of two tails is $\frac{1}{2}$. *The outcomes in the sample space (both tails: TT; not both tails: TH, HT, HH) aren't equally likely.*

On Your Own Exercises
Practice & Apply: 1–5, pp. 573–574
Connect & Extend: 9, 10, p. 577
Mixed Review: 16–24, p. 581

Problem Set B

Tamika was also curious about what would happen if she rolled two dice and considered one number to be the base and the other to be its exponent. Would the result more likely be even or odd?

1 You may have students work in pairs.

1. Conduct an experiment to predict whether an even or an odd result is more likely. Before you begin, assign one die as the base and the other as the exponent. Roll the dice 15 times, and record whether the result, $die1^{die2}$, is even or odd. Make a prediction based on your results.   Predictions will vary.

2 Ask students who can reason that these events are equally likely to test how well the experiment agrees with their results.

2. Because an odd number is just as likely to be rolled as an even number, you can analyze the possible combinations as you did in Problem Set A. Complete the table to indicate whether raising the given base to the given exponent has an odd or an even result.

	Even Exponent	Odd Exponent
Even Base	even	even
Odd Base	odd	odd

3. The results are equally likely.

3. Which is more likely to occur: an even result or an odd result?

4. Complete these probability statements.

   a. The probability that $die1^{die2}$ will be even is _____. $\frac{2}{4}$, or $\frac{1}{2}$

   b. The probability that $die1^{die2}$ will be odd is _____. $\frac{2}{4}$, or $\frac{1}{2}$

Share & Summarize

Suppose you spun these two spinners and added the results. Describe two ways you could determine whether an odd sum or an even sum is more likely.

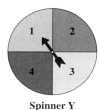

Spinner Y

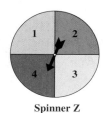

Spinner Z

3 Problem-Solving Strategy

Solve a simpler problem

Possible answer: Determine whether each of these combinations is odd or even: odd + odd, odd + even, even + odd, even + even. Determine the sum for each of the 16 possible number pairs, and compare the number of odd sums to the number of even sums.

Investigation 2

1 Introduce the *Rolling Differences* game to the class. You might play a round or two with a volunteer until students understand the rules, which are presented at the beginning of Problem Set C.

2 **Problem Set C** **Grouping: Pairs**
In this problem set, students play *Rolling Differences* to get a sense of whether the game is fair; they then analyze the probabilities. The end of the problem set presents the idea of a probability distribution, using a bar graph in which each bar represents a different outcome.

3 After pairs finish answering **Problem 2,** discuss the results in class. This should motivate students to want to analyze the game by creating an appropriate sample space.

4 Since the events in this situation include all the possible outcomes, with no overlap, the probabilities calculated in **Problem 5** must add to 1. You may want to point out this fact to students; they can use it in the rest of the problem set.

Investigation The Rolling Differences Game

Many games involve chance. Figuring out the probabilities of the various events involved in a game can help you determine whether the game is fair.

1 Introduce the game, possibly playing a round or two with a volunteer.

MATERIALS
- 2 dice
- graph paper

Problem Set C

Héctor and Mikayla are playing a game called *Rolling Differences*. On each round, they each roll a die and find the difference between the numbers. When the numbers are different, they subtract the lesser number from the greater number.

- Player 1 scores 1 point if the difference is 0, 1, or 2.
- Player 2 scores 1 point if the difference is 3, 4, or 5.

Each game consists of 10 rounds (dice rolls).

2 Have students work in pairs.

1. Who do you think is more likely to win a round, Player 1 or Player 2? Predictions will vary.

2. With a partner, play 10 rounds of *Rolling Differences*. Record who wins. Then, without switching sides—that is, score the second game the same as the first game—play another 10 rounds. Did the same player win both games? Answers will vary.

3 Discuss the results of Problem 2 with the class.

3. You can analyze this game by making a table of differences for all possible rolls. Complete this table to show the difference for each possible roll.

Player 2's Roll

–	1	2	3	4	5	6
1	0	1	2	3	4	5
2	1	0	1	2	3	4
3	2	1	0	1	2	3
4	3	2	1	0	1	2
5	4	3	2	1	0	1
6	5	4	3	2	1	0

Player 1's Roll (left label for rows)

4. How many of the 36 dice rolls produce a difference of 5? Which rolls are they? 2; 1 and 6, 6 and 1

5. Complete the table to show the probability of rolling each difference.

4 You may want to point out that the probabilities must add to 1.

Difference	0	1	2	3	4	5
Probability	6/36	10/36	8/36	6/36	4/36	2/36

LESSON 9.2 Probability Distributions **569**

Problem 6 has students create a bar graph to display the number of expected occurrences of each possible outcome. This is the basic idea behind a probability distribution.

Problem Set Wrap-Up If you didn't point out that the probabilities in Problem 5 add to 1, do so now. You might ask students why they think this should be so; you might remind them about situations in Lesson 9.1 in which they considered finding the probability that something did *not* happen. (See On Your Own Exercise 1 and Problems 10–12 in Problem Set F from Lesson 9.1.) In those situations, they should have noticed that all outcomes had to fall into one event or the other and that no outcomes could fall into both. This is true in this situation also, but there are more than two events to consider.

A discussion of **Problem 9** is also good to wrap up the problem set. Push students to think of as many ways as they can to assign points so that the game is fair; they may surprise themselves! In addition to the answer given on page 570, the following are possible answers:

- Player 1 scores 1 point if the difference is 0, 1, or 2; Player 2 score 2 points if the difference is 3, 4, or 5.

- Player 1 scores 1 point if the difference is 0, 1, or 5; Player 2 scores 1 point if the difference is 2, 3, or 4.

- Player 1 scores 2 points if the difference is 0 or 3; Player 2 scores 1 point if the difference is 1, 2, 4, or 5.

Share & Summarize
As you discuss this with the class, make sure all students see why the number of outcomes for one event are different from those of the other.

Troubleshooting If students have trouble generalizing, encourage them to begin listing the sample space with the resulting products. Note that a systematic process of creating the list might be sufficient to guide their thinking, and they may not need to complete their lists.

On Your Own Exercises
Practice & Apply: 6, 7, pp. 575–576
Connect & Extend: 11, 12, p. 578
Mixed Review: 16–24, p. 581

6. Make a bar graph to show the probability of each difference. Your completed bar graph will show the *probability distribution*—how the probabilities are distributed among the possible differences.

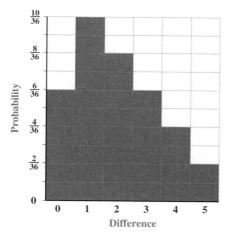

7. $\frac{24}{36}$, or $\frac{2}{3}$

9. Possible answer:
Player 1 scores
1 point if the
difference is even.
Player 2 scores
1 point it the
difference is odd.

7. Recall that Player 1 scores a point if the difference is 0, 1, or 2. What is the probability that Player 1 will score a point in a round?

8. Use your answer from Problem 7 to calculate the probability that Player 2 will score a point in a round. Does your table confirm your answer? $\frac{12}{36}$, or $\frac{1}{3}$; yes

9. *Rolling Differences* is unfair because one player has a greater probability of winning than the other. Try assigning points in a different way to make the game fair.

Share & Summarize

When two dice are rolled, the 36 possible pairs are equally likely. Why, then, are the chances of rolling numbers with a product of 25 different from the chances of rolling numbers with a product of 12?

Possible answer: The number pairs are equally likely, but since there is more than one way to roll certain products, the products are not equally likely.

1
• Point out that the sum of the probabilities in Problem 5 is 1, if you haven't already.

• Discuss Problem 9.

2
Make sure students see why the number of outcomes are different for these events.

Investigation 3

1 This bingo-like game is complicated enough to motivate analyzing the outcomes experimentally. You might copy and distribute Master 52, which reproduces the game board. Students can also copy the game board onto paper.

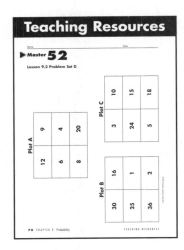

2 **Problem Set D** Grouping: **Pairs**
While it's best to play this game in pairs, if there are an odd number of students in the class, one group can have three students. Each player can take turns rolling both dice rather than two students each rolling one.

3 After partners have played several games, discuss the results of **Problem 2** with the whole class so students have a good sense of the class's experimental outcomes.

Investigation 3 The Land Grab Game

In this investigation, you will play a game called *Land Grab*. Analyzing the probabilities involved in the game can help you devise a winning strategy.

1 You might give copies of Master 52 to students.

2 Have students work in pairs.

MATERIALS
- 2 dice
- game markers
- graph paper

Problem Set D

Land Grab is played by two players. The game board shows three plots of land, each divided into six numbered sections.

Plot A	
12	9
6	4
8	20

Plot B	
30	16
25	1
36	2

Plot C	
3	10
24	15
5	18

Here are the rules for the game.

- Each player selects a different plot of land.
- Each player rolls one die, and the numbers on the two dice are multiplied.
- If the product appears in a section of the plot the player has selected (and it is not already covered), he or she puts a marker on that section.
- The first player to cover all the sections in his or her plot wins.

The challenge is to choose a plot that gives you the best chance of winning.

1. Play *Land Grab* with your partner. For this first game, one of you should choose Plot B and the other should choose Plot C. Before you start, make a prediction about who has a better chance of winning.   Predictions will vary.

Now play two or three more games with your partner. Choose a different plot of land for each game so you get a sense of how easy or difficult it is to win with the various plots.

2. On the basis of the games you played, which plot seems easiest to win with? Which seems most difficult to win with?
Answers will vary.

3 Discuss the results of Problem 2 with the class.

LESSON 9.2 Probability Distributions **571**

For **Problem 3,** students might record the probabilities on the game board:

Plot A

12 $\left(\frac{4}{36}\right)$	9 $\left(\frac{1}{36}\right)$
6 $\left(\frac{4}{36}\right)$	4 $\left(\frac{3}{36}\right)$
8 $\left(\frac{2}{36}\right)$	20 $\left(\frac{2}{36}\right)$

Plot B

30 $\left(\frac{2}{36}\right)$	16 $\left(\frac{1}{36}\right)$
25 $\left(\frac{1}{36}\right)$	1 $\left(\frac{1}{36}\right)$
36 $\left(\frac{1}{36}\right)$	2 $\left(\frac{2}{36}\right)$

Plot C

3 $\left(\frac{2}{36}\right)$	10 $\left(\frac{2}{36}\right)$
24 $\left(\frac{2}{36}\right)$	15 $\left(\frac{2}{36}\right)$
5 $\left(\frac{2}{36}\right)$	18 $\left(\frac{2}{36}\right)$

1 You may want to have students construct their bar graphs for **Problem 4** on overhead transparencies so they can be displayed for the whole class.

2 **Problem Set Wrap-Up** Discuss students' ideas for **Problem 5** as a wrap-up for this problem set. Students might enjoy discussing whether it would be a good idea to reassign products to plots of land to even out the chances of winning, as done below. If products were assigned to the plots so that no plot was easier to win than another, there would be no strategy to the game.

Plot A

12 $\left(\frac{4}{36}\right)$	9 $\left(\frac{1}{36}\right)$
6 $\left(\frac{4}{36}\right)$	25 $\left(\frac{1}{36}\right)$
16 $\left(\frac{1}{36}\right)$	36 $\left(\frac{1}{36}\right)$

Plot B

30 $\left(\frac{2}{36}\right)$	8 $\left(\frac{2}{36}\right)$
4 $\left(\frac{3}{36}\right)$	1 $\left(\frac{1}{36}\right)$
20 $\left(\frac{2}{36}\right)$	2 $\left(\frac{2}{36}\right)$

Plot C

3 $\left(\frac{2}{36}\right)$	10 $\left(\frac{2}{36}\right)$
24 $\left(\frac{2}{36}\right)$	15 $\left(\frac{2}{36}\right)$
5 $\left(\frac{2}{36}\right)$	18 $\left(\frac{2}{36}\right)$

3 **Share & Summarize**
Conduct this discussion with the entire class. As with most graphical displays, a bar graph showing a probability distribution communicates a lot of information in just a brief glance. By seeing probabilities as the heights of the bars, the observer can easily compare individual outcomes and possibly even see patterns, when they exist.

Troubleshooting Encourage students who are insecure about calculating probabilities to construct sample spaces using basic listing principles. For some, just beginning a list will get them thinking about its structure.

On Your Own Exercises
Practice & Apply: 8, pp. 576–577
Connect & Extend: 13–15, pp. 578–580
Mixed Review: 16–24, p. 581

Some sections of land are easier to cover than others. For example, a product of 25 can be rolled only one way (5 and 5), while a product of 12 can be rolled four ways (3 and 4, 4 and 3, 6 and 2, and 2 and 6), so the section labeled 12 is easier to cover than the section labeled 25.

3. Determine the probability of covering each section of land. Record your results in a systematic way.   See Additional Answers.

4. Make a bar graph to show the probability distribution for the products.

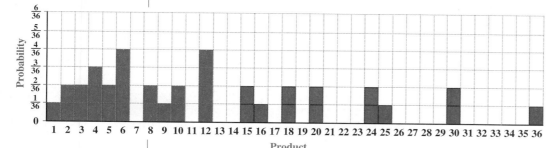

5. Use your results from Problems 3 and 4 to determine which plot of land—A, B or C—is easiest to win the game with. Explain how you decided.   See Additional Answers.

1 You may want to have students make their graphs on transparencies to display to the class.

2 Discuss Problem 5 as a wrap-up for the problem set.

3 Conduct this discussion with the class.

Share & Summarize

Possible answer: You can see at a glance which outcomes are more likely than others, which are most likely, and whether some are not possible at all.

You can list all the probabilities for a situation in a table, or you can make a bar graph. Discuss some of the advantages of showing a probability distribution in a bar graph.

Additional Answers
Problem Set D

5. Plot A; each of the numbers 1, 9, 16, 25, and 36 can be made in only one way, so the probability of any one of them is only $\frac{1}{36}$. Most of the other numbers can be made in two ways, and 4, 6, and 12 can be made in more than two ways. B has many of the least likely: only 8 chances out of 36. C has 12 chances out of 36. And A has the remaining 16 chances.

• **Additional Answers continued on page A690**

Teacher Notes

On Your Own Exercises

Practice & Apply

1. Two dice are rolled and the two numbers are added.

   a. Copy and complete the table to show all the possible sums.

   Die 1

+	1	2	3	4	5	6
1	2	3	4	5	6	7
2	3	4	5	6	7	8
3	4	5	6	7	8	9
4	5	6	7	8	9	10
5	6	7	8	9	10	11
6	7	8	9	10	11	12

   Die 2 (row labels)

1b. 11 sums; 2, 3, 4, 5, 6, 7, 8, 9, 10, 11, 12

   b. How many different sums are there? What are they?

1c. 7; 1 + 6, 2 + 5, 3 + 4, 4 + 3, 5 + 2, 6 + 1

   c. Which sum occurs most often? List all the ways it can be created.

   d. Complete the table to indicate whether the sum of each combination of even and odd numbers is even or odd.

   Die 1

+	Even	Odd
Even	even	odd
Odd	odd	even

   Die 2 (row labels)

1f. no; Possible explanation: You're more likely to get odd numbers on the spinners, which might make a difference. Also, there are 9 combinations, so odd and even cannot have even chances—the closest they can come is $\frac{4}{9}$ and $\frac{5}{9}$.

   e. What is the probability that the sum of two dice will be odd? $\frac{1}{2}$

   f. Suppose you spin these spinners and add the results. Can you use your table from Part d to find the probability that the sum will be odd? Explain.

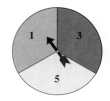

2. Suppose you spin these spinners and multiply the results.

   a. Predict whether an odd product or an even product is more likely.

   b. Determine the probability of spinning an odd product and of spinning an even product. Do your results agree with your prediction?

2a. Predictions will vary.

2b. probability of even: $\frac{6}{15}$ or $\frac{2}{5}$; probability of odd: $\frac{9}{15}$ or $\frac{3}{5}$; Conclusions will vary.

Investigation 1,
 pp. 566–568
Practice & Apply: 1–5
Connect & Extend: 9, 10

Investigation 2,
 pp. 569–570
Practice & Apply: 6, 7
Connect & Extend: 11, 12

Investigation 3,
 pp. 571–572
Practice & Apply: 8
Connect & Extend: 13–15

Assign Anytime
Mixed Review: 16–24

 impactmath.com/self_check_quiz

Quick Review
Math Handbook

hot words hot topics   Hot Topics pp. 232–238, 240–249

Exercise 5:
The fact that the dice have different numbers of faces automatically makes the dice distinguishable. Occasionally students are troubled by the fact that we treat normal dice as distinguishable even though they aren't, but in this case they understand the difference easily. If students don't see the counting principle to find the size of the sample space (just multiply the number of possible outcomes for each die), you may want to have them start a tree diagram to list the possible outcomes.

Just the facts

The shape of an 8-sided die is called an *octahedron*. The 8 faces of an octahedral die are equilateral triangles.

Just the facts

The shape of a 12-sided die is called an *dodecahedron*. The 12 faces of a dodecahedral die are regular pentagons.
4b. 24
4c. 13; $\frac{12}{144}$, or $\frac{1}{12}$

5b. 9, 10, 11, 12, and 13 all occur in eight ways; $\frac{8}{96}$, or $\frac{1}{12}$
5c. They are equally likely.

574 CHAPTER 9 Probability

3. Suppose you roll two 8-sided dice with faces numbered 1 to 8.

   a. How many possible number pairs can you roll? 64

   b. Complete the table to show all the possible sums of two 8-sided dice.

Die 1

+	1	2	3	4	5	6	7	8
1	2	3	4	5	6	7	8	9
2	3	4	5	6	7	8	9	10
3	4	5	6	7	8	9	10	11
4	5	6	7	8	9	10	11	12
5	6	7	8	9	10	11	12	13
6	7	8	9	10	11	12	13	14
7	8	9	10	11	12	13	14	15
8	9	10	11	12	13	14	15	16

(Die 2 labels the rows)

   c. What is the probability that a sum will be odd? $\frac{32}{64}$, or $\frac{1}{2}$

   d. What is the probability that a sum will be a prime number? $\frac{23}{64}$

4. Suppose you roll two 12-sided dice with faces numbered 1 to 12.

   a. How many possible number pairs can you roll? 144

   b. What is the greatest sum possible from a roll of two 12-sided dice?

   c. What sum is most likely? What is the probability of this sum?

5. Suppose you roll two dice: a 12-sided die with faces numbered 1 to 12, and an 8-sided die with faces numbered 1 to 8.

   a. How many possible number pairs can you roll? 96

   b. What sum is most likely? What is the probability of this sum?

   c. Is an odd sum or an even sum more likely?

6. Suppose two people play *Rolling Differences* with one 6-sided die, and one 8-sided die with faces numbered 1 to 8. The players follow these rules:

- Player 1 scores 1 point if the difference is 0, 1, or 2.
- Player 2 scores 1 point if the difference is 3, 4, 5, 6, or 7.

a. Make a table showing the probability of each difference being rolled.   See below.

6b. No; Player 1 has 27 chances out of 48 to score a point, while Player 2 has only 21 chances out of 48 to score a point.

b. Is this game fair? Explain.

c. Make a bar graph to show the probability distribution for this game.

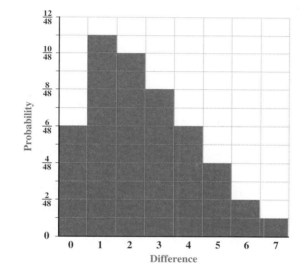

6d. This game; the probability that Player 2 will score a point is $\frac{12}{36}$, or $\frac{1}{3}$, or about 33%, with two ordinary dice, but improves to $\frac{21}{48}$, or almost 44%, with one die an octahedron.

d. Compare the rules for this game to the rules for the original *Rolling Differences* game (which involves two ordinary dice) described in Problem Set C. In which game does Player 2 have a better chance of winning? Explain.

6a.

Difference	0	1	2	3	4	5	6	7
Probability	$\frac{6}{48}$	$\frac{11}{48}$	$\frac{10}{48}$	$\frac{8}{48}$	$\frac{6}{48}$	$\frac{4}{48}$	$\frac{2}{48}$	$\frac{1}{48}$

7. Player 1; Player 1 scores on 34 of the 64 possible rolls.

7. Suppose two people play *Rolling Differences* with two 8-sided dice numbered 1 to 8. The players follow these rules:

• Player 1 scores 1 point if the difference is 0, 1, or 2.

• Player 2 scores 1 point if the difference is 3, 4, 5, 6, or 7.

Which player has the advantage? Explain your answer.

8. *Mixing Colors* is a two-player game that uses the spinners and game cards shown below.

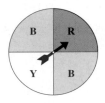
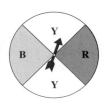

Card 1	
Y	B
B	Y

Card 2	
R	P
O	B

Card 3	
Y	G
P	O

Card 4	
R	Y
B	G

The letters on the spinners and game cards represent the colors red, blue, yellow, green, orange, and purple. Here are the rules.

• Each player selects a different game card.

• Each player spins a spinner. The colors on the two spinners are "mixed" to give a mixture color, as follows:

RR = R   BB = B   YY = Y   RY = O   RB = P   BY = G

• If the mixture color is on a player's game card (and is not already covered), he or she puts a marker on that section.

• The first player to cover all the sections on his or her game card wins the game.

a. Make a prediction about which game card gives the best chance of winning the game.   Predictions will vary.

b. Determine the probability of spinning each mixture color. Record your results in a systematic way.   See below.

8c, d. See additional answers

c. Make a bar graph to show the probability of spinning each mixture color.

d. Use your results from Parts b and c to determine which card gives the best chance of winning. Explain how you decided.

Exercise 9b:
This is a nice extension of Problem Set A. Ask students whether each possible combination is equally likely.

Connect & Extend

9a. 216

9b. Possible method: Determine whether each of these possible combinations is odd or even: odd × odd × odd, odd × odd × even, odd × even × odd, odd × even × even, even × even × even, even × even × odd, even × odd × even, even × odd × odd.

9c. Of the 8 possible combinations, only one, odd × odd × odd, results in an odd product. Therefore, rolling an even product is more likely.

10a. There are 6 possible rolls for each die, so there are $6^5 = 7,776$ possible outcomes.

10c. $\frac{6}{6^5}$, or $\frac{1}{6^4}$, or $\frac{1}{1,296}$

9. Imagine rolling three regular dice and multiplying all three numbers.

a. How many number triples are possible when you roll three dice?

b. *Without* finding the products of every possible roll, describe a way you could determine whether an odd product or an even product is more likely.

c. Use your method from Part b to determine whether an even product or an odd product is more likely.

10. Imagine rolling five regular dice and looking for outcomes when all five dice match.

a. How many different outcomes are possible on a roll of five dice? Explain.

b. In how many of the possible outcomes do all five dice match?   6

c. What is the probability of getting all five dice to match on a single roll?

d. Suppose Tamika is given three rolls to get five matching dice. On the second and third rolls, she may roll some or all of the five dice again.

On her first roll, Tamika gets three 3s, a 2, and a 6. She picks up the dice showing 2 and 6 and rolls them again. What is the probability that she will get two more 3s on this roll? $\frac{1}{36}$

8b.

Mixture Color	Red	Yellow	Blue	Green	Orange	Purple
Probability	$\frac{1}{16}$	$\frac{2}{16}$	$\frac{2}{16}$	$\frac{5}{16}$	$\frac{3}{16}$	$\frac{3}{16}$

LESSON 9.2 Probability Distributions **577**

Additional Answers

8c.

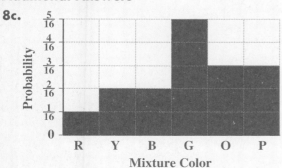

8d. Card 3 gives the best chance of winning because it has the most "high probability" colors. The probabilities of spinning the colors on Card 3 are $\frac{2}{16}$, $\frac{5}{16}$, $\frac{3}{16}$, and $\frac{3}{16}$. On Card 1, each color has only a $\frac{2}{16}$ chance of being spun. Card 2 has the same probabilities as Card 3 for three of its colors, but the fourth color, red, has only a $\frac{1}{16}$ probability of being spun compared to $\frac{5}{16}$ for green on Card 3. Card 4 has sections with probabilities $\frac{1}{16}$, $\frac{2}{16}$, $\frac{2}{16}$, and $\frac{5}{16}$, which are less than Card 3's.

11. Both players have the same chances of winning because Player 2 receives 2 points to make up for having only half as many ways to score.

12a. See below.

12b. $\frac{12}{36}$, or $\frac{1}{3}$

11. Two players each roll a six-sided die and find the difference of the numbers.

• Player 2 receives 2 points each time the difference is 3, 4, or 5.

• Player 1 receives 1 point each time the difference is 0, 1, or 2.

Which player has the advantage in this game? Explain your answer.

12. Kai wants to create a fair dice game for two people, using divisibility by 3. He decided on these rules:

• Each player rolls one die.

• The players find the sum of the two numbers.

• Player 1 scores if the sum is divisible by 3. Player 2 scores if the sum is *not* divisible by 3.

Kai isn't sure how many points each player should score each time.

a. Make a table showing the probability of each sum being rolled.

b. What is the probability that Player 1 scores on a given roll?

c. Kai decided to give 2 points to Player 2 when the sum isn't divisible by 3. For the game to be fair, how many points should Player 1 score each time the sum *is* divisible by 3?   4 points

13. *Mountain Climbing* is a two-player game involving two dice and this game board.

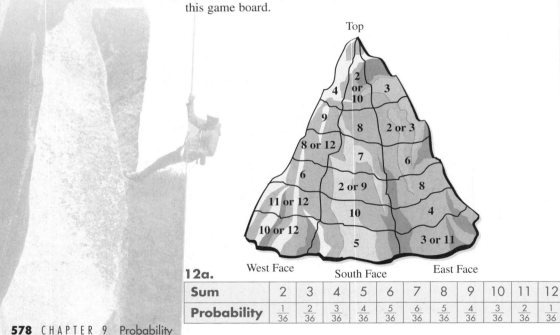

12a.

Sum	2	3	4	5	6	7	8	9	10	11	12
Probability	$\frac{1}{36}$	$\frac{2}{36}$	$\frac{3}{36}$	$\frac{4}{36}$	$\frac{5}{36}$	$\frac{6}{36}$	$\frac{5}{36}$	$\frac{4}{36}$	$\frac{3}{36}$	$\frac{2}{36}$	$\frac{1}{36}$

578 CHAPTER 9   Probability

In your
own
words

If you were deciding whether to play a game of chance, what would you figure out in order to decide whether the game is fair?

Here are the rules for *Mountain Climbing*.

- Each player selects a different face of the mountain to climb step by step.

- Each player rolls one die, and the results are added.

- If the sum appears as the next step on the face the player has selected, he or she puts a marker on that step. Players must proceed one step at a time from bottom to top.

- The first player to reach the top step wins.

The challenge is to choose a face that gives the best chance of winning.

a. Copy and complete these tables, which show the probability for reaching each step along each face of the *Mountain Climbing* game board.

West Face

Step	1	2	3	4	5	6
Probability	4/36	3/36	5/36	6/36	4/36	3/36

South Face

Step	1	2	3	4	5	6
Probability	4/36	3/36	5/36	6/36	5/36	4/36

East Face

Step	1	2	3	4	5	6
Probability	4/36	3/36	5/36	5/36	3/36	2/36

13b. the South Face

b. Which face gives the greatest probability of winning?

c. Which face gives the least probability of winning?   the East Face

14. In Investigation 3, you played the game *Land Grab*. Design a new six-section plot that is easier to win with than Plots A, B or C. Explain your reasoning.

Possible answer: This plot uses both of the numbers with a $\frac{4}{36}$ probability and the one with a $\frac{3}{36}$ probability, and no $\frac{1}{36}$ probabilities. No plot will give a better chance of winning than this one.

4	6
3	2
12	5

Exercise 15:
If you have time before assigning this exercise, you may find it useful to play a few rounds of the game with the class. The rules will rapidly become apparent.

Quick Check

Informal Assessment
Students should be able to:

✔ create sample spaces with equally likely outcomes for a variety of games of chance involving dice

✔ apply calculated probabilities to create strategies for winning a game of chance

15. *Hidden Dice* is a two-player game in which opponents take turns guessing one or both numbers on a pair of dice.

Players take turns rolling the dice and concealing the result. The rolling player announces that the sum of the two dice is "greater than or equal to 7" or "less than or equal to 7."

If the guessing player can correctly identify one of the dice, he or she scores 1 point. The guessing player may then keep the point or give it up for the opportunity to make a guess at the second die. The winner is the first player to score 10 points or to guess both dice correctly in the same turn.

a. Complete the table, which shows all the possible ways you can get a sum that is greater than or equal to 7.

15b.

Sum	Die 1	Die 2
2	1	1
3	1	2
	2	1
4	2	2
	1	3
	3	1
5	1	4
	4	1
	2	3
	3	2
6	3	3
	1	5
	5	1
	2	4
	4	2
7	1	6
	6	1
	2	5
	5	2
	3	4
	4	3

Sum	Die 1	Die 2
12	6	6
11	5	6
	6	5
10	5	5
	4	6
	6	4
9	4	5
	5	4
	3	6
	6	3

Sum	Die 1	Die 2
8	4	4
	3	5
	5	3
	2	6
	6	2
7	1	6
	6	1
	2	5
	5	2
	3	4
	4	3

b. Make another table showing all the possible ways you can roll a sum that is equal to or less than 7.

c. Consider the possible outcomes for a sum of greater than or equal to 7. Which number appears in the greatest number of outcomes? Give the probability that *that* number is on at least one die when the rolling player reports the sum is "greater than or equal to 7."

d. Consider the possible outcomes for a sum of less than or equal to 7. Which number appears in the greatest number of outcomes? Give the probability that *that* number is on at least one die when the rolling player reports the sum is "less than or equal to 7."

e. Suppose the rolling player announces that the sum is greater than or equal to 7, and you correctly guess that a 2 appears on one of the dice. How many possibilities are there for the remaining die, and what are they?   2 possibilities, 5 and 6

15c. 6, $\frac{11}{21}$
15d. 1, $\frac{11}{21}$

15f. A 1 appears only with a 6, so you can win the game by using your second guess.

15g. A 1 appears in only 2 of 21 possible number pairs.

f. Suppose the rolling player announces that the sum is greater than or equal to 7, and you correctly guess that a 1 appears on one of the dice. Explain why you should continue and give up 1 point for a guess at the other die.

g. What is the disadvantage of guessing 1 on your first guess when the sum is greater than or equal to 7?

h. What are the advantages and disadvantages of guessing 6 on your first guess when the sum is greater than or equal to 7?

Mixed Review

15h. Guessing 6 gives you the best chance of scoring a point in your turn but it leaves open all six (1–6) possibilities for the other die; that is, you have only a 1 out of 6 chance for a "quick" victory.

16. Match each equation to a graph.

a. $y = {}^-2x^2$ Graph B

b. $\frac{y}{2} = x^2$ Graph C

c. $y + 3 = 0.5x^2$ Graph A

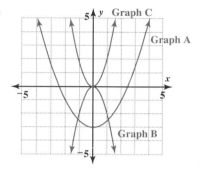

17. Write an equation to represent the value of K in terms of n. $K = 0.4^n$

n	0	1	2	3	4
K	1	0.4	0.16	0.064	0.0256

18. $\sqrt[3]{{}^-4}$, $\sqrt[5]{{}^-4}$, $\sqrt[7]{{}^-4}$, $\sqrt[9]{{}^-4}$, $\sqrt[11]{{}^-4}$

18. Order these numbers from least to greatest.

$$\sqrt[9]{{}^-4} \qquad \sqrt[3]{{}^-4} \qquad \sqrt[11]{{}^-4} \qquad \sqrt[5]{{}^-4} \qquad \sqrt[7]{{}^-4}$$

19.

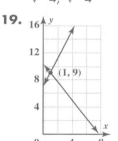

19. Draw a graph to estimate the solution of this system of equations. Check your answer by substitution.

$$y = 2x + 7$$
$$4x + 3y = 31$$

20. length: 24; slope: $\frac{1}{4}$

20. A line segment with length 8 and slope $\frac{1}{4}$ is scaled by a factor of 3. What are the length and the slope of the new segment?

Expand and simplify each expression.

21. ${}^-3a(2a - 3)$ $-6a^2 + 9a$

22. $(4k - 7)({}^-2k + 3)$
$-8k^2 + 26k - 21$

Simplify each expression.

23. $\frac{m - 3}{m(2m - 6)}$ $\frac{1}{2m}$

24. $\frac{7}{k - 2} - \frac{5}{2(k - 2)}$ $\frac{9}{2(k - 2)}$

LESSON 9.2 Probability Distributions **581**

a. Ben says there are four possibilities: even × even = even, even × odd = even, odd × even = even, odd × odd = odd. Three of these are even; therefore the probability of obtaining an even product is $\frac{3}{4}$. Explain what's wrong with his reasoning. *The outcomes are not equally likely.*

b. Calculate the correct probability of obtaining an even product in Tamika's game. Explain how you found your answer. $\frac{33}{42}$, or $\frac{11}{14}$; *There are 6 possible outcomes for rolling the die and 7 for the drawing. The sample space has 42 equally likely outcomes. Of these, 12 are even-even, 9 are even-odd, 12 are odd-even, and 9 are odd-odd. So 12 + 9 + 12 = 33 of the 42 outcomes produce an even number.*

Teacher Notes

Probability Investigations

Objectives

▶ To analyze probabilities in real-world situations

Overview (pacing: about 3 class periods)

Students grow up hearing about the results of state lotteries and sports playoffs. This lesson introduces methods of analyzing the chances of winning several lotteries and the fairness of various playoff schemes.

Advance Preparation

In Investigation 1, student pairs will need six identical pieces of paper and containers from which they can draw them. In Investigation 2, you may want to give groups copies of Masters 53, 54, and 55, the three-team and four-team playoff charts. Groups will also need four identical pieces of paper for this investigation.

Lesson Planner

	Summary	Materials	On Your Own Exercises	Assessment Opportunities
Investigation 1 page T582	Students analyze several simple lotteries.	• 6 identical slips of paper (per pair) • Container (1 per pair)	Practice & Apply: 1–3, p. 590 Connect & Extend: 6–9, pp. 591–593 Mixed Review: 13–26, p. 595	Share & Summarize, pages T586, 586 Troubleshooting, page T586
Investigation 2 page T587	Students analyze the probabilities involved in two methods of conducting playoffs.	• Master 53 (1 per group of 3) • 4 identical slips of paper (per group of 3) • 2 dice (per group of 3) • Master 54 (1 per group of 4) • Master 55 (1 per group of 4)	Practice & Apply: 4, 5, p. 591 Connect & Extend: 10–12, pp. 593–594 Mixed Review: 13–26, p. 595	Share & Summarize, pages T589, 589 Troubleshooting, page T589 Informal Assessment, page 594 Quick Quiz, page 595

This lesson gives students a chance to apply what they have learned about sample spaces and probability to situations and events that may be a part of their daily lives.

1 Explain how the basic "pick six numbers" game works: players choose six numbers from a large set and win if the six they have selected are chosen in a random drawing.

2 ## Think & Discuss
Read through the Think & Discuss with the class. Have students give a quick estimate of the chances of winning. Be sure students understand that they are to estimate the probability of winning and then the amount of time it is likely to take to win if they play the game twice a week. Record estimates so students can compare them with the precise answers they calculate at the end of Investigation 1.

Investigation 1

3 The investigation has students begin with a simpler case of the situation in the Think & Discuss that introduced the lesson. Remind students about this strategy, which they encountered in Lesson 9.1. Tell them that to start simple, they will first think about a lottery game in which the player must match two of six numbers.

4 ## Think & Discuss
Read this question with the class, and give students a minute or two to think about their predictions. They will do the calculations in Problem Set A.

Probability Investigations

Many people play state-run lottery games. There is an important social issue associated with these games: they often appear easier to win than they really are! If players knew their real chances of winning, they might make wiser decisions about whether and how often to play.

Think & Discuss

In one state's lottery game, participants choose six different numbers from 1 to 49. To win the grand prize, all six numbers must match those selected in a random drawing. The order of the numbers doesn't matter. For example, 3-32-16-13-48-41 is considered the same as 3-13-16-32-41-48.

This game has a drawing twice a week. Suppose you selected one group of six numbers for every drawing. Make a guess about how often you could expect to win the grand prize.

Answers will vary. The actual answer is about once every 13,983,816 drawings, or about once every 134,460 years.

By the end of this lesson, you will be able to find the exact answer to this problem.

Investigation 1 ▶ Analyzing Lottery Games

Let's start by analyzing some simple lottery games. Consider a lottery game in which you must match two out of six numbers.

Think & Discuss

To win the *2-of-6* lottery game, you must match two different numbers from 1 to 6 with those selected in a random drawing. How often do you think you could expect to win this game? Answer this question by completing this probability statement:

I estimate that I would win the 2-of-6 game once every _____ games.

Record the responses for the entire class on the board. Answers will vary. The actual answer is 15 (that is, $\frac{6 \cdot 5}{2}$).

Develop

1 **Problem Set A** Suggested Grouping: Pairs

In this problem set, students play the *2-of-6* lottery game using slips of paper. Pairs record results from their rounds and then the class compiles all results. Students then find the theoretical probabilities and compare them to their experimental results.

2 As students complete **Problem 1,** have them record their results on the board so they can complete **Problem 2.** The total will provide a good experimental sampling.

Problems 3–5 are important. The technique of finding the number of ordered pairs first and then dividing by the number of ways each pair can be ordered is readily extendable to games involving both more numbers to guess from and more numbers to match.

You may wish to point out the Just the Facts on this page, which alerts students to another probability term they will encounter in future mathematics courses— *combination.* Note that in this text the word combination is used to refer to an arrangement of objects. In future mathematics courses, students will use this term to specifically refer to a listing of objects in which order is *not* important.

About the Mathematics

In **Problem 1a–c** students are shown an intuitive strategy for finding the number of permutations of 6 numbers taken 2 at a time. In future mathematics courses, students will learn the following algorithm for finding the number of permutations of n distinct objects taken r at a time, which is noted $P(n, r)$.

$$P(n, r) = \frac{n!}{(n - r)!}$$

In this formula, $n!$, read "n factorial," is the product of n and all the counting numbers less than n. So, for example, the number of ways to draw 2 numbers out of 6 is $P(6, 2)$.

$$P(6, 2) = \frac{6!}{(6 - 2)!}$$
$$= \frac{6!}{4!}$$
$$= \frac{6 \cdot 5 \cdot 4 \cdot 3 \cdot 2 \cdot 1}{4 \cdot 3 \cdot 2 \cdot 1}$$
$$= 6 \cdot 5 \text{ or } 30$$

In **Problem 1e** students are shown an intuitive strategy for finding the number of combinations of 6 numbers taken 2 at a time. This method takes the number of permutations of 6 numbers taken 2 at a time and divides it by the number of ways to arrange those two numbers. This strategy is reflected in the following algorithm for finding the number of combinations of n distinct objects taken r at a time, noted $C(n, r)$.

$$C(n, r) = \frac{P(n, r)}{r!} \text{ or } \frac{n!}{(n - r)! \, r!}$$

So, for example, the number of combinations of 6 numbers taken 2 at a time is $C(6, 2)$.

$$C(6, 2) = \frac{6!}{(6 - 2)! \, 2!}$$
$$= \frac{6!}{4! \cdot 2!}$$
$$= \frac{6 \cdot 5 \cdot 4 \cdot 3 \cdot 2 \cdot 1}{(4 \cdot 3 \cdot 2 \cdot 1) \cdot (2 \cdot 1)}$$
$$= \frac{6 \cdot 5}{2 \cdot 1}$$
$$= \frac{30}{2} \text{ or } 15$$

- 6 identical slips of paper
- a container

2. Answers will vary.

3. 1-2, 1-3, 1-4, 1-5, 1-6, 2-3, 2-4, 2-5, 2-6, 3-4, 3-5, 3-6, 4-5, 4-6, 5-6; 15 pairs

Just the **facts**

An arrangement or listing of objects in which order is *not* important is called a *combination*.

4c. See Additional Answers.

4d. There are 6 choices for the first number, and each of those has 5 choices, so there are 30 in all.

Problem Set **A**

With a partner, follow these steps to model the *2-of-6* lottery game.

- Write the whole numbers from 1 to 6 on separate slips of paper. Place the slips in a container, and shake them.

- One partner should write down a two-number lottery pick.

- The other partner should select two numbers from the container.

- Record "win" if the selected number pair matches the recorded number pair and "lose" if it doesn't match. (Both numbers must match in order for you to win.)

- Return the numbers to the container, and shake the container.

- Keeping the same numbers for the lottery pick, repeat the process— drawing two numbers, recording "win" or "lose," and returning them to the container—until you have made 10 selections.

1. How many times out of 10 did you win the game? Answers will vary.

2. Combine your results with those from your classmates. Use the combined results to complete this statement:

In our class experiment, there was 1 winner every _____ games.

3. List all the possible pairs that can be drawn in the *2-of-6* lottery game. Remember, the order of the numbers doesn't matter; for example, 3-4 is the same as 4-3. How many pairs are there?

4. Instead of listing all the possibilities, you can use a shortcut to find the number of pairs.

a. How many ways are there to select the first number? 6

b. Once the first number is chosen, how many ways are there to select the second number? 5

c. If you multiply your answers from Parts a and b, you will have the number of pairs if order *did* matter. To see that this is true, draw a tree diagram showing the different combinations. How many different pairs would there be if order mattered?

d. Explain why you can just multiply the answers from Parts a and b to find the number of pairs.

e. Any pair of numbers can be arranged two ways; for example, 1-2 and 2-1. So, your total from Part c counts each number pair twice. To find the actual number of pairs, you need to divide your result from Part c by 2.

What is the total number of possible pairs for the *2-of-6* lottery game? How does this number compare to the number of possible pairs in the list you made in Problem 3? 15; the results are the same.

1 Problem-Solving Strategies

- Make a model
- Act it out

2 Have students record their answers to Problem 1 on the board.

• *Additional Answers on page A691*

Problem Set Wrap-Up A discussion of **Problem 6** makes a good wrap-up for this problem set. Comparing student results to predictions transitions into the Think & Discuss. Most students will probably agree that the game looks easier than it actually is.

Think & Discuss

After working Problem Set A and seeing how close their preliminary predictions were, students may be able to give a better prediction for this slightly more difficult problem. They still may not be aware of how quickly these probabilities change, though. Give students a minute or two to think about their predictions, and discuss how they think changing the numbers involved will change the probabilities.

If you give students enough time to calculate, some may apply the principle of counting to ordered triples and then divide by the number of ways three items can be ordered to obtain the correct answer. If so, record their "prediction" with the other predictions, and let students continue with Problem Set B.

5. If you choose just one pair in the *2-of-6* lottery game, what are your chances of winning? Record your answer by completing this probability statement:

The chances of winning are 1 out of __15__.

6. Answers will vary.

6. Compare your answer for Problem 5 to your class predictions from the Think & Discuss at the bottom of page 582. Do the data support the idea that the game looks easier than it really is?

As you probably would have guessed, the chances of winning a lottery game change as the number of choices and the number of matches required to win change.

1 Discuss Problem 6 and lead into the Think & Discuss.

Think & Discuss

In the *3-of-7* lottery game, players must match three different numbers from 1 to 7 with those selected in a random drawing. So, players have one more number to choose from, and they must match three numbers instead of two.

Think about how these changes would affect your chances of winning. Then complete this statement:

I estimate that I would win the 3-of-7 game once every ____ games.

Record the responses for the entire class on the board.
Answers will vary. The actual answer is 35 $\left(\text{that is, } \dfrac{7 \cdot 6 \cdot 5}{6}\right)$.

2 Give students a minute to think about how changing the numbers involved will change the probabilities.

1 **Problem Set B** Suggested Grouping: Pairs

In this problem set, students calculate probabilities for the *3-of-7* game, using the methods introduced in Problem Set A for the *2-of-6* game. This problem set will probably move more quickly than the last. Circulate as students work, and help pairs as needed.

If students are having trouble understanding how to order three items, you may want to refer them back to the CD problem of Lesson 9.1, Investigation 2; in particular, you may want to remind them of Kai's method in the Share & Summarize on page 554.

Problem Set B

1 You may have students work in pairs.

1. You can use the counting strategy from Problem Set A to calculate the number of possible triples for the *3-of-7* game.

   a. How many possibilities are there for the first number selected? 7

   b. Once the first number is chosen, how many possibilities are there for the second number? 6

   c. Once the first two numbers are chosen, how many possibilities are there for the third number? 5

   d. Multiplying your results from Parts a–c will give you the number of triples if order *did* matter—if, for example, 1-2-3 was considered different from 2-3-1. How many different triples would there be if order mattered? 210

   In your answer for Part d, each triple is included more than once. To find how many times each triple is counted, think about how many ways any triple of numbers can be arranged. For example, consider the numbers 1, 2, and 3.

   e. How many possibilities are there for the first number? 3

   f. Once the first number is chosen, how many possibilities are there for the second number? 2

   g. Once the first two numbers are chosen, how many possibilities are there for the third number? 1

   h. How many times is each triple counted in your answer to Part d? That is, how many ways are there to arrange three numbers? 6

   i. To find the actual number of triples, divide your result from Part d by your answer to Part h. What is the total number of possible triples in the *3-of-7* lottery game? 35

2. What are your chances of winning the *3-of-7* game? 1 out of 35

3. Compare your answer to Problem 2 to your class predictions for the Think & Discuss on page 584. Does the game look easier than it actually is? Answers will vary.

Example

1 Walk students through the Example. If they understand the basic principle, they should not be in doubt about what to do, although they may have some trouble with a particular step such as figuring out how many ways four items can be ordered or calculating $12 \cdot 11 \cdot 10 \cdot 9$.

If you have time, you may want to point out that an alternative to multiplying first is to set up a ratio of products and simplify by division where possible. For example, $\frac{12 \cdot 11 \cdot 10 \cdot 9}{4 \cdot 3 \cdot 2 \cdot 1}$ can be written in the form $\frac{12}{4} \cdot \frac{9}{3} \cdot \frac{10}{2} \cdot \frac{11}{1}$ which simplifies to $3 \cdot 3 \cdot 5 \cdot 11$, an easier product to calculate.

Share & Summarize

2 Have students work on these questions in pairs. Walk around to observe whether they are following the basic principle. When all pairs have answers, you might let a couple of them report their findings.

If you have time, you also might pose the following question:

> Given the low probability of winning a typical state-run lottery such as this one, why do you think they have such broad appeal? *Possible answers: If the prize is large, people are willing to ignore the odds; people may not understand their real chances; numbers like 13,983,816 may be too large for people to comprehend; people think they might get "lucky."*

Troubleshooting If students are having trouble, use the following examples to go back to listing outcomes using a tree diagram. Then help students generalize the counting structure for a particular tree diagram to any tree diagram having the same number of items.

Additional Examples

- How many ways can three items be arranged in order? $3 \cdot 2 \cdot 1$, or 6

- In how many orders can you read three books from a list of five books? $5 \cdot 4 \cdot 3$, or 60

- How many ways can three items be picked from five in any order? $\frac{60}{6}$, or 10

- List all the ways to pick three letters, in any order, from A, B, C, D, and E. *ABC, ABD, ABE, ACD, ACE, ADE, BCD, BCE, BDE, CDE*

On Your Own Exercises

Practice & Apply: 1–3, p. 590
Connect & Extend: 6–9, pp. 591–593
Mixed Review: 13–26, p. 595

You can use the techniques you developed in Problem Sets A and B to calculate the probability of winning other lottery games.

Calculate the probability of winning the *4-of-12* game. To do this, you need to find the number of possible ways 4 numbers can be selected from 12 numbers.

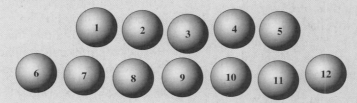

First think about the number of possibilities if order did matter. There would be 12 possibilities for the first number, 11 for the second, 10 for the third, and 9 for the fourth. So, if order mattered, the number of possibilities would be $12 \cdot 11 \cdot 10 \cdot 9$, or 11,880.

Any four numbers can be arranged in $4 \cdot 3 \cdot 2 \cdot 1$, or 24, ways. So, the product $12 \cdot 11 \cdot 10 \cdot 9$ counts each set of four numbers 24 times. To find the number of possible lottery selections, you must divide that result by 24:

$$\frac{12 \cdot 11 \cdot 10 \cdot 9}{4 \cdot 3 \cdot 2 \cdot 1} = \frac{11,880}{24} = 495$$

So, there are 495 ways four numbers can be selected. The probability of winning the game with a single ticket is $\frac{1}{495}$.

Share & Summarize

1. Calculate the probability of winning the lottery game described in the Think & Discuss on the top of page 582. Remember, this is a *6-of-49* game. Show your calculation.

2. If you select one group of six numbers for both drawings every week, how often could you expect to win? Show your calculation.

1. $\frac{49 \cdot 48 \cdot 47 \cdot 46 \cdot 45 \cdot 44}{6 \cdot 5 \cdot 4 \cdot 3 \cdot 2 \cdot 1}$
= 13,983,816, so the probability is $\frac{1}{13,983,816}$.

$\frac{13,983,816}{2(52)} \approx$ 134,460, so about once every 134,460 yr

1 Summarize students' work using the Example.

2 Have students work in pairs and observe whether they are following the basic principle.

Investigation 2

Some students are very much aware of the playoff structures for various sports leagues. You can introduce this investigation by asking for some examples of how playoffs work—for instance, the league playoffs for the World Series. If no students are able to offer examples, you might tell them about the NCAA college basketball tournament (sometimes called "March Madness").

The NCAA Tournament This tournament begins with 64 teams chosen for their record during the season or for winning particular tournaments. (In 2001, this number changed to 65 with the addition of a "play-in" game to determine the 64th team to play in the tournament. For the purposes of this example, tell students to ignore this additional game.) The 64 teams are divided into four divisions, with 16 teams in each. Six rounds are played, as follows.

The first two rounds are the quarter finals. Within each division, the 16 teams are paired up and pairs play. The 8 winners then pair up and play, leaving 4 winning teams in each division.

The four sets of division winners, called the "Sweet Sixteen," again are paired. The next round produces eight winners, called the "Elite Eight." Another round of games brings the number of winners down to four: the "Final Four." These four are the champions of each of the four regions.

The Final Four play a total of two games, and the winners of those go on to the championship game.

The structure itself is relatively straightforward. If all the teams are equally matched, each team has the same chances of winning. Realistically, though, the teams will not all be equally matched, so a team's chances of winning are influenced by the decisions about which teams pair up and where games will be played. Top-seed teams (that is, those ranked highest) are often paired with bottom-seed teams in the quarter finals; teams with strong season records often have to travel less to the playoff games. These decisions are made carefully, with many factors brought into consideration. ■

After an example has been presented, tell students that they will analyze some playoff structures, starting with fairly simple ones. If some students express (now or during the investigation) the opinion that this isn't math, you can explain that experiments are important in probability, because they can help you see why, for example, two teams might have the same or different probabilities. Without experimenting, it's sometimes very difficult to see where to begin analyzing a situation.

In addition, some students may have trouble accepting the playoff models, knowing that in reality one team will likely be better than the other. It is important to remind them that to analyze a situation, they may need to simplify it. By assuming the teams have an equal chance of winning, they can determine how much the structure of the playoff itself influences who wins. That would be much more difficult to do if they didn't make the equally likely assumption.

Some students may feel that since skill is involved, this is not a probabilistic situation. As mentioned on page T565, there are so many factors involved that using probabilities is often the best way to analyze the overall situation. Students will probably agree, if pressed, that a team with lesser skill may be able to win games against a team with greater skill. It is often the case that if two teams play several games, both will win at least one game. Remind students that although skill is involved, factors such as weather, some players being sick, and just having a "bad day" contribute to the outcome, so there is no way to accurately predict the outcome.

Problem Set C Grouping: **Groups of Three**
If your class size isn't divisible by 3, having a couple of groups of two is acceptable.

Pose and solve **Problem 1** with the entire class, and then read through the text following Problem 1 with the class.

Investigation 2 Analyzing Sports Playoffs

Many sports leagues end their seasons with some type of playoff. Playoff organizers must decide how many teams to include and how to structure the series of games. The organizers try to make the structure as fair as possible for all teams.

1 Discuss how some sports playoff tournaments are structured.

2 After working Problem 1 and reading the text with the class, have students work in groups of three.

MATERIALS
- 3-team playoff charts
- 3 identical slips of paper
- 2 dice

1. Team A: $\frac{1}{2}$;

  Team B: $\frac{1}{2}$

Problem Set C

You will now analyze two playoff structures, *Top Two* and *Top Three*.

Top Two: Teams A and B have the two best records at the end of the season. The two teams play, and the winner is declared the champion.

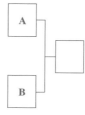

1. Assume the teams have the same chances of winning the game. What is the probability that Team A will win the championship? What is the probability that Team B will win?

Top Three: At the end of the season, Teams A, B, and C have the three best records. In the playoffs, Team B plays Team C, and the winner plays Team A for the championship.

You can work in a group of three to model the *Top Three* series. In your model, assume that each team has the same chances of winning each game.

To decide who will represent each team, label three identical slips of paper A, B, and C. Put them face down, mix them up, and have each player choose one.

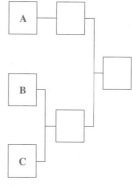

On a copy of the chart above, put the slips of paper on their starting positions. For each game, the two students representing the participating teams each roll a die. The student rolling the higher number wins the game and moves his or her slip of paper on to the next round. If there is a tie, the students roll again.

Develop

1 ▶ For **Problem 2,** groups will need a copy of the three-team chart. They can copy it from the text, or you can hand out Master 53. You might want to create a class table for this problem, compiling all the group results to get a larger experimental sample.

Students may have trouble understanding the logic in **Problem 4.** Parts a–c help students find the probability that Team B wins the tournament by considering eight tournaments and finding how many of those B is expected to win. Students should be able to answer **Part a** easily. You may need to reword **Part b** using their answer to Part a:

2 ▶ So Team B will advance to play Team A in four of the eight tournaments. Of those four games, how many do you expect Team B to win? 2

If students can't see how their answer to Part b helps them in **Part c,** you might ask:

Remember, the probability that an event occurs is the number of outcomes in the event divided by the total number of outcomes in the sample space. What do you think we mean by *outcomes* in this case? **the ways the tournament can be played out** What is the total number of outcomes in our sample space? 8 In how many outcomes did Team B win? 2

If they still don't see that the total number of outcomes—the number of ways the tournament can be played out—is eight, you might want to ask them to determine how many times Team A and Team C win; then they should be able to see that if B and C winning is two outcomes each (for a total of four) and A winning gives another four outcomes, there are eight outcomes total.

Using this kind of *model population* (the eight tournaments) is a powerful technique for calculating theoretical probabilities, and you may want to spend some class time discussing it. Model populations will be explored more explicitly in Chapter 10, using different contexts.

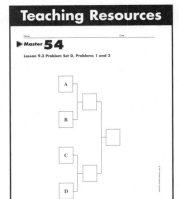

3 ▶ **Problem Set Wrap-Up** Conduct a class discussion of **Problem 5.** Students may have different ideas, drawing on their own experiences and knowledge of sports and playoffs in addition to the mathematical evidence from the problem set.

4 ▶ **Problem Set D** Grouping: **Groups of Four**
If your class size isn't divisible by 4, having a few groups of three is acceptable.

This problem set is similar to Problem Set C, so students can get into groups and begin work immediately. You may want to distribute Masters 54 and 55, which reproduce the four-team playoff charts.

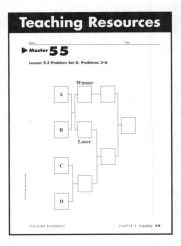

5 ▶ For **Problem 2,** students should combine their results with those of other groups. Creating a tally in a table similar to that in Problem Set C, Problem 2, is a good way to do this. You may want the class to discuss the results before moving on to the rest of the problem set.

2. Play the complete playoff series eight times, keeping a tally of the champion teams.

Team	Number of Championships
A	
B	
C	

3. Answers will vary. Most groups will find that Team A wins the most. Team A has an advantage because they must win only one game to be champions; Teams B and C each must win two games in a row.

3. Which team won the most championships? Why do you think this is?

4. If you assume the teams are equally likely to win each game, you can find the probability that each team will win the championship.

a. If this playoff series were played eight times, how many times would you expect Team B to beat Team C in the first game?   4

b. Of the number of times Team B beats Team C, how many times would you expect it to beat Team A in the final game?   2

c. Use your results to determine the probability that Team B will win the championship. $\frac{2}{8}$, or $\frac{1}{4}$

4d. Team A: $\frac{1}{2}$;
Team C: $\frac{1}{4}$

d. Use a similar method to determine the probabilities that Team A and Team C will win the championship. That is, imagine that the series is played eight times, and figure out how many times you can expect each team to win the championship.

5. Suppose a sports league with several teams is planning a special playoff. The organizers are considering including either the top two teams, using the *Top Two* structure, or the top three teams, using the *Top Three* structure. Discuss whether you think one playoff structure would be more appropriate than the other.   See below.

Next you will compare playoff structures involving four teams.

1 You may create a class table for Problem 2.

2 You may need to reword Part b.

3 Discuss Problem 5 with the class.

4 Have students work in groups of four.

5 You may want to discuss Problem 2 before the groups move on.

MATERIALS

- 4-team playoff charts
- 4 identical slips of paper
- 2 dice

2. Answers will vary. Each team should win about the same number of times.

Problems Set C Answer

5. Answers will vary. Many students will consider the three-team structure unfair and therefore inappropriate. Others may suggest that the unequal chances of winning could be used to balance other influences such as playing the series "away from home." Still others may think that if Team A finished the season with the best record, it "deserves" an advantage in the playoffs.

Problem Set D

At the end of the season, Teams A, B, C, and D are the top four teams. Here is one possible playoff structure.   **1.** Answers will vary.

1. Working in a group of four, play through the complete playoff series five times, keeping a record of the champion teams.

2. Combine your results with those from the other groups. Summarize what you find.

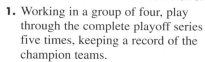

Develop

Again, groups should compile their results for **Problem 4.** Bring them together as they finish Problem 4, and let them discuss Problems 4 and 5 as a class.

Some students will have trouble answering **Problem 5.** It is enough if they understand appropriate suggested answers, from their classmates or from you.

Set groups to work on challenge **Problem 6** if there is time. The suggestion for attacking this problem is to create an "ideal" playoff model and play it out an appropriate number of times to determine the probabilities, as students did in Problem 4 of Problem Set C. Students will need to be careful, though, that all the possible win-lose combinations are considered. For example, Team A defeats Team B half the time; for the times when Team A wins, Team C must defeat Team D exactly half the time.

Share & Summarize

Let students discuss this in class. You may need to suggest that they review the various charts in *both* problem sets.

Troubleshooting If students have trouble with the Share & Summarize question, you can pose some leading questions, such as the following:

> Look at the three-team chart on page 587. Which team had the best chance of winning? A
>
> What was different for that team? *It played fewer games.*
>
> Does this difference happen with the other structures for the teams most likely to win? *yes*

On Your Own Exercises

Practice & Apply: 4, 5, p. 591
Connect & Extend: 10–12, pp. 593–594
Mixed Review: 13–26, p. 595

Here is another way to structure a four-team playoff.

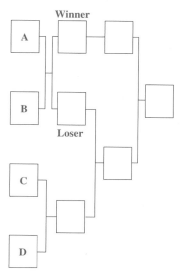

3. Work with your group to model this series. Play the complete series five times, keeping a tally of your results. Answers will vary.

4. Combine your results with those from the other groups. Summarize what you find.

5. Discuss any circumstances under which you think one playoff structure would be more appropriate than another.

★ **6. Challenge** For each structure in this problem set, determine the probability that each team will win the championship. Assume both teams are equally likely to win each game. (Hint: Imagine that a series is played eight times, and determine how many times you can expect each team to win the championship.)

Structure 1: Team A: $\frac{1}{4}$; Team B: $\frac{1}{4}$; Team C: $\frac{1}{4}$; Team D: $\frac{1}{4}$

Structure 2: Team A: $\frac{3}{8}$; Team B: $\frac{3}{8}$; Team C: $\frac{1}{8}$; Team D: $\frac{1}{8}$

Share & Summarize

In some of the playoff structures you examined, all the teams had an equal chance of winning the championship. In others, at least one team had a better chance than some of the other teams. What is the difference in the structures that allows one team to have a better chance? The teams that didn't have to play as many games had a better chance.

4. Answers will vary. Students should find that Teams A and B win a significantly greater number of times than Teams C and D.

5. Possible answer: The first structure would be good for a sports league that has four divisions, because it does not give advantage to one division winner over another.

1 Let students discuss Problems 4 and 5 as a class.

2 Problem-Solving Strategy

Act it out

3 You may need to suggest students review the charts in both problem sets.

On Your Own Exercises

On Your Own Exercises

Investigation 1,
pp. 582–586
Practice & Apply: 1–3
Connect & Extend: 6–9

Investigation 2,
pp. 587–589
Practice & Apply: 4, 5
Connect & Extend: 10–12

Assign Anytime
Mixed Review: 13–26

Exercise 1:
Make sure students know why it is important to distinguish individual but identically colored marbles. If some students object, ask them if the outcomes W-W, O-O, and W-O are equally likely.

Exercise 3:
Students need to realize that **Parts c and d** assume an "ideal" model in which the probabilities come out exactly according to calculation. For example, in **Part d,** it isn't likely that someone who plays for 45 years will actually win exactly every 9 years.

Practice 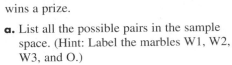 **Apply**

1a. W1-W2, W1-W3, W1-O, W2-W3, W2-O, W3-O

1. In the *Orange-and-White* game, three white marbles and one orange marble are placed in a bag. A player randomly draws two marbles. If the marbles are different colors, the player wins a prize.

   a. List all the possible pairs in the sample space. (Hint: Label the marbles W1, W2, W3, and O.)

   b. What is the probability of winning a prize? $\frac{1}{2}$

2. To win the *3-of-10* lottery game, players must match three numbers from 1 to 10 with those selected in a random drawing. Remember that order doesn't matter.

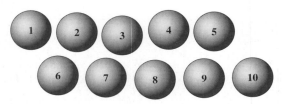

2a. 120 $\left(\text{that is, } \frac{10 \cdot 9 \cdot 8}{3 \cdot 2 \cdot 1}\right)$

   a. How many possible triples are there in the *3-of-10* lottery game?

   b. What are your chances of winning the *3-of-10* lottery game? $\frac{1}{120}$

3. To win the grand prize in the *Match 5* lottery game, players must match five numbers from 1 to 30 with those selected in a random drawing. Remember, order doesn't matter.

3a. 142,506 $\left(\text{that is,}\right.$
$\frac{30 \cdot 29 \cdot 28 \cdot 27 \cdot 26}{5 \cdot 4 \cdot 3 \cdot 2 \cdot 1}\left.\right)$

   a. How many different groups of five numbers are possible?

   b. If you bought a single ticket with five numbers, what is the probability you would win the grand prize? $\frac{1}{142,506}$

   c. The *Match 5* lottery game has a drawing three times a week. If you bought a ticket for each drawing—that is, if you played three times a week—how often could you expect to win the grand prize?   about once every 913 yr

   d. Suppose you bought 100 tickets for each drawing (with a different group of five numbers on each ticket). How often could you expect to win the grand prize?   about once every 9 yr

 impactmath.com/self_check_quiz

Quick Review
Math Handbook

Hot Topics
pp. 232–238,
240–249

★ indicates multi-step problem

4. Sports A volleyball league has two divisions. At the end of the season, Team A is in first place in Division 1, followed by Team B and Team C. Team D is in first place in Division 2, followed by Team E and Team F. League organizers have structured the playoffs as shown below.

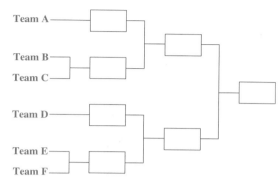

a. Model this series six times, keeping a tally of the champion teams. Flip a coin or roll a die to determine the winner of each game. Answer will vary.

b. Which team won the most championships? Answer will vary.

★ **c.** Determine the probability that each team will win the championship. Assume both teams in each game are equally likely to win. (Hint: Imagine that a series is played eight times, and determine how many times you can expect each team to win the championship.)

4c. Teams A and D each have a $\frac{1}{4}$ probability of winning the championship. Each of the other teams has a $\frac{1}{8}$ probability of winning.

6a. 6,840 (that is, 20 · 19 · 18)

6b. 720 (that is, 10 · 9 · 8)

Connect & Extend

5. Possible answer:

A
B
C
D
E
F

Teams A–D: Each has $\frac{1}{8}$ chance of winning; Teams E and F: Each has $\frac{1}{4}$ chance of winning.

5. Design a championship structure for six teams in which all teams play the first round. Assuming each team is equally likely to win a single game, find the probability that each team will win the championship. See margin.

6. Automobile license plates in one state consist of three different letters followed by three different digits. The state does not use vowels or the letter *Y*, which prevents slang words from accidentally appearing on license plates.

a. Each letter can appear only once on a given license plate. How many different sets of three letters are possible?

b. Each digit can appear only once on a given license plate. How many different sets of three digits are possible?

c. Altogether, how many different license plates with three letters followed by three digits are possible for this state? 4,924,800 (that is, 6,840 · 720)

Exercise 8:

As an extra challenge, ask students to verify that there are only 84 possible different triples. They can do this by listing all the possibilities or by listing a few and finding a pattern. Suggest to students that they start by listing all the possible triples when 1 is the only number they can choose. 1-1-1 Then list all the triples using 1 or 2 that have at least one 2. 2-1-1, 2-1-2, 2-2-2 Students should continue in this way, counting the number of triples in each group until they have listed all triples or until they see a pattern. The total number of triples possible is 1 + 3 + 6 + 10 + 15 + 21 + 28 or 84. Notice that from one group of triples to the next, the number of triples increases by the next counting number:
1 + **2** = 3; 3 + **3** = 6;
6 + **4** = 10; 10 + **5** = 15;
15 + **6** = 21;
21 + **7** = 28.

7b. 36; There are 6 ways to choose each number, so there are 6 · 6 or 36 possible pairs.

7c. 1-1, 1-2, 1-3, 1-4, 1-5, 1-6, 2-1, 2-2, 2-3, 2-4, 2-5, 2-6, 3-1, 3-2, 3-3, 3-4, 3-5, 3-6, 4-1, 4-2, 4-3, 4-4, 4-5, 4-6, 5-1, 5-2, 5-3, 5-4, 5-5, 5-6, 6-1, 6-2, 6-3, 6-4, 6-5, 6-6

7e. No; there are 2 ways to get a pair in which the numbers are different but only 1 way to get a pair in which both numbers are the same.

7f. A pair in which the numbers are different has a $\frac{2}{36}$ or $\frac{1}{18}$ chance of winning, while a pair in which the numbers are different has a $\frac{1}{36}$ chance of winning.

8a. 343; There are 7 ways to choose each number, so there are 7 · 7 · 7 or 343 possible pairs.

7. Suppose the *2-of-6* lottery game was modified so that after the first number was selected, that number was placed back into the group before the next number was selected. In this way, a number could be repeated, meaning pairs such as 2-2 and 3-3 would be possible.

a. Would your chances of winning be better or worse for this modified game? Explain.   Worse; there are more possible pairs.

b. How many possible pairs are there for this modified game, assuming that order *does* matter? Explain.

c. List all of the possible pairs from part b.

d. Since order really doesn't matter in this game, how many *different* pairs are there? (Remember, if order doesn't matter, 1-2 is the same as 2-1.)   21

e. Are all of the pairs considered in part d equally likely? Explain.

f. If you choose one number pair for this modified game, what is the probability you will win. (Hint: There are two cases to consider.)

8. Suppose the *3-of-7* lottery game was modified so that after each number was selected, that number was placed back into the group before the next number was selected. In this way, a number could be repeated, meaning triples such as 1-2-2 and 3-3-3 would be possible.

a. How many possible pairs are there for this modified game, assuming that order *does* matter? Explain.

b. Since order really doesn't matter in this game, 1-1-2, 1-2-1, and 2-1-1 are all the same triple. So there are only 84 possible *different* triples. Are all of these different triples equally likely? Explain.

c. If you choose one number triple for this modified game, what is the probability you will win. (Hint: There are three cases to consider.)

8b. No; there are 6 ways to get a triple in which none of the numbers are the same; 3 ways to get a triple in which two numbers are the same, but the third number is different; and only 1 way to get a triple in which all of the numbers are the same.

8c. A triple in which none of the numbers are the same has a $\frac{6}{343}$ chance of winning; a triple in which two numbers are the same has a $\frac{3}{343}$ chance of winning; and a triple in which all of the numbers are the same has a $\frac{1}{343}$ chance of winning.

592 CHAPTER 9   Probability

★ indicates multi-step problem

9b. It is the same.

9d. See Additional Answers.

9e. the *2-of-6* game;
Possible explanation:
You have the higher four
numbers in the numer-
ator and the lower four
in the denominator.
Since there are only six
numbers, the middle two
are in both numerator
and denominator, so
you can take them out.
That leaves only two
numbers in both parts of
the calculation, which is
what you have for the
2-of-6 game.

11b. Possible answer:
The second structure
shown in the answer
to Part a, in which
Team A does not
have to play the first
two rounds, might be
more appropriate if
Team A has a record
that indisputably sets
it above the other
teams, as it gives the other teams a more equal chance to get to the final game.

9. Challenge In the *4-of-7* lottery game, players must match four numbers from 1 to 7 with those selected in a random drawing.

a. If you select one group of four numbers, what is the probability that you will win this game? $\frac{1}{35}$

b. How does the probability of winning the *4-of-7* lottery game compare to the probability of winning the *3-of-7* lottery game (see your work in Problem Set B)?

c. Calculate and compare the probabilities of winning the *5-of-7* lottery game (match five numbers from 1 to 7) and the *2-of-7* lottery game (match two numbers from 1 to 7). They're the same, $\frac{1}{21}$.

d. Look back over the Example on page 586. Use similar calculations to explain what you discovered in Parts b and c.

e. What game has the same probability of winning as the *4-of-6* game? Explain.

10. Mr. Wegman takes a drive each Sunday afternoon. One Sunday, he decides to let probability determine his destination. The diagram shows the network of roads he is driving. He starts at Point A and drives toward Point B. Each time he reaches a fork in the road, he flips a coin to decide which path to take. If he flips heads, he goes to the left. If he flips tails, he goes to the right.

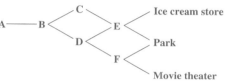

★ **a.** What is the probability Mr. Wegman will end at the movie theater? (Hint: Imagine he takes this drive eight times. How many times would you expect him to end at the movie theater?) $\frac{1}{8}$

★ **b.** What is the probability he will end at the park? $\frac{4}{8}$, or $\frac{1}{2}$

★ **c.** What is the probability he will end at the ice cream store? $\frac{3}{8}$

11. Sports In a particular sports league, five teams qualify for the final playoff. **11a.** See Additional Answers.

a. Design two ways of structuring the playoff series.

b. Describe a situation in which one playoff structure would be more appropriate than another.

Exercise 9:
This exercise gets at the symmetric structure of the matching game. The number of ways to choose *r* out of *n* items is the same as the number of ways to choose *n − r* out of *n* items. For an elegant way to look at it, note that choosing *r* items leaves out *n − r* items. Therefore, the number of ways to choose *r* items out of *n* must be the same as the number of ways of leaving out *n − r* items. You can then consider the left-out items to be those you chose in the first place.

Exercise 10:
The hint in **Part a** suggests students create an ideal model of eight trips. In applying this model, make sure students count the number of occurrences of the desired outcome in the model. Ideally, 4 of the 8 trips would involve driving from Point B to Point C. All of those trips would then go from Point C to Point E and 2 of the 4 would then go to the Ice cream store. So the branch B-C-E-Ice cream will occur two times out of 8 trips. The branch B-D-E-Ice cream will occur one time out of 8 trips. Therefore the destination of the ice cream store will occur ideally three times out of eight.

Additional Answers

9d. Possible answer: To find the probability for the *4-of-7* game, do this calculation: $\frac{7 \cdot 6 \cdot 5 \cdot 4}{4 \cdot 3 \cdot 2 \cdot 1}$. To find the probability for the *3-of-7* game, do this calculation: $\frac{7 \cdot 6 \cdot 4}{3 \cdot 2 \cdot 1}$. Factoring out $\frac{4}{4}$ in the first calculation shows that the results are the same. For the *5-of-7* game, the probability is $\frac{7 \cdot 6 \cdot 5 \cdot 4 \cdot 3}{5 \cdot 4 \cdot 3 \cdot 2 \cdot 1}$. For the *2-of-7* game, it's $\frac{7 \cdot 6}{2 \cdot 1}$. Factoring out $\frac{5 \cdot 4 \cdot 3}{5 \cdot 4 \cdot 3}$ in the first calculation shows that the results are the same.

• **Additional Answers continued on page A691**

Exercise 12:

If possible, give students a couple of days to work on this exercise, and then discuss answers in class. Students should use the probabilities to create an ideal model of this playoff. **Part d** is the most difficult part; students will need to multiply all the probabilities along each branch of the tree. Refer back to **Part c** if necessary, and help students calculate the number of games won by each team at each level.

Quick Check

Informal Assessment
Students should be able to:

✔ analyze probabilities in real-world situations

12. **Challenge** In Investigation 2, you always assumed that two teams have the same chances of winning a single game. For this exercise, assume that Team A has a 60% chance of defeating Team B in every game they play against each other.

a. Suppose there is a one-game tournament between the teams and the winner of the game wins the tournament. What is the probability that Team A will win? That Team B will win?   0.6, 0.4

Now suppose you have a "best two out of three" tournament. That means the teams play until one of them wins two games.

b. Use a tree diagram to show all the possibilities for the tournament. For example, in the first game, there are two branches:

A wins or B wins. (Hint: If A wins the first two games, is a third game played?)   See below.

c. Suppose the teams played 1,000 tournaments. In how many tournaments would you expect Team A to win the first game? In how many of those tournaments would you expect Team A to also win the second game?   600, 360 (that is, 0.6 · 600)

12d. AA: 360; ABA: 144; ABB: 96; BAA: 144; BAB: 96; BB: 160

d. For each combination in your tree diagram, use similar reasoning to find the number of tournaments out of 1,000 you would expect to go that way. For example, one combination should be ABB; in how many tournaments out of 1,000 would you expect the winner to be A, then B, and then B? (Hint: Check your answers by adding them; they should total to 1,000.)

e. Find the total number of tournaments out of 1,000 in which each team wins the tournament. What is the probability that Team A wins a tournament?   Team A: 648; Team B: 352; 64.8%

f. Which tournament, *one-game* or *best-two-out-of-three*, is better for Team B?   1-game

12b.

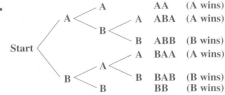

Mixed Review

13. Consider the line $y = ^-5x - 7$.

   a. A second line is parallel to this line. What do you know about the equation of the second line? The value of m is $^-5$.

   b. Write an equation for the line parallel to $y = ^-5x - 7$ that passes through the origin. $y = ^-5x$

   c. Write an equation for the line parallel to $y = ^-5x - 7$ that crosses the y-axis at the point $(0, ^-2)$. $y = ^-5x - 2$

   d. Write an equation for the line parallel to $y = ^-5x - 7$ that passes through the point $(3, 0)$. $y = ^-5x + 15$

14. **Life Science** The data in the table represent how a certain population of bacteria grows over time. Write an equation for the relationship, assuming the growth is exponential. $p = 5^h$

Hours from Start, h	Population, p
0	1
1	5
2	25
3	125

15.

15. Copy this picture. Create a design with rotation symmetry by rotating the figure several times about the point using a 30° angle of rotation.

16. Solve the inequality $0 > 5(7 - x) + 12x$. Draw a graph of the solution. $x < ^-5$

    <-- -8 -7 -6 -5 -4 -3 -2 -1 0 1 2 -->

Factor each expression.

17. $4h^2 - 2h$ $2h(2h - 1)$

18. $^-6a^2 + ab + b^2$
  18. $(3a + b)(^-2a + b)$

19. $^-4k^2 - 5kj - j^2$
  19. $^-(k + j)(4k + j)$

20. $2m^2 - 9 + 3m$
  20. $(m + 3)(2m - 3)$

Use the quadratic formula to solve each equation.

21. $3h^2 - 2h + ^-6 = 0$
  21. $\frac{2 \pm \sqrt{76}}{6}$ or $\frac{1 \pm \sqrt{19}}{3}$

22. $^-6a^2 + 3a = ^-4$
  22. $\frac{3 \pm \sqrt{105}}{12}$

23. $4k^2 = 5k + 2$
  23. $\frac{5 \pm \sqrt{57}}{8}$

24. $2m^2 - 12 = 6m$
  24. $\frac{6 \pm \sqrt{132}}{4}$ or $\frac{3 \pm \sqrt{33}}{2}$

Find the x-intercepts for the graph of each equation.

25. $(x - 5)^2 - 49 = 0$ 12, $^-2$

26. $6x^2 + 36 - 30x = 0$ 2, 3

Exercises 18 and 19: Students may factor out $^-1$ and leave it as shown in the answer to Exercise 19, or they may prefer to leave it within one of the binomial factors, as shown in the answer to Exercise 18. Either is acceptable.

Quick Quiz

1. A homeless shelter raises money with a grab bag that contains 10 identically wrapped packages. Inside each of 4 of the packages is $1; the other 6 contain play money. To play, you pay $3 and then randomly select 3 packages.

   a. In how many different ways can you pick 3 packages? $\frac{10 \cdot 9 \cdot 8}{6}$, or 120, ways

   b. To win the maximum of $3, all 3 packages must have real money in them. In how many different ways can you win $3? $\frac{4 \cdot 3 \cdot 2}{6}$, or 4, ways

   c. If none of the packages you choose hold real money, you end up contributing $3. In how many different ways can this happen? $\frac{6 \cdot 5 \cdot 4}{6}$, or 20, ways

   d. What is the probability that you will win $3? $\frac{4}{120}$, or $\frac{1}{30}$

   e. What is the probability that you will end up contributing $3? $\frac{20}{120}$, or $\frac{1}{6}$

• **Quick Quiz continued on page A692**

Chapter Summary

This summary helps students recall the major topics of the chapter.

Vocabulary

Students should be able to explain each of the terms listed in the vocabulary section.

Problem-Solving Strategies and Applications

The questions in this section help students review and apply the important mathematical ideas and problem-solving strategies developed in the chapter. The questions are organized by mathematical highlights. The highlights correspond to those in "The Big Picture" chart on page 541a.

Questions 1 and 2:

Make sure students actually construct the lists.

VOCABULARY
sample space

1. 10 games; AB, AC, AD, AE, BC, BD, BE, CD, CE, DE

Chapter Summary

In this chapter, you found the sizes of *sample spaces* for several situations. Sometimes this required counting all the possible ways a group of items could be selected from a larger group. Other times you had to figure out the number of ways a group of things could be ordered.

You can find the sample space for a situation by systematically listing all the possibilities. You learned that you can sometimes discover a pattern to help you determine the size of the sample space without listing all the outcomes.

You also found the probabilities of events for various situations, and you determined whether one event was more likely than another. You saw that sometimes finding probabilities can help you make decisions or devise game-winning strategies.

Strategies and Applications

The questions in this section will help you review and apply the important ideas and strategies developed in this chapter.

Making a systematic list of every possible outcome

1. Ally, Brevin, Carol, Doug, and Evan are setting up a chess tournament among themselves that will be a round-robin tournament—that is, every participant will play every other participant once. How many games will there be? Make a systematic list of every possible tournament pairing.

2. In science class, Ally, Brevin, Carol, and Doug are assigned to sit next to one another in the first row.

    a. List all the arrangements in which Ally sits in the first seat, then all the arrangements in which Brevin sits in the first seat, and so on.

    b. How many different arrangements are there? **24**

A First	B First	C First	D First
ABCD	BACD	CABD	DABC
ABDC	BADC	CADB	DACB
ACBD	BCAD	CBAD	DBAC
ACDB	BCDA	CBDA	DBCA
ADBC	BDAC	CDAB	DCAB
ADCB	BDCA	CDBA	DCBA

 impactmath.com/chapter_test

Using a pattern or shortcut to find the size of a sample space without listing every outcome

3a. Possible explanation: Nine different players could bat first, leaving eight different players to bat second, seven different players to bat third, and so on, so you can multiply $9 \cdot 8 \cdot 7 \cdot 6 \cdot 5 \cdot 4 \cdot 3 \cdot 2 \cdot 1$; 362,880 orders.

4. Possible explanation: There are $12 \cdot 11 \cdot 10 \cdot 9 \cdot 8 = 95{,}040$ ways to order 5 players chosen from a team of 12, but since order is unimportant, divide by the number of ways to order 5 players, which is $5 \cdot 4 \cdot 3 \cdot 2 \cdot 1 = 120$. The result is $95{,}040 \div 120 = 792$.

3. The manager of a baseball team is responsible for assigning the nine players to a batting order.

   a. Explain how you can find the number of different batting orders *without* listing all the possibilities. How many batting orders are possible?

   b. How many different batting orders are possible if one of the nine players, the pitcher, always bats ninth? 40,320

4. Suppose a basketball coach has 12 players. *Without* listing all the possibilities, explain how you can find the number of different 5-player teams the coach could create. How many teams are possible?

Determining the probability of an event

5. In Question 1, you determined all the possible pairings for a round-robin chess tournament. Imagine that each pairing is written on a slip of paper. The slips are placed into a container and mixed. One slip is then chosen at random.

   a. What is the probability that the chosen names are Doug and Evan? $\frac{1}{10}$

   b. What is the probability that Doug or Evan (or both) is included in the chosen pairing? $\frac{7}{10}$

   c. What is the probability that the chosen names contain neither Doug or Evan? $\frac{3}{10}$

6a. $\frac{12}{24}$, or $\frac{1}{2}$

6. In Question 2, you listed all the ways four students could be arranged in a row. Use your list to answer these questions.

   a. If seats are assigned randomly to the four students, what is the probability that Brevin and Carol will sit next to each other?

   b. If seats are assigned randomly to the four students, what is the probability that Doug will sit at one end of the row? $\frac{13}{24}$

Review and Self-Assessment **597**

Question 8:
This requires students to calculate a probability in order to determine the appropriate strategy for a number-guessing game. You may need to help students understand the rules of the game. Have them try playing a round or two, if necessary.

★ indicates multi-step problem

Using probability to determine whether a game is fair

7. Héctor is trying to invent a two-player game that involves rolling two dice and adding the results. He is considering several scoring rules.

7a. No; the probability that Player 1 will win is $\frac{16}{36}$, and the probability that Player 2 will win is $\frac{20}{36}$.

7b. No; the probability that Player 1 will win is $\frac{16}{36}$, and the probability that Player 2 will win is $\frac{20}{36}$.

7c. yes; Possible explanation: Although Player 2 is three times as likely to score on a given roll, Player 1 receives 3 times as many points, so in 36 games they are both expected to get 9 points.

★ **a.** Suppose Player 1 scores 1 point for a sum of 2, 3, 4, 9, 10, 11, or 12, and Player 2 scores 1 point for any other sum. Is this game fair? Explain.

★ **b.** Suppose Player 1 scores 1 point when the sum is 6, 7, or 8. Otherwise, Player 2 scores 1 point. Is this game fair? Explain.

★ **c.** Suppose Player 1 scores 3 points when the sum is 11 or 12, and Player 2 scores 1 point when the sum is 3, 4, or 5. For other sums, neither player scores. Is this a fair game? Explain.

Using probability to make decisions

8. *Higher or Lower?* is a two-player game in which opponents take turns guessing whether the sum of the numbers on a pair of rolled dice will be higher than 7 or lower than 7. The play of one turn proceeds as follows:

- Each player rolls one die. The guessing player for the roll makes his or her roll in full view; the nonguessing player conceals his or her roll.

- The guessing player then guesses "higher than 7" or "lower than 7." The guess is made with the knowledge of one die but not the other.

- The guessing player scores 1 point if he or she is correct. The nonguessing player scores 1 point if the guess is incorrect. If the sum is 7, no points are awarded.

Suppose you are the player guessing higher or lower.

★ **a.** The first die shows a 2. Should you guess the sum will be "higher than 7" or "lower than 7"? What is the probability you will be correct? lower; $\frac{4}{6}$, or $\frac{2}{3}$

★ **b.** The first die shows a 4. Should you guess the sum will be "higher than 7" or "lower than 7"? What is the probability you will be correct? higher; $\frac{3}{6}$, or $\frac{1}{2}$

★ indicates multi-step problem

Demonstrating Skills

9. Suppose you have seven chairs in a row. How many different seating orders are possible for seven people? 5,040

★ **10.** At Barak's Burgers you can order a cheeseburger with up to seven different condiments: mustard, catsup, pickles, onions, tomatoes, lettuce, and mayonnaise. How many different cheeseburgers are possible, including a plain cheeseburger with no condiments? 128

11. The *21-and-5* lottery game requires players to match 5 numbers drawn randomly from 21. How many different groups of 5 numbers are possible? 20,349

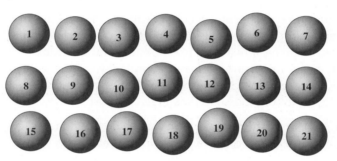

Question 10:
This question may confuse some students. Students can calculate the possibilities separately: how many burgers contain all 7 condiments, exactly 6 of the 7, exactly 5 of the 7, and so on, ending with the number having 0 of the 7 condiments. Then just add the results: $1 + 7 + 21 + 35 + 35 + 21 + 7 + 1 = 128$. Alternatively, students might realize that there are 7 condiments that can be either "on" or "off," giving 2^7, or 128, possibilities.

Question 11:
You may want to ask students to give you the uncalculated form for the answer,
$$\frac{21 \cdot 20 \cdot 19 \cdot 18 \cdot 17}{5 \cdot 4 \cdot 3 \cdot 2 \cdot 1},$$
and possibly explain it, to be sure they are not just generalizing without understanding.

Modeling with Data

Chapter Overview

There is usually a "story" behind real data: rising school enrollment may be due to improving school conditions; numbers of cavities may decrease after introduction of fluoride in water. Reading the stories often requires organizing the data and using the tools of statistics to find and explain patterns in the data. A bit of "messiness" has to be tolerated in real data, too.

In this chapter, students develop and use skills in statistical interpretation on real data, including the 1854 cholera epidemic in London, one year's records of gasoline consumption and mileage, and the most common first names across several decades. They organize and reorganize data, find measures of central tendency, create algebraic expressions that model data, and display data visually with maps and graphs in order to understand what the data say about the situations they come from.

The lab investigation for this chapter is an exploration of Geographic Information System (GIS) software. This optional investigation is presented in the Teaching Resources, Masters 58a–58e. If you wish to present this interesting material, you will need to request a free CD-ROM from Environmental Systems Research Institute, *www.esri.com* (see page 615a). Be aware that it will take time for the CD to arrive in the mail, so you may want to visit the Web site immediately.

the **Big Picture**

Chapter 10 Highlights	Links to the Past	Links to the Future
Analyzing data presented in tables (10.1)	**Elementary Grades:** Understanding tables **Courses 1 and 2:** Recognizing patterns in tables	**High School and College:** Working with data and statistics
Using visual displays to identify trends (10.1, 10.2)	**Course 2, Chapters 1–4:** Recognizing various types of relationships from graphs **Course 2:** Identifying appropriate displays for data	**High School and College:** Understanding linear and nonlinear correlations **High School and College:** Using concrete and abstract visual representations to convey information
Creating and using models (10.2)	**Course 2, Chapters 1–3:** Using equations to represent graphs	**High School and College:** Applying mathematics to real-world situations through models

Lesson Objectives	Pacing	Materials		NCTM Standards	Hot Topics
10.1 Data Patterns in Tables and Graphs page 601b • To sort and organize data appropriately • To use tables, graphs, and maps to reveal trends that may not be obvious in data • To interpret data in a plausible manner	5 class periods	• Computers with spreadsheet software (optional) • Graphing calculators • Master 56 (optional) • Master 57 • Master 60 (optional) • Rulers • Compasses • Graph paper • Computers with GIS software (optional) • Masters 58a–58e (optional) • Master 59 (optional)		2, 5, 6, 7, 8, 9, 10	pp. 222–230
10.2 Models, Data, and Decisions page 630a • To make predictions from data • To create an economic model for a simple business • To create a population model and use it to make predictions	5 class periods	• Graphing calculators • Graph paper • Master 60 (optional) • Computers with spreadsheet software (optional) • Protractors (optional)		2, 5, 6, 7, 8, 9, 10	pp. 214–220

Key to NCTM Curriculum and Evaluation Standards: 1=Number and Operations, 2=Algebra, 3=Geometry, 4=Measurement, 5=Data Analysis and Probability, 6=Problem Solving, 7=Reasoning and Proof, 8=Communication, 9=Connections, 10=Representation

Assessment Opportunities

Standard Assessment

Impact Mathematics offers three types of formal assessment. The Chapter 10 Review and Self-Assessment in the Student Edition serves as a self-assessment tool for students. In the Teacher's Guide, a Quick Quiz at the end of each lesson allows you to check students' understanding before moving to the next lesson. The Assessment Resources include blackline masters for chapter and quarterly tests.

- **Student Edition** Chapter 10 Review and Self-Assessment, pages 652–658
- **Teacher's Guide** Quick Quizzes, pages A675, 651
- **Teaching Resources** Quick Quiz, Master 59
- **Assessment Resources** Chapter 10 Test Form A, pages 246–249; Chapter 10 Test Form B, pages 250–252

Ongoing Assessment

Impact Mathematics provides numerous opportunities for you to assess your students informally as they work through the investigations. Share & Summarize questions help you determine whether students understand the important ideas of an investigation. If students are struggling, Troubleshooting tips provide suggestions for helping them. On the Spot Assessment notes appear throughout the teaching notes. They give you suggestions for preventing or remedying common student errors. Assessment Checklists in the Assessment Resources provide convenient ways to record student progress.

- **Student Edition** Share & Summarize, pages 604, 608, 612, 615, 634, 636, 637, 641
- **Teacher's Guide** On the Spot Assessment, pages T604, T610, T633 Troubleshooting, pages T604, T608, T612, T615, T634, T636, T637, T641
- **Assessment Resources** Chapter 10 Assessment Checklists, page 298

Alternative Assessment, Portfolios, and Journal Ideas

The alternative assessment items in *Impact Mathematics* are perfect for inclusion in student portfolios and journals. The In Your Own Words feature in the Student Edition gives students a chance to write about mathematical ideas. The Performance Assessment items in the Assessment Resources provide rich, open-ended problems, ideal for take-home or group assessment.

- **Student Edition** In Your Own Words, pages 625, 648
- **Assessment Resources** Chapter 10 Performance Assessments, pages 253–256

Assessment Resources

The Assessment Resources provide a chapter test in two equivalent forms, along with additional performance items. The performance items can be used in a variety of ways. They are ideal for take-home assessment or in-class group assessment.

- Chapter 10 Test Form A, pages 246–249
- Chapter 10 Test Form B, pages 250–252
- Chapter 10 Performance Assessment, pages 253–256
- Chapter 10 Assessment Solutions, pages 257–259

A semester test, with performance items, is also provided in the Assessment Resources in two equivalent forms. This test covers material in the whole course, with emphasis on Chapters 6–10. In addition, an algebra proficiency test is provided.

Ch. 10 Test Form A	Ch. 10 Test Form B	Ch. 10 Perf. Assess	Semester 2 Tests

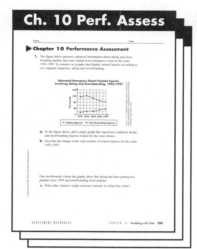
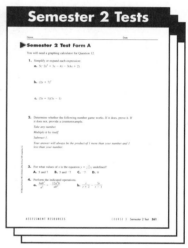

Additional Resources

- **Math Skills Maintenance Workbook,** 35
- **Investigations for the Special Education Student in the Mathematics Classroom,** 3, 4, 5, 6, 9
- **What's Math Got To Do With It? Videos,** Level 3, Video 4; Level 3, Video 5
- **StudentWorks™ CD-ROM**
- **Reading and Writing in the Mathematics Classroom**
- **Using the Internet in the Mathematics Classroom**

ExamView® Pro

Use ExamView® Pro Testmaker CD-ROM to:

- Create Multiple versions of tests.
- Create Modified tests for Inclusion students with one mouse click.
- Edit existing questions and Add your own questions.
- Build tests aligned with state standards using built-in State Curriculum Correlations.
- Change English tests to Spanish with one mouse click and vice versa.

Introduce

Using data is important in our "information age." To introduce the chapter, you might have students read the section "It Makes Good Census." As noted here, data such as those collected in the census is available in almanacs and other resource books, and the information could be anything from population makeup (race, ethnicity, gender, and so on) to how people spend their leisure time. Social trends such as access to technology can be tracked using data gathered at different times, and *model populations* can be created to better understand how certain characteristics might be distributed throughout a population or even passed down from generation to generation.

Throughout this chapter, it might be fun to have students bring in data they find in newspapers or magazines. You can discuss what story, if any, the data tell.

Think About It

Students should pose at least one question that can be answered using Census data. Then, provide students with the resources to find current Census data so that they might answer their question. If the Internet is available, use the government Web site www.census.gov.

Modeling with Data

Real-Life Math

It Makes Good Census The United States Constitution mandates that a census of the U.S. population be conducted every 10 years. This complicated process requires that every U.S. citizen be counted.

Detailed information about each citizen is collected and analyzed as part of the census. For example, age, race, religion, and education data are collected and analyzed. These analyses enable us to make generalizations and draw conclusions about the U.S. population.

Think About It What would you like to know about the U.S. population? Write a few questions, and then use an almanac, the Internet, or another resource to find the answers.

Family Letter

Dear Student and Family Members,

Throughout the past year, we have seen mathematics at work in several situations. In this chapter, we will look more closely at how to work with data, including data from many real-world contexts. We will use tables to organize data, look for trends, and draw conclusions. We will use visual displays, including a map describing a historic cholera outbreak in London. Using the map, we will gather evidence to determine the source of the epidemic.

■ Pump sites

∵ Deaths from cholera

Copyright 1991 National Geographic Society Publications Art

In the second half of the chapter, we will use *mathematical models*. For example, we will use equations to model population growth and make predictions. We will also analyze a business using tables, and use a model population to explore how left-handedness might change from one generation to another.

What can you do at home?

You might ask your student about the London cholera outbreak or the other situations he or she is learning to analyze. You might also explore information in the newspaper together and look for patterns: Are there patterns in the temperatures displayed on the weather map?

Another version of the Family Letter, available in English and Spanish, is found in the Teaching Resources. You may want to send a copy of this letter home with your students.

Mathematical Background

The study of mathematics often involves the production of numerical data, much of it generated as we evaluate literal expressions in order to solve equations or to understand relationships that are not obvious. In addition, though, people who do not study mathematics are regularly confronted with numerical data.

The mathematics of this chapter is fairly straightforward: students organize data sets, find measures of central tendency, and compare statistical measures. Some of the basic concepts (such as using mean, median, and mode as measures of clustering within a numerical data set) were introduced in Courses 1 and 2 using real, but limited, data sets. Here, some of the limits (particularly how smooth or "nice" the data are) are lifted, and students try to make sense of large and relatively "messy" data sets that more realistically reflect the complicated natures of many natural and social environments.

Organizing and Sorting Data often come to us as a seemingly haphazard collection of numerical values. Simply making a table imposes an order or organization on any collection of numbers, and that order might reveal patterns or trends in the data. By reorganizing and retabulating the data, one can display relationships that were hidden in the original tabulation, and often make one data set serve several very different purposes. For example, the chapter opens with test score data from two classes taught by the same teacher in a high school served by two towns. This data set can be tabulated to compare the test scores of students according to town or class; with more data (which the school would have but which are not given in the text), the data could be organized according to other types of data as well.

Deriving New Data Not only can data sets be tabulated in different ways for different purposes, but they can also be used as the basis for calculating new data sets. A dated record of miles traveled and gas purchased provides a vague sense of gas consumption. If the table is extended to include the calculated measure of miles per gallon, that vague sense is made more precise. Furthermore, this table might be matched with a table of temperatures to create a new table that explores a possible relationship between temperature and gas consumption.

Displays and Correlation An important part of data analysis is to gain some experience constructing and interpreting visual displays of real data. Data within a set might be characterized by a pie chart or circle graph. Data trends across time are readily depicted by line and bar graphs. In some cases, data that have a geographical base can be displayed on a map, revealing unexpected patterns and suggesting new conclusions.

When data appear to follow some sort of pattern, one often says there is some *correlation* between the variables in the data. For example, statistics for a recent Major League baseball season are displayed in these graphs:

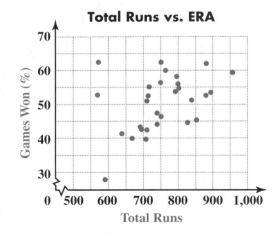

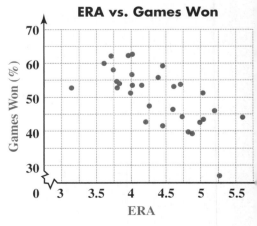

• **Teaching notes continued on page A692**

Data Patterns in Tables and Graphs

Objectives

▶ To sort and organize data appropriately

▶ To use tables, graphs, and maps to reveal trends that may not be obvious in data

▶ To interpret data in a plausible manner

Overview (pacing: about 5 class periods)

In this lesson, students turn realistic raw data into useful information by organizing and analyzing the data with the aid of tables and graphs. They begin by rearranging and presenting the data in tabular form. Then they move on to making graphs, looking for trends in the tabulated data, and using maps and graphs to help them discover trends. Much of this lesson reviews earlier skills and concepts that students have developed in the past three years.

Note that Masters 58a–58e provide an optional lab investigation, using Geographical Information Systems (GIS) software, which you might teach after Investigation 4. Notes for the lab can be found on pages 615a and 615b.

Advance Preparation

You may want to allow students to use spreadsheets for Investigations 1–3. Graphing calculators are used in Investigation 2, and Master 56 has instructions for using the Texas Instruments TI-83 Plus to create scatterplots and line graphs. For Investigation 4, each group or pair of students will need a copy of Master 57, Snow's Map of London, as well as a ruler, a compass, and graph paper. See page 615a for preparation information for the optional lab investigation.

	Summary	Materials	On Your Own Exercises	Assessment Opportunities
Investigation 1 page T602	Students reorganize a table of data to help them analyze the information.	• Computers with spreadsheet software (optional)	Practice & Apply: 1–3, p. 616 Connect & Extend: 11, 12, pp. 623–625 Mixed Review: 20–33, pp. 629–630	On the Spot Assessment, page T604 Share & Summarize, pages T604, 604 Troubleshooting, page T604
Investigation 2 page T605	Students organize data and explore connections between variables. Raw data are extended by including calculations using the data.	• Graphing calculators • Master 56 (optional) • Master 59 (optional) • Master 60 (optional) • Spreadsheets (optional)	Practice & Apply: 4, p. 617 Connect & Extend: 13–15, pp. 625–626 Mixed Review: 20–33, pp. 629–630	Share & Summarize, pages T608, 608 Troubleshooting, page T608
Investigation 3 page T608	Students look for trends by examining data sets that are not overtly quantitative or that contain so much data that it's hard to make sense of them.	• Spreadsheets (optional)	Practice & Apply: 5–8, pp. 617–621 Connect & Extend: 16–18, pp. 626–628 Mixed Review: 20–33, pp. 629–630	On the Spot Assessment, page T610 Share & Summarize, pages T612, 612 Troubleshooting, page T612
Investigation 4 page T612	Students explore a real-life historical problem in which both maps and graphs turned out to be useful presentations of data that led to important analyses.	• Master 57 • Rulers • Compasses • Graphing calculators (optional) • Graph paper	Practice & Apply: 9, 10, pp. 621–623 Connect & Extend: 19, p. 629 Mixed Review: 20–33, pp. 629–630	Share & Summarize, pages T615, 615 Troubleshooting, page T615 Informal Assessment, page 630 Quick Quiz, page A675
Lab Investigation page 615a	**Optional** Students explore maps as displays of data using Geographical Information System software.	• Computers with GIS Software (see page 615a) • Master 58a–58e		

You may want to begin the lesson by reading the introductory paragraphs with the class. Then move into the Think & Discuss.

Think & Discuss
These open-ended questions will help students look back at things they already know but will not necessarily be thinking about at this time.

 To give everyone a chance to provide input, you might start this activity with a brief period of silent writing in which each student collects his or her thoughts, which they can then share in small groups. Finally, pool the class's ideas in a whole-class discussion. Be sure students understand that there are no "right" answers to these questions.

If it seems appropriate, you might also invite a brief discussion of the conflict between access to data and privacy; the popularity of the Internet makes many students aware of these two "rights," although most students will probably never have considered the potential that each of these rights has for violating the other.

Investigation 1

This investigation presents fictional data from a small high school that serves two communities, Northtown and Southtown. Raw data for 44 algebra students include their scores on an algebra pretest, their hometowns, and the time of day their algebra classes meet.

 You may want to begin by reading the introductory paragraphs with the class and then discussing the table on page 603.

Data Patterns in Tables and Graphs

1 Discuss accessing and interpreting data.

The times in which you are living have been called the *information age* because the amount of information available is increasing faster than ever before. Through the Internet, you can find an enormous amount of data, on almost any topic you can think of, in a matter of minutes.

Just having data won't help you, however, if you can't interpret the data. By organizing and analyzing data, you can sometimes discover trends and connections that will help you understand the information better.

Just the facts

If you have access to the Internet, you may be interested in *fedstats.gov*, where you can find some of the data collected by the U.S. government.

Think & Discuss

What kinds of data do you think your school might have about you? How might the school use these data? See ① in Additional Answers.

In math class, you have often collected and drawn conclusions from data. Consider some investigations in which you collected numerical data earlier this year and then formulated a conjecture. How did you use mathematics to make sense of the collected data?

Possible answer: From data in tables, we conjectured the type of relationship and then derived an equation and checked values against the data. From experimental evidence, we determined whether a game of chance was fair or not fair and checked conclusions with theoretical probabilities.

2 Let students share their thoughts in small groups and then discuss as a class.

Investigation ▶ 1 Analyzing Data Using Tables

Schools often collect data about test scores of groups of students and use them to evaluate the performance of the students and the schools.

One high school draws its students from two small towns, Northtown and Southtown, each with one middle school. At the beginning of the school year, students in algebra classes take a test to determine how well prepared they are. The results of the algebra pretest for two classes are given on the opposite page.

The designation "S" in the "Town" column indicates that the student was from Southtown, and "N" indicates the student was from Northtown. The letter "M" in the "Class" column represents the morning algebra class, and "A" represents the afternoon class.

3 Read these paragraphs and discuss the table on page 603.

602 CHAPTER 10 Modeling with Data

Additional Answers

① Possible answer: Name, birth date, phone numbers, standardized test scores, medical information; phone numbers might be used for emergencies or for teacher/parent conferences; test scores might be used to determine which classes a student should take; medical information might be used in case of emergencies.

Develop

1 The order of students in the table is apparently random: the students are numbered 1–44, and there is no indication how these numbers are assigned.

If your students ask, you might speculate that the numbers represent alphabetical order or perhaps merely the order in which the recorder wrote down the data. If students have ID numbers in your school—and if they know their own numbers—it might be of interest to figure out how those numbers are assigned and to speculate why they exist at all. You might ask:

> Could a student be uniquely identified by first and last name if no ID numbers were used? *Not necessarily; for example, there might be two students named "Michael Smith" or some other common name, especially in a large school.*

> Is specific information (such as expected year of graduation from high school) encoded into part of an ID number? Are numbers assigned alphabetically within each class? Are they ever reused?

Tell your students that they will be analyzing the test scores and comparing them with hometown and class meeting time.

2 The paragraph following the table notes that the vice principal calculated the mean score for all 44 students. This is a good time to review the measures of center (mean, median, and mode) if you wish.

3 ## Problem Set A Suggested Grouping: Pairs

This problem set focuses on comparing the students' hometowns. Although it is structured as a pencil-and-paper activity, it can also be done on a computer by students who are familiar with sorting data on a spreadsheet. Using a spreadsheet program will require an initial time investment in order to enter the data, but that investment could pay off in the ease of making corrections, and the same data can be used for Problem Set B.

You may want to direct students to use a ruler or other straightedge to help them read large tables.

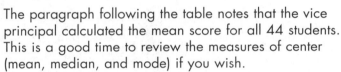

Problem-Solving Strategies **Problem 1** invites several possible solutions:

- Students might sort the original table by town.
- Students might create a pair of tables, one for each town.
- Students might make a single table listing the scores from each town.

In any case, it will be useful to sort each hometown's scores, either from lowest to highest or from highest to lowest. (The table in the answer provided has two columns of scores, each sorted from lowest score to highest.) You might suggest to any students who don't sort by score that they look ahead to Problem 3, which clearly motivates this choice.

Problems 2–4 serve primarily to review measures of central tendency. The calculations in Problems 2 and 3 are straightforward and offer the possibility of a discussion of the significance of a 2.5-point difference in the means and a 1.5-point difference in the medians. Taken together, these differences can offer some small insight into the *spread* of the two data sets. Since there is a larger difference in the means than the medians, one could conclude that either Southtown has a few students with much higher scores than the others or that Northtown has a few students with much lower scores. The raw data shows that Southtown does have all the students with scores of 100.

You may want to tell students they will be able to get a *quantitative* (numerical) measure to help them decide whether the differences are significant after they have studied more mathematics, perhaps in a statistics course in college or an advanced mathematics course in high school.

Algebra Pretest Results

Student	Score	Town	Class	Student	Score	Town	Class
1	100	S	A	23	54	N	A
2	81	N	M	24	72	N	A
3	55	S	M	25	100	S	M
4	74	N	A	26	66	S	A
5	58	N	A	27	90	S	M
6	59	S	A	28	84	N	A
7	94	N	M	29	68	N	M
8	72	N	A	30	73	N	M
9	100	S	M	31	44	S	M
10	100	S	M	32	82	N	A
11	77	N	A	33	60	S	A
12	94	S	A	34	79	S	M
13	66	N	M	35	94	S	A
14	85	N	M	36	89	N	A
15	63	S	A	37	69	N	A
16	74	S	M	38	69	N	M
17	90	N	M	39	62	S	M
18	66	N	A	40	87	N	M
19	59	S	M	41	76	N	A
20	92	S	A	42	70	S	M
21	73	S	M	43	100	S	A
22	81	N	M	44	88	S	A

1 Discuss the table.

The vice principal used the scores to compare the mathematics preparation of students in the two towns. He first calculated the mean score for all 44 students. He then created a new table that would help him compare the performance of students in the two towns.

2 You may want to review the measures of center.

3 You may have students work in pairs.

Problem Set A

1. Design a table that could help the vice principal make a town-to-town comparison of the scores.   See Additional Answers.

2. Find the mean score of the entire group of 44 students and the mean score of the students from each town. Compare these statistics for the two towns.

2. About 77.02 for the entire group, 75.77 for Northtown, 78.27 for Southtown; Southtown's mean is 2.5 points higher than Northtown's.

3. Find the median score of the entire group of 44 students and the median score of the students from each town. Compare these statistics for the two towns.
75 for the entire group, 75 for Northtown, 76.5 for Southtown; Southtown's median is 1.5 points higher than Northtown's.

LESSON 10.1   Data Patterns in Tables and Graphs   **603**

• **Additional Answers on page A693**

Problem 4 asks some factual questions to help students summarize the data and consider the open-ended question in **Part e:** which town's middle school prepares students better?

On the Spot Assessment

If students feel they are unable to make an assessment of the two towns, acknowledge that it's not easy to summarize all the different aspects they have considered. This can be a frustrating experience for many students. They may also feel they don't have enough information, which is a valid concern.

You might point out that in many jobs, it's necessary to make the best decision possible with limited information. Impress on them the importance of using the information they *do* have to state a conclusion and give the reasons they believe one town does better than the other, even if they feel the justification for their conclusion is not strong. Encourage them to make such a statement (that the justification is not strong) if they feel it's necessary.

Problem Set Wrap-Up Let students briefly discuss their answers to Problem 4e as a class. You may want to point out that unless results are very clear, the analysis of a particular data set might have different interpretations.

After students have taken a few moments to discuss their conclusions, bring them back to the main point of this investigation: that reorganizing can help in analyzing data. You can refer to some specific observations that students made during their discussion, and ask whether they would have made those observations as easily from the original table. Clearly, students could calculate means and even medians from the original table, but it would have been much more of a chore to do so.

Bringing students back to the original data table can also serve as a good lead-in to Problem Set B.

 Problem Set B Suggested Grouping: Pairs or Individuals

You may want to tell students they will consider the same data as in Problem Set A, but for different purposes.

As in Problem Set A, **Problem 1** calls for a rearrangement of the table to highlight particular data. Once again, it's helpful to divide the table into two categories, according to when the class meets, and to sort the scores within each category.

 Problem 2 is a less structured version of Problems 2–4 from Problem Set A. This time students are given looser guidelines but should still consider the standard statistical measures. If necessary, you can hint that students should refer to those problems and answer similar questions, but try to let them discover this themselves.

 ## Share & Summarize

Questions 1 and 2 focus on the organization of the data in tables, while **Question 3** asks about the types of information students gathered from the tables. Again, you may want to ask students whether the information was more easily found from the original table or from their reorganized tables.

Troubleshooting If students are having difficulty with this material, you might refer them to earlier work with measures of central tendency. You could also collect or invent data similar to those presented in the table at the beginning of the lesson, and then ask the same sorts of questions about the new data, prompting students and supplying some insights of your own as necessary.

Students will have more experience organizing and analyzing data in the rest of the lesson, so you can continue even if they are still struggling with these ideas.

 ### On Your Own Exercises

Practice & Apply: 1–3, p. 616
Connect & Extend: 11, 12, pp. 623–625
Mixed Review: 20–33, pp. 629–630

4b. Yes; they both have 11 students above the class median.

4d. Southtown, 10

4e. See Additional Answers.

4. Assuming the test gives an accurate indication of each student's preparation, consider what these scores might mean about the preparation of students from the two towns.

a. Which town has a wider range of student scores?   Southtown

b. Do the towns have the same number of students above the overall median? If not, which has more students above the median?

c. Five students scored 100 on the test. Which town is each of these top scorers from?   All five are from Southtown.

d. Which town has the lowest test score? How many points' difference is there between the lowest scores for the two towns?

e. Based on these data, which town's middle school do you think prepares students better? Explain your reasoning.

Problem Set B   See Additional Answers.

The same data are often used for quite different purposes. The vice principal was comparing the performance of students from two *towns*. The teacher of the two classes wondered whether either *class* was better prepared.

1. Construct a table to make the teacher's analysis easier. That is, find a way to display the data so you can more easily differentiate the scores for the two classes, morning and afternoon.

★ **2.** Do you think the data support a conclusion that one class is better prepared than the other? Justify your answer. You may want to consider mean, median, mode, range, or other factors.

Share & Summarize Answers

1. Possible answer: I thought about what I was trying to find out about the data and ignored the extra information.

2. Possible answer: Advantage: The single table gives all the information without having to repeat the scores. Disadvantage: You can't really sort the information in a way that makes both town and class easy to compare.

Share & Summarize

In this investigation, you used a table of data to create two new tables to help you analyze the information in the original table.

1. For each new table, how did you decide how to reorganize the original table?

2. Consider the table on page 603. Give an advantage and a disadvantage to presenting the data in the single table, rather than the two individual tables you created in Problem Sets A and B.

3. What things did you look at when trying to form conclusions about the differences between students from the two towns or the two classes?   Possible answer: mean, median, mode, range, the high and low scorers in each case

604 CHAPTER 10   Modeling with Data

1 • Encourage students to make a decision.

• Discuss Problem 4e.

2 You may have students work in pairs or on their own.

3 If necessary, prompt students to answer questions similar to those of Problem Set A.

4 Discuss these questions.

**Additional Answers
Problem Set A**

4e. Answers will vary. Southtown may provide stronger opportunities for top students, since their best scorers all got perfect scores. Northtown may provide stronger opportunities for low and average students, since their lowest score was 10 points above Southtown's lowest score.

• Additonal Answers continued on page A693

Investigation 2

In this investigation, students continue to organize and analyze data. While they compared two sets of single-variable data (scores) in Investigation 1, here they will work with and look for trends in sets of two-variable data. In some cases, students will use the raw data to calculate additional data that they can analyze. Note that the data presented show only very slight trends.

 1 You might introduce the investigation by explaining Lydia's situation (wanting her parents to have a newer car) or by having students read the introductory text, individually or as a class.

 2 **Think & Discuss**

Point out to students that they can sometimes easily see a *general* trend in data before proceeding to a detailed analysis. (Sometimes, of course, an analysis is needed to see any trend at all.)

Students should see immediately that the price of a new car is rising every year; some may want to consider now whether the relationship between price and year is linear, exponential, or some other type of relationship. Let them know that this is a more detailed level of analysis than what is necessary at this first glance at the problem, then tell them they will have a chance to consider what type of relationship fits the data in Problem Set C.

When you move the discussion to the second question, you might tell students that it's important to consider not just what the trend might be, but what might cause it as well. There isn't enough information in this case to say for certain what the cause is, but in general, this kind of speculation can give analysts ideas for what other data they might want to consider for a situation.

 3 **Problem Set C** Suggested Grouping:
Pairs or Individuals

This problem set reviews the use of graphs to present data visually. You may need to review the general shape of linear, quadratic, and exponential graphs, along with their algebraic representations in the equations $y = mx + b$, $y = ax^2 + bx + c$, and $y = ab^x$.

Prior to **Problem 1,** students use their calculators to graph the data points. They may recall how to create plots from Chapter 1, but you may need to go over the directions on Master 56 with them. (Step 5 on the master includes directions for creating a line graph, which students will do in Lesson 10.2.)

Students may need help with the suggestion that 1981 be treated as Year 1 as they enter the data. You may want to ask them how using the actual years would affect the graph. Point out that there is nothing to be gained by having 1984 blank years and that the graph's scale would be impractical.

You may also want to invite a discussion of which variable, *year* or *price,* belongs on which axis. Mathematically, it does not matter, but it should seem more natural to consider *price* as a function of *year* than to consider *year* as a function of *price,* so *year* is a better choice for the independent variable (horizontal axis).

Their plots should look similar to this:

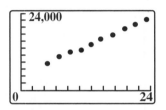

Problem 1 also asks students to find an equation if the relationship between year and price appears linear. In fact, the data points do not quite lie on a straight line, but they are certainly more nearly linear than they are quadratic or exponential. If students disagree with the suggestion that the relationship is linear, you might ask them to justify their reasoning. If they say the points obviously don't lie on a line, you can remind them that real data often aren't "nice." Ask them whether the data are *close enough* to linear that they would feel confident using a line to estimate prices for years between points, or even for years after 2003.

Problem-Solving Strategies There are several ways students might find the equation in Problem 1:

- The simplest and quickest way is to use a graphing calculator to compute a regression line for the data. (The sample answer on page 605 was found in this way.) Some students may recall doing this, but not exactly how. You can give them Master 60, which includes instructions for quadratic and exponential regression as well. Students will use these other forms in Lesson 10.2.

- They can plot the points by hand and try drawing a line themselves, perhaps using a clear ruler to position as many points above the line as below.

• *Teaching notes continued on page A694*

Investigation Organizing Data

Lydia wants her parents to buy a new car. When her parents argued that new cars are expensive, Lydia decided to try to convince them that they should buy a new car now (rather than wait a year or two until she was ready to drive and would undoubtedly be asking for the keys!).

Although she would have preferred a sports car, Lydia knew her parents would be more likely to listen if she talked about a midsize model like the one they currently owned. She collected the data below about the base price of their model of car each year.

Price of New Car

Year	Price	Year	Price
1985	$8,449	1995	$15,775
1987	10,598	1997	17,150
1989	11,808	1999	18,922
1991	12,698	2001	19,940
1993	14,198	2003	21,319

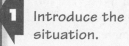

Think & Discuss

Describe the trend in the data. Possible answer: Each year the price rises.

What might cause the price to change the way it does?
  Possible answers: inflation, more features assumed to be "basic"

MATERIALS

graphing calculator

1. linear; Possible equation:
$y = 702x + 5,254$

Problem Set C

Plot the data from Lydia's table on your calculator. It will help if you treat 1981 as Year 1.

1. Use your graph to decide whether the relationship between year and price appears to be linear, quadratic, exponential, or some other type of function. If it appears to be linear, find an equation for a line that seems to be a good fit for the data.

2. Assume the price continues to increase in the same way. Use your equation to find out how much Lydia's parents would save by buying this year's model rather than waiting two years.
Possible answer: If the current year is 2005, the price would be about $22,804, which is $1,404 less than the 2007 estimated price of $24,208.

LESSON 10.1 Data Patterns in Tables and Graphs **605**

1 Introduce the situation.

2 Discuss the *general* trend in the data; the type of relationship doesn't matter at this stage.

3 You may have students work in pairs or on their own.

4 You might ask what the average annual increase is or whether students think Lydia's argument should convince her parents.

Read the text at the top of the page with the class. You might point out that Lydia doesn't know whether the odometer readings will support her or her parents.

Access
for all Learners

Language Diversity Be sure students know what an *odometer* is before they start this problem set. See the Just the Facts at the top of the page.

Problem Set D Suggested Grouping: Pairs or Individuals

Problems 1 and 2 are straightforward calculations that are used later. No interpretation is necessary, although the fuel economies for July and November are strikingly different.

Stress to students that **Problem 3** asks for a single table, not two.

Although **Problem 4** asks a purely factual question, many students may notice that the months listed are probably cold ones (depending on where Lydia lives, of course). If this observation occurs, it naturally leads into Problem Set E.

Just the facts

An odometer measures the distance a vehicle has traveled.

Lydia's parents weren't convinced, so Lydia decided to find more information. Her father kept a monthly record of odometer readings and the amount of gas bought for the family car. Lydia studied the records, hoping the data might suggest that the car was using so much gas that it would save money to replace it with a model with better fuel economy.

She prepared this record for 12 months, starting with the gasoline bought in June 2003. The second column shows the odometer reading (rounded to the nearest mile) on the last day of the month. The third column shows the gallons of gasoline bought during that month.

Month	Odometer Reading (mi)	Gasoline Bought (gal)
May	119,982	
Jun	121,142	42.8
Jul	122,564	36.6
Aug	126,354	139.7
Sep	127,459	42.0
Oct	128,106	26.5
Nov	128,919	34.7
Dec	129,939	41.5
Jan	131,052	44.6
Feb	131,695	27.2
Mar	132,430	29.6
Apr	134,114	60.0
May	135,135	35.3

Problem Set D

1. How many miles did the car travel during the year? What was the average number of miles driven per month?   15,153; 1,262.75

2. Fuel economy is often measured in miles per gallon. Calculate this measure for July and November to the nearest tenth.

3. Construct a table that shows the miles driven and the fuel economy (in miles per gallon) for each month.   See Additional Answers.

4. Which four months show the worst fuel economy? List them in order, starting with the worst.   Nov, Feb, Oct, Dec

2. July: 38.9; November: 23.4

• Additional Answers on page A694

Margin notes:

1 Introduce the new set of data.

2 You may have students work in pairs or on their own.

3 Stress that a single table, not two, is requested.

Develop

Problem Set E Suggested Grouping: Pairs or Individuals

In this problem set, students consider the possible effect of temperature on fuel economy. They inspect a graph of *temperature* versus *fuel economy* for any noticeable trend.

Read the introductory text with your students. You may want to ask them where they think Lydia lives. She is clearly in the Northern Hemisphere, since the coldest months are January and February; and she doesn't live too far north, since January's average is only slightly below freezing, nor too far south, since the temperatures do get fairly low.

Problem 2 asks about a possible connection between temperature and fuel economy. (See the discussion of *correlation* in the Mathematical Background on page 601a). Some students will feel there is a connection; others may not. The colder months do all seem to have relatively poor fuel economy, but the warmer months don't all have good fuel economy.

In **Problem 3** students identify and remove the outlier (July). There's even less of a correlation in this case. Suggest to students who have worked quickly and have extra time that they might try to find a line and graph it to see how well it fits the data. A regression line will lie in the midst of the points, but many points will seem quite far from the line.

Problem Set F Suggested Grouping: Pairs or Individuals

This problem set explores the possibility that the car gets more miles per gallon when it is driven longer distances. The Share & Summarize on page 608 will invite an explanation for this possibility.

In **Problem 1** students return to the question of sorting data in different ways, as they did in Investigation 1.

Problem 2 asks students to use a graph rather than a table to analyze the theory that fuel economy is related to miles driven. As usual, a visual representation helps us view the trends in the data.

1. Answers will vary, perhaps depending on where a student lives or has lived. In many parts of the country, the mean temperature for June will look low and that for December will look high.

**Problem Set E
Answers**

2. Possible answer: There may be a connection but not much of one. There are some low-fuel-economy months when it wasn't that cold.

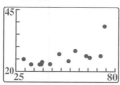

3. Possible answer: Although there may be a slight connection, there doesn't seem to be much of one.

Problem Set E

It is natural to wonder what caused the fuel economy to be better in some months than others. Lydia suspects that it's related to temperature; she thinks the car gets fewer miles per gallon in cold weather.

To test her theory, she researched the average temperatures in her city for the months during which she had data. From the Internet, she obtained the average of the daily mean temperatures, in °F, for each month.

Average Daily Mean Temperatures

Jun	Jul	Aug	Sep	Oct	Nov	Dec	Jan	Feb	Mar	Apr	May
64.6	74.3	72.5	66.3	54.4	44.6	39.1	29.5	33.6	39.4	49.2	58.2

1. Are any of the monthly temperature records surprising? Why?

2. Use your calculator to plot the (*temperature, fuel economy*) data. (The fuel economy data, in mpg, can be found in your answer to Problem 3 of Problem Set D.) Adjust the window settings to fill the screen with the data, as much as possible. Does there seem to be a connection between these two variables? Explain.

3. There should be one point on your graph that looks far from the others. Make a new graph without including that point. Adjust the window settings to fill the screen with the remaining data points. Now do you think there is a connection between temperature and fuel economy? Explain.

Problem Set F

Lydia's father said that he thought the car got fewer miles per gallon in months when they didn't drive much. Lydia decided to use her data to test his theory.

1. Construct a table that could be used to more easily see whether the fuel economy is worse in low-mile months and better in high-mile months. Can you see any evidence in your table to support Lydia's father's theory?   See Additional Answers.

2. Plot the (*miles driven, fuel economy*) data on your calculator. Does there seem to be a connection between these two variables? Explain. Possible answer: There seems to be a connection but not much of one. Two points seem really far from the general trend.

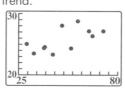

• **Additional Answers on page A694**

Share & Summarize

These questions make comparisons among different problem sets.

Question 1 stresses the difference between graphing data points that are already stated and data points that must first be calculated.

Question 2 asks students to compare how strong the connections between the variables are; this is difficult to quantify without knowledge of more advanced statistics, so students will have to use visual clues from the graphs. They might argue either way. Some students might find it frustrating that there is no clear answer here. You can point out that it's sometimes just as important to conclude that there is *no* connection as it would be to find such a connection. Then move to Question 3, which gives another possibility.

Question 3 opens up some discussion of the possibility of multiple causes; in this case the warmest months were also those with the most highway driving. You also might want to point out that the car might have been driven a lot over short distances in some of the months with high mileage and low economy. Students might be interested in thinking of ways they might test these conjectures. Gathering data for more than one year would certainly be helpful, for example.

Tips from **Teachers**

"You may want to ask your students to brainstorm other explanations for the possible trends in the data. For example, the car may have had more maintenance or repair work done during the summer months and so had better mileage."

Troubleshooting Most students should be gaining confidence and skill in organizing and sorting data and in developing plausible explanations for trends in the data. There will be further opportunities for practice in the rest of the lesson and chapter, so mastery is not important at this point, but it is a good idea to identify those students who may need extra support in the next investigations and lesson.

On Your Own Exercises

Practice & Apply: 4, p. 617
Connect & Extend: 13–15, pp. 625–626
Mixed Review: 20–33, pp. 629–630

Investigation 3

This investigation extends the idea of looking for trends by examining data sets that contain so much data that it's hard to make sense of them.

Introduce the investigation by reading through the introductory text with your students.

1. Possible answer: In Problem Set E, I had to use my calculation of fuel economy; in Problem Set F, I had to use my calculations of both miles driven and fuel economy. It was necessary because the variables I needed to graph weren't given in the tables; I had to make the calculations to get the data I needed.

Share & Summarize

2. Possible answer: It's difficult to say. The graph of miles driven seems to show a stronger connection but not by much.

1. In Problem Set C, you plotted the data from a given table. In Problem Sets E and F, however, you had to do something to the given data before plotting. In each case, what data *did* you graph, and why couldn't you graph the given data?

2. Compare the temperature graph (from Problem Set E) that you feel is most helpful to the graph of miles driven (from Problem Set F). Which graph suggests a stronger connection between the variables?

3. Lydia's brother Kyle observed that the family usually took their longer trips in the summer. He reasoned that fuel economy would be better on longer trips, since he had read that highway driving gives better fuel economy than city driving. Do the data fit this observation? Explain.   Yes; the best months for fuel economy were in the summer (plus April).

1 You might point out that concluding there is no connection can be just as important as finding one.

2 Introduce the investigation.

Investigation ▶ 3 Looking for Trends

The Social Security Administration has collected information on the names given to newborn boys and girls in the United States.

The two tables show the three most common names for newborn boys and girls in the United States for each year from 1900 through 2002. Each table lists the years in which each name was in first, second, and third place. To conserve space, the tables don't show the "19" part of the years, so the entry "87, 88, 90–93" represents the years 1987, 1988, 1990, 1991, 1992, and 1993.*

*Source: These data are derived from information at the Social Security Administration Web site, *www.ssa.gov.*

You may want to give students time to scan these tables before they start the problem set on page 610. You might encourage discussion about possible similarities and differences between the names in your particular group of students and those in the tables; a conversation about the variation across the years and why these names might be more popular would give students a useful perspective as they answer the questions to come.

Boys' Names

Name	First Place	Second Place	Third Place
Christopher		72, 73, 75, 81–93	74, 76–80, 94
David	60, 61, 63	58, 59, 66–70	56, 62, 64, 71–72
Jacob	99, 2000–2002	95, 97, 98	96
James	35, 40, 42, 43, 45–47, 49, 52	27, 30, 31, 33, 34, 36–39, 44, 48, 50, 51, 55, 57, 65	00–17, 19–22, 24, 25, 28, 29, 32, 41, 53, 59, 67, 68, 73
Jason		74, 76–80	75, 81
John	00–25, 50	26, 28, 29, 32, 41, 47, 62–64, 71	27, 30, 31, 33–40, 42–46, 48, 49, 51, 52, 54, 60, 61, 65, 66, 69, 70
Joshua			89, 90, 92, 93, 2000
Matthew		94, 96	82–88, 91, 95, 97–99, 2000–2001
Michael	53, 55–59, 62, 64–98	54, 60, 61, 99, 2000–2002	63
Robert	26–34, 36–39, 41, 44, 48, 51, 54	21–25, 35, 40, 42, 43, 45, 46, 49, 52, 53, 56	18, 47, 50, 55, 57, 58
William		00–20	23, 26

Girls' Names

Name	First Place	Second Place	Third Place
Alexis			99
Amanda			79–82, 86–88, 91
Amy		74–77	73
Anna			00–02
Ashley	88, 91	85–87, 89, 90, 92–95	83, 84, 96
Barbara		37–44	32, 33, 35, 36, 45
Betty		27–34	25
Brittany			89, 90
Deborah		54, 55	53
Debra			56
Dorothy		20–26	12–15, 17–19, 27–31
Emily	95–99, 2000–2002		94
Hannah		98, 99, 2000	2001–2002
Helen		00–02, 04–19	03, 20–24, 26
Jennifer	70–84	69	85
Jessica	85–87, 89, 90, 92–94	78, 80–84, 88, 91, 96	95
Karen			65
Kimberly			67, 68, 70
Linda	47–52	45, 46, 53, 58	54, 55, 57, 59
Lisa	62–69	61, 70	71, 72
Madison		2001–2002	2000
Margaret		03	04–11, 16
Maria		65–67	60, 62–64
Mary	00–46, 53–61	47–52, 62–64	66
Melissa		79	76–78
Michelle		68, 71–73	69, 74, 75
Patricia			37–44, 46–52
Samantha			98
Sarah		97	92, 93
Shirley		35, 36	34
Susan		56, 57, 59, 60	58, 61
Taylor			97

1 You may have students consider or discuss these tables before continuing.

Problem Set G Suggested Grouping: Pairs or Small Groups

This problem set poses a variety of questions about the popularity of various names. Because there is no obvious way to measure popularity, several possible ways to quantify it are suggested.

Before setting students to work, discuss the tables on page 609 as a class; be sure students understand how the tables are set up and what the data in each column mean. Having students work in pairs or small groups can help them interpret the tables and think about trends by presenting different perspectives.

Problem 1 starts by suggesting scanning the "First Place" columns as a natural way to begin. By this measure, it's absolutely clear that over the course of a century the most popular boys' names are Michael and John and the most popular girls' names are Mary and Jennifer. Students may also observe that John and Mary used to be the most common names but haven't been so for many decades. (Despite the common use of "John Smith" and "John Doe" as generic names, note that John hasn't been the number-one name in three quarters of a century, with the single exception of 1950!)

In **Problem 1c,** a point system is suggested. Because calculating points for all the names would be tedious, students are asked to guess at the "candidate names" to evaluate. Note that John rises closer to the top in this new system, and Mary is still way out in front. If it is appropriate for your students, you might ask them to discuss this pair of alternative measures in a voting context; for example, if they were voting for class president, would the results differ if everyone cast 3 votes for their first choice, 2 for their second, and 1 for their third, rather than the traditional method of casting a single vote for one's favorite candidate?

Problem 4 calls for interpretation, and students may have some interesting explanations, especially if some of them have names included in the lists. They may also have some creative ideas about why there are many girls' names with short-term popularity but no such apparent boys' names. Regional differences in first names may show up in your class, depending on where your school is located and how many students have moved from elsewhere. You may want to point out that the names in the table represent popularity of that particular name. Similar names with different spellings were not considered when determining popularity. So, for example, data for the name Sara is not included when determining the popularity of the name Sarah.

After students have answered Problem 4, you might pull the class together to examine the two tables on page 611.

Problem Set G

Michael and Mary were discussing the information in the tables on page 609. Looking at the first table, Michael said, "Hey, I've got the most popular name of the century!"

"Not true," said Mary, who was looking at the second table. "My name is the most popular."

1. Consider how you might decide which name is the most popular for the years listed in the table.

   a. Using the total number of years in first place as your measure, determine the two most popular boys' names and the two most popular girls' names.

   b. Considering the total number of years each name was in first place, who would you say was right, Michael or Mary? Defend your answer.

   c. Lee suggested a different measure: assign 3 points for each first-place appearance, 2 for each second, and 1 for each third. Scan the list to pick out four likely top boys' names and four likely top girls' names, using Lee's measure, and calculate the scores for those eight names. Which two boys' names and two girls' names are rated most popular this way?

2. Which do you think changes more frequently: the popularity of particular boys' names or the popularity of particular girls' names? Write a sentence or two defending your answer.

3. Which names have stayed in the top three for the most *consecutive* years? Explain.

4. Which names made sudden appearances into the top three for only 1 to 3 years and then disappeared? Do you have any explanation for the popularity of these particular names?

Data can be organized in many ways. For example, on the opposite page are two new tables for the girls' names.

   • The first table combines the names into 10-year intervals. The number in parentheses after a name tells how many years in that interval that name was in the given place.

   • The second table gives the number of years each name was in first, second, and third place. It also lists the maximum number of consecutive years each name was in each place.

If you wish, have the class examine these tables. You might ask them which of the three tables (including the "Girls' Names" table on page 609) they like best, and why. This question will be revisited in the Share & Summarize on page 612, though, so let them discuss it just enough to encourage thought about how the information is presented. Problem 5 on page 612 will also get them thinking about the various presentations.

Interval	First Place		Second Place		Third Place	
1900–1909	Mary (10)		Helen (9)	Margaret (1)	Anna (3) Margaret (6)	Helen (1)
1910–1919	Mary (10)		Helen (10)		Margaret (3)	Dorothy (7)
1920–1929	Mary (10)		Dorothy (7)	Betty (3)	Helen (6) Dorothy (3)	Betty (1)
1930–1939	Mary (10)		Betty (5) Barbara (3)	Shirley (2)	Barbara (4) Patricia (3)	Dorothy (2) Shirley (1)
1940–1949	Mary (7)	Linda (3)	Barbara (5) Mary (3)	Linda (2)	Patricia (9)	Barbara (1)
1950–1959	Linda (3)	Mary (7)	Mary (3) Deborah (2)	Linda (2) Susan (3)	Patricia (3) Linda (4) Susan (1)	Deborah (1) Debra (1)
1960–1969	Mary (2)	Lisa (8)	Susan (1) Mary (3) Michelle (1)	Lisa (1) Maria (3) Jennifer (1)	Maria (4) Karen (1) Kimberly (2)	Susan (1) Mary (1) Michelle (1)
1970–1979	Jennifer (10)		Lisa (1) Amy (4) Melissa (1)	Michelle (3) Jessica (1)	Kimberly (1) Amy (1) Melissa (3)	Lisa (2) Michelle (2) Amanda (1)
1980–1989	Jennifer (5) Ashley (1)	Jessica (4)	Jessica (6)	Ashley (4)	Amanda (6) Jennifer (1)	Ashley (2) Brittany (1)
1990–1999	Jessica (4) Emily (5)	Ashley (1)	Ashley (5) Sarah (1)	Jessica (2) Hannah (1)	Brittany (1) Sarah (2) Jessica (1) Taylor (1)	Amanda (1) Emily (1) Ashley (1) Samantha (1) Alexis (1)
2000–2002	Emily (3)		Hannah (1)	Madison (2)	Madison (1)	Hannah (2)

You might ask students to briefly discuss which table they like best, to get them thinking about the different presentations.

Name	Total Years			Maximum Consecutive Years		
	1st Place	2nd Place	3rd Place	1st Place	2nd Place	3rd Place
Alexis	0	0	1	0	0	1
Amanda	0	0	8	0	0	4
Amy	0	4	1	0	4	1
Anna	0	0	3	0	0	3
Ashley	2	9	3	1	4	2
Barbara	0	8	5	0	8	2
Betty	0	8	1	0	8	1
Brittany	0	0	2	0	0	2
Deborah	0	2	1	0	2	1
Debra	0	0	1	0	0	1
Dorothy	0	7	12	0	7	5
Emily	8	0	1	8	0	1
Hannah	0	3	2	0	3	2
Helen	0	19	7	0	16	5
Jennifer	15	1	1	15	1	1
Jessica	8	9	1	3	5	1
Karen	0	0	1	0	0	1
Kimberly	0	0	3	0	0	2
Linda	6	4	4	6	2	2
Lisa	8	2	2	8	1	2
Madison	0	2	1	0	2	1
Margaret	0	1	9	0	1	8
Maria	0	3	4	0	3	3
Mary	56	9	1	47	6	1
Melissa	0	1	3	0	1	3
Michelle	0	4	3	0	3	2
Patricia	0	0	15	0	0	8
Samantha	0	0	1	0	0	1
Sarah	0	1	2	0	1	2
Shirley	0	2	1	0	2	1
Susan	0	4	2	0	2	1
Taylor	0	0	1	0	0	1

LESSON 10.1 Data Patterns in Tables and Graphs **611**

Problem 5 asks students to re-answer some earlier questions in the light of new tables and then to discuss whether the new tables make those analyses easier or harder.

Problem 6 doesn't require the use of any particular table; students may derive their answers from any of the three tables. This rather open-ended question invites a discussion of "major trends" without defining or narrowing that term, and it talks about the beginning, middle, and end of the century without specifying boundaries. One thing that is clear is the complete change in popular girls' names over the course of the century.

Problem 7 describes one of the few situations in which the mode is a more useful measure of central tendency than the mean or the median, although it doesn't mention the word *mode*. This is an opportunity to review the mode; earlier investigations in this lesson have brought up means and medians. This problem is another open-ended problem for which many answers can be defended.

Problem 8 asks for an extrapolation that can be compared to real historical data. You should accept any reasonable response if supported by an appropriate explanation. The actual boys' names most used in 1899 were John, William, and George; the most popular girls' names were Mary, Anna, and Margaret. Of course, George and Margaret could not reasonably be predicted from the given table.

Access
for all **Learners**

Extra Challenge Ask students to think about the information given in the original tables on page 609 and decide what they think the best way to present the data might be. Encourage them to think of presentations other than the three given in this investigation.

You might then direct them to the data on the Social Security Administration Web site, *www.ssa.gov.* (See the Top 10 Services.) The information in the text has been deliberately presented in a form different from that site's table. Students may be interested in whether their decisions about the best presentation is similar to the Social Security Administration's decision; if it isn't, they can compare the Web site's presentation to their own, giving advantages and disadvantages of both.

Share & Summarize

After having been immersed in a great number of details, students now step back and look at the big picture. **Question 1** asks them to compare the tables themselves rather than the data they contain. **Question 2** invites so many possible responses that you may want students to brainstorm individually, then discuss in small groups, and finally report back to the whole class. Those whose names don't appear on the lists—and they will almost certainly be a majority of your students—may well have questions about their own names.

Tips
from **Teachers**

"Depending on the dynamics of my class, I like to invite a brief discussion of the origins of my students' own names."

Troubleshooting If students seem to be having trouble considering advantages and disadvantages of various data presentations, have them look at their answers to Problem 5 again. You also might ask them whether there is any information given in the first table that they can't get from the other two; for example, exact years are not included in the two additional tables. This may also help them consider what data are not given in the first table.

On Your Own Exercises

Practice & Apply: 5–8, pp. 617–621
Connect & Extend: 16–18, pp. 626–628
Mixed Review: 20–33, pp. 629–630

Investigation 4

This investigation presents a real-life historical problem—a *cholera* epidemic in London of 1854—in which both maps and graphs are useful presentations of data that led to a lifesaving conclusion. This interdisciplinary investigation involves history, geography, and science in addition to mathematics.

If students find the use of maps particularly interesting, and if there is time left in the school year, you might follow this investigation with the optional lab investigation presented on Masters 58a–58e in the Teaching Resources. (See pages 615a and 615b.)

• **Teaching notes continued on page A694**

5–8. See Additional Answers.

5. Using the first table on page 611, find the answers to Problem 1 (Parts a and c), Problem 3, and Problem 4 again, for just the girls' names. Then find the answers one more time, using the second table. Describe how each arrangement of the data makes it easier or harder to answer the questions.

6. Describe any major trends you see over the course of the century. For example, can you see any significant differences in popular names toward the end of the century as opposed to the beginning or the middle of the century?

7. Suppose you are designing wall hangings with babies' names on them that you plan to sell through a toy company that distributes nationwide. You want to sell as many as possible, but the toy company has agreed to carry only six boys' names and six girls' names at first, to see how well customers like the product. Predict the most popular names for the current year, and support your prediction with an explanation.

8. Predict the most-used names for 1899 (the year before the data shown in the table). Support your prediction with an explanation.

Share & Summarize

1. Compare the advantages and disadvantages of the three tables in this investigation.   See Additional Answers.

2. Write a question about the most popular names that you would like to answer but don't have enough data to do so.
Possible questions: What are the actual numbers of babies with each name? What names were in fourth place?

 You may want to have students share answers in small groups and then report to the class.

Investigation 4 From Maps to Graphs

As you've seen, a large table filled with data can be hard to analyze. A visual display, such as a graph, of the information in a table sometimes makes essential patterns apparent immediately. A map is sometimes the best visual display of data.

① Possible answer: cities; borders of states and countries; roads and highways; physical characteristics like mountains, lakes, and rivers

② Possible answer: weather maps, infrared (heat) maps, maps of the human brain

Think & Discuss

What sort of geographic data is usually presented on a map?   See ①.

Have you seen maps that present other types of information? What sort of information?   See ②.

② Use these questions to introduce the investigation.

612 CHAPTER 10   Modeling with Data

Additional Answers
Problem Set G
5–8. See page A695.

Share & Summarize

1. Possible answer: The table organized by 10-year intervals is relatively compact, and it was easier to use for some of the questions. The table giving year totals was easy to use to answer all of the questions, but it gives no information about when a particular name was most popular; the other two do. The original table gives the most information, although it isn't easy to read.

Read the text at the top of the page with the class, and have students look at the map. You might want to ask a couple of questions to make sure they are reading the map properly, for example:

How many pump sites are shown on this map? 11

How many cholera deaths occurred in the block next to Saville Row (in the lower-left corner)? 5

Problem Set H Suggested Grouping:
Small Groups or Pairs

This problem set contains an extensive exploration of the use of maps and graphs. The context is a true story in which analysis of a map was key to finding the cause of an epidemic. Each group or pair of students will need a copy of Master 57, which is an enlarged version of the map.

You may want to discuss **Problem 1** as a class. Students should be able to agree that there seem to be more deaths near the center of the map.

Be sure students read the text between Problems 1 and 2, at the bottom of page 613 and the top of page 614. You may want to read this with the whole class.

In 1854, the Broad Street area of London suffered a severe outbreak of *cholera,* a serious bacterial infection of the small intestine. A London physician, John Snow, was determined to stop the spread of this disease.

Dr. Snow recorded the locations of the victims' homes on a map of this section of the city. At the time, London did not have pipes bringing the public water supply directly into homes and business. The map shows the locations of the public pumps that residents used as their water source.

1 Introduce and discuss the map, being sure students are reading it correctly.

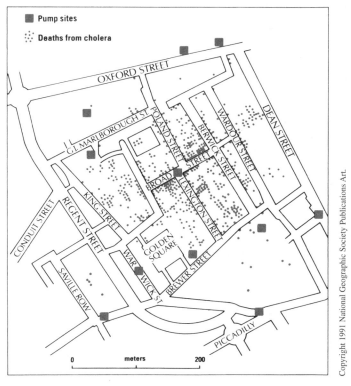

■ Pump sites

⠿ Deaths from cholera

Copyright 1991 National Geographic Society Publications Art.

2 You may have students work in small groups or in pairs after discussing Problem 1 as a class.

3 Be sure students read this text.

MATERIALS

- Snow's map of London
- ruler
- compass
- graph paper

Problem Set H

1. Possible answer: There are many in the center of the map and fewer near the edges.

1. What pattern, if any, do you observe in the deaths?

As Dr. Snow studied the pattern of deaths on the map, he noticed that they seemed to be concentrated in certain locations. Even though many people lived around Oxford Street, Regent Street, and Piccadilly, there were few cholera deaths in those areas. The visual display of deaths on the map convinced him that drinking water was the likely cause of the epidemic—and that the Broad Street pump, where the deaths clustered most densely, might be the source.

LESSON 10.1 Data Patterns in Tables and Graphs **613**

For **Problem 3,** students should draw circles on their copies of the map, using the scale distances they created in **Problem 2** for the radii. (The sample answer for Problem 2 uses the scale for Master 57, not the one for the map in the student text.) The exact center used will vary from student to student, but it should be within the Broad Street pump symbol. Each student should use the same center for all of their circles.

Problems 4 and 5 require careful and detailed counting that may be best done in groups.

Student answers will depend on several things. Exact position of the circles' centers can make a small difference, as can what students do with deaths that occur on a circle (the boundary of two rings) or that are too close together to count accurately. Encourage students to decide for themselves what to do in those cases, but you may need to suggest ideas. For boundary cases, students can consider how much of the symbol is in which ring. If there are several that seem to be cut in half, they might count half of them in one ring and half in the other. For dense areas, students should just make estimates.

If you have students who are particularly adept with their calculators, you might want to let them figure out how to create the histogram for **Problem 6** using a graphing calculator.

Note in **Problem 7** that the greatest number of deaths occur fairly close to the pump, but not in the closest ranges. If students feel that they have done something wrong, encourage them to respond based on the work they have done, even though the data or the analysis seems incorrect. (See the notes for Problem 10.)

Problem 8 demonstrates that measures of central tendency are not applicable to every single-variable context. Because the calculations are not only tedious but ultimately meaningless, students are asked only to interpret measures that have already been calculated.

Dr. Snow was interested in how far each cholera death was from the Broad Street pump. A length representing 200 meters is given on the map. It will be convenient to have a much smaller distance—such as 25 meters—to help you analyze what was happening.

2. Divide the 200-meter length on your map in half to make 100-meter intervals. Divide each part in half again to make 50-meter intervals. Finally, divide each 50-meter segment in half to make 25-meter intervals.   See below.

3. Draw several circles on your map, using the Broad Street pump as the center. Give the circles radii of 25, 50, 75, . . ., and 200 meters. This will create eight rings of 25-meter width about the pump, something like this: See student work.

4. Consider the innermost circle to be Ring 1, and the area between the innermost circle and the next circle to be Ring 2. Count the number of victims who lived within Ring 3. Describe the distance of the residences of this ring from the Broad Street pump.   See below.

5. Count the number of victims who lived in each of the other rings, and list them in a table. You will be adding two more columns to your table later, so leave space.

6. Construct a histogram with the distance from the Broad Street pump on the horizontal axis and the number of victims on the vertical axis. Give each bar a width of 25 meters.

7. Do your table and histogram support the conclusion that there are more deaths closer to the pump? Explain.

8. Kai used his own table to calculate the median, mode, and mean for the distance of the victims' residences from the pump. To make things simpler, he rounded distances according to the number of the ring in which the victim lived. For example, for all people in Ring 1, he used the distance 12.5 m; for Ring 2, he used 37.5 m; and for Ring 3, he used 62.5 m.

Kai found a median of about 87.5 m, a mode of about 62.5 m, and a mean of about 78.3 m. Consider what these measurements might mean in terms of the cholera epidemic. What useful information, if anything, do these statistics reveal about the situation?
Answers will vary, but most students should realize that they don't reveal anything particularly useful.

2. 0   25   50   75   100 125 150 175 200
└─┴─┴─┴─┴─┴─┴─┴─┘

4. Answers will vary, depending on the location of the center of the rings and judgment calls about deaths that occur on their borders. There are approximately 120 deaths within Ring 3. The victims lived from 50 m to 75 m from the pump.

Just the **facts**

The circles you draw in Problem 3 are concentric because they have the same center.

5, 6. See Additional Answers.

7. Possible answer: No; there are more deaths in Ring 3 than any other, and the first ring (closest to the pump) has relatively few deaths.

1 Encourage students to make decisions about ambiguous cases.

2 Encourage students to respond based on their data, even if they feel the data or analysis can't be correct.

614 CHAPTER 10   Modeling with Data

• **Additional Answers on page A695**

Problem 9 raises an important but subtle point: rings of equal width do not have equal area and therefore do not represent equal amounts of land. Using the area of two circles to find the area of a ring might be new to some students. The conclusion here is that using *population density,* or equal-area rings, provides a far stronger correlation with the distance from the Broad Street pump than the count from equal-width rings did. **Problem 10** supports that conclusion in a graph.

Share & Summarize

These questions ask students to look back at all they have done and comment on the uses, and usefulness, of the map, the table, the statistical measures, and the graphs.

Troubleshooting Because of the complexity of this investigation, many students may have difficulty understanding how each problem fits in with the context. Frequent reminders of the historical situation and of Dr. Snow's goals may help them focus on the important issues that mathematics is serving here.

On Your Own Exercises

Practice & Apply: 9, 10, pp. 621–623
Connect & Extend: 19, p. 629
Mixed Review: 20–33, pp. 629–630

Remember

The area of a circle with radius *r* is πr^2.

9a. about 1,963 m²

9b. See the table in the answer to Problem 5.

9. As you counted dots on the map, you might have noticed that each ring covers more area than the next smaller ring. For example, Ring 2 has 3 times the area of Ring 1!

   a. Ring 1 represents a circular piece of land with radius 25 m. What is the area, in square meters, covered by that ring?

   To calculate the area of each ring, you have to find the area of two circles and subtract. For example, the area of the shaded ring to the right is the area of the large circle minus the area of the small circle.

   b. Find the area of each ring, and add a column to your table from Problem 5 to list these new data.

   c. Now, by dividing the number of victims in a ring by the area of that ring, find the number of victims per square meter for each ring. Add another column to your table to record this information, called the *population density* of the victims, to the nearest ten-thousandth.   See the table in the answer to Problem 5.

   d. Does the pattern in the population density support the conclusion that there are more deaths closer to the pump? Explain. See Below.

10. Make a plot of the (*ring number, population density*) data.
   See Additional Answers.

Dr. Snow's presentation, complete with maps and tables, convinced the city administration that water from the Broad Street pump was to blame for the cholera epidemic. When the handle was removed so people could no longer get water from that pump, the epidemic subsided.

Just the facts

Dr. Snow had to work hard to convince people of his conclusions. In the mid–nineteenth century, not much was known about the spread of disease. His work with cholera is a classic example in *epidemiology*, the study of diseases that spread rapidly through a population.

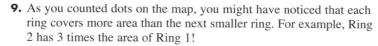

Share & Summarize

1. Consider the map; the table; the mean, median, and mode; the histogram; and the plot showing population density versus ring number. Explain why each is or is not useful in supporting Dr. Snow's conclusion about the relationship between the number of deaths and the distances from the victims' residences to the Broad Street pump.   See Additional Answers.

2. Which display or statistic provides the clearest support for such a connection?   Arguments can be made for either the original map, which gives a lot of information at just a glance, or the population-density plot, which supports the conclusion with numbers.

1 Discuss the usefulness of the various tools used.

9d. Yes; the density increases as you move through the rings toward the pump.

Additional Answers
Problem Set H

10.

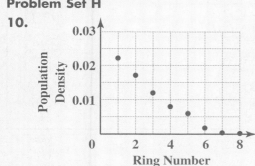

• **Additional Answers continued on page A695**

Lab Investigation

Suggested Grouping: Small Groups

This optional lab investigation extends the use of maps as displays for data by introducing students to a Geographic Information System, or GIS. Professional versions of this software can be extremely helpful in any field in which location is an important part of the data being analyzed. The lab allows students to explore some basic features of GIS software as they examine information displayed on maps of the United States and all of North America.

Materials and Preparation

For this lab, students will need access to a Geographic Information System (GIS) called *ArcVoyager Special Edition* to investigate spatial data. This software is available free from Environmental Systems Research Institute (ESRI); you can request a CD-ROM for both Macintosh and Windows computers from the Web site *www.esri.com*. Look for links to the software for schools and libraries. Allow time for the company to mail the CD. (A downloadable version for the PC, *ArcExplorer*, is also available. However, it differs in several ways from *ArcVoyager*, so you would need to work through this lab on your own before giving it to students so you will be familiar with those differences.)

It is highly recommended that you take the time to work through this lab investigation yourself before presenting it to your students. You may want to explore some of the options not used in the lab or to read through the tutorial supplied in the software's help guide.

It will be easiest if you have a shortcut or alias for the *ArcVoyager* program on the desktops of the computers; then students can just double-click on the icon to start the program. Otherwise, you may need to direct students how to open the program. Consult your computer's help guides for creating shortcuts and aliases, if necessary.

In addition, each student will need a copy of Masters 58a–58e.

What Is a GIS?

This first section gives students an opportunity to see what the GIS screen looks like, and to consider the information given on that screen, without the pressure of trying to create it themselves.

> 1. Possible answer: Earthquakes, and in some cases volcanoes, cluster together to make lines and curves on the map. There are many earthquakes and volcanoes down the western coasts of both North and South America.

Try It Out

You may need to direct students to find the software so they can open it. For the Macintosh version, students will need to click "OK" when the program asks them to wait for the *ArcVoyager Guide,* and again after they have chosen the "US Reference Map."

Give them some time to play with the zoom and pan (hand) tools. Depending on the speed of the computers, redrawing the map with each change can take several seconds.

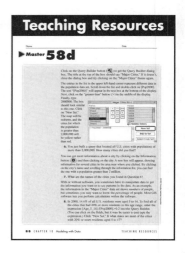

2. Possible answer: There are more major cities near the coastline; many major U.S. cities are in the eastern half of the country.

3. Possible answer: It is easier to see patterns or trends when you zoom out (view more of the country), and it is easier to see individual cities and their sizes when you zoom in.

Make and Test a Hypothesis

4. Hypotheses will vary, and, while many may not seem likely, all should be accepted as long as groups can explain their thinking.

5. Students should test their ideas using appropriate themes. You may need to point out the "Population Density" theme (scrolling down the theme list if necessary) to give students more to work with than just where the large cities are located.

Query the Data

With the Windows version of the software, the yellow symbols might be easier to see if students choose the "Population Density" theme to show the states using a color with greater contrast.

Students may need help typing the expression in **Question 8.** If they double-click on the fields and then type, they will delete the field. After double-clicking, they must click in the text box or use the right cursor arrow to place the cursor at the end of the expression and before the parenthesis, and then type.

6 and 7. There are 3 cities: Los Angeles, Chicago, and New York.

8. Most of the cities are in California and Texas, with a few (including a large city) in Michigan.

What Did You Learn?

Give students time to perform at least one query on their own. Although the directions ask them to use the "Major Cities" data, some may want to use other data sets, for example, looking at earthquakes with high (or low) magnitudes. Using the "Major Cities" data, students may try such queries as the following:

[Asian_pi]/[Pop2000] > 0.25 (More than 25% of the population is Asian or Pacific Islander.)

[Divorced]/([Age_18_64] + [Age_65_up]) > 0.15 (More than 15% of the adult population is divorced.)

[Age_65_up]/[Pop2000] > 0.2 (More than 20% of the residents are age 65 or older.)

Teaching Resources

▶ Master **58e**

On Your Own Exercises

Investigation 1,
   pp. 602–604
Practice & Apply: 1–3
Connect & Extend: 11, 12

Investigation 2,
   pp. 605–608
Practice & Apply: 4
Connect & Extend: 13–15

Investigation 3,
   pp. 608–612
Practice & Apply: 5–8
Connect & Extend: 16–18

Investigation 4,
   pp. 612–615
Practice & Apply: 9, 10
Connect & Extend: 19

Assign Anytime
Mixed Review: 20–33

Exercise 1:

This exercise will probably reinforce the idea that organization is important. Note that two different independent (and non-numerical) variables can be considered here: the store and the artist. You may need to focus students' attention on one of these at a time. If there is time, you may get students engaged in a discussion of real-world pricing, something of considerable interest to most teens.

Exercise 2c:

If students consider only the mean price in their answers, you may want to ask them what they think will happen if Aviva's CD is removed from the table: Would InstantMusic's mean still be lower than Castle's?

Practice & Apply

In Exercises 1–3, use this information:

Economics Ben decided to write an article for the school newspaper comparing compact disk (CD) prices in several stores. He found the prices of five current releases at three local stores and at an Internet music site and listed them in a table.

1. Possible answer: Some stores charge a wide variety of prices, while others have prices that are about the same, except for Aviva, whose CD is higher in all the stores. It also seems that some artists' CDs are priced relatively lower at all the stores and that other artists' CDs, Aviva's in particular, are more expensive.

CD Prices

Store	Artist	Price
Castle	A K Mango	$12.19
Castle	Screaming Screamers	12.50
Castle	Front Street Girls	13.09
InstantMusic	A K Mango	13.25
InstantMusic	Front Street Girls	13.25
InstantMusic	Screaming Screamers	13.49
InstantMusic	Out of Sync	13.59
GLU Sounds	Front Street Girls	13.95
Castle	Out of Sync	14.29
GLU Sounds	A K Mango	14.50
Pineapples	A K Mango	14.99
InstantMusic	Aviva	15.00
GLU Sounds	Out of Sync	15.49
GLU Sounds	Screaming Screamers	15.50
Pineapples	Screaming Screamers	15.99
Pineapples	Front Street Girls	16.00
Pineapples	Out of Sync	16.25
GLU Sounds	Aviva	16.75
Pineapples	Aviva	18.89
Castle	Aviva	19.00

2b. Castle: $14.21; InstantMusic: $13.72; GLU Sounds: $15.24; Pineapples: $16.42

2c. Possible answer: Castle, because they have the lowest price for all but the most expensive CD; or InstantMusic, because they have the lowest mean price.

3b. A K Mango: $13.73; Screaming Screamers: $14.37; Front Street Girls: $14.07; Out of Sync: $14.91; Aviva: $17.41

1. Study Ben's table, and write a brief paragraph describing the most noticeable differences in CD prices.

2. Consider how CD prices vary from store to store.

   a. Reorganize the table to make it easier to compare the stores' prices for the various CDs. (Abbreviate the store and artist names if you want to.)   See Additional Answers.

   b. What is the mean price of the CDs in each store?

   c. Which store would you recommend for the best price in general? Explain your choice.

3. Consider the prices for each artist's CD.

   a. Reorganize the table to make it easier to compare the prices for a particular CD.   See Additional Answers.

   b. What is the mean price of each artist's CD?

 impactmath.com/self_check_quiz

Quick Review
Math Handbook

hot **words**
hot **topics**   Hot Topics
pp. 222–230

• **Additional Answers on page A696**

4. Ecology You can find data about air pollution and other environmental issues on the U.S. Environmental Protection Agency (EPA) web site, *www.epa.gov.*

Garbage-Disposal Methods, 1960–2000
(in millions of tons per year)

	1960	1970	1980	1990	2000
Recycled or Composted	5.6	8.0	14.5	33.2	67.7
Combustion (Burning)	27.0	25.1	13.7	31.9	33.7
Discarded in Landfills	55.5	87.9	123.4	140.1	130.6
Total	88.1	121.1	151.6	205.2	232.0

Source: *Characterization of Municipal Solid Waste in the U.S.: 2001 Update*, U.S. Environmental Protection Agency, Washington, D.C.

Remember

The *percentage increase* is the difference in two quantities divided by the original quantity and expressed as a percentage.

4c. Possible answer: There does seem to have been a dramatic improvement.

4e. Possible answer: People have been recycling increasing portions of their garbage each year.

Ellis and Gabriela want to use the garbage-disposal data to help decide whether people are recycling more or less than they used to.

a. What is the percentage increase in tons of waste recycled or composted in 2000 compared to 1960? about 1,100%

b. Graph the amount of waste recycled or composted over the years 1960–2000. See below left.

c. Ellis argued that the answer to Part a and the graph from Part b show that recycling has improved a great deal in the last few decades. Do you agree? Why or why not?

d. Gabriela argued that they should compute a ratio for each year: the amount of waste recycled or composted to the total amount of waste generated. Make a table showing this ratio, as a decimal, for each year in the original table. Then graph the ratios over the 1960–2000 period. See Additional Answers.

e. What does your graph from Part d tell you about whether people are recycling more or less than they used to?

5. Social Studies In Investigation 3, you considered tables listing the most common names for newborns in the United States. When a name falls from first place, you might expect it to descend slowly, in which case it would appear in the second or third position for a year or two. For which years does this actually happen? Are there years when it doesn't happen (meaning the first-place name must have fallen to fourth place or lower)?
In every case, for boys and girls, when a name dropped out of first place it appeared in second or third place the following year.

4b.
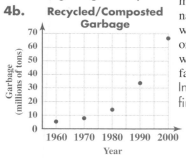
Recycled/Composted Garbage

Additional Answers

4d.

Year	Ratio of Waste Recycled or Composted to Total Generated
1960	0.064
1970	0.066
1980	0.096
1990	0.162
2000	0.292

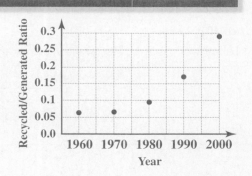

Exercises 6–8:

Students may not be aware that a candidate who wins the plurality of the votes for president in one state normally captures all the electoral votes for that state. Point out that the presidency is one of the few offices for which we do not vote directly and that a candidate can (and often does) receive a majority of the electoral votes without winning a majority of the popular vote.

Each state has an electoral vote equal to the number of members of Congress for that state. This results in non-proportional numbers of electoral votes, since every state has two votes for its senators (two per state) plus a number of votes equal to its number of representatives (which are apportioned proportionally). A small state with 5% of the population of California has three representatives and two senators, for 5 votes. If electoral votes were proportional, California would then need to have 100 votes instead of the 54 it does have.

6a. Answers will vary; there were more Republicans elected.

6b. See Additional Answers.

6c. Possible answer: Add a column listing the number of electoral votes for each state.

6d. Answers will vary. There is no easy way to do this with so many states and so many years; however, students might suggest reordering the table according to the number of electoral votes or repeating a year for every *x* electoral votes a state has. (For example, a student repeating years for every 5 electoral votes would repeat each of MO's entries twice for its 11 electoral votes.)

Social Studies In Exercises 6–8, use the table on the opposite page, which gives the years in which each party's presidential candidates received the most votes in each state from 1948 to 2000.

There were 14 elections during those years. In the table, the two major parties—Democrats and Republicans—have their own categories. All other parties are included in the "Other" category. Note that Alaska (AK) and Hawaii (HI) did not become states until 1959. Also, the District of Columbia (DC), although not a state, received voting status similar to that of each state beginning in 1964.

6. In a presidential election, the candidate receiving the most votes in a state wins that state. Each state counts for a certain number of points, called *electoral votes,* with some states worth more than others because of population differences. For Parts a and b, assume each state is worth the same number of electoral votes.

   a. Just from looking at the table, try to guess whether more Democrats or more Republicans were elected president in the years listed.

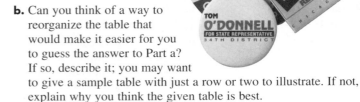

   b. Can you think of a way to reorganize the table that would make it easier for you to guess the answer to Part a? If so, describe it; you may want to give a sample table with just a row or two to illustrate. If not, explain why you think the given table is best.

   Now consider how you might try to make a more accurate guess using each state's actual number of electoral votes. For example, Alaska—and many other states—has only 3 electoral votes, while California has 54.

   c. How might you modify the table to reflect this information?

   d. **Challenge** To determine who actually won each election, you should add the electoral votes of the states that each candidate won. A candidate must have at least 270 electoral votes to win.

   How would you use the number of electoral votes for each state to help guess which party has had more candidates win elections, without actually calculating the winner each year?

Additional Answers

6b. Possible answer: Instead of listing the years for each state, list the states who voted for each party, by year:

Year	Democratic	Republican	Other
1948	AZ, AR, CA, CO, FL, GA, ID, IL, IA, KY, MA, MN, MO, MT, NV, NM, NC, OH, OK, RI, TN, TX, UT, VA, WA, WV, WI, WY	CT, DE, IN, KS, ME, MD, MI, NE, NH, NJ, NY, ND, OR, PA, SD, VT	AL, LA, MS, SC

Years in Which Each Party's Presidential Candidate Received the Most Votes

	Democrat	Republican	Other		Democrat	Republican	Other
AL	52, 56, 60, 76	64, 72, 80, 84, 88, 92, 96, 2000	48, 68	MO	48, 56, 60, 64, 76, 92, 96	52, 68, 72, 80, 84, 88, 2000	
AK	64	60, 68, 72, 76, 80, 84, 88, 92, 96, 2000		MT	48, 64, 92, 96	52, 56, 60, 68, 72, 76, 80, 84, 88, 2000	
AZ	48, 96	52, 56, 60, 64, 68, 72, 76, 80, 84, 88, 92, 2000		NE	64	48, 52, 56, 60, 68, 72, 76, 80, 84, 88, 92, 96, 2000	
AR	48, 52, 56, 60, 64, 76, 92, 96	68, 72, 80, 84, 88, 2000		NV	48, 60, 64, 92, 96	52, 56, 68, 72, 76, 80, 84, 88, 2000	
CA	48, 64, 92, 96, 2000	52, 56, 60, 68, 72, 76, 80, 84, 88		NH	64, 92, 96	48, 52, 56, 60, 68, 72, 76, 80, 84, 88, 2000	
CO	48, 64, 92	52, 56, 60, 68, 72, 76, 80, 84, 88, 96, 2000		NJ	60, 64, 92, 96, 2000	48, 52, 56, 68, 72, 76, 80, 84, 88	
CT	60, 64, 68, 92, 96, 2000	48, 52, 56, 72, 76, 80, 82, 88		NM	48, 60, 64, 92, 96, 2000	52, 56, 68, 72, 76, 80, 84, 88	
DE	60, 64, 76, 92, 96, 2000	48, 52, 56, 68, 72, 80, 84, 88		NY	60, 65, 68, 76, 88, 92, 96, 2000	48, 52, 56, 72, 80, 84	
DC	64, 68, 72, 76, 80, 84, 88, 92, 96, 2000			NC	48, 52, 56, 60, 64, 76	68, 72, 80, 84, 88, 92, 96, 2000	
FL	48, 64, 76, 96	52, 56, 60, 68, 72, 80, 84, 88, 92, 2000		ND	64	48, 52, 56, 60, 68, 72, 76, 80, 84, 88, 92, 96, 2000	
GA	48, 52, 56, 60, 76, 80, 92	64, 72, 84, 88, 96, 2000	68	OH	48, 76, 92, 96	52, 56, 60, 65, 68, 72, 80, 84, 88, 2000	
HI	60, 64, 68, 76, 80, 88, 92, 96, 2,000	72, 84		OK	48, 64	52, 56, 60, 68, 72, 76, 80, 84, 88, 92, 96, 2000	
ID	48, 64	52, 56, 60, 68, 72, 76, 80, 84, 88, 92, 96, 2000		OR	64, 88, 92, 96, 2000	48, 52, 56, 60, 68, 72, 76, 80, 84	
IL	48, 60, 64, 92, 96, 2000	52, 56, 68, 72, 76, 80, 84, 88		PA	60, 64, 68, 76, 92, 96, 2000	48, 52, 56, 72, 80, 84, 88	
IN	64	48, 52, 56, 60, 68, 72, 76, 80, 84, 88, 92, 96, 2000		RI	48, 60, 64, 68, 76, 80, 88, 92, 96, 2000	52, 56, 72, 84	
IA	48, 64, 88, 92, 96, 2000	52, 56, 60, 68, 72, 76, 80, 84		SC	52, 56, 60, 76	64, 68, 72, 80, 84, 88, 92, 96, 2000	48
KS	64	48, 52, 56, 60, 68, 72, 76, 80, 84, 88, 92, 96, 2000		SD	64	48, 52, 56, 60, 68, 72, 76, 80, 84, 88, 92, 96, 2000	
KY	48, 52, 64, 76, 92, 96	56, 60, 68, 72, 80, 84, 88, 2000		TN	48, 64, 76, 92, 96	52, 56, 60, 68, 72, 80, 84, 88, 2000	
LA	52, 60, 76, 92, 96	56, 64, 72, 80, 84, 88, 2000	48, 68	TX	48, 60, 64, 68, 76	52, 56, 72, 80, 84, 88, 92, 96, 2000	
ME	64, 68, 92, 96, 2000	48, 52, 56, 60, 72, 76, 80, 84, 88		UT	48, 64	52, 56, 60, 68, 72, 76, 80, 84, 88, 92, 96, 2000	
MD	60, 64, 68, 76, 80, 92, 96, 2000	48, 52, 56, 72, 84, 88		VT	64, 92, 96, 2000	48, 52, 56, 60, 68, 72, 76, 80, 84, 88	
MA	48, 60, 64, 68, 72, 76, 88, 92, 96, 2000	52, 56, 80, 84		VA	48, 64	52, 56, 60, 68, 72, 76, 80, 84, 88, 92, 96, 2000	
MI	60, 64, 68, 92, 96, 2000	48, 52, 56, 72, 76, 80, 84, 88		WA	48, 64, 68, 88, 92, 96, 2000	52, 56, 60, 72, 76, 80, 84	
MN	48, 60, 64, 68, 76, 80, 84, 88, 92, 96, 2000	52, 56, 72		WV	48, 52, 60, 64, 68, 76, 80, 88, 92, 96	56, 72, 84, 2000	
MS	52, 56	64, 72, 76, 80, 84, 88, 92, 96, 2000	48, 60, 68	WI	48, 64, 68, 76, 88, 92, 96, 2000	52, 56, 60, 72, 80, 84	
				WY	48, 64	52, 56, 60, 68, 72, 76, 80, 84, 88, 92, 96, 2000	

Exercise 7:
You might point out that in analyzing data, it is sometimes necessary to assign a precise definition to a vague term or phrase. Here, the meaning of "largely Democrat" or "largely Republican" is debatable, but students are asked to assume a precise meaning for these terms. Of course, this definition may or may not be the meaning that others would give them.

Exercise 8:
The "other" candidate who received Mississippi's electoral votes in 1960 was actually a Democrat who was not the candidate chosen and endorsed by the Democratic National Convention. In other cases, the candidate was an independent, or third party, candidate.

7a. Democrat: DC, HI, MN; Republican: AK, AZ, CO, ID, IN, KS, MS, NE, NH, ND, OK, SD, UT, VA, WY

7b. Republican: 1964; Democrat: no year

7c. Answers will vary. Sorting the data by the number of times Republicans (or Democrats) won each state might help. The given table seems good because you can just scan the entries for low numbers of years won, although trying to find which years are common to most is a little more difficult with the states in question spread out like this.

In Exercises 7 and 8, refer to the information on pages 618 and 619.

7. Suppose that if the Democratic candidates have lost in a state no more than three times from 1948 to 2000, that state is considered to be "largely Democrat" during this period. Similarly, a state in which the Republican candidates have lost no more than three times is considered "largely Republican" during this period.

a. Name all the states that are largely Democrat or largely Republican, by this definition.

b. For the states that are largely Republican, in which years were most of them won by the Democratic candidate? For the states that are largely Democratic, in which years were most of them won by the Republican candidate?

c. Can you think of a way to reorganize the table that would make it easier to find the answers to Parts a and b? If so, describe it; you may want to give a sample table with just a row or two to illustrate. If not, explain why you think the given table is best.

8. There were a few years in which a candidate other than the Republican or Democratic candidate won a state.

a. List the states and the years. See below.

b. What do you notice about the states? (Hint: Locating them on a map may be helpful.) See Additional Answers.

c. Can you think of a way to reorganize the table that would make it easier to determine the answers to Parts a and b? If so, describe it; you may want to give a sample table with just a row or two to illustrate. If not, explain why you think the given table is best.

Answers will vary. Because there were so few of these states, the given table works as well as any other, although the fact that all the states are Southern would have been immediately obvious if the table were organized by region.

8a. Alabama, Georgia, Louisiana, Mississippi, and South Carolina; 1948, 1960, and 1968

Additional Answers

8b. Possible answer: Most of the states choosing the "other" candidate in 1948 also chose the "other" candidate in 1960; all five states choosing "other" candidates were Southern states, four east of the Mississippi River.

In Exercises 9 and 10, use this information:

Social Studies Aftermath Inc. offers after-school math classes for seventh and eighth graders in Massachusetts. During one year, 603 students were enrolled in the program. Use the following data, which show the number of students in Aftermath, the total population of seventh and eighth graders, and the percentage of the seventh- and eighth-grade population enrolled.

Students Enrolled in Aftermath

City or Town	Number Enrolled	Population (Grades 7–8)	Percent Enrolled
Boston	98	8,873	1.104
Braintree	40	828	4.831
Brockton	2	2,505	0.080
Brookline	52	899	5.784
Cambridge	3	1,061	0.283
Canton	35	433	8.083
Cohasset	5	191	2.618
Dedham	29	457	6.346
Duxbury	2	461	0.434
Easton	26	537	4.842
Hanover	2	390	0.513
Hingham	45	511	8.806
Mansfield	18	535	3.364
Marshfield	2	688	0.291
Medfield	2	347	0.576
Milton	77	630	12.222
Needham	5	605	0.826
Newton	7	1664	0.421
Norwell	17	286	5.944
Quincy	69	1,290	5.349
Randolph	4	646	0.619
Westwood	52	330	15.758

Source: Adapted from information at the Massachusetts Department of Education Web site, *www.doe.mass.edu.*

9c. Answers will vary. Luna's reasoning seems more solid; it's likely that Boston sends more just because it has so many seventh and eighth graders. However, there are many reasons Westwood might have a greater fraction: some special arrangement between Westwood and Aftermath; the program has become popular there and spread by word of mouth; the schools have no extra-help programs of their own, or perhaps it's an affluent city whose citizens can more easily afford to send their children to such a program.

9. Luna suspects that the town or city sending the *most* students must be where Aftermath is located. Orlando thinks the town or city sending the greatest *percentage* of students must be where Aftermath is located.

a. Which town or city sends the most students to Aftermath? Boston

b. Which town or city sends the greatest percentage of its seventh and eighth graders to Aftermath? Westwood

c. Who do you think is more likely to be correct, Luna or Orlando? Explain your reasoning.

10. Geography For this exercise, refer to the information on page 621.

This is a map of Eastern Massachusetts.

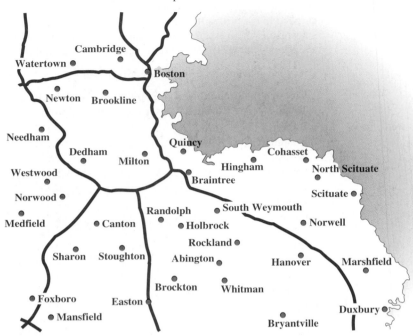

10a. Cambridge is farthest north, Mansfield is farthest south, Medfield is farthest west, and Duxbury is farthest east.

10b. Possible answer: Braintree or Quincy

10c. It removes Medfield and Duxbury from their positions as farthest west and east, respectively, making Needham farthest west and Norwell farthest east. Braintree or Quincy is still in the middle.

a. Of all the cities and towns that send any number of students to Aftermath, which is farthest north? Farthest south? Farthest west? Farthest east?

b. Lydia suspects that Aftermath is located somewhere in the middle of all the towns and cities listed in the table. Where would that be?

c. Consider only cities and towns sending three or more students. How does that change your answers to Parts a and b?

d. Explain why it might be reasonable to exclude towns with fewer than three students from your analysis.

e. Make your best guess about the location of the Aftermath program, and explain your reasoning.

10d. If a town sends only one or two students, it might not mean anything statistically or geographically. They might be children of faculty members, for example.

10e. Possible answer: Braintree or Quincy because they are the most central.

622 CHAPTER 10 Modeling with Data

Connect & Extend

In Exercises 11 and 12, use this information:

An important branch of mathematics is *cryptology,* the study of making and breaking codes. Its uses range from deciphering intercepted enemy messages in wartime to encrypting credit card information over the Internet.

A simple—but not very secure!—method of sending secret messages is the use of a substitution table. This method is used in cryptogram puzzles in your daily newspaper. To send a message, it is helpful to present the entries in a substitution table in alphabetical order, like this:

Input	a	b	c	d	e	f	g	h	i	j	k	l	m	n	o	p	q	r	s	t	u	v	w	x	y	z
Output	C	F	I	L	O	R	U	X	A	D	G	J	M	P	S	V	Y	B	E	H	K	N	Q	T	W	Z

Remember

This table represents a *function* since it provides a unique output for each input.

To avoid confusion, it's useful to use lower-case letters for your original (English) message and upper-case letters for your secret message, as the table shows. To write a message, look up each letter in the top row and change it to the corresponding letter in the bottom row. For example, to write "come here," you would send ISMO XOBO.

11. Using the original table as it is sorted is a nuisance when you are *deciphering* a message.

11b. See Additional Answers.

    a. Suppose you receive the message BOHKBP AMMOLACHOJW. Translate it into plain English. "return immediately"

    b. Make a new table in which the *outputs* are in alphabetical order.

    c. Use your new table to decipher the message WSK CBO ISB-BOIH. "you are correct"

Just the facts

Cryptology played a part in the victory of the Allies in World War II. Mathematician Alan Turing, among others, had a critical role in breaking the Enigma code used by the Germans.

Exercises 11 and 12: Concern about security and privacy over the Internet, where data such as e-mail messages and credit-card numbers are often encrypted, has revived interest in cryptology. The systems used on the Internet are of course far more sophisticated than the system described in these problems. Students who are particularly interested in this topic might enjoy doing some library or Internet research on the topic.

Additional Answers

11b. In this version the two rows have been interchanged, since it's conventional to work from top to bottom.

A	B	C	D	E	F	G	H	I	J	K	L	M	N	O	P	Q	R	S	T	U	V	W	X	Y	Z
i	r	a	j	s	b	k	t	c	l	u	d	m	v	e	n	w	f	o	x	g	p	y	h	q	z

Exercise 12:
Students who are interested in puzzles like these (often called *cryptograms*) may be able to find more in a daily newspaper or magazines such as *Games*. The following is a more detailed way to use the frequency table to analyze the message:

The two most frequent letters in the message are "L" and "K" and in English are "e" and "t." The 2-letter word "LC" is probably "to," since "e_" doesn't give a common English word. That means "K" is probably "e." "CSL" is then "o_t" so it's likely "out." The next four most frequent letters are "C," "E," "I," and "M"; these are probably four of "a," "i," "n," "o," and "r"; though "C" may be "o," as already guessed. First words in a sentence beginning with "T" are often "th" words, like "the" or "this." So if "F" is "h," the first word may begin with "th" and be followed by a 2-letter word that happens to be the last 2 letters of the first word: "this is" comes to mind. "IV" must have a vowel; "a" is the only one left (other than "y"), so it's probably "an." (It can't be "at" or "as" because "t" and "s" are taken.) "KIEU" is "eas_," so "U" is probably "y." The rest, one might guess at using the deciphered words as clues.

a	7.3
b	0.9
c	3.0
d	4.4
e	13.0
f	2.8
g	1.6
h	3.5
i	7.4
j	0.2
k	0.3
l	3.5
m	2.5
n	7.8
o	7.4
p	2.7
q	0.3
r	7.7
s	6.3
t	9.3
u	2.7
v	1.3
w	1.6
x	0.5
y	1.9
z	0.1

Source: Trinity College Web site, *www.trincoll.edu/depts/cpsc/cryptography/caesar.html*.

Just the facts

The construction of secret messages is cryptography. Breaking codes is cryptanalysis. Both are part of cryptology.

12. **Challenge** Refer to the information on page 623.

If you intercept someone else's encrypted message and don't know the table that was used to construct it, you have a problem to solve: breaking the code.

To solve a code, it is helpful to have some idea of which letters are most frequent in English and what combinations of letters are typical. In the short encoded message in Part a of Exercise 11, for instance, the letter "O" occurs three times; since "e" is the most common letter in English, you might guess (correctly) that "O" represents "e" in this message.

The table at left shows one estimate of the frequencies of letters in English text, as percentages.

a. Use the letter frequencies as a guide in attempting to translate the message below. It will help to start with a blank table in which the inputs are in alphabetical order. Fill in your guesses about the outputs (in pencil!) as you go along, and soon a pattern will emerge. "this is not an easy example to figure out"

b. Explain how you solved Part a. See Additional Answers.

The table above comes from a Web site. You can find letter-frequency tables from many sources that differ in the percentages assigned to the letters of the alphabet.

c. Explain why sources might have apparently contradictory tables for frequencies of letters in English. See below.

d. Explain why a particular message, like the one above, might *not* have the same letter frequencies as those in the table. See Additional Answers.

12c. Possible answer: The sources from which the data were gathered probably differ.

Additional Answers

12b. Possible answer: You can find the frequency of each letter in the coded message and compare it to the letter-frequency table; all the letters in the coded message may not appear with exactly the same frequency, but you can get some helpful information.

12d. Possible answer: Specific texts vary in their letter frequencies (for example, a short passage might include no e's but would still contain vowels), use of words in a particular context (for example, a discussion of zoos might have more z's than is typical), and even deliberate efforts to confuse (for example, if you knew your message might be intercepted, you might intentionally write something with unusual letter frequencies).

In Exercises 13–15, use this information:

Ecology Automobiles are an essential mode of transportation at this point in U.S. history. Unfortunately, they are also a major source of air pollution. In recent years, a series of technological improvements has reduced the amount of pollution emitted per mile driven, but people are driving more miles.

The following figure includes a line graph and a bar graph. The line graph displays the average per-vehicle emissions (estimated) from 1960 through 2015. The bar graph shows the vehicle miles traveled (in billions) for these years. Certain assumptions have been made for the estimates of future emissions, such as no increase in regulations, no cutbacks in driving, and no unexpected improvements in technology.

Exercises 13–15:
The actual data in this exercise are augmented with projected data. By this point, students are very familiar with this kind of pairing of the real with the projected.

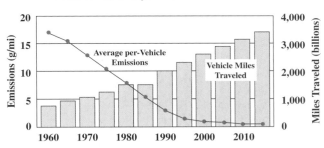

Comparison of the Number of Miles Driven and Emissions per Vehicle in the U.S.

Source: "Automobiles and Ozone," Fact Sheet OMS-4 of the Office of Mobile Sources, the U.S. Environmental Protection Agency, Jan 1993.

13. Possible answer: Yes; they have been (or even have more than made up for it), but the assumptions for the future are that they will not continue to do so.

14. See Additional Answers.

13. At first glance, do the improvements (as indicated by the line graph) seem to be keeping up with the increase in miles driven (as indicated by the bar graph)? Explain.

14. Paul claimed that the total amount of pollutants produced by cars in 2010 will be less than that in 1960 due to technological improvements. Sara claimed that the total amount of pollutants from cars will be greater in 2010 than in 1960. Who do you think is correct? Explain your answer, using the graphs to justify your reasoning.

LESSON 10.1 Data Patterns in Tables and Graphs **625**

Additional Answers

14. Possible answer: Paul; in 1960, there were approximately 750 billion vehicle miles with emissions of about 17 g/mi, for about 12.8 trillion grams of hydrocarbon; in 2010, there were approximately 3.15 trillion miles at about 0.5 g/mi, for about 1.6 trillion grams of hydrocarbon. So, there is less hydrocarbon expected in 2010 than there was in 1960.

15b. See Additional Answers.

15c. It increased and then decreased, and from the graph we expect it to be about the same (slight increase) from 2010 to 2015.

15d. Possible answer: Per-vehicle emissions could stay at about 0.5 g/mi; assuming vehicle miles traveled is increasing linearly, the miles traveled would be about 4,150 billion.

15e. Possible answer: Using 0.5 g/mi emission and 4,150 billion miles traveled, about 2,075 billion grams.

Just the facts

Earthquake data are collected and exchanged by countries throughout the world. Teams of scientists examine the data in hopes of discovering patterns that might allow them to predict future earthquakes.

15. Use the graphs on page 625 to create a new graph by following these directions.

a. Complete the following table, giving an approximation of the average amount of emissions from cars each year.

Note: Values in table are approximations.

Year	Average per-Vehicle Emissions (grams of hydrocarbon per mile)	Vehicle Miles Traveled (billions)	Total Emissions (billions of grams of hydrocarbon)
1960	17	750	12,750
1965	15.5	950	14,725
1970	13	1,150	14,950
1975	10.5	1,250	13,125
1980	7.5	1,500	11,250
1985	5.5	1,500	8,250
1990	3	2,000	6,000
1995	1.5	2,300	3,450
2000	1	2,600	2,600
2005	0.75	2,850	2,138
2010	0.5	3,150	1,575
2015	0.5	3,400	1,700

b. Draw a graph displaying the average number of grams of hydrocarbon produced per year for each year on the original graphs.

c. Describe how the amount of hydrocarbon produced by cars changed over the observed and predicted years.

d. Use the graphs to predict the average per-vehicle emissions and vehicle miles traveled in 2030.

e. Calculate the estimated grams of hydrocarbon that cars will produce in 2030, and add these data to your graph.

16. Earth Science Diana decided to do her science project on the frequency of earthquakes. She already knew that an earthquake's magnitude is sometimes measured on a scale of positive numbers called the *Richter scale*. This scale is not linear: a quake measuring 7 is very severe—10 times as severe as one measuring 6; a quake measuring 8 is devastating.

Diana conjectured that there were more earthquakes of higher magnitude than lower. She explained her hypothesis by saying that she often reads about major earthquake disasters but rarely hears about small quakes. Do you agree with Diana's hypothesis? If not, why not? See Additional Answers.

Additional Answers

15b. Possible graph:

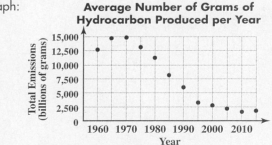

Average Number of Grams of Hydrocarbon Produced per Year

16. Possible answer: Her hypothesis is not very reasonable. Large earthquakes are more newsworthy and probably not more frequent.

In Exercises 17 and 18, use this information:

Earth Science Diana (see Exercise 16) browsed through earthquake pages on the Internet and found the U.S. Geological Survey National Earthquake Information Center. The following table was on one of their Web pages.

17b, c. See Additional Answers.

17d. Possible answer: Although you can see from looking at the table that decreasing magnitude results in a very sharp increase in the average number of earthquakes, the histogram makes the pattern more dramatic.

Just the facts

Major earthquakes, which can result in the deaths of thousands of people, occur along the edges of large fragments of Earth's crust—called *plates*—that grind together as they shift.

Table 1
Frequency of Occurrence of Earthquakes

Description	Magnitude	Average Number Annually
Great	8 and higher	1
Major	7–7.9	17
Strong	6–6.9	134
Moderate	5–5.9	1,319
Light	4–4.9	13,000 (estimated)
Minor	3–3.9	130,000 (estimated)
Very Minor	2–2.9	1,300,000 (estimated)

Source: U.S. Geological Survey National Earthquake Information Center Web site, *wwwneic.cr.usgs.gov.*

17. Look carefully at Table 1.

   a. Do the data support Diana's hypothesis (in Exercise 16)? no

   b. Use the data from Table 1 to construct a histogram that shows the average annual number of earthquakes at each magnitude level. Give each bar a width of 1 unit of Richter magnitude.

   c. What significant difficulties did you have when constructing your histogram?

   d. Does your histogram emphasize any patterns that connect frequency with magnitude?

Additional Answers

17b.

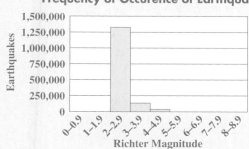

Frequency of Occurence of Earthquakes

17c. If the histogram is on a sheet of paper of reasonable size, the bars for earthquakes of magnitude greater than 4 will be so short they can't be read.

18. Diana (see Exercises 16 and 17) had a second hypothesis: that the frequency of earthquakes increased during the twentieth century. Again, she referred to the coverage of earthquakes in the news media: "Every year we hear about more of them!"

She then found a table that appeared to trace the magnitude and frequency of quakes from the years 1992 to 2003.

Table 2

Magnitude	1992	1993	1994	1995	1996	1997	1998	1999	2000	2001	2002	2003
8.0–9.9	0	1	2	3	1	0	1	0	1	1	0	1
7.0–7.9	23	15	13	22	21	16	11	18	14	15	13	13
6.0–6.9	104	141	161	185	160	129	117	128	158	126	132	128
5.0–5.9	1,541	1,449	1,542	1,327	1,223	1,118	979	1,106	1,345	1,243	1,198	954
4.0–4.9	5,196	5,034	4,544	8,140	8,794	7,938	7,303	7,042	8,045	8,084	8,603	7,121
3.0–3.9	4,643	4,263	5,000	5,002	4,869	4,467	5,945	5,521	4,784	6,151	7,004	6,524
2.0–2.9	3,068	5,390	5,369	3,838	2,388	2,397	4,091	4,201	3,758	4,162	6,420	6,652
1.0–1.9	887	1,177	779	645	295	388	805	751	1,026	944	1,137	2,101
0.1–0.9	2	9	17	19	1	4	10	5	5	1	10	107

Source: U.S. Geological Survey National Earthquake Information Center Web site, *wwwneic.cr.usgs.gov.*

18a. Possible answers: It does seem like there have been more earthquakes in the years towards the end of the 20th century than might be expected. In general, though, the figures are slightly below the century-long averages, except in the 5.0–5.9 ages.

18c. All magnitudes under 4; according to Table 1, these low magnitudes should be registering thousands, hundreds of thousands, even millions of quakes for the lowest magnitudes, but Table 2 shows hundreds down to single digit for the lowest magnitudes.

a. Look carefully at Table 2. Do the data seem to support Diana's hypothesis at any or all magnitude levels?

b. In which years from 1992 to 2003 did the number of earthquakes with magnitude 7.0–7.9 reach or exceed the long-term average given in Table 1 on page 627? 1992, 1995, 1996, 1999

c. If you compare the two tables, something seems very wrong. For which magnitudes of earthquakes are the data in Table 2 *so* different from the data in Table 1 that you just can't believe they are correct? Explain.

d. Returning to the Internet, Diana examined Table 2 more closely. She discovered that this table includes only those earthquakes whose locations could be determined by the Geological Survey National Earthquake Information Center. How does this information explain the surprising numbers in Table 2? See below.

e. Describe at least two ways to use the data in Table 2 to better analyze the patterns in the table. (Ignore the rows for magnitudes less than 4.) Possible answer: Find averages for the given years; graph the data for each magnitude.

18d. Possible answer: Earthquakes with magnitudes under 4 are probably not strong enough for their locations to be determined by an instrument that is not close by.

19. Answers will vary.

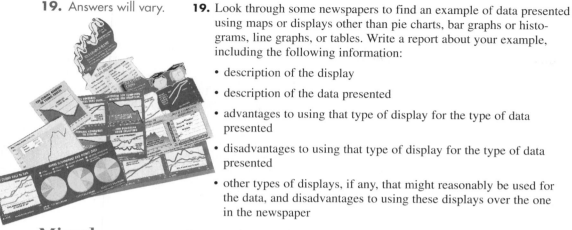

19. Look through some newspapers to find an example of data presented using maps or displays other than pie charts, bar graphs or histograms, line graphs, or tables. Write a report about your example, including the following information:

- description of the display

- description of the data presented

- advantages to using that type of display for the type of data presented

- disadvantages to using that type of display for the type of data presented

- other types of displays, if any, that might reasonably be used for the data, and disadvantages to using these displays over the one in the newspaper

Mixed Review

Factor each expression.

20. $2n^2 - 6n$ $2n(n - 3)$

21. $4a^2 - 1$ $(2a + 1)(2a - 1)$

22. $3x^2 - 9x - 30$ $3(x + 2)(x - 5)$

Expand and simplify each expression.

23. $2(g + 3)(2g - 7) + g(2g^2 + 3)$ $2g^3 + 4g^2 + g - 42$

24. $x + 2 - (x + 1)(3x + 4) + 2(8 - x)$ $-3x^2 - 8x + 14$

25. $0.5t + 3t - 1.5(t + 1)(7t + 1)$ $-10.5t^2 - 8.5t - 1.5$

Make a rough sketch showing the general shape and location of the graph of each equation.

26. $y = x^2 - 3x - 4$

27. $y = \frac{3}{x - 1} + 2$

28. $y = x^3 + 3$

Evaluate or simplify without using a calculator.

29. $\left(\frac{1}{7}\right)^3$ $\frac{1}{343}$

30. $2\sqrt[4]{81a^6}$, where a is nonnegative

31. 3^{-3} $\frac{1}{27}$

32. $\sqrt[3]{\left(\frac{8}{125}\right)^2}$ $\frac{4}{25}$

26.

27.

28.

30. $6a\sqrt[4]{a^2}$ or $6a\sqrt{a}$

Quick Check

Informal Assessment
Students should be able to:

✔ sort and organize data appropriately

✔ use tables, graphs, and maps to reveal trends that may not be obvious in data

✔ interpret data in a plausible manner

33. Statistics Surveys are often used to estimate a characteristic of a large group of people based on a relatively small group of people.

For example, a recent study found that about 1,050 of the 1,500 American adults surveyed said they found news helpful when making practical decisions, but only about 795 trusted what their local television anchors told them. Network anchors were believed by about 675 people, newspaper reporters by about 465, and radio talk-show hosts by only 210 people.

There were about 200 million American adults in the year of the survey. As you answer the following questions, assume the survey's sample was representative of all American adults at that time. That is, assume the proportions in the sample are the same as the proportions for all American adults.

33a. $\frac{1,050}{1,500} = \frac{x}{200,000,000}$; about 140,000,000; 70%

a. Set up and solve a proportion to estimate how many American adults found news helpful when making practical decisions. What percentage is this?

33b. $\frac{795}{1,500} = \frac{x}{200,000,000}$; about 106,000,000; 53%

Set up and solve a proportion to estimate how many American adults trust each of the following news sources. Then find the estimated percentage of American adults who trust each news source.

33c. $\frac{675}{1,500} = \frac{x}{200,000,000}$; about 90,000,000; 45%

b. local television anchors

c. network anchors

33d. $\frac{465}{1,500} = \frac{x}{200,000,000}$; about 62,000,000; 31%

d. newspaper reporters

e. radio talk-show hosts

33e. $\frac{210}{1,500} = \frac{x}{200,000,000}$; about 28,000,000; 14%

630 CHAPTER 10   Modeling with Data

• *Quick Quiz on page A697*

10.2

Models, Data, and Decisions

Objectives

▶ To make predictions from data

▶ To create an economic model for a simple business

▶ To create a population model and use it to make predictions

Overview (pacing: about 5 class periods)

In this lesson, students will go beyond the process of drawing direct conclusions from data to construct mathematical models. They will use their models to interpret data and make predictions.

Advance Preparation

In Investigation 1, students will need graph paper; you may want to distribute copies of Master 60, Fitting Curves on the Texas Instruments T1-83 Plus, as well. Graph paper will also be useful in Investigations 2 and 4.

Lesson Planner

	Summary	Materials	On Your Own Exercises	Assessment Opportunities
Investigation 1 page T632	Students create models to fit data and use the models to make predictions.	• Graphing calculator • Graph paper • Master 60 (optional)	Practice & Apply: 1, 2, p. 642 Connect & Extend: 8, 9, pp. 645–646 Mixed Review: 16–28, pp. 650–651	On the Spot Assessment, page T633 Share & Summarize, pages T634, 634 Troubleshooting, page T634
Investigation 2 page T634	Students analyze a business and create a simple model for it.	• Graphing calculator • Graph paper (optional)	Practice & Apply: 3, 4, p. 643 Connect & Extend: 10, pp. 647–648 Mixed Review: 16–28, pp. 650–651	Share & Summarize, pages T636, 636 Troubleshooting, page T636
Investigation 3 page T636	Students explore a model for starting a new business and consider a variety of variables and possibilities.	• Computers with spreadsheet software (optional)	Practice & Apply: 5, 6, p. 644 Connect & Extend: 11–14, p. 648 Mixed Review: 16–28, pp. 650–651	Share & Summarize, pages T637, 637 Troubleshooting, page T637
Investigation 4 page T638	Students investigate model populations, specifically, handedness in humans.	• Graph paper or protractor	Practice & Apply: 7, p. 644 Connect & Extend: 15, p. 649 Mixed Review: 16–28, pp. 650–651	Share & Summarize, pages T641, 641 Troubleshooting, page T641 Informal Assessment, page 651 Quick Quiz, page 651

Think & Discuss

1. You can introduce this lesson with the Think & Discuss, which sets the stage for the data interpretation in the first investigation.

2. Read the introductory text with the class. It will help if you let students work for a brief time, perhaps in pairs, to calculate the average speed of the rocket over each 2-second time interval. Then bring the class together to discuss the questions.

10.2 Models, Data, and Decisions

In Lesson 10.1, you drew conclusions directly from data. In this lesson, you will construct mathematical models to help you interpret data sets and make predictions from them.

Think & Discuss

Every detail about a rocket launch is controlled by computers. Suppose that for one launch, a computer calculated the height of the rocket every 2 seconds and produced the following data.

Time (s)	Height (m)	Time (s)	Height (m)
0	0	14	1,344
2	48	16	1,704
4	144	18	2,064
6	288	20	2,424
8	480	22	2,784
10	720	24	3,144
12	1,008	26	3,504

① The speed increases for the first 14 s and stays constant afterward.

② about 14 s

③ Answers will vary. At launch, a rocket begins to eject gas at a fairly high speed, decreasing its own mass and increasing its own velocity. The loss of mass is continuous until all the fuel has been burned, at which point the rocket would travel at a constant speed (ignoring air resistance and other external forces).

- Describe what is happening to the *rate* at which the rocket's height changes over the 26 seconds that are recorded. See ①.

- At what time does the nature of the rocket's motion change? See ②.

- Do you think the computed data are reasonable? Why or why not? See ③.

1 Use this activity to introduce the lesson.

2 You might let students work in pairs to calculate the average speed over each interval.

LESSON 10.2 Models, Data, and Decisions **631**

Investigation 1

This investigation moves from the analysis of data called for in the Think & Discuss on page 631 to predictions that go beyond the data. Students will model data using different types of relationships.

1 You can segue from the Think & Discuss into Problem Set A by pointing out that if students can write an equation or equations that fit the data, they can estimate the rocket's heights at times other than those listed.

2 **Problem Set A** Suggested Grouping: Pairs
This problem set begins by asking students to construct a graph, which is the most immediate way to see the behavior of the rocket's motion, even for people who do not primarily think in visual ways.

Problem 2a has students compute first and second differences up to the break point; students should see that the initial motion is quadratic. In **Problem 2b** they use their calculators to find a quadratic expression for the data, a process similar to that for linear regression, which students used in Chapter 1. The directions below, for the Texas Instruments TI-83 Plus graphing calculator, are reproduced on Master 60, which you may want to distribute to students. (Steps 4 and 5 on the master include the possibility of linear and exponential relationships as well.)

1. Enter the data into lists L1 and L2. Use L1 for the independent variable. (See Master 56 for instructions on entering data, if needed.)

2. Access the STAT menus by pressing [STAT].

3. Press [→] to highlight **CALC** at the top of the screen.

4. Select **5:QuadReg** by pressing [5] or by pressing [↓] four times and then pressing [ENTER].

5. Press [ENTER]. The display will give values for a, b, and c to use in the equation $y = ax^2 + bx + c$.

For **Problem 3,** students can use linear regression for the data from the break point on, or they can use the constant difference as the slope and calculate the y-intercept.

In **Problem 4,** students consider when each equation should be used. Some may be unsure what to do for $t = 14$. Ideally, students should restrict that input to one or the other equation, but it doesn't matter in which domain they choose to include it.

About the Mathematics

The height of the rocket is a function of time. Because it requires more than one function rule, the height function is call a *piecewise-defined function*; that is, it's defined in two pieces, for time before and including 14 seconds and for time after 14 seconds:

$$h(t) = \begin{cases} 6t^2 + 12t & \text{if } 0 \leq t \leq 14 \\ 180t - 1{,}176 & \text{if } t > 14 \end{cases}$$

Note that in this function definition, the quadratic expression is used to calculate $h(14)$. Because the two expressions are equal when $t = 14$, the definition could have required using the linear expression for $h(14)$.

3 **Problem Set Wrap-Up** Review students' equations for Problems 2b and 3b and their predictions for **Problem 5**. Although most students will probably use their equations for Problem 5, some may prefer to use a table or a graph to make each prediction. You may want to ask students to discuss the advantages and disadvantages of each method. Some people are helped by the precision of the table, others by the visual immediacy of the graph. Tell students that this process of modeling data using equations is an important application of mathematics, used in both business (finance, economics, marketing, and so on) and scientific (physics, chemistry, ecology, and so on) settings.

Investigation ▶ 1 ◀ Data and Algebra

If you can write equations that describe the rocket-launch data given on page 631, you will be able to predict the rocket's height at times not given in the table.

page 631

MATERIALS
• graph paper
• graphing calculator

Problem Set A

1. Draw a graph by plotting the rocket-launch data. Use the horizontal axis for time since launch (in seconds) and the vertical axis for height (in meters). Connect the points using line segments.

2. The point at which the nature of the data changes is called a *break point*. Consider just the data points up to the break point you identified in the Think & Discuss.

   a. Calculate the first and second differences between the height values. What type of relationship does there seem to be between time and height?

   In Chapter 1, you used a graphing calculator to find a *line of best fit* for data that seemed approximately linear. In the same way, you can use your calculator to fit curves to data that show nonlinear trends.

   b. Enter the data for the points before the break point. Then use your calculator to find an equation of the type you answered in Part a that describes the relationship between time t and height h.

3. Now consider just the data beginning with the break point and continuing after that point.

   a. What type of relationship does there appear to be between time and height for these data?   linear

   b. Write an equation that describes the relationship between time t and height h for these data. $h = 180t - 1{,}176$

4. For what times should you use the equation you wrote in Problem 2 to estimate the rocket's height? For what times should you use your equation from Problem 3?   times up to 14 s, times beyond 14 s

5. Predict the rocket's height at 3 seconds, 15 seconds, and 23 seconds.

2a. First differences are 48, 96, 144, 192, 240, 288, 336; all second differences are 48; quadratic.

2b. $h = 6t^2 + 12t$

5. 90 ft; 1,524 ft; 2,964 ft

1.

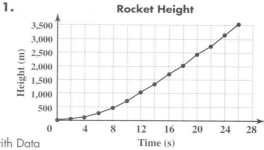

Rocket Height

(Height (m) on vertical axis from 0 to 3,500; Time (s) on horizontal axis from 0 to 28)

---

1 Point out that with equations that fit the data, students can estimate the rocket's height at the other times.

2 You may have students work in pairs.

3 Problem-Solving Strategies

• Use a graph
• Make a table

1 Read the text at the top of the page with the class.

If you wish, point out that the rocket data are perfectly quadratic from 0 to 14 seconds and perfectly linear after 14 seconds. Then ask students whether they think the data are real or fictitious. They should recognize that real data isn't likely to follow equations so precisely.

You might then point out that while this is true, it's still reasonable for a model rocket to follow equations closely. For other data sets, such as human activities (including population growth), it might be even more difficult to fit an equation closely. In Problem Set B, students will work with such a data set.

2 ### Problem Set B Suggested Grouping: Pairs
In a transition from Problem Set A, students move from the relatively predictable behavior of a model rocket to the less predictable behavior of masses of human beings. Population growth is often exponential, although a wide variety of factors can influence a simple exponential model.

For Problems 1 thru 3, students use their graphing calculators. You may want to give them copies of Master 62, Blank Calculator Graphs, for recording rough sketches of their graphs. It's best not to require a high degree of accuracy here; their sketches should just be enough to help you see that they produced a graph with more or less the correct shape.

3 For **Problem 1,** students use their calculators to plot the (*year, population*) data and connect the points with line segments. To make a line graph, students can follow the instructions for making a scatterplot except for the choice of the type of plot. On the Texas Instruments TI-83 Plus, the first "Type" icon is a scatterplot and the second is a line plot. (See Master 56 for more complete instructions for the TI-83 Plus.)

You may want to help students create the graph, and then ask:

> Are there sections of the graph that seem very different from other sections? *Possible answer: It seems that population didn't grow as rapidly as one might have expected around the 1930s.*

> Can you think of any reasons for the difference? *Depending on students' history backgrounds, they might say that perhaps there was less migration into California at that time, or perhaps there was less population growth in general because of the Depression.*

 4 In **Problem 2,** students will need to use *exponential regression* to fit a curve to the data. You shouldn't need to explain this to the whole class, except maybe to point out that this is the same process they used for the quadratic regression in Problem Set A. The only difference is in the final selection of the choice of regression equation. Master 60 gives instructions for using exponential regression on the Texas Instruments TI-83 Plus. (On the STAT CALC menu of the TI-83 Plus, students should select choice **0:ExpReg.** Values of *a* and *b* will be given for an equation of the form $y = ab^x$.)

Note that students would not find the same exponential function if they kept all four digits of the year instead of following the suggestion of using years after 1900; the coefficient (*a*) will be extremely small (about 3.6236×10^{-22}).

For **Problem 3,** students will differ in their judgment of whether their equation "does a good job of fitting the data," since there's no objective measure of "good" in this context without using the *correlation coefficient,* which students will encounter if they study more advanced statistics.

 5 In **Problem 4,** using $t = 0$ for 1900 will require students to use $t = {}^-10$ for 1890. If a student is unsure what to do, ask:

> What value of *t* represents 1902? 1901? 1900? *2, 1, 0* So what value of *t* do you think should represent 1899? 1890? $^-1, {}^-10$

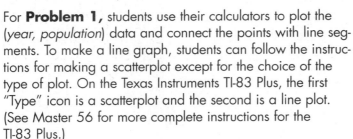

On the Spot Assessment

Watch for students who use "years after 1900" in one part of the problem and the actual year in another. Ask them what the variable *t* represents; if they answer incorrectly, try not to just correct them. Have them compare their equation to the table if necessary.

If you have the time, you may want to explore whether an absolute error or a percentage error provides a better measure of how accurate the prediction is for **Problem 5.** If students prefer the absolute error, you can clarify the difference with a more dramatic example, such as an error of 58 when reporting the number of people in the state in which you live versus an error of 58 when reporting the number of students in your class. It will be clear that, as is often the case, the percentage error is a better measure.

Even though equations can help model a rocket's motion, many things will affect an actual flight, such as shifting winds and flaws in the rocket's construction.

Human activities can be even more difficult to describe with mathematics. For example, population growth is often exponential in nature, so we might expect to be able to find an exponential equation that approximately fits population data over time. However, events often alter the expected pattern of population growth.

 Discuss how precisely data are likely to follow a curve or line.

 You may have students work in pairs.

MATERIALS
graphing calculator

Problem Set B

1. Possible answer: Yes; it starts out rising slowly and ends up rising rapidly.

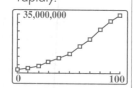

3. Possible answer: It does a fairly good job; most of the points are close to the curve.

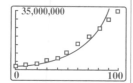

4. Possible answers: about 1,360,000 and about 61,000,000

The table gives population data for the state of California from 1900 through 1990.

Enter the data into your calculator. Use *years after 1900* as the input; for example, 1910 is $t = 10$ and 1970 is $t = 70$.

California Population	
Year	**Population**
1900	1,485,053
1910	2,377,549
1920	3,426,861
1930	5,677,251
1940	6,907,387
1950	10,586,223
1960	15,717,204
1970	19,971,069
1980	23,667,764
1990	29,760,021
2000	33,871,648

Source: *World Almanac and Book of Facts 2003.* Copyright © 2003 World Almanac Education Group, Inc.

 Help students create the graph, using Master 56.

 You may need to help students find the exponential regression choice on their calculators.

Help students unsure what value of *t* to use for 1890.

1. Use your calculator to graph the population of California over time, connecting the points with line segments. Make a sketch of your graph. Does the graph look roughly exponential? Explain.

2. Use the calculator's curve-fitting features to find an exponential function *C* for which the input is the years after 1900, *t*, and the output is the (approximate) population of California in that year. Write the base of the exponent to the nearest ten thousandth.   See below.

3. Now enter your equation into the calculator and graph it. Plot the data on the same graph, without connecting the points. Do you think the equation does a good job of fitting the data? Explain.

4. Use the equation to predict the population of California in the year 1890 and in the year 2010.

5. The actual population of California in 1890 was 1,213,398. How does this compare to your prediction in Problem 4?
Possible answer: It's a little less (about 12% difference, which is relatively close).

2. Possible function: $C(t) = 1,868,788(1.0322^t)$, where *t* is years after 1900

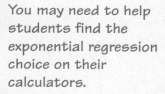

Share & Summarize

These questions are fairly general, so you should probably focus students' attention on coming up with concrete examples to support their thinking. In particular, students may be better able to answer **Question 2** if they create (or are given) a data set and think about how to find a reasonable model for that particular set. If necessary, give them one of the data sets from On Your Own Exercise 9 on page 646.

Troubleshooting It's OK to move on if students are not fully confident with the work in this investigation. They will have more practice in the next investigation.

On Your Own Exercises

Practice & Apply: 1, 2, p. 642
Connect & Extend: 8, 9, pp. 645–646
Mixed Review: 16–28, pp. 650–651

Investigation 2

So far, students have worked with data measured in physical and (with population) historical contexts. This investigation moves on to a future-oriented model, in which the purpose of the model is to make predictions and aid in decision making.

You might introduce the investigation by reminding students that in Investigation 1, they did some work finding equations that seemed to fit data. Then tell them they will create a similar model for a business situation.

Problem Set C Suggested Grouping: Individuals

This problem set is fairly straightforward. Simple calculations support intuitive conclusions. The problem set serves in part as a review of basic concepts ranging from arithmetic to the nature of linear and quadratic functions, and the scenario is a good example of using a quadratic model in a realistic economic situation. The problem set is also similar to optimization problems students solved in Chapter 8. Here, the goal is to find a price that gives maximum profit.

For the comparison in **Problem 4,** the important thing is for students to recognize that the baby-sitters earned less even though they were charging more per hour.

1. Possible answer: You can use them to make predictions for where other data points might be. For example, with the population data, we predicted the population for years before and after the times in the data set. We could also have predicted the population for years between those given, such as 1983.

Share & Summarize

In this investigation, you used your graphing calculator to find equations that model different types of data.

1. How are such models useful? Give an example if it helps explain.

2. Suppose you want to find an equation that models a particular set of data. Describe the steps you would take to find a reasonable model. Possible answer: Graph the data to see if they have a particular shape so you can choose a type of equation to use. Then use a graphing calculator to find an equation for that type of relationship.

Investigation ▶2▶ Modeling a Simple Economic Problem

Equations are constructed not only by aerospace engineers and population scientists, but also by economists and business analysts. In this investigation, you will analyze a business and create a simple model for it.

1 Focus students on creating examples to support their thinking.

2 Remind students they fit equations to data in Investigation 1.

3 You may have students work on their own.

MATERIALS
• graphing calculator
• graph paper (optional)

Problem Set C

Tamika lives in a neighborhood with lots of young children and not very many teenagers, so there is a great demand for baby-sitters. She and four of her friends decided to pool their efforts and start a baby-sitting business.

The five friends began by charging $3 per hour. They quickly had lots of business—almost more than they could handle! In fact, they did a combined total of 120 hours of baby-sitting in each of the first few months.

1. How many hours per month, on average, did *each* friend work? 24

2. How much income per month, on average, did *each* friend earn from baby-sitting? $72

Adam suggested they could make more money by tripling their hourly rate. Unfortunately, most people didn't want to pay $9 per hour, so they went elsewhere for baby-sitters. Business dropped to a total of 60 hours over the next 2 months—less than what the group was used to getting in a *single* month.

3. How many hours per month, on average, did each friend work during these two months? 6

4. How much income per month, on average, did each friend earn from baby-sitting? How did this compare with their income when they were charging only $3? $54; each earned $18 per month less.

For **Problem 7,** you can have students create their graphs on paper or using their calculators.

Note that three data points won't allow students to get a clear idea of the possible shape of the graph. However, of the equations students have studied, only quadratics (and cubics) change from increasing to decreasing like this, so students will likely focus on quadratic equations. Keep an eye out for students spending a lot of time considering this question, and encourage them to just record their initial thoughts and go on.

The analysis in **Problems 8–10** relies on the assumption that the price charged per hour and the amount of work the group received are related linearly.

Access
for all **Learners**

Early Finishers You may want to discuss with students how realistic Hilda's assumption is. In fact, the (*rate, hours of baby-sitting*) data are collinear, but students may feel this would not be the case in their own neighborhoods. You can point out that, unless they were to collect more data, the friends would need to make some sort of assumption. You might then ask what they feel a better assumption might be.

Depending on your class, you might challenge students to use their own assumptions to find a rate that gives the maximum profit. Note that their assumptions may or may not lead to rate-income relationships they can model easily. For example, they may feel that the relationship between hourly rate and hours of baby-sitting is an exponential decay function $y = ab^r$, which leads to the income function $i(r) = r(ab^r)$. However, they may be able to find constants to model the rate-hours data, instead, by using exponential regression, for example. Then they can just multiply the resulting expression by r to get the income function.

5. $84; this is their highest income yet.

6.

Hourly Rate	Income per Baby-sitter
$3	$72
7	84
9	54

7. Possible answer: quadratic (parabola)

Baby-Sitter Income

8a. the number of hours lost by raising the rate $1

8b. the number of hours they get when they charge nothing at all

8c. quadratic; Possible answer: yes

Rebecca then suggested lowering the hourly rate to $7. "We might not get as much business as we had the first few months," she reasoned, "but we will get more than in the past two!" They received calls for 60 hours of baby-sitting during the next month alone.

5. How much income, on the average, did each friend get from baby-sitting for this month? How did this compare with their average monthly income when they were charging $9 and $3?

Finally, Hilda proposed that they graph all these results. "We could find an equation for a curve that fits the data points," she said, "and then determine how much we should charge to earn the maximum possible income."

6. Make a table with hourly rate in the first column and average monthly income per baby-sitter in the second. Fill the table using the information from Problems 1–5.

7. Graph the data in your table. What kind of curve might describe the relationship between hourly rate and average monthly income?

When you create a model to fit data, you must sometimes make assumptions to help decide what kind of relationship to use. In this case, Hilda proposed that the connection between the rate and the hours of baby-sitting they get might be linear—that is, for every dollar they raise their rate, they lose a certain number of hours.

8. Using Hilda's assumption, the number of hours each sitter works, on average, is a linear expression like $a - br$, where a and b are constants and r is the hourly rate.

   a. What does the value of b represent?

   b. What does the value of a represent? (Hint: What happens when r is 0?)

   c. Each baby-sitter's income is the rate multiplied by the number of hours worked, or $r(a - br)$. What kind of expression is $r(a - br)$? Does this support your answer to Problem 7?

9. Use your calculator to fit an equation for income i of the type you answered in Part c of Problem 8 to the data in your table from Problem 6. $i = -3r^2 + 33r$

10. Use your equation to determine the hourly rate that results in the greatest average monthly income. Use the Trace feature on your calculator, if needed. What is the rate, and what is the income?
rate: $5.50; income: $90.75

1 Encourage students to record their initial thoughts and then continue.

2 You may want to discuss how realistic Hilda's assumption is.

LESSON 10.2 Models, Data, and Decisions **635**

Share & Summarize

These questions are applicable only if students have completed both Investigations 1 and 2.

1 Encourage students to consider reasons in the situations or data sets for the difference in the approaches. For example, in Investigation 1, students used the shape of the data points to choose a probable shape for the curve. In Investigation 2, there weren't enough data points to be able to see a shape, so additional information had to be assumed.

Troubleshooting Students who baby-sit or perform other such tasks to produce income may focus too much on nonmathematical considerations. You may need to redirect them to consider the level of abstraction in the investigation: although the situations are not especially abstract, the analysis requires acceptance of the given assumptions whether or not students consider those assumptions realistic.

On Your Own Exercises

Practice & Apply: 3, 4, p. 643
Connect & Extend: 10, pp. 647–648
Mixed Review: 16–28, pp. 650–651

Investigation 3

This investigation is considerably more complex than the last. Instead of being limited to a single-variable hourly rate, it considers a variety of variables and possibilities. The scenario is in many ways more realistic than the baby-sitting one, although it also requires a great many assumptions that could be challenged, ranging from cost of materials and tools to estimations of potential sales. If you know people who have started their own business and have created a business plan, you might invite them in as guest speakers, but be sure to provide an accurate description of the mathematical level of your class. If they can pitch their presentation to an appropriate level of sophistication, it could provide a rare opportunity for students to see how mathematics is used in the real world.

Because students will be creating a fairly complicated table, and revising it in the Share & Summarize on page 637, you can have them use spreadsheets, if they are available.

2 You might introduce the lesson by reminding students about the baby-sitting business of Investigation 2. Tell them they will now consider a new business and a different kind of mathematical model, creating tables instead of writing and examining equations. Read the introductory text with the class.

3 **Problem Set D** Suggested Grouping: Pairs
This problem set calls for calculations based on a mathematical model and conclusions that are drawn from those calculations.

4 Before letting students work on the problems, read through the given assumptions. They are too much to absorb all at once, but if students understand each individual point, the problems that follow will help them pull together the information. The Share & Summarize asks students to make recommendations about which assumptions seem unrealistic; if a student objects to some of the assumptions, ask him or her to accept them for now with the reassurance that the class will return to the objection later.

Share & Summarize

Compare your work in Investigations 1 and 2.

1. How are the approaches used to find models for the data similar in the investigations?

2. How are the approaches different?
Possible answer: In Investigation 1, we chose a type of curve based on the shape of the data points. In Investigation 2, we used an assumption about the situation to choose the type of curve.

Investigation 3 Starting a Business

Evita and Tariq noticed that there were quite a few broken bicycles—and lots of discarded bicycle *parts*—lying by the side of the road in their town. They would see a frame in one place, a rear wheel in another, and a bike missing its wheels in a third. They decided to form a business recovering old bicycle parts and rebuilding good bicycles from ones that no longer worked. They couldn't resist calling their business *Re-cycle*.

Problem Set D

Before starting their business, Evita and Tariq researched and collected statistics from others who had been successful at this kind of business. They decided to construct a mathematical model of how their Re-cycle project might go for 5 years. The model required several assumptions:

• They would need some tools. Evita estimated their cost to be $600.

• Tariq predicted they could rebuild 12 bicycles the first year. He thought that after the first year, they would have a better idea about what they could find where. With greater experience, each year they could rebuild 10 more bicycles than the previous year.

• Tariq also predicted they could sell 7 bicycles the first year, and that in each subsequent year they could sell 50% more bicycles than the preceding year.

• They would need to buy some bicycle parts, since they couldn't be sure they would find working versions of everything they needed. Evita estimated they would have to spend about $1,000 on parts in each of the first two years. She also thought that, in each year after the first two, they would have to spend $200 more on parts than the preceding year.

• Evita predicted they could sell a rebuilt bicycle for an average price of $250 this year, and that for each of the next 4 years the price would increase. Tariq and Evita agreed that a yearly increase equal to 10% of the previous year's price seemed reasonable.

In **Problem 2,** you may find that some students round down, some round up, and some round to the closest whole number. A good argument for rounding down is given in the sample answer. A good argument for rounding off to the closest whole number is that the calculations are based on imprecise assumptions.

Problem 5 provides a nice opportunity to use a spreadsheet. If you wish, you could extend the spreadsheet horizontally or vertically by making additional assumptions or adding in other factors, such as taxes. You can also use it to demonstrate the power of a spreadsheet by changing the assumptions and instantly seeing the dynamic changes in results.

Share & Summarize

These questions ask for a re-examination of the basis for assumptions made in the situation, based on students' experiences. This includes challenging explicit and implicit assumptions, as well as the very real point that advertising costs money. Open up discussion to anything students feel might be relevant to the planning involved in the bicycle business.

Troubleshooting Students may become overwhelmed by the significant increase in complexity of this investigation over the preceding one. The problems were designed to narrow the focus to one type of cost or projection at a time, in order to help reduce this complexity, but you may want to help them consider each point individually.

On Your Own Exercises

Practice & Apply: 5, 6, p. 644
Connect & Extend: 11–14, p. 648
Mixed Review: 16–28, pp. 650–651

1. Calculate the expected costs that Evita and Tariq will incur each year. (Tools don't have to be bought after the first year.)

2. Calculate the expected number of bicycles they will sell each year. Decide what to do when the model predicts a fractional number of bicycles, and justify your decision.

3. Now find the number of bicycles the friends will build each year. How many extra bicycles will Re-cycle have on hand at the end of each year? (Remember to include the leftovers from the previous year.)   build: 12, 22, 32, 42, 52; on hand: 5, 17, 34, 54, 73

4. Calculate the price to be charged per bicycle each year.

5. Copy the table, and complete it with information from Problems 1–4 and by calculating the values for the last two columns. *Gross income* is simply the amount of money taken in. *Net profit* is the amount of money left after all costs have been paid. Answers will vary slightly, depending on how students round.

Year	Costs	Bikes Sold	Price per Bike	Gross Income	Net Profit
1	$1,600	7	$250.00	$1,750.00	$150.00
2	1,000	10	275.00	2,750.00	1,750.00
3	1,200	15	302.50	4,537.50	3,337.50
4	1,400	22	332.75	7,320.50	5,920.50
5	1,600	33	366.03	12,078.99	10,478.99

6. What is Re-cycle's predicted net profit over the 5-year period? Possible answer: $21,636.99

Share & Summarize

1. In the business model for Re-cycle, many assumptions had to be made. Although you don't know the conditions in their town, which of their assumptions would you ask Evita and Tariq to reconsider, and why?

2. Evita and Tariq planned on advertising to help sell their bikes, but they neglected to consider that advertising costs money!

   a. Revise your table with an added assumption of spending $500 per year on advertising. What is the net profit for each year?

   b. What is the new predicted net profit over the 5-year period? Possible answer: $19,136.99

Investigation 4

This investigation introduces the notion of a model population, related to but different from models using a function or even a spreadsheet. The concept is presented using genuine research on a topic that may interest many of your students, particularly left-handed students who are frustrated living in a "right-handed world."

1 You may want to introduce this lesson by asking which students are left-handed and then asking, how many of those students have a relative who is left-handed. Then read the opening paragraphs with the class.

The estimates for handedness in men and women are from the article "Hand Preference and Age in the United States" from the journal *Neuropsychologia* (A. N. Gilbert and C. J. Wysocki, 1992).

Think & Discuss

2 These questions call for some basic intuition about probability and sampling. For most students this will be a review of concepts they have already learned.

3 Follow the Think & Discuss by defining *model population,* as given in the text before Problem Set E.

4 **Problem Set E** Suggested Grouping: Small Groups

This problem set employs a model population of 1,000 people, 500 each of men and women. Note that the paragraph before the problem set refers to a model of 100 women. If students are puzzled about this change, you can suggest that a larger group is easier to work with, since there's less chance of working with a fraction of a person.

5 In **Problem 2,** stress that this model represents a "typical" (or even "ideal") group that fits the experimental data exactly, so it's possible to give an accurate count of left-handed men and women, even though in a real sample the counts would probably not be exactly as predicted.

6 The proportions described at the bottom of the page can be confusing for students. It may be useful to help students summarize this situation.

Handedness of Children

When parents are both right-handed:

- 9.5% of children are left-handed
- 90.5% of children are right-handed

When exactly one parent is right-handed:

- 19.5% of children are left-handed
- 80.5% of children are right-handed

When parents are both left-handed:

- 26.1% of children are left-handed
- 73.9% of children are right-handed

These proportions were taken from "The Genetics of Handedness, Cerebral Dominance and Lateralization" by I. C. McManus and M. P. Bryden, in *Handbook of Neuropsychology, Volume 6: Developmental Neuropsychology* (I. Rapin and S. J. Segalowitz, Eds., pp. 115–144; Amsterdam: Elsevier Science).

Investigation ▶4 Model Populations

Scientists are increasingly interested in why some people are left-handed, because left-handed patients may recover faster from some ailments than right-handed patients do. They may also be less likely to develop certain disorders in the first place.

Estimates vary, but one estimate is that 12.6% of males and 9.9% of females are left-handed. To make things easier in the problems that follow, assume that approximately 10% of women and 13% of men are left-handed.

Think & Discuss

No; on average, there will be 10 in every group of 100, but that doesn't mean there will be exactly 10 in a particular group.

• Does it follow from the estimates that in a group of 100 women, selected randomly, exactly 10 will be left-handed? Explain.

• Is it possible that all 100 of a group of 100 randomly selected women will be left-handed?   Yes, though it's very unlikely.

When you imagine a fictitious group of 100 women and say that 10 are left-handed, you have created a *model population* that fits the data exactly. Creating such a model is often helpful in answering complex questions about characteristics in the real population.

Problem Set E

MATERIALS

graph paper or protractor

1. See Additional Answers.

An imaginary population of 500 men and 500 women can be used as a model of left- and right-handedness.

1. Draw a graph of the model—either a bar chart or a pie chart—that visually shows the number of right- and left-handed people in the group.

2. How many adults (male or female) in your model are left-handed? What percentage of the total population is that?   115, 11.5%

Left-handedness seems to be genetic: left-handed adults are more likely to have left-handed children. One pair of scientists concluded from a study that if both your parents are right-handed, you have a 9.5% chance of being left-handed. Your chances rise to 19.5% if one of your parents is left-handed and to 26.1% if *both* are left-handed.

Sidebar (right margin):

1 Discuss the incidence of left-handedness.

2 Use these questions to review probability and sampling.

3 Define *model population*.

4 You may have students work in small groups.

5 Stress that the model represents an "ideal" group, allowing exact numbers.

6 Help students summarize this information.

Additional Answers
Problem Set E

1. Possible graphs:

Handedness in 1,000 People

■ Right-handed
■ Left-handed

Men   Women

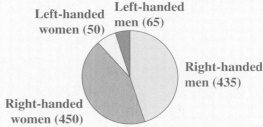

Handedness in 1,000 People

Left-handed women (50)
Left-handed men (65)
Right-handed men (435)
Right-handed women (450)

Students may be confused by the use of the word *likely* in **Problems 3–5,** since they may be thinking of probability situations. The word is used here to remind students that this is merely a model. In a real sample of 1,000 people, one wouldn't see exactly the predicted results.

Problem Set Wrap-Up Review student answers, especially for **Problems 6 and 7,** which demonstrate the power of model populations. It would be more difficult to try to predict how many left-handed children will be in the next generation using other methods.

You may want to point out that students' results rely on estimated percentages: the percentages of men and women who are left-handed, and the percentages of children who are left-handed depending on the handedness of their parents. If the studies these estimates came from were inaccurate, the results would also be inaccurate.

Just the facts

There have been many myths and super-stitions about left-handedness. Records even show that in the sixteenth century people were burned at the stake just for being left-handed.

3. 391 or 392; Possible explana-tion: Of the 500 men, 435 are right-handed, and of the 435 women married to those men, about 391.5 are right-handed.

4. 6 or 7; Possible explanation: Of the 500 women, 50 are left-handed, and of the 50 men married to those women, about 6.5 are left-handed.

5. about 102; Possible explanation: Parts a and b gave 391.5 + 6.5 = 398 couples, so the remaining 102 should consist of one right-hander and one left-hander.

6a. About 74; 9.5% of 2(391.5) is 74.385.

6b. About 3; 26.1% of 2(6.5) is 3.393.

Suppose the 500 men in the model each marry one of the 500 women. Assume that handedness of a potential spouse is not a factor in who mar-ries whom. That is, assume that in each couple, the chances that the man is left-handed are 13% and that the woman is left-handed are 10%.

3. How many of the couples are likely to consist of two right-handed people? Explain how you found your answer.

4. How many of the couples are likely to consist of two left-handed people? Explain how you found your answer.

5. How many of the couples are likely to consist of one right-handed person and one left-handed person? Explain.

6. Suppose each couple has exactly two children.

   a. Consider the children of couples in which both parents are right-handed. About how many of those children would you expect to be left-handed? Show how you found your answer.

   b. Now consider the children of couples in which both parents are left-handed. How many of those children would you expect to be left-handed? Show how you found your answer.

   c. Finally, consider the children of couples in which one parent is left-handed and the other is right-handed. How many of those children would you expect to be left-handed? Show how you found your answer.   About 40; 19.5% of 2(102) is 39.78.

   d. The 500 couples have a total of 1,000 children. How many of those children would you expect to be left-handed? What percent-age of all the children is that?   about 117 children, 11.7%

7. Compare the percentage of left-handed adults to the percentage of left-handed children in this group. What do you think this might mean about left-handedness far into the future?   The percentage of left-handed children is 0.2% higher than the percentage of left-handed adults; a very long time from now, there may be just as many left-handed people as right-handed people.

1 Discuss answers, especially for Problems 6 and 7.

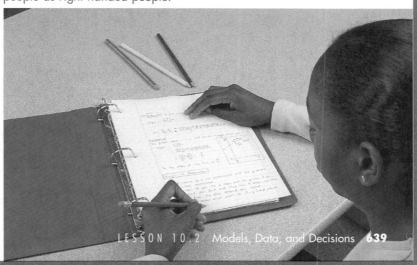

LESSON 10.2 Models, Data, and Decisions **639**

1 Before letting students work on Problem Set F, you might ask if any know what a *paradox* is, or if they can give an example of a paradox, such as the fact that you can save money by spending money (buying more of an item can lower the unit price).

 2 **Problem Set F** **Suggested Grouping: Pairs**
This problem set represents the most advanced level of abstraction in the chapter. Because it presents an apparently paradoxical situation, you may want to be especially careful with students who are uncomfortable with mathematics and skeptical of mathematical results. They may come out with the wrong interpretation, thinking that a mathematical model can appear to explain anything, even things that aren't true.

 3 Depending on your students, you may want to read to the bottom of page with the class and give them an opportunity to ask questions about the situation. If they are all fairly good readers, you might prefer to have them read the whole problem set with their partners.

Evan's approach of creating an extreme example is a good strategy for exploring apparently paradoxical situations. Sometimes a result will appear that isn't apparent in more balanced examples. To take a familiar example, the distinction between mean and median is most vividly seen in a sample that includes an outlier.

 4 Students may also be confused by the language. Evan is "creating" classes, but remind your students that this is a fictional model designed to explore possibilities; he isn't literally creating classes.

Sometimes a mathematical model can help us understand data that are hard to believe or seem contradictory. A situation that appears to be contradictory is known as a *paradox*. In Problem Set F, you will consider one paradox and discover why it can actually be true.

Problem Set F

Evan's younger twin sisters, Hannah and Elana, attend a small elementary school. There are only two fifth-grade classrooms in the school; Hannah is in the Green Room and Elana is in the Blue Room. The twins told Evan the following things:

- The average height of the boys in the Blue Room is greater than that of the boys in the Green Room.

- The average height of the girls in the Blue Room is greater than that of the girls in the Green Room.

- The combined average height of everyone in the Blue Room is *less* than the combined average height of everyone in the Green Room!

Evan was skeptical. "If *both* the boys *and* the girls in the Blue Room are taller than their Green Room classmates," he reasoned, "it seems the Blue Room should, in general, have taller students."

The twins insisted this wasn't the case. Evan decided to try to create a model population for which this odd situation could have occurred. Then at least he would know it was possible.

He reasoned that the paradox couldn't occur unless the two classes had different ratios of girls to boys. To create an extreme example, Evan distributed 30 girls very unevenly—27 in one room, 3 in the other—and 30 boys in the opposite way.

Green Room

Blue Room

Discuss what a *paradox* is, and maybe ask for examples.

You may have students work in pairs.

You may want to read through this text as a class or have students read with their partners.

Remind students that Evan is using fictional classes, not literally creating them.

A possible strategy for completing Evan's tables is as follows:

- In the Green Room, if 27 girls had an average height of 56 inches, their total was 1,512 inches; the 3 boys with an height of 54 inches had a total of 162 inches. So the total of the heights is 1,674 inches, with an average of 55.8 inches.

- In the Blue Room, there are only 3 girls, so increasing their average heights won't affect the class average by much. However, increasing the average height for the 27 boys will significantly change the class average. We want the average height of the class to be low, so make the boy's average height only a little higher than for the Green Room, say 55 inches. That's 1,485 inches total. To keep the Blue Room's average height less than the Green Room's, the total has to be 1,673 or less. That leaves up to 188 inches to distribute to the 3 girls—their heights can be greater than the average height of the girls in the Green Room!

Share & Summarize

These questions ask students to cast a critical eye on the assumptions and methodology they have been using. This might be best handled as a guided class discussion, since it would be very difficult for individuals or small groups. For **Question 2a,** in addition to some of the challenges in the sample answer on page 641, students may mention single parents, infertility, multiple births, and same-sex couples.

Question 3 is a challenge, but it's important for students to think about why something might sound paradoxical—especially when the paradox is based on assumptions that students may not realize they are making.

Troubleshooting This lesson gave students a new tool with which they can explore mathematical situations—especially statistical ones. If they had trouble understanding the *usefulness* of model populations, you might ask them to actually try using percentages or other methods to find how the percentage of left-handed people might change from one generation to the next.

If they had trouble questioning assumptions and evaluating their reasonableness, remind students that they already have a lot of experience with the world and how it works. While they should never assume that everyone's life (or family, or neighborhood, and so on) is similar to theirs, they can use their own experiences as counterexamples to show that some assumptions will not *always* be true. Point out that they will have to use their best judgment of how reasonable the assumption is *for the purposes of the problem being explored,* even if it clearly won't always be true. They will get better at such judgment calls as they gain more experience.

On Your Own Exercises

Practice & Apply: 7, p. 644
Connect & Extend: 15, p. 649
Mixed Review: 16–28, pp. 650–651

1. Possible answer: It makes it easier, since I'm able to find percentages and add with real numbers rather than just percentages. Without the model, I would have had to find percentages of percentages and try to add them. It would have been a lot more difficult to keep track of what the numbers meant.

2a. Possible answers: Equal number of men and women; not likely for a large population (it certainly won't be exact) but may be reasonable. Every person gets married; definitely won't be true for a real population. Handedness of a potential spouse is not a factor; this is debatable, as some people might meet spouses at a support group for left-handed people, or something like that. However, the assumption is more likely to be true than, say, a similar assumption for very tall or short people. Every couple has exactly two children; this is not likely to be true.

By adjusting the average heights of the girls and the boys, Evan tried to see whether it was possible to match the situation at the school. He started by assigning heights to the boys and girls in the Green Room. Then he needed to create a Blue Room class that had a lower average overall height than the Green Room class, even though both the boys and the girls were taller than those in the Green Room.

Below are the tables Evan began. Try to complete the tables in a way that meets the conditions of the problem. Possible answers are given in the Blue Room table.

Green Room

	Girls	Boys	Total
Students	27	3	30
Average Height (in.)	56	54	55.8

Blue Room

	Girls	Boys	Total
Students	3	27	30
Average Height (in.)	58	55	55.3

Share & Summarize

In Problem Set E, you used a model to predict how the percentage of left-handers might change from one generation to the next.

1. Consider trying to predict this change by working with percentages rather than with a model population. What advantage does working with the model have?

2. When you worked with the model, you were asked to make several assumptions.

   a. List the assumptions. Decide whether each assumption is reasonable for a real population, like that of the United States.

   b. How do you think it might change your prediction if the assumptions you listed are not true? See Additional Answers.

3. **Challenge** Think about the paradox in Problem Set F. Can you see the key to this paradox? That is, can you see why it sounds impossible but actually isn't?
   Possible answer: When you first consider the situation, you probably assume there are about the same number of boys as girls in each room. If that's not true, it's easy for a few girls (or boys) to be really tall or really short without affecting the average by a whole lot.

1 Discuss these questions with the class.

2 If students don't see the usefulness of model populations, you might ask them to answer the problem set questions using other methods.

Additional Answers
Share & Summarize

2b. Possible answer: Not a lot, because much of it will probably balance out. Being left-handed isn't likely to make you not marry or not have children. Left-handers might be a little more likely to seek out other left-handers, and their children would have the greatest chance of being left-handed; that might increase the number of left-handed children by a little, but probably not by much. The number of men and women aren't exactly even, but probably close enough that it won't have a big effect either. If couples have more or fewer children, the percentage of left-handers might change at a different rate.

On Your Own Exercises

**On Your
Own
Exercises**

Investigation 1,
pp. 632–634
Practice & Apply: 1, 2
Connect & Extend: 8, 9

Investigation 2,
pp. 634–636
Practice & Apply: 3, 4
Connect & Extend: 10

Investigation 3,
pp. 636–637
Practice & Apply: 5, 6
Connect & Extend: 11–14

Investigation 4,
pp. 638–641
Practice & Apply: 7
Connect & Extend: 15

Assign Anytime
Mixed Review: 16–28

Exercise 1:
Part f should not be assigned unless graphing calculators are available to students when they complete these exercises. Note that there is no indication here of what is propelling the toy car.

Exercise 2:
Assign **Part d** only if students have access to graphing calculators when they complete these exercises. Students may be able to find the equation if they remember that exponential equations have a growth or decay factor; in this case, though, they would need to divide subsequent temperatures and then take the square root, because the times are in 2-minute intervals. You may want to discuss this with your students after they have completed the homework assignment.

Practice & Apply

1a. See Additional Answers.

1b. The car travels at a constant speed for the first 4 s and then speeds up over the next 5 s.

1e. quadratic; Possible explanation: The second differences are all 2.

2a. See Additional Answers.

2c. From 50°C, about 12 min; from 100°C, about 18 min. No; water at 100°C will lose more heat in a minute than water at 50°C, but water at 100°C still has to fall to 50°C before it can freeze, and from that point it takes just as much time to freeze as water that started at 50°C.

1. **Physical Science** The table shows the distance a toy car has traveled from its starting point at various times. The car is moving in a straight line.

   a. Make a graph of the data.

   b. Describe the car's motion.

   c. When is the break point? That is, at what time does the car's motion change? around 4 s

   d. Write an equation for the distance d the car has traveled, in feet, from time $t = 0$ seconds to the break point. $d = 2t$

   e. Does the motion after the break point seem to be quadratic or exponential? Explain why you think so.

   f. Use a graphing calculator to find an equation for the distance d the car has traveled for times after the break point. $d = t^2 - 6t + 16$

Time (s)	Distance (ft)
0	0
1	2
2	4
3	6
4	8
5	11
6	16
7	23
8	32
9	43

2. **Physical Science** Crystal once heard that liquids cool faster when they are hotter. A friend said that meant you should use hot water—not cold—to make ice cubes quickly. This didn't make much sense to Crystal, so she decided to conduct an experiment to see just how hot water cools.

   She boiled some water and put a thermometer in the liquid. When the mercury stopped rising, she recorded the temperature and then put the water in her freezer. Every 2 minutes she checked the temperature, recording her results in a table.

   a. Plot the data from her table.

   b. What kind of relationship does there appear to be between these variables? exponential

   c. Consider the time it would take water at 50°C to cool to 15°C in Crystal's freezer. Then consider the time it would take water to cool from 100°C to 15°C. Do you think her friend was right—that she should use hot water to make ice cubes? If not, what does it mean to say that hot water cools faster? Support your answer.

   d. Use a graphing calculator to find an equation relating the water temperature T to the time t after Crystal put the water in the freezer. $T = 120(0.9^t)$

Time (min)	Temp (°C)
0	120
2	97
4	79
6	64
8	52
10	42
12	34
14	27
16	22
18	18
20	15

impactmath.com/self_check_quiz

• **Additional Answers on page A698**

3. Economics David designs and makes jewelry boxes to sell at crafts fairs. At a special week-long fair, he introduced a new design. He priced the boxes at $30 each, but they weren't as popular as he had hoped: he didn't sell any the first day. The next day he lowered the price to $20 and sold 10 boxes. He thought he might do even better if he lowered the price to $10; he sold 20 at that price.

a. Find David's *revenue* (the amount of money he received) for these boxes on each of the first three days of the fair. $0, $200, $200

b. Assume that the number of boxes sold is related to their price by a linear relationship. The revenue is then the price p times a linear expression involving the price, such as $a - bp$. What type of relationship is there between the price and the revenue?   quadratic

3c. $15; Possible explanation: Since $10 and $20 gave the same revenue, the vertex is halfway between these prices.

c. Suppose David wants to take in the most money possible and that he has enough jewelry boxes to fill whatever demand there is for them. What price should he try for the rest of the fair? Explain your answer. (Hint: Consider the symmetry in graphs of the type of relationship you answered for Part b, and use the revenues for the first three days.)

Exercise 3c:
If students have access to graphing calculators, they can use quadratic regression to find an equation that fits the data. Assuming that $30 is the lowest point at which people would stop buying the boxes, the equation is $y = -x^2 + 30x$.

4. Economics Aysha makes handblown glass ornaments. She found that, for one style of ornament, the amount of money she received for selling them depended on the price she asked. She created this graph to estimate her revenue (money received) on a single day for any price.

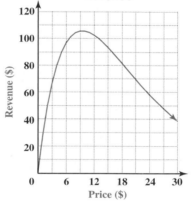

Revenue

4a. $9 or $10, about $105
4b. about $5 and about $16

a. Approximately what price gives the greatest revenue for a single day? What is the corresponding revenue?

b. What price or prices would give a revenue of about $89?

c. Aysha considers more than just the amount of money she receives when she prices her ornaments. She also considers the cost of creating each ornament, both in the time she spends and the cost of the materials.

If Aysha had to choose between the two prices you found in Part b, which she should choose? Explain why.
$16; she'll earn the same revenue for selling fewer items, which means less money spent on materials and less time taken to create the ornaments.

Quick Review
Math Handbook

 Hot Topics
pp. 214–220

This is an unusual exercise because it asks students to think of reasonable assumptions that will give a particular outcome. You may want to ask students what this tells them about the assumptions they use. Ideally, someone entering into a serious business (as opposed to a "for fun" or "for spending money" business like the one Evita and Tariq are creating) would be very careful about the assumptions they make and try to support them with real data.

Exercise 7:

Testing, whether medical or product testing, is an important context in which model populations are very helpful. Although it's possible to determine the number of *false positives* and *false negatives* you might expect from a test without using a model population, the model makes the analysis relatively easy to understand. (Note that Exercise 15 uses the terms *false positive* and *false negative*.)

---

5. −$1,350, −$150, $1,237.50, $3,620.50, and $7,978.99; $11,336.99

6. See Additional Answers.

7a. Answers will vary.

7b. 40; 4 will test negative.

7c. 960; 48 will test positive.

---

5. Suppose Evita and Tariq were overly optimistic about the cost of parts in their Re-cycle business of Problem Set D. Suppose they will really spend $2,000 the first year, and in each subsequent year they will spend $400 over the previous year. If you include $500 per year for advertising, what is the new profit each year? Over the 5 years?

6. Consider Evita and Tariq's Re-cycle business in Problem Set D. Make appropriate changes in their assumptions so that the business has a negative net profit over the 5-year period. Defend each of your changes by explaining why it is plausible.

7. Life Science Medical tests sometimes give incorrect results. Suppose that one disease occurs in 4% of the population and that a test that screens for this disease misdiagnoses a healthy person 5% of the time and an ill person 10% of the time.

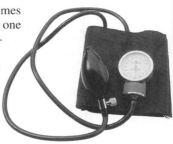

a. Suppose you take the test and the result is positive, suggesting that you have the disease. What do you estimate is the probability that you really have it?

Now consider a model population of 1,000 people, with 4% of those people afflicted by the disease.

b. How many people in the model have the disease? How many of these are expected to be reported by the test as *not* having the disease—that is, how many are expected to incorrectly test negative?

c. How many people in the model do not have the disease? How many of these will be expected to incorrectly test positive?

d. Copy and complete the table using your results from Parts b and c.

	Population	Tests Positive	Tests Negative
Has Disease	40	36	4
Doesn't Have Disease	960	48	912
Total	1,000	84	916

e. What is the probability that a person who tests positive actually has the disease? $\frac{36}{84}$, or about 42.9%

f. What is the probability that a person who tests negative doesn't have the disease? $\frac{912}{916}$, or about 99.6%

• Additional Answers on page A698

Connect & Extend

8a. Answers will vary.

8. Social Studies The table gives population data for the United States from 1900 through 2000.

a. Here is a plot of these data. What kind of relationship—for example, linear, quadratic, or exponential—do you think best describes these data?

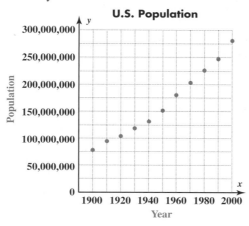

U.S. Population

Year	Population
1900	76,212,168
1910	92,228,496
1920	106,021,537
1930	123,202,624
1940	132,164,569
1950	151,325,798
1960	179,323,175
1970	203,302,031
1980	226,542,203
1990	248,709,873
2000	281,421,906

Source: *World Almanac and Book of Facts 1999.* Copyright © 2003 World Almanac Education Group,

b. The graph is repeated twice below. On one, an exponential curve of best fit, about $y = 0.0022(1.0129^x)$, is included. On the other, a line of best fit, about $y = 2,019,000x - 3,772,000,000$, is included. Identify which is the line and which is the exponential curve.

i.

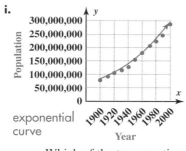

exponential curve

ii.

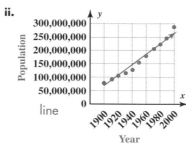

line

8c. The exponential equation; answers will vary.

8d. about 72,986,000; about 339,806,000

8e. Possible answer: It's lower but still fairly close (about 14% lower than the estimate).

c. Which of the two equations appears to fit the data better? Does this agree with your answer to Part a?

d. Use the equation that fits better to estimate the population of the United States in the years 1890 and 2010.

e. The actual population of the United States in 1890 was 62,979,766. How does this compare to your estimate in Part d?

Exercise 9d:
Without a calculator, students could find the equation for the regular polygon angle (Part c) using such strategies as guess-check-and-improve, or by creating a system of equations and solving it by substitution.

9. **Challenge** For Parts a–c, choose the graph below that you think will best fit the data.

a. burning rate for light to heavy fabric reciprocal, $y = \frac{A}{x}$

Density of Fabric (g/m²)	50	100	150	200	250	300	350	400
Speed of Burning (cm/s)	15.4	7.9	5.2	3.9	3.1	2.6	2.2	2.0

b. a braking car on dry concrete quadratic, $y = Ax^2$

Speed of Car (mph)	20	25	30	35	40	50	60	70
Stopping Distance (ft)	16	25	36	49	64	100	144	196

c. regular polygon angle reciprocal, $y = \frac{-A}{x} + B$

interior angle

Sides of the Polygon	3	4	5	10	15	20	25	30
Interior Angle (degrees)	60	90	108	144	156	162	165.6	168

Quadratic Functions

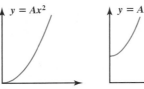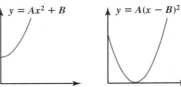

$y = Ax^2$ $y = Ax^2 + B$ $y = A(x - B)^2$ $y = -Ax^2 + B$

Exponential Functions

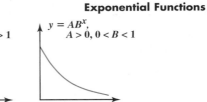

$y = AB^x,$ $A > 0, B > 1$ $y = AB^x,$ $A > 0, 0 < B < 1$

Reciprocal Functions

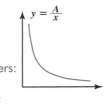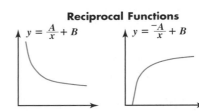

$y = \frac{A}{x}$ $y = \frac{A}{x} + B$ $y = \frac{-A}{x} + B$

9d. Possible answers:
a. $y = \frac{780}{x}$
b. $y = 0.04x^2$
c. $y = \frac{-360}{x} + 180$

9e. See tables for possible answers.

d. Choose *one* table above. Use the general equation given with the graph to help find a specific equation relating the two variables.

e. Use your equation to find the missing value in your chosen table.

10. Economics The manager of a small fast-food company was reviewing the restaurant's profits. The company had been operating only 5 years. The first year saw no profit, but profits had been positive each year since. Profits had increased at first and then decreased some when the company was preparing for an expansion. The current year's sales suggested the profits that year would be only $5,000. However, the manager projected major profit increases, predicting that the company's profit would reach $35,000 in 2 years.

a. Assuming the current year is Year 0, which of these graphs best represents the information above? Graph A

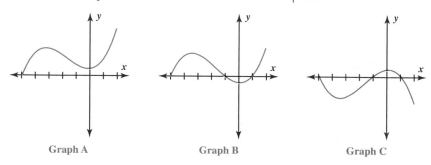

Graph A   Graph B   Graph C

b. Match each function to a graph from Part a.

   i. $P(x) = 1,000(x + 5)(1 - x^2)$ Graph C

   ii. $P(x) = 1,000(x + 5)(x^2 + 1)$ Graph A

   iii. $P(x) = 1,000(x + 5)(x^2 - 1)$ Graph B

c. Use the function that matches the graph you chose in Part a to check that the profit in the current year (that is, Year 0) is $5,000. Calculate the profit from 4 years ago and the profit in 2 years.

d. Choose one of the other functions, and assume it is the profit function for a rival fast-food company. Write a paragraph like the one at the beginning of this exercise, describing the company's profit over the last 5 years and the predictions for the next few years. Use your imagination to include some reasons for changes!

10c. $P(0) = 1,000(5)(1) = 5,000$; $P(^-4) = 1,000(1)(17) = 17,000$; $P(2) = 1,000(7)(5) = 35,000$

10d. Possible answer: For Graph C: The profit in the first year was $0, and a bad series of commercials kept people from trying the new restaurant. After a couple of years, a new ad firm was able to interest people, and although the company was still losing money, they weren't losing as much. By Year 4, the company was breaking even and actually began making a profit. Unfortunately, a popular TV news magazine just reported unhealthy conditions at 90% of the chain's restaurants, and the manager's TV interview didn't go well, so they expect to experience a large drop in profits that will be very difficult to recover from.

Exercises 11–14:
These exercises focus students on hidden assumptions. Identifying unspoken assumptions helps students not just in mathematical modeling, but in debate and philosophy (logic and proof).

In your
own words

In what ways can mathematical models be helpful to someone who is starting a business? What advice would you give about using such models?

11–14. See Additional Answers.

For the situations described in Exercises 11–14, answer Parts a–d.

a. What two variable quantities are related in the situation?

b. What assumptions were made about how the quantities varied?

c. What type of function—linear, quadratic, exponential, or reciprocal—would best model the situation if the assumptions were correct?

d. Do you find the assumptions reasonable in the context? Why?

11. Héctor can run 100 meters in 12 seconds, so it will take him about 2 minutes to run 1 kilometer.

12. Lydia and her brother go to the movies every week, and together it costs $15 to get in. If their sister were to go with them, it would cost $22.50 to get in.

13. An 8-inch-diameter pizza will feed one hungry student quite well, so a 16-inch pizza should feed four students.

14. Ben's grandmother put $1,000 in a savings account. By the end of a year, the amount had increased to $1,050, so by the end of the second year it will have increased to $1,100.

Additional Answers

Possible answers:

11a. distance run and time

11b. The time will be the same for the first 100 m as for every other 100 m.

11c. linear

11d. No; it's not easy to keep up that pace for more than a few seconds.

12a. number of people and cost to get in

12b. each person's ticket costs the same

12c. linear

12d. Yes; unless one of them is a lot younger or a lot older, the price for each will be the same.

13a. size of pizza and number of students it will feed

13b. the students each eat about the same amount

13c. quadratic

13d. No; if one of the students is an athlete, he or she might eat a lot more than a smaller or a younger student.

14a. amount in bank and time after initial deposit

14b. Interest is based only on the original amount (simple interest, not compound).

14c. linear

14d. probably not, because most bank accounts use compound interest

648 CHAPTER 10 Modeling with Data

15. Life Science A test for one fairly common medical condition has false-positive results of 30% (meaning 30% of healthy persons are wrongly reported to have the condition) and false-negative results of 10% (10% of people with the condition are wrongly reported to be healthy). The disease is present in about 10% of the population.

a. Create a sample population that represents the results of testing for the condition, and display the results in a table like the one below.   Possible answer:

	Population	Tests Positive	Tests Negative
Doesn't Have Condition	900	270	630
Has Condition	100	90	10
Total	1,000	360	640

b. What is the probability that someone who tests negative doesn't have the condition? $\frac{630}{640}$, or about 98.4%

c. What is the probability that someone who tests positive actually has the condition? $\frac{90}{360}$, or 25%

A new test has been created for the condition. The designers have found that the new test gives false-positive results 10% of the time and false-negative results 30% of the time.

15d. See Additional Answers.

d. Using your population size from Part a, create a table that displays the results of testing for the condition using the new test.

e. What is the probability that someone who tests negative with the new test doesn't have the condition? $\frac{810}{840}$, or about 96.4%

f. What is the probability that someone who tests positive with the new test actually has the condition? $\frac{70}{160}$, or 43.8%

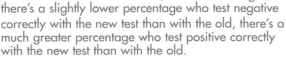

g. Compare your answers to Parts b and e, and compare your answers to Parts c and f. Which test do you think is better, the original test (with a relatively high percentage of false positives) or the new test (with a high percentage of false negatives)? Explain.
Possible answer: The new one, because although there's a slightly lower percentage who test negative correctly with the new test than with the old, there's a much greater percentage who test positive correctly with the new test than with the old.

Additional Answers

15d. Possible answer:

	Population	Tests Positive	Tests Negative
Doesn't Have Condition	900	90	810
Has Condition	100	70	30
Total	1,000	160	840

**Mixed
Review**

Expand each expression.

16. $\frac{4}{7}\left(\frac{1}{2}t + 12\right)$ $\frac{2}{7}t + \frac{48}{7}$

17. $x(4 - 13x)$ $4x - 13x^2$

18. $0.2(72v - 3)$ $14.4v - 0.6$

Find the value of n in each equation.

19. $3.582 \times 10^n = 3{,}582{,}000$ 6

20. $n \times 10^7 = 34{,}001$ 0.0034001

21. $82.882 \times 10^3 = n$ 82,882

22. $28.1 \times \frac{1}{10^3} = n$ 0.0281

23. Graph this inequality on a number line, and give three values that satisfy it.   See below.

$$-3 \le y < 7$$

24. In how many ways can the letters on the sign be ordered?   5,040

Find an equation for each line described.

25. passing through the point $(3, {}^-14)$ and parallel to the line
$y = 16x - 2$ $y = 16x - 62$

26. passing through the points $({}^-8, 9)$ and $({}^-1, 3)$ $y = {}^-\frac{6}{7}x + \frac{15}{7}$

27. with slope 0 and passing through the point $(2, 0.5)$ $y = 0.5$

23. Possible values: $^-3, 0, 6.9$

28. Technology Computers use a *binary* number system, a system that has 0 and 1 as its only digits. Each digit (0 or 1) is called a *bit*.

Computers translate everything—including letters—into series of 0s and 1s. Using only one bit, there are two possible series: 0 and 1. Using two bits, there are four possible series: 00, 01, 10, and 11. Because of the use of binary numbers, powers of 2 show up in many ways when you analyze how computers work.

a. To be able to distinguish 26 lower-case letters and 26 upper-case letters, a computer needs at least 52 different series. What is the least number of bits that will give at least 52 series? How many series will that many bits give? 6 bits, 64 series

b. In actuality, a single letter or symbol, called a *character,* is identi-fied using a *byte,* which is 8 bits. (Notice that 8 is a power of 2.) How many different characters can be identified using a single byte? 2^8 or 256

c. A *kilobyte* is not 1,000 bytes, as you might think. It's actually 1,024 bytes, because 1,024 is a power of 2. What power of 2 is 1,024? 2^{10}

d. How many *bits* (not bytes) are in 1 kilobyte? Express your answer as a power of 2. 2^{13}

Quick Check

Informal Assessment
Students should be able to:

✔ make predictions from data

✔ create an economic model for a simple business

✔ create a population model and use it to make predictions

Quick Quiz
Ryan gave a survey to the students at a local elemen-tary school. He used their responses to find the aver-age number of comic books owned by students in each age group.

Age	Average Number of Comic Books
6	25
7	40
9	57
10	58
11	56
12	51

1. Make a graph of these data.

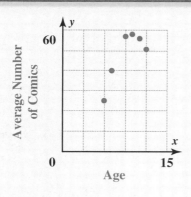

2. Would a linear, quadratic, or exponential model be best for these data? Explain your reasoning. Quadratic; the data rise fast, then rise slowly, and then fall.

3. Use your calculator's quadratic regression feature to find an equation that seems to fit the data. Possible equation: $y = {}^-2x^2 + 41x - 148$

4. Use your equation to predict the average number of comic books owned by 8-year-olds and 13-year-olds at this school. 52 and 47, respectively

Chapter Summary

Chapter Summary

This summary helps students recall the major topics of the chapter.

Problem-Solving Strategies and Applications

The questions in this section help students review and apply the important mathematical ideas and problem-solving strategies developed in the chapter. The questions are organized by mathematical highlights. The highlights correspond to those in "The Big Picture" chart on page T599a.

Questions 1–3:

These all concern the Major League baseball statistics on page 653.

1a. Answers will vary. Based on just the number of runs, the AL looks better. The mean number of runs for the AL is 788, but only 747 for the NL. The median for the AL is 793, but the median for the NL is only 737.5.

1b. Possible answer: Split it into two tables, one for the AL and one for the NL, still sorted by the number of runs.

In this chapter, you worked with various kinds of displays for organizing and analyzing data. You reorganized tables to make it easier to see trends in the variables. In some cases, you made calculations using the given data in order to produce the data you really needed.

You also worked with models of different types. You fit curves to data, using the shape of the data points or assumptions about the situation to select the type of curve to use. Sometimes, though, an algebraic equation wasn't helpful, so you used tables and *model populations* to analyze situations and predict outcomes.

MATERIALS

graphing calculator

Strategies and Applications

The questions in this section will help you review and apply the important ideas and strategies developed in this chapter.

Analyzing data presented in tables

The table on page 653 gives 2003 statistics for all the Major League baseball teams: total number of runs, percentage of games won, and earned run average (ERA). The earned run average (ERA) gives the average number of runs the *opposing* teams earned per inning. The teams all played approximately the same number of games.

1. Evita and Marcus were arguing about which league had better teams, the American League or the National League.

   a. Use the table to compare the number of runs each team scored over the year. Based on just this one statistic, which league would you think has better teams? Support your answer.

   b. How could you reorganize the table to make it easier to answer Part a?

2. Evita and Marcus want to compare the teams in each region rather than in each league. How could they reorganize the table to make this task easier?   Possible answer: Make three tables, one for each region.

 impactmath.com/chapter_test

2003 Major League Baseball Statistics

Team	Total Runs	Games Won (%)	ERA	League	Region
Los Angeles	574	52.5	3.16	National	West
Detroit	591	26.5	5.30	American	Central
New York Mets	642	41.0	4.48	National	East
San Diego	678	39.5	4.87	National	West
Cincinnati	694	42.6	5.09	National	Central
Cleveland	699	42.0	4.21	American	Central
Montreal	711	51.2	4.01	National	East
Milwaukee	714	42.0	5.02	National	Central
Tampa Bay	715	38.9	4.93	American	East
Arizona	717	51.9	3.84	National	West
Chicago Cubs	724	54.3	3.83	National	Central
Anaheim	736	47.5	4.28	American	West
Baltimore	743	43.6	4.76	American	East
Florida	751	56.2	4.04	National	East
Pittsburgh	753	46.3	4.64	National	Central
San Francisco	755	62.1	3.73	National	West
Oakland	768	59.3	3.63	American	West
Philadelphia	791	53.1	4.04	National	East
Chicago White Sox	791	53.1	4.17	American	Central
Seattle	795	57.4	3.76	American	West
Minnesota	801	55.6	4.41	American	Central
Houston	805	53.7	3.86	National	Central
Texas	826	43.8	5.67	American	West
Kansas City	836	51.2	5.05	American	Central
Colorado	853	45.7	5.20	National	West
St.Louis	876	52.5	4.60	National	Central
New York Yankees	877	62.0	4.02	American	East
Toronto	894	53.1	4.69	American	East
Atlanta	907	62.3	4.10	National	East
Boston	961	58.6	4.48	American	East

Source: MLB.com

Using visual displays to identify trends

3. The baseball statistics from page 653 are plotted below.

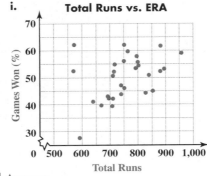

i. Total Runs vs. ERA

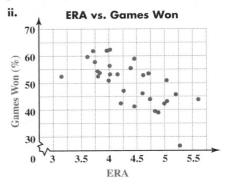

ii. ERA vs. Games Won

3a. See Additional Answers.

4a. Possible answer: The most farmland is in the center of the country, and a little to the west, although most of the western states (except California) are on the lower end. Montana and Texas may be the most important farming states.

4b, c. See Additional Answers.

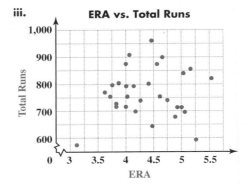

iii. ERA vs. Total Runs

a. Which plot or plots do you think show some connection between the given variables, even a weak one? Which do you think show no connection at all? Explain.

b. Which plot do you think shows the strongest connection between the variables?   Possible answer: Plot i

4. On the opposite page are two displays of the United States.

a. Describe the pattern in the first map, which categorizes the states by amount of farmland, in millions of acres. Using that map, which states do you think may be the most important farming states?

b. Describe the pattern in the second map, which categorizes the states by the portion of their land used for farming. Using that map, which do you think may be the most important farming states?

c. Which map do you think gives a better sense of how important farming is to each state? Explain.

654 CHAPTER 10   Modeling with Data

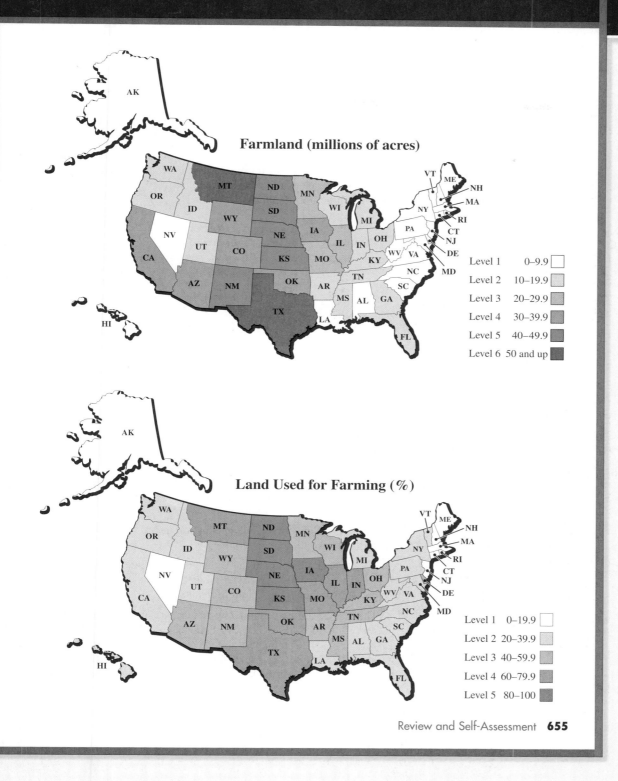

Farmland (millions of acres)

Level 1   0–9.9

Level 2   10–19.9

Level 3   20–29.9

Level 4   30–39.9

Level 5   40–49.9

Level 6   50 and up

Land Used for Farming (%)

Level 1   0–19.9

Level 2   20–39.9

Level 3   40–59.9

Level 4   60–79.9

Level 5   80–100

Question 5:

This requires graphing calculators. Students without access to a graphing calculator at home will need time in class. The possible answer given for **Part b** is rounded from the exponential regression equation found using a Texas Instruments TI-83 Plus and is an extremely good fit. Note that students cannot round the base to fewer than five digits or they will get a constant function. The example function, with the data points plotted, looks like this:

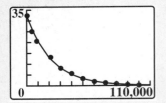

Creating and using models

5. Have your ears ever "popped" as you changed elevation, perhaps when driving up or down a mountain or landing or taking off in an airplane? The popping is caused by changes in *air pressure*. As your altitude or elevation increases, the pressure exerted by the air on your ears lessens.

A *barometer* is a device that measures air pressure. Mercury in the barometer rises and falls depending on the air pressure. The table shows the average barometer reading of air pressure, in inches of mercury, at various altitudes.

Altitude (ft)	Average Air Pressure (in. of mercury)
0 (sea level)	29.92
5,000	24.90
10,000	20.58
20,000	13.76
30,000	8.90
40,000	5.56
50,000	3.44
60,000	2.14
70,000	1.32
80,000	0.82
90,000	0.51
100,000	0.33

Source: *New York Public Library Science Desk Reference.* New York: Macmillan, 1995.

a. Plot the (*altitude, average air pressure*) data on your calculator. What kind of relationship appears to exist between the two variables?   exponential (decay)

b. Use your calculator to find an equation that models the relationship between these two variables.

5b. Possible answer: $y = 32.737425(0.999954)^x$, where y is pressure and x is altitude

c. The highest mountain in the United States is Mount McKinley in Alaska, at 20,320 ft. Use your model to estimate the average air pressure at the top of Mount McKinley.

5c. Possible answer: about 12.86 in. of mercury

5d. Possible answers: about 0.65 and 0.11 in. of mercury, respectively

d. The highest altitude attained by an airplane in a horizontal flight was 85,068.997 ft, by U.S. Air Force captain Robert C. Helt on July 28, 1976. The highest altitude ever attained by an airplane was 123,523.58 ft, by Alexander Fedotov of the USSR on August 31, 1977. Use your model to estimate the average air pressures at these two altitudes.

6. Hernando, an accountant, is reviewing the Algora Corporation's taxes. The company owns stock in three other companies, giving Algora the following percentage ownership in each.

Company	Ownership Percentage
Binomi	20%
The Co-Efficiency Company	40%
Diagon Inc.	30%

In examining these other companies, Hernando found that they each own stock in Algora! Binomi owns 15%, Co-Efficiency owns 25%, and Diagon owns 10% of Algora.

a. Create a model by supposing that there are 1,000 shares, or equal-sized pieces, of the Algora Corporation. Binomi owns 15% of them, or 150 shares. How many of the 1,000 shares of Algora are owned by Co-Efficiency? By Diagon? 250, 100

b. Since Algora owns 20% of Binomi, you might consider 20% of Binomi's 150 shares of Algora to be owned by Algora *through* Binomi. That is, Algora owns 30 shares through Binomi. Find the number of shares Algora owns through Co-Efficiency and through Diagon. 100, 30

c. Together the three other companies own 50% of Algora. Suppose Algora itself still owns the remaining 50% of the 1,000 shares. How many shares does Algora own in total, including the shares owned through other companies? 660

d. What percentage of Algora is owned by the company itself? 66%

Demonstrating Skills

7. The table lists the federal minimum hourly wage from 1978 to 2003. Suppose a person works 40 hours each week at minimum wage, for 50 weeks each year. Create a new table giving the person's annual (yearly) income for each rate.

Federal Minimum Hourly Wage, 1978–2003

Effective Date	Minimum Wage	Annual Income
Jan 1, 1978	$2.65	$5,300
Jan 1, 1979	2.90	5,800
Jan 1, 1980	3.10	6,200
Jan 1, 1981	3.35	6,700
Apr 1, 1990	3.80	7,600
Apr 1, 1991	4.25	8,500
Oct 1, 1996	4.75	9,500
Sep 1, 1997	5.15	10,300

8a. inverse variation

8b. linear

8c. quadratic

8d. exponential growth

8e. exponential decay

8. Match each graph with the type of relationship—linear, quadratic, exponential growth, exponential decay, or inverse variation—that best describes it. Use each type of relationship once.

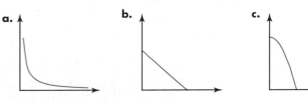

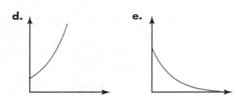

APPENDIX

Trigonometry

Trigonometric Ratios

Explain to students that this lesson will bring together some of the ideas that they have studied previously regarding linear relationships, specifically the relationship of slope and angles in a right triangle. They will also be using some of the work they did with similar triangles in exploring the relationships of sides in right triangles.

Think & Discuss

Draw the right triangle in the Think & Discuss on the chalkboard or overhead. Have students work in pairs to answer the questions, which provide a review of finding the slope of a line. After checking to see that students have arrived at the correct answer, explain that so far, calculating $\frac{\text{rise}}{\text{run}}$ is the only way they know how to find the slope of a line. By the end of the lesson, they will discover another way to find the slope of the line that does not rely on being able to identify the coordinates of two points on a line.

Investigation 1

In this investigation, students measure lengths of legs in similar right triangles to begin an exploration of the tangent ratio. They construct right triangles, each with a 40° angle, and explore the ratio of the legs opposite and adjacent to that angle. They notice that since two of the three angles in their triangles are congruent, the triangles must be similar, and therefore the ratio of the legs is constant. In the next investigation, they will give this ratio a name—the tangent of an angle.

The idea of sides "opposite" or "adjacent to" an angle has not yet been introduced. In this particular triangle, the shorter leg will be opposite the 40° angle. So the ratio of the shorter leg to the longer leg will be the ratio of the opposite side to the adjacent side, or the tangent ratio. This terminology will be introduced in the next investigation.

Have students discuss the text at the bottom of page 660 and the top of page 661 about determining the height of a tree if you know the length of its shadow. As a whole class, discuss why it may be possible to figure out the height of the tree using rulers of different lengths. If students cannot explain this, let the question remain unanswered. Tell students that by the end of the investigation, they will have a better idea of what quantities are important in these calculations. Do not spend more than 5 minutes on this question.

Trigonometric Ratios

There are many ways to look at linear relationships. In Chapter 1 you looked at direct variation and other linear relationships in words, tables, graphs, and equations. You also looked at the slopes of lines on graphs and in equations. Let's look at lines from a different perspective.

1 Draw this right triangle on the chalkboard or overhead.

Think & Discuss

Look at the right triangle in this drawing. What are the coordinates of the end points of the hypotenuse?   (1, 2) and (4, 6)

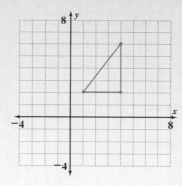

How would you find the slope of the line connecting these points?
The rise is $6 - 2 = 4$. The run is $4 - 1 = 3$. So the slope is $\frac{\text{rise}}{\text{run}}$ or $\frac{4}{3}$.

In this lesson, you will learn a way to find the slope of a line by thinking of that line as the hypotenuse of a right triangle. You will be able to find the slope by using the angles in the triangle even if you don't know the coordinates of the endpoints of the hypotenuse. But first, you will review some of your work with similar triangles.

Investigation ▶ 1 ▶ Special Ratios

You can determine the height of a tree if you know the length of its shadow and the height and the length of a shadow of some other object, such as a ruler. To do this you can use the length of the tree's shadow, the height of the ruler, and the length of the ruler's shadow to set up a proportion.

2 Discuss the text at the bottom of page 660 and top page 661 as a class.

Explore

In this Explore, students construct right triangles using protractors and rulers. They might find it easier to construct these triangles using graph paper, with the legs on horizontal and vertical lines. Have students work in groups of 3 or 4 to do these steps. You may need to provide some guidance on how to construct a right triangle with one 40° angle. As a class, ask students what they would do first in constructing such a triangle: would they construct the right angle first or the 40° angle first? The order is arbitrary, but some students may find that constructing the 40° angle first is easier. Students may be tempted to "eyeball" the right angle; encourage them to measure this angle as well. The more precise they are in their measurements, the greater the likelihood that they will come close to the anticipated answer. Tell students that all of the information from their group should be recorded in the table; each person needs to construct his or her own triangle.

After groups have finished, ask each group to report the decimal ratio in their last column. Record each group's answers on an overhead. These decimals should all be the same, or close to the same number (0.84). Ask students why they think they are all getting the same results. Students should be able to articulate that since all the triangles they constructed are similar to each other (they all have a right angle and a 40° angle), the ratios of the corresponding sides should be the same.

$$\frac{\text{ruler } (R)}{\text{ruler shadow } (S_R)} = \frac{\text{tree } (T)}{\text{tree shadow } (S_T)}$$

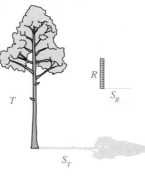

When using proportions like these, you only need to know three of the measurements to determine the fourth measurement.

But some of these measurements are not really important by themselves. For example, you could use rulers of different lengths casting their different length shadows, and you *still* could figure out the height of the tree. Can you explain why? If the *actual length* of the ruler is not really important, then what is?

MATERIALS

protractors

rulers

① Answers will vary. The ratios should all be approximately equal to the tangent of 40°, which is about 0.84.

② Students should see that, even though there will be minor differences in the ratios due to measurement error, the ratios are roughly all the same, regardless of the lengths of the triangle's legs.

③ All the triangles are similar since they have a right angle and a 40° angle. In similar triangles, corresponding sides are proportional.

Explore

Each person in your group should do the following:

- Draw a right triangle with one angle that measures 40°. Make sure your triangle is not congruent to anyone else's in your group.

- Measure the length of each leg of your right triangle.

- Make a table like the one below and record the lengths of the legs of your triangle. Express the ratio of the shorter leg to the longer leg as $\frac{S}{L}$. It is not necessary to reduce this fraction. Finally, convert that fraction to a decimal.

Shorter leg length (S)	Longer leg length (L)	Ratio $\frac{S}{L}$ (fraction)	Ratio $\frac{S}{L}$ (decimal)

- Collect the measurements and ratios from the other members of your group and record them in your table so you have all the information.   See ①.

- Compare the ratios from your group's measurements. What do you notice about the ratios?   See ②.

- Compare the ratios of the measurements of your entire class. Is the same thing still true?   Yes, it should still be true.

- Why do you think this is happening? Why *should* this be true? See ③.

Trigonometric Ratios   **661**

Develop

Problem Set A Suggested Grouping: Whole Class

In this problem set, students use the information they collected in the Explore. This problem set is intended to be done as a whole class discussion, with students volunteering answers to each question.

Problem 1 involves students proving that all the triangles they have constructed are similar.

Problem 3 can be done orally as students continue to work with corresponding sides in similar triangles. Note that in **part b,** there is more than one ratio that has the same value as $\frac{b}{e}$: $\frac{c}{f}$ and $\frac{a}{d}$. It might be worthwhile to ask students the difference between **part b,** and **parts a and c:** in **part b,** the ratio is of sides in different triangles, and in **parts a and c,** the ratios are of sides in the same triangle.

Problem Set Wrap-Up After students have finished problems 1–3, you may want to have them read the text following Problem Set A. It may be helpful to write the words *opposite* and *adjacent* on the board and have students record a picture of a right triangle with the legs labeled in their notebooks. Make sure that students understand that these terms will be used in the next problem set to identify the sides in a right triangle.

Problem Set B Suggested Grouping: Pairs or Small Groups

In this problem set, students are asked to reverse the process they used previously: they are given the ratio of the legs opposite and adjacent to an angle and asked to find the measure of the angle. One question you might pose as students begin to work on these problems is, given the ratio of the legs in a right triangle, how many right triangles can be constructed with that ratio? Students should be able to explain that there are an infinite number of right triangles with the given ratio, but they would all be similar to each other.

Problems 1–4 allow students to think about equivalent ratios in constructing their triangles.

Problem Set A

1. Yes, because they all have a right angle, and one other angle that is congruent. Since two of the three angles are congruent, the triangles must be similar.

1. Consider all the triangles that you and your classmates drew for the Explore activity. Are the triangles all similar? Explain.   See margin.

2. Imagine you have another right triangle with a 40° angle.

   a. What is the ratio, to the nearest hundredth, of its shorter leg to its longer leg?   The same. About 0.84.

   b. Suppose the longer leg is 14 inches. How long is the shorter leg?
   About $0.84 \cdot 14$ or about $11\frac{3}{4}$ in.

3. Given the two similar triangles shown, fill in the missing parts of each proportion.

   a. $\frac{c}{b} = \frac{?}{?}$ $\frac{f}{e}$

   b. $\frac{b}{e} = \frac{?}{?}$ and $\frac{?}{?}$ $\frac{c}{f}$ and $\frac{a}{d}$

   c. $\frac{f}{d} = \frac{?}{?}$ $\frac{c}{a}$

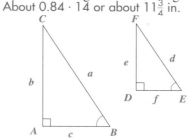

1 You may have students work as a class.

VOCABULARY
opposite leg
adjacent leg

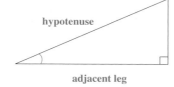

In each of the triangles above, one of the acute angles is marked. One of the legs is **opposite** this angle, or across from it. The other leg is **adjacent**, or next to, the acute angle.

As you work on the next Problem Set, pay attention to the relationship of an angle to the legs that are opposite and adjacent to it.

2 You may want to have students record one of these labeled right triangles in their notebooks.

MATERIALS

protractors
rulers

1–2. See Additional Answers for possible drawings.

Problem Set B

For each problem, draw a right triangle such that the ratio of the lengths of the leg opposite ∠A and the leg adjacent to ∠A is the same as the ratio given. As you are drawing, be sure that you have labeled one of the *acute* angles ∠A. Measure and draw the legs of the triangle to fit the ratio. Then find the measure of ∠A.

1. $\frac{\text{leg opposite } \angle A}{\text{leg adjacent } \angle A} = \frac{1}{4}$ or 0.25   m∠A ≈ 14°

2. $\frac{\text{leg opposite } \angle A}{\text{leg adjacent } \angle A} = \frac{1}{2}$ or 0.5   m∠A ≈ 27°

3 You may have students work in pairs or small groups.

Additional Answers
Problem Set B

1. Triangles will vary but should be similar to the one shown.

2. Triangles will vary but should be similar to the one shown.

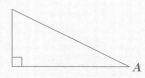

1 **Problem Set Wrap-Up** You may want to discuss **Problem 5** as a whole class. Students should be able to visualize what is happening to the legs as the angle measure increases.

2 **Share & Summarize**
These questions emphasize the method students used in developing the ratio of adjacent and opposite legs in a right triangle. Students should be able to describe the process they used in answering Question 1. It may be helpful to have a whole class discussion on Questions 1 and 2. As an alternative, students can enter their answers in their journals to be used as a way of introducing the next investigation.

Troubleshooting If students are having difficulty in constructing the triangles, you may want to develop a template for each step in the process. Some students may also have difficulty reading the protractor or using the ruler. If this is the case, you may want to model using the tools either on an overhead or in small groups. Some students may also have difficulty distinguishing between the legs of a right triangle and the hypotenuse. It may be helpful to have a right triangle drawn on the board during the entire class with the different sides labeled (adjacent leg, opposite leg, hypotenuse) so that students have a constant visual image of the distinctions.

On Your Own Exercises

Practice & Apply: 1–5, p. 674

Investigation 2

In this investigation, students define the ratio of the leg opposite an angle in a right triangle to the adjacent leg as the tangent of that angle. Students use graphing calculators to find the tangent of an angle. They then solve problems that use the tangent to find the lengths of missing sides in right triangles.

3 Begin the class by explaining to students that the special ratio they worked with in the previous investigation has a name: the *tangent* of an angle. Write the definition on the board, and have students record this in their notebooks.

> The *tangent* of an acute angle is the ratio of the length of the leg opposite that angle to the length of the leg adjacent to that angle in a right triangle. The abbreviation for tangent is tan. This definition can be written as
>
> $$\tan \angle A = \frac{\text{leg opposite } \angle A}{\text{leg adjacent } \angle A}.$$

It is important for students to differentiate between the tangent of an angle, which is the ratio of two sides of a triangle, and the angle itself, which is measured in degrees (or radians). Students should think of the tangent of an angle as a function of that angle, where the input is the angle, and the output is the ratio of the leg opposite that angle to the leg adjacent to that angle.

3-4. See Additional Answers for possible drawings.

5. ∠A increases. If the length of the adjacent leg is fixed and the length of the opposite leg is increased, the ratio of the leg opposite ∠A to the leg adjacent ∠A increases. As the opposite leg gets longer, ∠A must increase.

3. $\frac{\text{leg opposite } \angle A}{\text{leg adjacent } \angle A} = \frac{4}{3}$ or 1.3333 . . .   m∠A ≈ 53°

4. $\frac{\text{leg opposite } \angle A}{\text{leg adjacent } \angle A} = \frac{5}{2}$ or 2.5   m∠A ≈ 68°

5. What happens to the size of ∠A as the ratio increases? Why is this happening?

Share & Summarize

1. Look back at the triangles and ratios you found in the Explore section at the beginning of Investigation 1. The last question in the Explore asked you to explain why you got the results you did. What do you think now?   See Additional Answers.

2. How large and how small can the ratios of the legs of a right triangle be?   See Additional Answers.

3. In Problem Set A, Problem 2, you knew only the length of one leg of a right triangle. Still, you were able to figure out the length of the other leg using a ratio. What feature of the triangle does that ratio depend on? Its size? Its angles? Its position?
The ratio of legs in a right triangle depends only on one of the two acute angles.

Investigation ▶ 2 ▶ The Tangent of an Angle

V O C A B U L A R Y
tangent

The special ratio you looked at in the previous investigation has a name. The **tangent** of an acute angle ∠A is the ratio of the length of the leg opposite ∠A to the length of the leg adjacent to ∠A in a right triangle. The abbreviation for tangent is *tan*.

$$\tan \angle A = \frac{\text{leg opposite } \angle A}{\text{leg adjacent } \angle A}$$

You can use the tangent to calculate the length of a side in a right triangle that you cannot measure or, if the triangle is graphed on the coordinate plane, whose endpoints you do not know.

Trigonometric Ratios   **663**

1 You may want to discuss Problem 5 as a whole class.

2 You may want to discuss Questions 1 and 2 as a class.

3 Have students record the definition of tangent in their notebooks.

Additional Answers
Problem Set B

3. Triangles will vary but should be similar to the one shown.

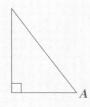

4. Triangles will vary but should be similar to the one shown.

Develop

 Think & Discuss

This Think & Discuss reinforces the idea that any right triangle with a 20° angle will have the same tangent ratio, regardless of the size of the triangle. Students should be comfortable articulating this fact. Have them talk about it in small groups before they share their answers with the class.

Example

Ask students to read the Example on page 664. Working with the whole class, model how you would solve the problem by setting up the equation $\tan 28° = \frac{?\ mi}{110\ mi}$. Ask students how they would solve this problem using a protractor and ruler. Then tell them that calculators can produce the values of the tangent of any angle; they no longer need to construct triangles to approximate these values.

Demonstrate how to find the tangent of 28° on a graphing calculator. When students enter the keystrokes on their own calculators, pause for a minute to ask them what the decimal 0.5317 indicates. They should be able to explain that this decimal represents the ratio of the leg opposite a 28° angle in a right triangle to the leg adjacent to that angle. Ask them for possible leg lengths that would yield this ratio. Whenever students find the tangent of an angle on a calculator, ask the question of what the number means.

Now finish solving the equation, making sure that students feel comfortable with each step in the process. When they get the answer of 58.49 miles, ask them if this number makes sense, given the values in the right triangle for one angle and one side.

② Draw a right triangle with a 20° angle. Measure the length of the leg opposite that angle, and the length of the leg adjacent to that angle. Then find the ratio of the opposite leg to the adjacent leg by dividing the lengths.

Think & Discuss

Suppose you have several right triangles, each with a 20° angle. Why would the tangent ratio of the 20° angle be constant in all of these triangles, no matter the triangle's size? How can you be sure of this? See Additional Answers.

Since a 20° angle has the same tangent no matter what right triangle it is in, you can refer to the tangent of 20°, or tan 20°, in general terms. How could you find tan 20° using only a ruler and a protractor? See ②.

You have used the tangent ratio to calculate the lengths of legs in a right triangle. In the following problems, you will use this technique in a variety of situations.

MATERIALS

graphing calculator

EXAMPLE

Find the length of the leg opposite the 28° angle in the triangle.

$$\tan 28° = \frac{\text{opposite leg}}{\text{adjacent leg}}$$

$$\tan 28° = \frac{? \text{ mi}}{110 \text{ mi}}$$

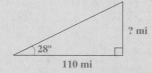

? mi

28°

110 mi

To find the tan 28°, you could certainly draw a right triangle that has an acute angle measuring 28°, measure the lengths of its legs, and calculate the ratio $\frac{\text{opposite leg}}{\text{adjacent leg}}$. Fortunately, you can also find tan 28° using a scientific or graphing calculator. On a graphing calculator, press [MODE] [↓] [↓] [→] [ENTER] to be sure that your calculator is in degree mode. Then press [TAN] 28. The calculator should display 0.531709432 which is about 0.5317.

Let x = the unknown length in miles.

Now finish the equation.

$$\tan 28° = \frac{x \text{ mi}}{110 \text{ mi}}$$

$$0.5317 = \frac{x \text{ mi}}{110 \text{ mi}}$$

$$0.5317 \cdot 110 \text{ mi} = x \text{ mi}$$

$$58.487 = x$$

So the length of the leg opposite the 28° angle is about 58.49 miles.

Problem Set C will give you some practice using the tangent to find lengths of sides in right triangles.

1 Have students work in small groups and then share their answers with the class.

2 Ask how students would solve this problem using a protractor and a ruler.

3 Demonstrate how to find tan 28° on a graphing calculator.

Additional Answers

Share & Summarize

① The reason all the ratios would be the same is that all the right triangles are similar. (They each have a right angle and a 20° angle. If two pairs of corresponding angles are congruent, the triangles are similar.) Since the triangles are similar, the ratios of the lengths of their legs will be equivalent. Writing the ratio as a decimal is another way to write a ratio in simplest form. So if all those equivalent ratios are written in reduced form, they should all be the same.

Develop

1 **Problem Set C** Suggested Grouping: Pairs or Small Groups

In this problem set, students practice using the tangent of an angle to find lengths of missing sides in right triangles.

2 On the **Spot Assessment**

In solving **Problem 2,** watch for students who set up the equation $\tan 62° = \frac{22.7 \text{ cm}}{x \text{ cm}}$ and forget that x is in the denominator. You may want to model how to solve this equation with the entire class, or anticipate before they get to that problem that there will be some confusion on how to solve it. Multiplying both sides by x may be easiest in this situation.

Alternatively, to avoid having the variable in the denominator, you may want to mention that they can determine the other acute angle of the right triangle, which is 28°, and use that angle to create the equation $\tan 28° = \frac{x \text{ cm}}{22.7 \text{ cm}}$.

3 In **Problems 3 and 4,** students should realize that in order to get x in the numerator, which produces an equation that is easier solve, they need to choose the angle they are to take the tangent of carefully. You may want to refer to this when you go over these problems.

Problem Set C

Find the value of *x* in each of the triangles shown below. Round your answers to the nearest hundredth.

1.

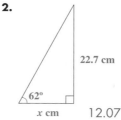

5.2 ft
40°
x ft
4.36

2.

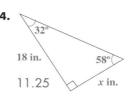

22.7 cm
62°
x cm   12.07

3.

72°
3 m
18°
x m
9.23

4.

32°
18 in.
58°
11.25   *x* in.

5. For safety and comfort, a landing airplane must approach a runway at an angle of about 3°. At what altitude is a plane that it is still 1,000 horizontal feet away from touching down on a runway? Round to the nearest foot.   52 ft

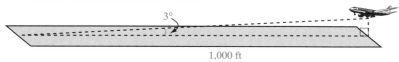

3°

1,000 ft

6. Caity is trying to estimate the height of a flagpole. Using her protractor, she estimates the angle measure from her eye up to the top of the flagpole to be about 34°.

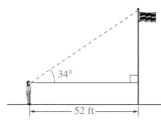

34°
—52 ft—

6b. She forgot to add the distance from the ground up to her eye. That distance plus 35 feet would give her the height of the flagpole.

a. Caity knows she is 52 feet away from the flagpole. She uses those numbers to calculate the opposite leg of the right triangle shown in the drawing above to the nearest foot. What answer does she get?   35 ft

b. She submits that number for her answer, but her teacher tells her she is not correct. What did she forget to do?

1 You may have students work in pairs or small groups.

2 You may want to solve Problem 2 with the entire class.

3 In Problems 3 and 4, students should choose the angle that will result in an equation with x in the numerator.

Develop

 Problem 7 gives students an opportunity to think about conversions between feet and miles. You may want to remind them or ask them if they can tell you that there are 5,280 feet in a mile.

 Problem 8, part b requires that students use the answer to part a and the Pythagorean Theorem to find the hypotenuse of a right triangle. You may need to review this theorem with students.

Pythagorean Theorem
If a and b are the measures of the legs of a right triangle and c is the measure of the hypotenuse, then $a^2 + b^2 = c^2$.

Problem Set Wrap-Up Have students present their solutions to **Problem 5** as a way of assessing if they understand how to solve an equation using the tangent function. Ask them how they might solve this problem if they did not have a calculator.

7. Two hikers come to a deep gorge with steep, almost vertical, cliffs. Since they have no way to cross it, they need to find out how much rope they will need to climb down the side of the gorge to the path at the bottom. They decide to approximate the height of the cliff by taking some measurements.

They are able to estimate that the angle from where they are standing to the bottom of the opposite cliff is about 60°. They know from their map that the width of the gorge is about $\frac{1}{2}$ mile, or about 2,640 feet. About how deep is the gorge?

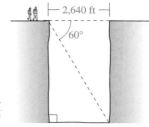

About 4,570 feet or a little less than $\frac{7}{8}$ of a mile

8. Erica has to clean out the leaves from the gutters on her house. She knows that to be safe she should put her ladder at an angle of about 75° to the ground. She wants to figure out how far from the house to put the ladder and how long a ladder she will need to reach the roof.

8a. 6.7 ft or about $6\frac{3}{4}$ ft

a. If her house is about 25 feet to the roof, how far out from the house should she put the foot of her ladder?

b. How long of a ladder will she need to the nearest foot?   at least a 26-foot ladder

9a. Possible answer: The tree and its shadow form a similar triangle to the triangle that Luisa creates. Because the triangles are similar, Luisa knows that the angle formed by the tree and the imaginary line to the top of the shadow is also 36°. She measures the length of the tree's shadow. Then she sets up the equation tan 36° = $\frac{\text{tree's shadow}}{\text{height of tree}}$.

9. Challenge The students in Mr. Claus's math class are trying to determine the height of a tree outside the school.

Luisa places her ruler vertical to the ground as shown. She then places one end of a yardstick at the end of the ruler's shadow and leans the yardstick on the ruler so that it forms a right triangle.

She then measures the angle formed by the ruler and the yardstick and finds that it is about 36°. Using this information and the length of the tree's shadow, Luisa is able to determine the height of the tree.

a. Explain how Luisa determines the tree's height.

b. If she knows that the length of the tree's shadow is 42.5 feet, what is the height of the tree?   58.5 ft

1 Problem 7 gives students an opportunity to think about conversions between feet and miles.

2 Students may need a review of the Pythagorean Theorem in order to solve part b of Problem 8.

1 Share & Summarize

This question requires students to have some understanding of the meaning of the tangent function as it relates to the ratio of the legs of a right triangle. You may want to have students discuss this question in small groups, and have the groups report to the whole class their thinking about the question. As an extension, you may want to ask what is known about a right triangle if the tangent of one of the acute angles is less than 1 or greater than 1.

Troubleshooting If students are having difficulty finding the missing lengths of right triangles, you may want to provide some additional examples that are similar to **Problem 1.** It is important that students make sense of the equations they create, and that they are able to explain in words what it means to find the tangent of an angle. For some students, the difficulty may lie in the mechanics of solving the equation; for others, the conceptual meaning of tangent may be confusing. Asking them to clarify steps in the process of solving and setting up the equation may help to address the specific issue that is causing a problem.

On Your Own Exercises

Practice & Apply: 10–13, p. 675
Connect & Extend: 22–24, pp. 677–678

Investigation 3

The goal of this investigation is to connect the slope of a line with the tangent function. Students are introduced to the idea that relationships are proportional only if the slope (or rate) is constant.

2 Think & Discuss

Begin the class by having students read the Think & Discuss on page 667. Have them work on the four questions in pairs or small groups. This is the first time they explore the connection between rate, slope, and the tangent of an angle. Students should be able to answer these questions relatively easily and quickly. The aim of the Think & Discuss is for students to notice that the speed, the slope, and the tangent are all expressed by the same number. Since this investigation includes three problem sets, move on to Problem Set A as soon as you can.

Share & Summarize

In a certain right triangle, the tangent of one of the acute angles is 1.

1. What does this triangle look like?

2. How do you know? If the tangent of one of the angles is 1, then the ratio of the length of the opposite leg to the length of the adjacent leg is $\frac{1}{1}$. That means the legs must be the same length.

Investigation 3 ▶ Connections Between Tangent, Slope, Rate, and Proportionality

In this investigation, you will see how rate (or speed) may be connected to the slope of a graph and the tangent of an angle.

Think & Discuss

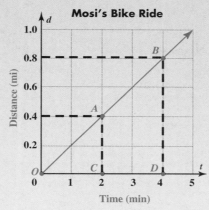

Mosi's Bike Ride

Mosi rode his bike from home to school at a constant speed. The graph above shows the distance Mosi traveled. Two minutes after he started, he was 0.4 mile away from his home. Two minutes later, he was 0.8 mile away. Point A has coordinates (2, 0.4); point B coordinates (4, 0.8); point O coordinates (0, 0); point C coordinates (2, 0); and point D coordinates (4, 0).

What is Mosi's speed in miles per minute?   0.2 mi/min

What is the slope of $\overrightarrow{OA}$? of $\overrightarrow{OB}$?   Both slopes are 0.2.

What is the tangent of $\angle AOC$?   0.2

What do you notice about the speed of Mosi's bike, the slope of the line, and the tangent of the angle?   They are all expressed by the same number.

Develop

Problem Set D Suggested Grouping:
Pairs or Small Groups

In this problem set, students explore the ways in which they calculate the slope of the line *OA* and the tangent of ∠*AOC*. The first three questions investigate the connections between the speed, the slope, and the tangent. The next two questions introduce the idea that proportional relationships are those in which you can make proportions. It also connects graphs with the ideas of similarity from geometry.

Note that in **Problem 4,** students review the concept of direct variation. You should go over this problem with the whole class. Students should understand that since the graph is a straight line starting at the origin, the relationship between distance and time is proportional.

In **Problem 5,** students should see the similarity of the two triangles *AOC* and *BOD*, since they both have a right angle, and both contain ∠*O*.

On the **Spot**
Assessment

In **Problem 5,** some students may have trouble seeing the two different triangles, △*AOC* and △*BOD*, since they overlap. If this is a problem, you may want to draw the triangles separately to the side of the graph and mark the equal angles.

Problem Set Wrap-Up Have students share their answers to **Problem 1, Problem 4,** and **Problem 5** as a way of assessing their understanding of the connection between slope and the tangent of an angle, as well as the proportional relationship between distance and time.

Problem Set E Suggested Grouping:
Pairs or Small Groups

In this problem set, the first three questions about Sancha's graph develop the connections between proportionality of relationships and the possibility of making proportions or equivalent ratios. The next three questions develop the idea that it is necessary to have a constant speed (rate) in order to be able to make a proportion.

Problems 2 and 3 should help students see that since the ratios $\frac{AC}{OC}$ and $\frac{ED}{OD}$ are not the same, a proportion cannot be made. Therefore, the entire graph does not represent direct variation.

Problem Set D

Look back at the graph on page 667.

1. Compare the ways you calculated the slope of the $\overrightarrow{OA}$ and the tangent of $\angle AOC$. How are they similar or different?

2. Express in words the meaning of the ratio $\frac{AC}{OC}$. Express in words the meaning of the ratio $\frac{BD}{OD}$.

3. Compare the ratios $\frac{AC}{OC}$ and $\frac{BD}{OD}$. Can you make a proportion with these ratios? Why or why not?

4. Is the relationship on the graph one of direct variation (is it proportional)? Why or why not?

5. Are $\triangle AOC$ and $\triangle BOD$ similar? Explain.

Problem Set E

Sancha started to bike with Mosi and rode beside him for two minutes. Then she became tired and went more slowly. Four minutes after they started, she was 0.6 mile away from home. Here is a graph showing both Mosi's and Sancha's progress.

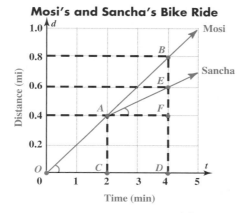

Mosi's and Sancha's Bike Ride

1. Express in words the meaning of the ratio $\frac{AC}{OC}$. Express in words the meaning of the ratio $\frac{ED}{OD}$.

2. Compare the ratios $\frac{AC}{OC}$ and $\frac{ED}{OD}$ for Sancha. Can you make a proportion with these ratios? Why or why not?

3. Is the graphed relationship for Sancha one of direct variation (is it proportional)? Why or why not?

Develop

In **Problems 4 and 5,** students should also notice that the tangent of $\angle AOC$ and the tangent of $\angle EAF$ are not the same.

Problem Set Wrap-Up Discuss **Problem 7** as a class. Bring out the connection here between the fact that the relationship is not proportional, the tangents are not equal, the slope is not constant, and the speeds are not constant.

Problem Set F Suggested Grouping: Pairs or Small Groups

In this problem set, the first three questions develop the idea of the rate and the slope connection, even in non-proportional relationships. The next two questions explore the inability to make proportions in a non-proportional relationship.

Discuss **Problem 3** as a class. Students should find that the hourly rate and the slope represent the same number. You may want to ask why this is true.

Problem 4 gets at an important question of the meaning of the respective ratios $\frac{AC}{OC}$ and $\frac{BD}{OD}$. Students should be comfortable in stating that these are both the ratio of total pay to the number of hours worked.

Problem Set Wrap-Up Go over **Problems 5 and 6** with the entire class. Students should be able to articulate that since the ratios are not the same, the relationship is not proportional. Make sure that they understand that they can simply look at the graph, note that it does not pass through the origin, and conclude that this it not a proportional relationship.

4a. 0.2 mi/min

4b. 0.1 mi/min

5. tan ∠AOC =
0.2; tan ∠EAF =
0.1

6. No; for the first 2
minutes the slope
of her graph is
$\frac{0.4}{2}$ or 0.2, but
over the next
2 minutes, the
slope of her
graph is $\frac{0.2}{2}$ or
0.1

4. a. What is Sancha's speed during the first two minutes of her ride?

b. What is her speed during the second two minutes?

5. What is the tangent of ∠AOC? What is the tangent of ∠EAF?

6. Does the graph of Sancha's bike ride have a constant slope over the first 4 minutes? Explain.

7. What should be true about the speed in order for the ratios $\frac{AC}{OC}$ and $\frac{ED}{OD}$ to be equal?   The average speed over the interval OC should be equal to the average speed over the interval OD.

Problem Set F

Hannah works as a Homework Helper for an elementary school. She is paid a fixed amount of $20 for being available each weekend, even if she is not needed. If she is needed, she is paid an additional $5 for each hour she works. The graph below shows how Hannah's pay on weekends depends on the number of hours worked.

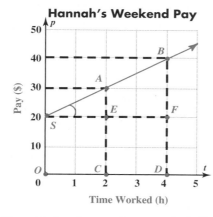

Hannah's Weekend Pay

1. What is Hannah's hourly rate of pay, not including the fixed amount?

2. What is the slope of the line on the graph?   5

3. Compare the hourly rate and the slope. How are they similar or different?

4. Express in words the meaning of the ratio of $\frac{AC}{OC}$. Express in words the meaning of the ratio $\frac{BD}{OD}$.

5. Compare the ratios $\frac{AC}{OC}$ and $\frac{BD}{OD}$ for Hannah. Can you form a proportion with these ratios? Why or why not?
No; the ratios are not equivalent.

6. Is the relationship on the graph a proportional one? Why or why not?
No; the graph does not start at the origin.

Problem Set F

1. $5 per hour

3. The hourly rate and the slope are expressed by the same number.

4. $\frac{AC}{OC}$: Hannah is paid $30 for 2 hours of work for an average rate of $15 an hour; $\frac{BD}{OD}$: Hannah is paid $40 for 4 hours of work for an average rate of $10 an hour. Both represent the ratio of total pay to time.

1 Discuss Problem 7 as a class.

2 You may have students work in pairs or small groups.

3 Discuss Problem 3 as a class.

4 Discuss Problems 5 and 6 as a class.

Share & Summarize

This question requires students to understand the connection between the slope of line and the tangent of the angle that the line makes with the x-axis. Make sure that students understand why they are getting the same (or approximately the same) answers to parts a and b in Question 2.

Troubleshooting If students are having difficulty seeing the connection between the slope of a line and the tangent of the angle the line makes with the x-axis, have them construct their own situation by doing the following: Ask them to take a piece of graph paper and draw any line that intersects the x-axis (with positive slope). Have them measure, with a protractor, the angle that this line makes with the x-axis. Now have them calculate the slope of the line using any method they choose (or you may suggest that they form a right triangle with this angle as one of the angles.) Ask them how they would find the tangent of that angle if they didn't have a calculator. They should be able to tell you that they would find the ratio of the leg opposite the angle to the leg adjacent to the angle. Ask them how that ratio differs from finding the slope of a line, or rise over run. Then ask them to check their answers using the calculator.

On Your Own Exercises

Practice & Apply: 20–21, pp. 676–677
Connect & Extend: 27, p. 679

Investigation 4

In this investigation, students explore two more ratios in right triangles: the sine and cosine. They will use an approach similar to the one they used with the tangent ratio: constructing similar right triangles and measuring sides to form the appropriate ratios. Students may have already noticed that there are other constant ratios in right triangles, and therefore the exploration with sine and cosine may take less time than the work with the tangent ratio. Students will also make conjectures about the range of values for sine and cosine and their relationship to the relative sides of right triangles.

You may want to tell students that the concepts they are studying are part of a branch of mathematics called trigonometry. Refer them to the origin of the word *trigonometry* in the Just the Facts on page 671.

Think & Discuss

Draw right triangle *ABC* with the right angle at *C* on a chalkboard or overhead. Label the sides *a*, *b*, and *c*. You might begin by asking students to look at $\angle A$ and state its tangent. Write the ratio $\frac{a}{b}$ on the board, and ask students if there are other ratios that can be formed using sides *a*, *b*, and *c*. Some students may think that the ratio $\frac{a}{b}$ is the same as $\frac{b}{a}$. It is important to reinforce that there is a distinction here. You might even ask which angle has as its tangent the ratio $\frac{b}{a}$ ($\angle B$, not $\angle A$.) They should be able to come up with all six ratios. You can mention to students that each of these ratios has a name, but in this investigation they will only look at two of these ratios.

1. Hannah's hourly rate of pay is $5. The slope of the graph is 5. This is the tangent of ∠ASE and also of ∠BSF in the graph.

2a. tan 40° ≈ 0.84

2b. Students will choose different points, but the $\frac{rise}{run}$ between these points should be reasonably close to 0.84.

Share & Summarize

1. Consider the hourly rate of pay and the slope of Hannah's graph. Which angle's tangent is equal to these?

2. This graph shows a line making an angle of 40° with the *x*-axis.

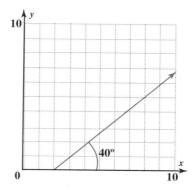

   a. Find the slope of the line using the tangent ratio.

   b. Find two points on the line and carefully measure their coordinates. Then find the slope of the line from your two points.

   c. Compare your answers to Part a and Part b.
   They are nearly equal, because they are both measures of the slope of the same line. They are not exactly equal because both are approximations.

Investigation ▶4▶ The Sine and Cosine

In the previous investigations, you worked with the tangent ratio by constructing right triangles. You selected one of the acute angles, measured the legs opposite and adjacent to that angle, and then formed the ratio of those legs.

Think & Discuss

Given right triangle *ABC* with sides *a*, *b*, and *c*, how many different ratios of sides can you form? State all of them.
6: $\frac{a}{b}$, $\frac{b}{a}$, $\frac{c}{a}$, $\frac{a}{c}$, $\frac{c}{b}$, and $\frac{b}{c}$

1 Make sure students understand why they are getting approximately the same answers to parts a and b.

2 Draw this triangle on the chalkboard or overhead.

Develop

 Problem Set G Suggested Grouping: Pairs or Small Groups

In this problem set, students construct three different right triangles, each with one angle measuring 65°. They might find it easier to construct these triangles using graph paper, with the legs on horizontal and vertical lines. They then look at the ratio of the length of the leg opposite that angle and the hypotenuse. They will learn that this ratio has a special name, the sine of an angle. It may be helpful to write the definition of sine on the board, and next to it, as review, the definition of tangent.

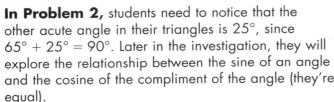 **Problem 1, part d,** is worth stressing. Students should be able to articulate that in any right triangle with a 65° angle, the ratio of the length of the opposite leg to the length of the hypotenuse has to be the same, since all right triangles with a 65° angle are similar (since all of the corresponding angles are equal). Have students hold up their different sized, but similar, triangles, and ask different pairs to share their decimal ratios from part c. They should take comfort in the fact that their ratios are equal, or at least quite close to each other.

In Problem 2, students need to notice that the other acute angle in their triangles is 25°, since 65° + 25° = 90°. Later in the investigation, they will explore the relationship between the sine of an angle and the cosine of the compliment of the angle (they're equal).

Problem Set Wrap-Up After students have finished Problems 1 and 2, you may want to write the definition of the sine of an angle on the board and have students record the definition in their notebooks. Make sure that students understand that this ratio is constant for any specific angle in similar right triangles.

 Problem Set H Suggested Grouping: Pairs or Small Groups

This problem set mirrors the process used in Problem Set G, except the function used is the cosine. You may want to suggest that pairs or groups of students divide the work among each other so that the measuring does not become too tedious.

Looking at $\angle A$, you know that the ratio $\frac{a}{b}$ has been given the special name of tangent. In fact, there are names for each of the other ratios as well. These ratios are the focus of a branch of mathematics called *trigonometry*. In this investigation, you will work with two more of these ratios.

Problem Set G

1. Draw three different right triangles that have one angle measuring 65°.

a. Measure the length of each leg opposite the 65° angle and each hypotenuse.   Answers will vary.

b. Make a table with these headings and record each measure. Then calculate the ratio of the opposite leg to the hypotenuse, and write it as a fraction and as a decimal.   Answers will vary. The decimal ratio should be approximately 0.91.

Opposite leg	Hypotenuse	Ratio (fraction)	Ratio (decimal)

c. What is true about this ratio?   It is approximately the same for each of the triangles.

d. Will this ratio be the same for any right triangle with a 65° angle? Explain your answer.   Yes; Since all right triangles that have one angle measuring 65° must be similar to each other, the ratio of their corresponding sides are proportional.

The name given to this ratio is **sine.** The abbreviation for sine is *sin*.

$$\sin \angle A = \frac{\text{leg opposite } \angle A}{\text{hypotenuse}}$$

2. How can you use your triangles to approximate sin 25°? What is your approximation?

Problem Set H

1. Use the three right triangles that you drew for Problem 1 in Problem Set G.

a. Measure the length of each leg adjacent to the 65° angle.

b. Make a table with these headings and record each measure. Then calculate the ratio of the adjacent leg to the hypotenuse, and write it as a fraction and as a decimal.   Answers will vary. The decimal ratio should be approximately 0.42.

Adjacent leg	Hypotenuse	Ratio (fraction)	Ratio (decimal)

c. What is true about this ratio?   It is approximately the same for each of the triangles.

d. Will this ratio be the same for any right triangle with a 65° angle? Explain your answer.   Yes; Since all right triangles that have one angle measuring 65° must be similar to each other, the ratio of their corresponding sides are proportional.

Problems 2 and 3 allow students to begin to think about the issue of the range of values the cosine can assume. If students seem confused, you may want to suggest that they try to draw a right triangle with an adjacent leg equal to 5 and a hypotenuse equal to 4. They should discover the contradiction.

About the Mathematics

If appropriate, you may want students to know that when they take a course in trigonometry, they will be working with angles between 0 and 360 degrees, as these definitions are extended to the unit circle. There are, in fact, three additional ratios (secant, cosecant, and cotangent) which are also used in trigonometry.

Problem Set Wrap-Up Add cosine to the list on the board you have created, and include tangent as well. If students need help memorizing the definitions of sine, cosine and tangent, one tool that has become a staple in many classrooms is the mnemonic device SOH-CAH-TOA, which are the first letter of each word in the ratios for sine, cosine, and tangent.

$$\mathbf{s}\text{in } A = \frac{\mathbf{o}\text{pp}}{\mathbf{h}\text{yp}}$$

$$\mathbf{c}\text{os } A = \frac{\mathbf{a}\text{dj}}{\mathbf{h}\text{yp}}$$

$$\mathbf{t}\text{an } A = \frac{\mathbf{o}\text{pp}}{\mathbf{a}\text{dj}}$$

You may want to mention to students that these ratios have uses in many fields, such as architecture, engineering, surveying, and astronomy.

Example

The method used in the Example is similar to the one used in working with the tangent function on the calculator. Go through the Example with the class, making certain that they can locate the sine and cosine keys.

Problem Set I Suggested Grouping: Pairs or Small Groups

In this problem set, students apply the sine and cosine functions to solve problems involving missing lengths of sides.

2. Marcus is correct. If the cosine of an angle is the ratio of the length of the adjacent leg to the hypotenuse, the cosine can never be greater than 1, since the hypotenuse is always the largest side.

The name given to this ratio is **cosine.** The abbreviation for cosine is *cos.*

$$\cos \angle A = \frac{\text{leg adjacent } \angle A}{\text{hypotenuse}}$$

2. Ian said he found a right triangle where the cosine of one of the angles was $\frac{5}{4}$. Marcus said that was impossible. Explain who was correct and why.

3. Challenge How small can the sine and cosine of an angle be in a right triangle? How large can they be?

In Problem Set I, you will use your calculator to solve problems involving lengths in right triangles. You should use the sine and cosine keys, $\boxed{\text{SIN}}$ and $\boxed{\text{COS}}$ respectively, in the same way you used the tangent key to find the sines and cosines of angles.

EXAMPLE

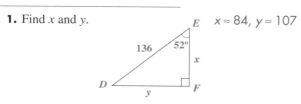

How can you find the length of the leg opposite the 34° angle?

$$\sin 34° = \frac{\text{opposite leg}}{\text{hypotenuse}}$$

$$\sin 34° = \frac{?}{165}$$

Press $\boxed{\text{SIN}}$ 34. The calculator should display 0.559192903 which is about 0.5592.

$$0.5592 = \frac{x}{165}$$

$$0.5592(165) = x$$

$$92.3 = x$$

Problem Set I

1. Find x and y.

$x \approx 84$, $y \approx 107$

2. A car is traveling on a road that has an incline of 4°. If the car travels 1,500 feet on this road, how much has its elevation changed to the nearest foot?   105 ft

Problem-Solving Strategy

1 Problem-Solving Strategy

Draw a diagram

2 You may want students to know about the mnemonic device SOH-CAH-TOA.

3 Work through the Example with students to be sure they can locate the sine or cosine keys.

4 You may have students work in pairs or in small groups.

Additional Answers

3. The ratio must be larger than 0 but can get as close to 0 as you like. The opposite or adjacent leg can get very small, approaching 0, and the hypotenuse can be any length. The ratio must be smaller than 1, but can get arbitrarily close to 1 as the opposite leg or adjacent leg approaches the length of the hypotenuse.

Problem 3 assesses whether students understand that 0.2 represents a ratio of two lengths in a right triangle, which is a fundamental understanding in developing the trigonometric ratios. If they are having difficulty knowing where to begin, you may want to ask, "Where did 0.2 come from?" They may think of 0.2 as $\frac{2}{10}$, $\frac{1}{5}$, $\frac{4}{20}$, etc. —any ratio equivalent to $\frac{1}{5}$. Using these equivalent ratios, they can think about similar right triangles with these lengths as the side adjacent (numerator) and the hypotenuse (denominator).

Problem 4 develops the idea that in any right triangle ABC, where $\angle C$ is a right angle, $\sin A = \cos B$. Students should draw a specific right triangle first, and then calculate the sine of one of the acute angles and the cosine of the other acute angle. This will help them articulate what is happening regarding the adjacent and opposite legs.

Share & Summarize

These questions emphasize the process used in developing the tangent, sine, and cosine functions: creating similar triangles and using the proportionality of the lengths of the sides to determine constant ratios. It is very important for students to be able to describe this process in words.

Troubleshooting If students are having difficulty with understanding the definitions of tangent, sine, and cosine, you may want to draw two similar right triangles, with the lengths of each of the sides given. Ask students to set up as many equal ratios as they can, using the numbers for lengths. Then make the transition to focusing on one of the acute angles, and the relationship of the adjacent leg to the hypotenuse and the opposite leg to the hypotenuse, before you generalize.

If students are having difficulty solving equations involving the sine and cosine, have them work with simpler equations first, such as $\frac{x}{2} = 7$. If they eventually set up a problem and need to take the sine of an angle (by entering it on the calculator), ask them what the number means that comes up on the display. Continue to reinforce the connection between the decimal representation and the ratio of two sides of a right triangle.

On Your Own Exercises

Practice & Apply: 6–9, 14–19, pp. 676–677
Connect & Extend: 25, 26, 28, pp. 678–680

3. Colin found the cosine of one of the angles in a right triangle was 0.2. Find the lengths of all sides in at least two right triangles for which this could be true. How many right triangles are there in all? **Possible answers: 2, 9.8, 10; 1, 4.9, 5; an infinite number**

4. Challenge Anson claimed that no matter what right triangle he examined, the sine of one of the acute angles was always equal to the cosine of the other acute angle. In other words, in the triangle shown, sin A = cos B. Do you think Anson is correct? Why or why not? **Yes, Anson is correct. The leg adjacent to one of the acute angles is the opposite leg for the other acute angle. Therefore, their sines and cosines are equal.**

1 You may want to ask, "Where did 0.2 come from?"

2 Problem-Solving Strategy

Draw a diagram

3 It is important that students be able to describe the process used in developing the tangent, sine, and cosine functions.

Share & Summarize

1. You are now familiar with the right triangle ratios tangent, sine, and cosine. What is the relationship of these ratios to similar triangles?

2. Which of the ratios—sine, cosine, or tangent—can be greater than 1? Explain your answer.

3. David found sin 30° on his calculator to be 0.5. Explain in words what this means in terms of the legs of a right triangle with a 30° angle. **If the sin 30° is 0.5, that means the ratio of the leg opposite the 30° angle to the hypotenuse is $\frac{1}{2}$. Therefore, the sides could be 1 and 2, 2 and 4, 5 and 10, etc., as long as the leg opposite is half the hypotenuse.**

1. The reason all the ratios are constant for any given angle in a right triangle is that all the right triangles are similar. Since the triangles are similar, the ratios of the lengths of their sides will be equivalent.

2. Only the tangent ratio can be greater than 1, when the opposite leg is greater than the adjacent leg. The sine and cosine can never be greater than 1, since the hypotenuse has to be the longest side of the triangle, and the hypotenuse is in the denominator of each of these ratios.

On Your Own Exercises

**On Your
Own
Exercises**

Investigation 1,
   pp. 660–663
Practice & Apply: 1–5

Investigation 2,
   pp. 663–667
Practice & Apply: 10–13
Connect & Extend: 22–24

Investigation 3,
   pp. 667–670
Practice & Apply: 20–21
Connect & Extend: 27

Investigation 4,
   pp. 670–673
Practice & Apply: 6–9,
   14–19
Connect & Extend: 25,
   26, 28

Exercise 1:
Part a, is a multi-step
problem, since students
first need to realize that
$\frac{x}{y} = \frac{a}{b}$, and then solve the
appropriate proportion.
You may want to ask
students different ways in
which they solved this
proportion. As an exten-
sion, you can ask students
which angle has a tangent
of 0.2.

Exercise 2:
In part a, when students
are solving this propor-
tion, the missing length
y is in the denominator,
which makes the proportion a bit trickier to
solve. To avoid having y in the denominator,
you may want to ask students what the value
of $\frac{b}{a}$ is, given $\frac{a}{b}$ is 0.25. Then they can use
the equation $\frac{4}{1} = \frac{y}{19.6}$.

Practice & Apply

1. Consider these similar right triangles.

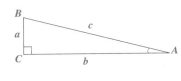

a. $\frac{x}{y} = \frac{1}{5}$, and $b = 2.4$ inches. Find the length of a.   0.48 in.

b. What is $\frac{1}{5}$ in decimal form?   0.2

c. What is $\frac{a}{b}$ in decimal form?   0.2

2. Consider these similar
right triangles.

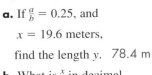
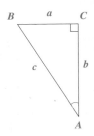

a. If $\frac{a}{b} = 0.25$, and
   $x = 19.6$ meters,
   find the length y.   78.4 m

b. What is $\frac{x}{y}$ in decimal
   form?   0.2

Each of the following ratios compares the leg opposite $\angle A$ to the leg
adjacent to $\angle A$. Copy the triangle and label $\angle A$.

3. $\frac{4}{3}$

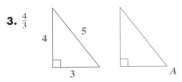

4. $\frac{24}{7}$

5. $\frac{5}{12}$

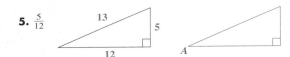

6. $\sin A = \frac{15}{17} \approx 0.88$;

$\cos A = \frac{8}{17} \approx 0.47$;

$\tan A = \frac{15}{8}$ or 1.875

7. $\sin A = \frac{21}{29} \approx 0.72$;

$\cos A = \frac{20}{29} \approx 0.69$;

$\tan A = \frac{21}{20}$ or 1.05

8. $\sin A = \frac{33}{65} \approx 0.51$;

$\cos A = \frac{56}{65} \approx 0.86$;

$\tan A = \frac{33}{56} \approx 0.59$

9. $\sin A = \frac{12}{37} \approx 0.32$;

$\cos A = \frac{35}{37} \approx 0.95$;

$\tan A = \frac{12}{35} \approx 0.34$

In Exercises 6–9, find the numerical value of sine, cosine, and tangent of the angle marked A.

6.

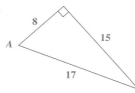

7.

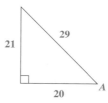

8.

9.

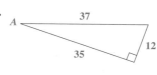

In Exercises 10–19, use a calculator to find the value of x and/or y to the nearest hundredth.

10.

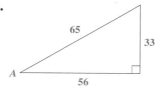

4.75

11.

19.27

12.

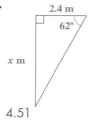

4.51

13.

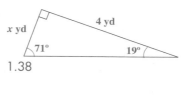

1.38

14.

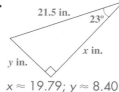

$x \approx 19.79$; $y \approx 8.40$

15.

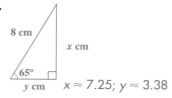

$x \approx 7.25$; $y \approx 3.38$

Trigonometric Ratios **675**

16.

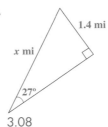

1.4 mi

x mi

27°

3.08

17.

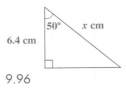

50°   *x* cm

6.4 cm

9.96

18.

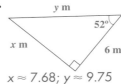

y m

52°

x m

6 m

$x \approx 7.68$; $y \approx 9.75$

19.

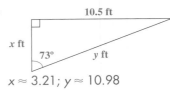

10.5 ft

x ft

73°   *y* ft

$x \approx 3.21$; $y \approx 10.98$

20a. See Additional Answers.

20e. The ratio of *AC:OC* describes the number of dollars you pay for 5 cones divided by 5. The ratio of *BD:OD* describes the number of dollars you pay for 10 cones divided by 10. Both give you the price for one cone.

20f. These ratios are equal because they are equal to the price of one cone. Equal ratios form can a proportion.

20h. Yes; The relationship is a direct variation because its graph is that of a line passing through the origin.

20. At the Ice Cream Club, each ice cream cone costs $1.50.

a. Graph this relationship with the number of cones from 0 and 15 on the *x*-axis and the cost of cones from $0 to $25 on the *y*-axis.

b. What is the slope of the line you graphed?   1.5

c. Plot the points (0, 0), (5, 0), and (10, 0) and label them *O*, *C*, and *D* respectively. Draw a vertical line through point *C* and label the point where this line meets your graph *A*. Draw a vertical line through point *D* and label the point where this line meets your graph *B*.   See Additional Answers.

d. What is the tangent of $\angle BOD$? Compare it with the slope of the line.   1.5; They are the same.

e. Express in words the meaning of ratio $\frac{AC}{OC}$. Express in words the meaning of ratio $\frac{BD}{OD}$.

f. Compare ratios $\frac{AC}{OC}$ and $\frac{BD}{OD}$. Can you make a proportion with these ratios? Why or why not?

g. If you express these two ratios as one number, what does this number represent?   These ratios are equal to the price of one cone.

h. Is the relationship graphed a direct variation? Why or why not?

i. Are $\triangle AOC$ and $\triangle BOD$ similar? Why or why not?   These triangles are similar because they are both right triangles and have a common angle.

676   Trigonometric Ratios

Additional Answers
20a, c. Ice Cream Costs

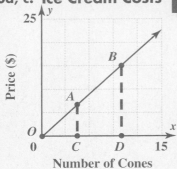

21a. Possible answer: Two cars started out traveling at the same speed. Then, one of the cars slowed down, so that 60 minutes after starting, the first car was 60 miles away from the start and the second car was 45 miles away from the start.

21b. Possible answer: Both of them represent the ratio of total miles traveled to the number of minutes that have passed.

21d. No; The graph of OAE is not linear.

21e. 1; 0.5

21f. tan $\angle AOC = 1$; tan $\angle EAF = 0.5$

21h. The average speed over the interval OC should be equal to the average speed over the OD.

Connect & Extend

21. Look at the graph below.

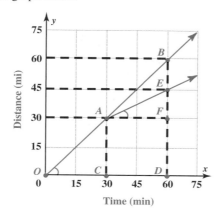

a. Write a problem about a real-life situation that could be represented by this graph.

b. Express in words the meaning of the ratio $\frac{AC}{OC}$. Express in words the meaning of the ratio $\frac{ED}{OD}$.

c. Compare the ratios $\frac{AC}{OC}$ and $\frac{ED}{OD}$. Can you make a proportion with these ratios? Why or why not?   You cannot make a proportion, because the ratios are not equal.

d. Does the graph of OAE represent a relationship with direct variation (a proportional relationship)? Why or why not?

e. What is the slope of $\overrightarrow{OA}$? What is the slope of the $\overrightarrow{AE}$?

f. What is the tangent of $\angle AOC$? What is the tangent of $\angle EAF$?

g. Is the slope of OAE constant?   no

h. If this were a graph of speed, what should be true about the speed in order for the ratios $\frac{AC}{OC}$ and $\frac{ED}{OD}$ to be equal?

22. Airports need to know the height of the cloud cover in order to control air traffic landing and taking off. One method the airport employees can use is to beam a light straight up, and measure the angle from a distant location up to the light on the clouds. One night, an airport employee stood 250 feet from the light and measured this angle as 70°. How high was the cloud cover that night?   about 687 ft

Trigonometric Ratios **677**

Some students may forget to subtract 200 from their answer after they find the height that the balloon is off the ground.

Exercise 25:
Students need to realize that the length of the kite string is the hypotenuse of the triangle. Again, watch for students who have difficulty solving an equation where the variable is in the denominator.

In y o u r
own
words

Explain the connection between the slope of a line and the tangent of an angle.

23. A hot air balloon is hovering directly over a 200-foot tower for power lines. The pilot in the balloon is concerned that he has enough clearance to be safe and radios his assistant on the ground. The assistant quickly moves to a place 100 feet from the center of the tower and estimates the measure of the angle up to the bottom of the balloon's basket as 65°. About how much clearance does the balloon have?
about (214 − 200) ft or 14 ft

24. As a sailboat passes a river buoy, the crew drops the anchor. Once the anchor hits the bottom of the river, the boat continues past the buoy another 50 feet before the line goes taut and the boat comes to a stop. The captain estimates that the measure of the angle between the anchor line and a straight line down to the bottom of the river is 48°. About how deep is the river at that point?   about 45 ft

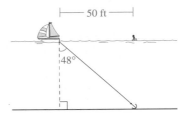

25. Jessica kneels a horizontal distance of 20 feet from the kite she is flying. Holding the end of the kite string to the ground, she estimates the angle the string makes with the ground to be 35°.

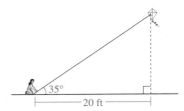

Estimate the length of kite string Jessica has let out to the nearest tenth of a foot.   about 24.4 ft

26. The tailgate of a moving truck is 2 feet above the ground. The incline of the ramp used for loading the truck is 15° as shown. Find the length of the ramp to the nearest tenth of a foot.   7.7 ft

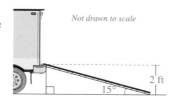

Not drawn to scale

2 ft

15°

27. Look at the drawing of the staircase.

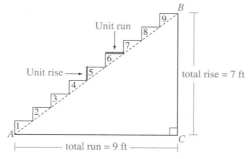

Unit run

Unit rise

total rise = 7 ft

total run = 9 ft

27b. No; The unit rise is 9.3 in., which is not between 6 and 8 in. In addition, the unit rise plus the unit run is 21.3 in., which is not between 17 and 18 in.

27e. This ratio is also equal to the slope of $\overrightarrow{AB}$.

27f. These ratios are equal and both equal to the slope of the staircase. Therefore, you can form a proportion with these ratios.

27g. These ratios are equal to the tangent of ∠BAC. You can calculate the tangent by dividing the total rise by the total run.

a. Calculate the unit rise and the unit run for the steps of the staircase. Round to the nearest tenth of an inch if necessary.
unit rise: 9.3 in., unit run: 12 in.

b. Building manuals have specifications for building staircases. In one such manual it states that the unit rise on a staircase needs to be in the range of 6–8 inches, and that the total of the unit rise plus the unit run needs to be between 17 and 18 inches. Is the staircase pictured above built to code? Why or why not?

c. What is the ratio of the unit rise to the unit run?   9.3:12 or 0.78

d. How is this ratio related to the slope of the staircase, or the slope of $\overrightarrow{AB}$?

e. Calculate the ratio of total rise to total run of the staircase. How is this ratio related to the slope of the staircase or $\overrightarrow{AB}$?

f. Compare the ratios of the unit rise to the unit run and the total rise to total run. Can you form a proportion with these ratios? Why or why not?

g. How are these ratios related to the tangent of ∠BAC? How would you find the tangent of this angle?

h. Draw a graph which shows how the height you reach depends on the number of stairs you climb.   See Additional Answers.

i. What is the slope of the line on the graph? How is the slope related to the slope of the staircase, to the ratio of unit rise to unit run, and to the tangent of ∠ABC? $\frac{7}{9}$ or about 0.78; they are all equal.

Trigonometric Ratios   **679**

Additional Answers
27h. Number of Stairs vs. Height

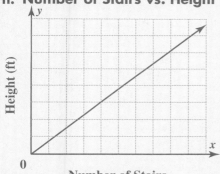

Height (ft)

0

Number of Stairs

Exercise 27:
Students might find it helpful to make the connection between the unit rise to unit run ratio and the total rise to total run, to finding the slope of a line using two different pairs of points. Regardless of which points they choose, the slope is constant.

This may be the first time students have used a trigonometric table to find the sine, cosine, and tangent of angles. You may want to examine this table as a whole class to see if the numbers make sense. Note that you can only estimate the measure of angle *CBE* if you have this table, unlike using a calculator. You can explain to students that some tables give values for parts of degrees as well (there are 60 minutes in every degree) so that estimates can be refined.

Exercise 28c:

In fact, the measure of ∠*CBE* is the same no matter the measure of diagonal *BD*, since the ratio of $\frac{EC}{BE}$ is $\frac{x}{0.5x}$. No matter the value of *x*, $\frac{x}{0.5x}$ always simplifies to $\frac{1}{0.5}$ or 2, and the angle measure whose tangent is 2 is between 60° and 65°.

20b. Since the diagonals bisect each other, $EB = 0.5x$ and $EC = x$. The diagonals are also perpendicular, so △*BEC* is a right triangle with ∠*E* as its right angle. The tangent of ∠*CBE*, is equal to the ratio $\frac{EC}{BE}$ or $\frac{x}{0.5x}$. This ratio simplifies to $\frac{1}{0.5}$ or 2. Thus, the tangent of ∠*CBE* is 2. Derrick can use the trigonometric table to find an angle measure whose tangent is about 2.

28. Derrick drew a rhombus and then drew in the diagonals of that rhombus as shown below.

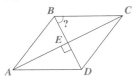

a. When Derrick measured the diagonals, he found that diagonal *AC* was twice as long diagonal *BD*. If the length of diagonal *BD* is *x*, express the length of diagonal *AC* in terms of *x*   2x

b. Derrick is trying to estimate the measure of ∠*CBE*. He knows that the diagonals of a rhombus bisect each other and are perpendicular. He also has the following table of trigonometric values at his disposal.

Trigonometric Table

Degrees	Sine	Cosine	Tangent
0	0.0000	1.0000	0.0000
5	0.0872	0.9962	0.0875
10	0.1736	0.9848	0.1763
15	0.2588	0.9659	0.2679
20	0.3420	0.9397	0.3640
25	0.4226	0.9063	0.4663
30	0.5000	0.8660	0.5774
35	0.5736	0.8192	0.7002
40	0.6428	0.7660	0.8391
45	0.7071	0.7071	1.0000
50	0.7660	0.6428	1.1918
55	0.8192	0.5736	1.4281
60	0.8660	0.5000	1.7321
65	0.9063	0.4226	2.1445
70	0.9397	0.3420	2.7475
75	0.9659	0.2588	3.7321
80	0.9848	0.1736	5.6713
85	0.9962	0.0872	11.4301
90	1.0000	0.0000	....

Explain how Derrick could estimate the measure of ∠*CBE*.

c. If the measure of diagonal *BD* is 6 inches, estimate the measure of ∠*CBE*.   Answers will vary but should be between 60° and 65°.

Chapter 6 Mathematical Background

Page 357a Notes, continued

Multiplying Two Binomials In this chapter, students use a geometric model as well as the distributive property to multiply binomials of the form $(a + b)(c + d)$, getting $ac + bc + ad + bd$. Using a geometric model can serve two important purposes:

- It shows that the equivalence of these two expressions makes sense and agrees with what our eyes tell us ought to be.

- In case we forget the rule, we can draw the diagram to help reconstruct the rule.

	c	d
a	ac	ad
b	bc	bd

It is important to note that the formula

$$(a + b)(c + d) = ac + bc + ad + bd$$

is quite a bit more general than the drawing, which illustrates only the case in which a, b, c, and d are all positive. The formula holds even when some values are negative, but in these cases the geometric models are harder to draw and interpret.

Three cases of multiplying binomials are especially important:

$$(a + b)^2 = (a + b)(a + b) = a^2 + 2ab + b^2$$

$$(a + b)(a - b) = a^2 - b^2$$

$$(a - b)^2 = (a - b)(a - b) = a^2 - 2ab + b^2$$

These types of expressions arise often in algebra, so students need to recognize them and know how to convert them from one form to the other.

Combining Like Terms The rules for combining like terms are a direct application of the distributive property, although this is not explicitly mentioned in the text. For example, $3u + 12u = 15u$ because $3u + 12u = (3 + 12)u = 15u$.

Algebraic Fractions Chapter 6 also introduces algebraic fractions, that is, fractions with variables—such as $\frac{1}{x}$, $\frac{a^2 - 1}{a + 1}$, and $\frac{xy}{x^2 - y^2}$. The rules for adding, sub-tracting, and multiplying algebraic fractions are the same as the analogous rules for numeric fractions.

The chapter concludes with a discussion of solving equations that contain algebraic fractions. One common strategy to solve such equations is to "clear" the equation of fractions by multiplying both sides by the product (or least common multiple) of the denominators. For example, to solve $\frac{x + 7}{2x - 4} = 5$, you might multiply both sides by $2x - 4$ to get $x + 7 = 5(2x - 4)$.

This strategy relies on the fact that $\frac{a}{b} = c$ if and only if $a = bc$. However, this is true only if $b \neq 0$. If $b = 0$, we have $\frac{a}{0} = c$, which makes no sense; however, $a = 0c$ says that $a = 0$. Multiplying by an expression that is equal to 0 for some value of the variable may result in an equation that has more solutions than the orignal equation. For example, given $\frac{x - 2}{2x - 4} = 5$, students might multiply by $2x - 4$ and find the solution $x = 2$. However, $2x - 4$ is equal to 0 when x is 2, so the students would effectively be multiplying by 0. This equation has no solution.

The phenomenon of obtaining solutions of an equation that turn out *not* to be solutions is referred to as *introducing extraneous roots*. There is always a danger of introducing extraneous roots when multiplying an equation by an expression that contains a variable. Students must be careful to check their answers by substituting them into the *original* equation.

Lesson 6.1

Page T364 Notes, continued

Problem-Solving Strategies Students may have various approaches in Problem 1.

- Students may think of subtracting $10(2x - 0.5)$ as adding the opposite, or $+ {}^-10(2x - 0.5)$.

- Students might distribute the 10 first, getting $20x - 5$, and then subtract the entire result, $^-20x + 5$.

Lesson 6.3

Page T392 Notes, *continued*

Additional Examples Expand each expression.

$(x + 3)^2$ $x^2 + 6x + 9$

$(y - 8)^2$ $y^2 - 16y + 64$

$(7 + h)^2$ $49 + 14h + h^2$

$\left(c - \frac{1}{2}\right)^2$ $c^2 - c + \frac{1}{4}$

On Your Own Exercises

Practice & Apply: 1–13, p. 396
Connect & Extend: 27–32, p. 397
Mixed Review: 42–49, p. 399

Lesson 6.4

Page 410 Quick Quiz

Quick Quiz

1. Consider the equation $y = \frac{3}{(x + 1)(x - 2)}$.

   a. What is the value of y when $x = 4$? $\frac{3}{10}$

   b. For what values of x is y undefined? $^-1$, 2

2. Every week the manager of a school cafeteria buys $1,000 of bread from a bakery warehouse. One week the bread sells for b dollars per loaf. The next week the price rose a quarter of a dollar per loaf.

   a. Write an expression for the total quantity of bread, in loaves, the manager purchased during the first and second weeks combined. $\frac{1,000}{b} + \frac{1,000}{b + 0.25}$

   b. For what values of b does your expression from Part a not make *mathematical* sense? 0, $^-0.25$

   c. For what additional values of b, if any, does your expression not make sense in this situation? *Possible answer: negative values, values with decimal parts smaller than hundredths; Some students may mention large values (it doesn't make sense to charge $100 per loaf, for example).*

3. Simplify each fraction.

   a. $\frac{5rs}{10r^3}$ $\frac{s}{2r^2}$

   b. $\frac{2(d + 3)}{4d^2 + 12d}$ $\frac{1}{2d}$

   c. $\frac{4 - x}{3(x - 4)}$ $-\frac{1}{3}$

4. Find each product or quotient.

   a. $\frac{5}{6f} \cdot \frac{3f^2}{10}$ $\frac{f}{4}$

   b. $\frac{5ab}{7} \div \frac{10ab^3}{21}$ $\frac{3}{2b^2}$

Chapter 7 Mathematical Background

Page 431a Notes, *continued*

For the factored equation to be true, either $mx + n = 0$ or $px + q = 0$. That is, x must equal either $\frac{^-n}{m}$ or $\frac{^-q}{p}$. In general, it is assumed that m, n, p, and q are integers.

There are two special cases of quadratic equations for which factoring is quick and easy: *perfect squares* and *differences of two squares*. In solving a quadratic equation, students should first check whether it fits one of these two forms. This should eventually become a quick, almost automatic evaluation.

If a quadratic is a perfect square, it can be written in the form $(mx + n)^2 = 0$, where m and n can be positive or negative. Perfect-square quadratic equations have only one solution, $x = \frac{^-n}{m}$.

Perfect-square quadratics always have the expanded form

$$m^2x^2 + 2mnx + n^2 = 0$$

That is, for $ax^2 + bx + c = 0$, the coefficient a and constant c are perfect squares, m^2 and n^2, respectively; and the coefficient of the middle term, b, is twice the product of m and n. Examples include the following:

$$4x^2 + 4x + 1 = 0 \quad \text{or} \quad (2x + 1)^2 = 0$$

$$x^2 - 12x + 36 = 0 \quad \text{or} \quad (x - 6)^2 = 0$$

• *continued on next page*

A second special type of quadratic equation that can be easily factored are those that can be written as *the difference of two squares*. An equation of the form

$$p^2x^2 - q^2 = 0$$

can be factored as

$$(px + q)(px - q) = 0$$

Examples include the following:

$$16x^2 - 4 = 0 \quad \text{or} \quad (4x + 2)(4x - 2) = 0$$
$$a^2 - 81 = 0 \quad \text{or} \quad (a + 9)(a - 9) = 0$$

Some other quadratic equations can be factored into two fairly simple binomials. Finding the factors is a matter of systematic trial and error, and it's not easy to know in advance whether factors can be found. It is easier to factor equations in which the coefficient on the x^2 term is 1 than those in which this coefficient is some other integer, because you know that the coefficients of the x terms in the factored form must be 1.

For example, to solve the equation $x^2 + 8x + 12 = 0$, rewrite it in the form $(x + m)(x + n) = 0$. The product of m and n must be 12, and their sum must be 8. The numbers 6 and 2 meet this requirement, so the factored form is

$$(x + 6)(x + 2) = 0$$

The solutions are $^-6$ and $^-2$.

When the middle term of the expanded form has a negative coefficient, or the constant term is negative, the process is similar.

$x^2 - 8x + 12 = 0; (x - 6)(x - 2) = 0; x = 6 \text{ or } x = 2$

$x^2 + 4x - 12 = 0; (x + 6)(x - 2) = 0; x = ^-6 \text{ or } x = 2$

$x^2 - 4x - 12 = 0; (x - 6)(x + 2) = 0; x = 6 \text{ or } x = ^-2$

Some equations cannot be solved easily by this method. For example, $x^2 + 8x - 12 = 0$ cannot be factored using only integers, because there are not two integers whose product is $^-12$ and whose sum is 8.

Solving Quadratic Equations Using the Quadratic Formula It's a fact that most quadratic equations cannot be factored using only integers. However, any quadratic equation in the form $ax^2 + bx + c = 0$ can be solved using the quadratic formula,

$$x = \frac{-b \pm \sqrt{b^2 - 4ac}}{2a}$$

This formula can be derived by a method called *completing the square*, in which an equation of the form $ax^2 + bx + c = 0$ is rewritten in the form $(x + h)^2 = k$. The resulting solution, $x = ^-h \pm \sqrt{k}$, is identical to the quadratic formula because $h = \frac{b}{2a}$ and $k = \frac{b^2 - 4ac}{4a^2}$. See the derivation on page 466.

The equation $x^2 + 8x + 12 = 0$ was solved earlier by factoring. For that example,

$$b^2 - 4ac = 64 - 48 = 16$$
$$x = \frac{-8 \pm \sqrt{16}}{2} = ^-4 \pm 2 = ^-6 \text{ or } ^-2$$

This solution is the same as the solution found by factoring.

The equation $x^2 - 8x - 12 = 0$ could not be solved by factoring. For this example,

$$b^2 - 4ac = 64 - (^-48) = 112$$
$$x = \frac{8 \pm \sqrt{112}}{2} = 4 \pm 2\sqrt{7}$$

The quadratic formula also reveals how many solutions an equation has, using the *determinant*, $b^2 - 4ac$:

- If $b^2 - 4ac > 0$, the determinant has two real square roots, so the equation has two solutions.
- If $b^2 - 4ac = 0$, the equation has only a single solution, $x = \frac{-b}{2a}$.
- If $b^2 - 4ac < 0$, the determinant has no real square root, so there are no solutions (in the domain of real numbers).

Additional Notes & Answers, continued

Lesson 7.1

Page 441 Quick Quiz

Quick Quiz

1. Solve the equation $3(x - 2)^2 + 1 = 13$ by back-tracking. Show the flowchart you use. *0, 4*

2. Solve each equation.

  a. $\sqrt{4x - 3} = 3$ *3*

  b. $\frac{2}{5x + 3} = 4$ $-\frac{1}{2}$

  c. $\frac{6}{x^2} + 1 = 25$ $\pm\frac{1}{2}$

  d. $(4 - y)^3 + 4 = 31$ *1*

3. Find exact solutions to the following equation.

$$(x - 4)^2 - 7 = 0 \quad 4 \pm \sqrt{7}$$

Lesson 7.4

Page 479 Teaching Notes, continued

Exercise 5:
You may want to ask students which method was more efficient, factoring or the formula. In this case, students should have recognized the difference of squares, which makes factoring much easier.

Exercise 6:
Make sure students understand that only the positive solution makes sense in this context.

Exercise 11:
Students might approach **Part c** in various ways.

Problem-Solving Strategies

- Students may realize that because the ball reaches a maximum height, there is just one solution to the equation $40t - 16t^2 + 5 = M$, where M is the maximum height. Students must rewrite this equation in the form $ax^2 + bx + c = 0$ and then realize that $b^2 - 4ac$ is 0.

- Students may actually graph the quadratic equation $y = 40x - 16x^2 + 5$ and look at the y-coordinate of the vertex for the maximum height.

Page 481 Additional Answers

17b.

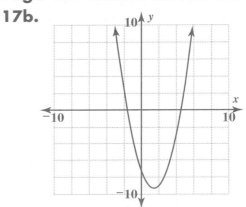

19b. There is a maximum area.

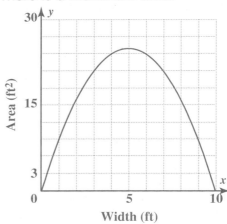

Page 482 Quick Quiz, continued

5. A baseball is thrown upward with a starting velocity of 30 feet per second from 5 feet above the ground. The equation describing the height h of the ball in feet after t seconds is $h = 30t - 16t^2 + 5$. Will the ball travel as high as 100 feet? *no*

Chapter 8 Mathematical Background

Page 487a Notes, *continued*

Functions as Consistent and Unique The most basic part of the definition of *function* is that, for a given input, a function gives exactly one output. That is, for a particular input *x*, you cannot have $f(x) = a$ some of the time and $f(x) = b$ at other times. In terms of the function-machine analogy, this means that a machine must behave in a *consistent* way. This consistency allows us to speak of *the* output *b* corresponding to the input *x* or *the* value of *f* at *x*.

When first introduced to functions, people often get the idea of the *uniqueness* of the outputs confused with a related, but very different, idea. For functions, different outputs cannot be given for the same input. However, different inputs *can* give the same output. A simple example to illustrate the distinction is the *squaring* function, $f(x) = x^2$. Note that for any input *x*, the function always gives the same output (any number has a unique square). However, *different inputs* can give the *same output*; for example, $f(-2) = f(2) = 4$ and $f(-3) = f(3) = 9$.

Domain Sometimes, just what inputs a given function can "process" is a concern. For example, for the reciprocal function, $g(x) = \frac{1}{x}$, the number 0 is not allowed as an input. This leads to the notion of the *domain* of a function, which is the set of *legitimate* inputs to that function. For the function $f(x) = x^2$, *all* inputs are legitimate, so the domain of *f* is the set of *all* real numbers. For $g(x) = \frac{1}{x}$, the domain is the set of all *nonzero* real numbers.

In some cases, the domain of a function may be further restricted by the *context* in which the function arises. Students have already encountered this idea, although not using function notation. For example, the number of diagonals of any regular polygon with *n* sides can be described using the function $D(n) = \frac{n(n-3)}{2}$. The formula itself is valid for *all* real numbers, but in the context of the problem, only positive integers greater than or equal to 3 make sense. Thus the domain of the diagonal function *D* (the set of integers $n \geq 3$) is *not* the same as the domain of the expression $\frac{n(n-3)}{2}$ (the set of *all* real numbers).

Domains can also have an explicit restriction. For example, one can define a function *k* in this way: $k(s) = 3s + 4$ where $3 < s \leq 15$. The domain is restricted to $3 < s \leq 15$, but only because the definition makes it so. Students will not encounter this type of restriction in this course, but it will become important in future courses. (For example, when discussing inverse relationships of trigonometric functions, such domain restrictions are used to ensure that the inverses will, in fact, be functions.)

Range While the domain of a function is the set of all legitimate inputs, the *range* of a function is the set of all possible outputs. For example:

$f(x) = x^2$ Domain: all real numbers

                       Range: all non-negative real numbers (since x^2 can't be negative)

$g(x) = \frac{1}{x-1}$ Domain: all real numbers, $x \neq 1$

                       Range: all nonzero real numbers

Composition of Functions *Composition* of functions is a powerful idea. Given two functions *f* and *g*, you can create a new function *h* by applying *f* to an input and then applying *g* to the result. Students encountered this idea when working with geometric transformations in Chapter 5; the transformations are functions that act upon geometric objects.

Using the function machine model, we can think about *hooking up* an *f*-machine and a *g*-machine. Suppose $f(x) = 2x$ ("double") and $g(x) = x + 1$ ("add 1"):

Function *h*

Now, applying *f* and then *g* gives the function $h(x) = 2x + 1$. Notice that composition of functions is a *noncommutative* operation, that is, the *order* in which the machines are hooked together matters. Applying *g* and then *f* gives a function $k(x) = 2(x + 1)$. It's easy to see that the functions *h* and *k* are not the same.

• **continued on next page**

A function may be composed with itself. For example, if $g(x) = x + 1$, the composition of g with g gives a function $h(x) = (x + 1) + 1 = x + 2$.

Function h

Similarly, hooking the doubling function f to itself gives $k(x) = 2(2x) = 4x$. This is sometimes referred to as *reiterating* a function. Many fractals are created using function iteration.

Non-numerical Functions Functions need not involve numbers. As noted earlier, geometric transformations, such as reflections and translations, are functions. The generality of the concept of a function is illustrated by the following examples:

- The *state capital* function C: input a state; output a city. For example, C(Illinois) = Springfield; C(New York) = Albany.

- The *mother* function M (assigns to each person his or her biological mother): input a person (female or male), output a woman. For example, M(Lourdes) = Madonna; M(Hamlet) = Gertrude.

- The *word length* function L: input a word; output a number. For example, L(cat) = 3; L(antidisestablishmentarianism) = 28.

It's helpful—and fun—to give students opportunities to invent some of their own non-numerical functions. If you build a nice library of imaginative functions in your classroom, you can use them to check out ideas like domain and range. For example, the *mother* function makes it clear that several inputs can have the same output (full siblings have the same mother). Furthermore, while any person can be an input, only certain women can be an output. Note, however, that there is no *grandmother* function: a person can have only *one* biological mother, but, since everyone has *two* biological grandmothers, the output of a grandmother "function" would not be unique.

Page 489 Additional Answers, *continued*

⑧ Every whole number (other than 1) has at least two factors: itself and 1. Composite numbers have even more. If the input is 8, the output could be 1, 2, 4, or 8.

⑨ The area of a rectangle is determined not by just one measurement but two (length and width). A rectangle with length 10 can have area 10 (width 1), 200 (width 20), and so on.

⑩ There are many ways to rearrange the letters in most words. For *cat*, there are five possible rearrangements (not counting the original): *cta, act, atc, tac, tca*.

Page 496 Additional Answers

Share & Summarize

1. Possible answers: 7 more than $^-3$ times the input; 3 times the input number subtracted from 7; $f(t) = 7 - 3t$; $f(t) = ^-3t + 7$.

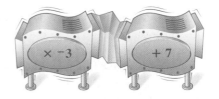

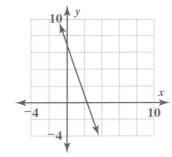

Input	Output
0	7
$^-1$	10
1	4
$\frac{2}{3}$	5

Page 515 Additional Answers, *continued*

2a.

2b. All four graphs have the same shape. Each is a translation of f: g, 1 unit to the right; h, 2 units to the right; and j, 1 unit to the left.

2c. Possible answer: $m(x) = \frac{1}{x + 2}$, $k(x) = \frac{1}{x - 5}$

3. They are similar in that the graph of the next function in each set is translated 1 unit to the right of the graph of the previous function. They are different in that the functions in each set are of different types: Problem 1 has quadratic functions, and Problem 2 has inverse variations.

4. $g(x) = (x - 1)^2$; Possible explanation: For $g(x) = (x - 1)^2$, the output is 9 for an input of 4, so (4, 9) is on the graph of this function.

Page T522 Teaching Notes, continued

Investigation 3

In this investigation, students use the x-intercepts of the graph of a quadratic function to determine the associated parabola's line of symmetry and vertex. The symmetry properties of parabolas allow us to find the line of symmetry and the turning point from the factored form. For example, the x-intercepts of $f(x) = (x - 5)(x + 1)$ are 5 and $^-1$, and therefore the line of symmetry passes halfway between these two, at $x = 2$. The vertex is therefore $(2, ^-9)$. With this information, a parabola can be drawn fairly efficiently. The kind of reasoning used here—finding the solutions to a quadratic equation when the quadratic part of the rule has been factored—relies on the multiplication property of 0, which students studied in Chapter 7.

You might begin the investigation by reminding students that in Investigation 2, they used a particular form of a quadratic function to find the vertex and the line of symmetry. Read the definition of *x-intercepts* in the text with them, and explain that they will learn how they can use x-intercepts to find the vertex and the line of symmetry of a parabola.

Think & Discuss

Students should be able to see, without much prompting, that the x-intercepts of a function f are the solutions to $f(x) = 0$. You may need to remind them, though, that $f(x)$ is the output variable, that is, $y = f(x)$. If necessary, draw a quick sketch of a parabola that crosses the x-axis in two places, and have them identify the x-intercepts. Ask what the y value is for those intercepts, and have them connect the y value to the value of $f(x)$.

Page 532 Additional Answers, continued

22c.

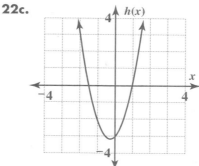

24. two solutions

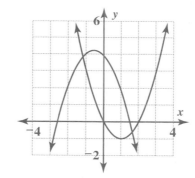

25. two solutions

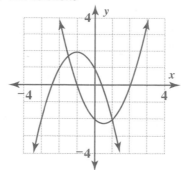

26. no solutions

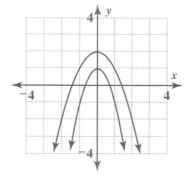

27. three solutions: ⁻2.2, 0, and 2.2

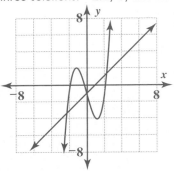

28. one solution: about 2.6

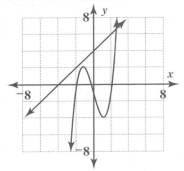

29. one solution: about 2.2

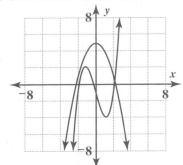

30a.

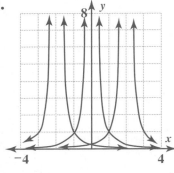

30b.

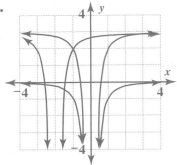

Page 534 Additional Answers

43a. Possible answer: 0.4, ⁻2.4

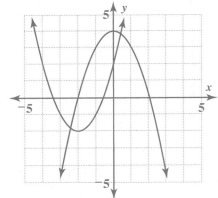

Page 537 Quick Quiz, *continued*

4. Consider the function $f(x) = x^2 - 4x + 7$.

   a. Complete the square to find the coordinates of the vertex of the graph of f. $f(x) = (x - 2)^2 + 3$; vertex (2, 3)

   b. Sketch its graph without using a graphing calculator.

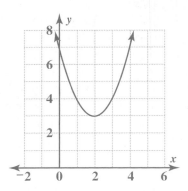

5. Use a graphing technique to approximate the solutions of the equation $2x + 1 = x^2 - 3$. about ⁻1.2 and 3.2

Page 537 Additional Answers, continued

60a.

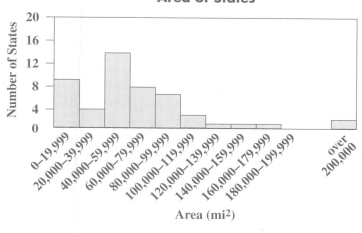

Area of States

60b.

Stem	Leaf
0	1545 2489 5543 8721 9350 9614
1	0555 0931 2407
2	4230
3	2020 5385 6418
4	0409 2143 2774 4825 6055 8430
5	1840 2419 3179 3819 4556 6272 7914 9425
6	5498 5755 9704 9898
7	0700 1300 7116 7354
8	2277 3570 4899 6936
9	6716 7814 8381
10	4094
11	0561 3998
12	1589
13	
14	7042
15	
16	3696
.	
.	
.	
26	8581
.	
.	
.	
66	3267

Chapter 9 Mathematical Background

Page 543a Notes, continued

Counting without Listing The act of listing outcomes suggests strategies for counting outcomes without listing. In the previous example, the branches of the tree diagram are created from 10 choices that each have 9 subsequent choices. Thus, the tree contains 90 branches and the sample space contains 90 equally likely outcomes. Similarly, for a single roll of two dice, there are 6 ways the first die can be rolled followed by 6 ways the second die can be rolled, for a sample space of 36 equally likely outcomes.

Although the problem of counting outcomes in sample spaces is inherently interesting to some, the purpose behind the activity is thoroughly practical: information about the probability of two events can be useful in making strategic decisions. Chapter 9 demonstrates this principle by having students analyze appropriate strategies for games of chance involving dice and spinners. More complicated games suggest that it can be useful to look at the distribution of probabilities. In particular, if counting outcomes is not possible, experimental probability distributions can help in making choices.

Lesson 9.1

Page 564 Quick Quiz, continued

2. Joe's combination lock is opened by dialing three different numbers chosen from the digits 1 to 5 in the proper order.

a. How many possible combinations are there? 60

b. What is the probability that the combination number contains two numbers that are the same? 0

Joe remembers that the correct combination numbers for his lock differ successively by 1. For example 1, 2, 3 and 5, 4, 3 are possible combinations.

c. How many combinations are possible for Joe's lock? Explain. *six; There are three combinations that increase by 1: (1, 2, 3); (2, 3, 4); (3, 4, 5). Each can be reversed to create a combination that decreases by 1, so there are six combinations.*

d. Joe randomly chose a combination (using numbers that differ successively by 1). What is the probability that he chose the correct one? $\frac{1}{6}$

The same company makes a different type of combination lock in which the numbers can be repeated. For example, 151 is a valid combination.

e. How many combinations are there for this kind of lock? Explain. 125; *There are five choices for the first number, five for the second, and five for the third.*

f. If the combination is assigned randomly, what is the probability that it will contain three numbers that are the same? $\frac{5}{125}$, or $\frac{1}{25}$

Lesson 9.2

Page 572 Additional Answers, continued

3.

Product	Probability
1	$\frac{1}{36}$
2	$\frac{2}{36}$
3	$\frac{2}{36}$
4	$\frac{3}{36}$
5	$\frac{2}{36}$
6	$\frac{4}{36}$
8	$\frac{2}{36}$
9	$\frac{1}{36}$
10	$\frac{2}{36}$
12	$\frac{4}{36}$
15	$\frac{2}{36}$
16	$\frac{1}{36}$
18	$\frac{2}{36}$
20	$\frac{2}{36}$
24	$\frac{2}{36}$
25	$\frac{1}{36}$
30	$\frac{2}{36}$
36	$\frac{1}{36}$

Lesson 9.3

Page 583 Additional Answers

4c. 30 pairs

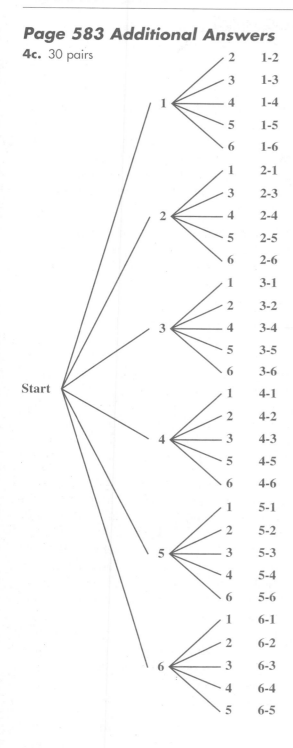

Page 593 Additional Answers, *continued*

11a. Possible answers:

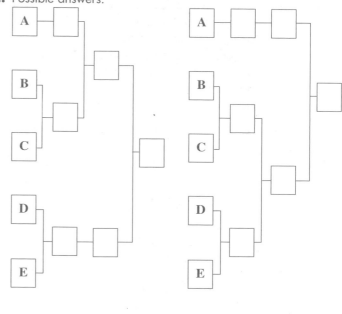

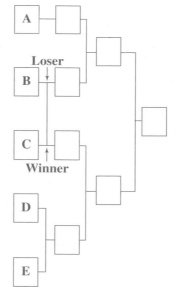

Page 595 Quick Quiz, *continued*

2. One state has several soccer leagues. To determine the champion of each league, the third-place and fourth-place teams play each other. The winner of this match plays the second-place team. The winner of this plays the first-place team. Assume that before the tournament, Team A is in first place, Team B is in second, Team C is in third, and Team D fourth.

   a. Draw a diagram of the playoff structure.

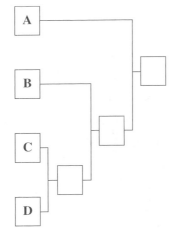

   b. Suppose that each team has an equally likely chance of winning any game. What is the probability that Team A will win the playoff? $\frac{1}{2}$

   c. Is this championship structure fair? Explain why or why not. *Against fairness is the argument that if all teams really have the same chance, Team A is given an unfair advantage. In favor of fairness, one might argue that Team A won the league and therefore deserves the best chance.*

Chapter 10 Mathematical Background

Page 601a Notes, *continued*

There seems to be some correlation, or connection, between the total runs by a team and the number of games the team won. Although the points do not lie on a line, there appears to be some vaguely linear relationship: as the total runs increases, the percentage of games won tends to increase. However, there seems to be little correlation, if any, between a team's average ERA and the total number of runs.

Correlation has a precise mathematical definition, and through a formula, a value can be assigned to indicate how well two variables are correlated linearly. In this chapter, students just consider visually how "well-connected" two variables seem.

Modeling and Decisions Analyzing data is necessary to make informed decisions, and it often helps to fit a mathematical model to the data. For example, one might ask whether a time-dependent data set is close enough to linear to allow a future data point to be predicted with a reasonable degree of accuracy. Graphing calculators make sophisticated curve fitting simple, so students can fit data sets to models that are quadratic, cubic, or even exponential in nature.

The task of interpreting the nature of large and complex data sets and inferring likely probabilities from them is often made easier by referring to an "ideal" model population representing the data. For example, suppose that an electronics company knows that, on average, 10% of the microchips it produces are defective. They subject each chip to a test to see whether it can be used in a computer or other device. Unfortunately, 2% of the time the test falsely reports the chip is defective when it is not, and 5% of the time it fails to report the chip as defective when it is. The company wants to determine the probability that a defective chip will get by the test; that is, they want to find the ratio of defective chips that pass the test to the total number of chips that pass the test.

The simplest way to work out the probabilities in such a complicated situation is to create an "ideal" population, say of 1,000 chips. Of these, 100 will be defective and

900 good. Of the 100 defective chips, the test will fail on 5%, reporting 5 falsely as good. Of the 900 good chips, the test will falsely report 2%, or 18, as defective; therefore 882 will be reported as good. The total number of chips passing the test will be 882 + 5, or 887. Of these, 5 will be defective. Therefore the probability of a defective chip being used is $\frac{5}{882}$, or about 0.0057.

Page 603 Additional Answers, *continued*

Problem Set A

1. Possible table:

Northtown Scores	Southtown Scores
54	44
58	55
66	59
66	59
68	60
69	62
69	63
72	66
72	70
73	73
74	74
76	79
77	88
81	90
81	92
82	94
84	94
85	100
87	100
89	100
90	100
94	100

Page 604 Additional Answers, *continued*

Problem Set B

1. Possible table:

Morning	Afternoon
44	54
55	58
59	59
62	60
66	63
68	66
69	66
70	69
73	72
73	72
74	74
79	76
81	77
81	82
85	84
87	88
90	89
90	92
94	94
100	94
100	100
100	100

2. Possible answer: Although the morning class has a higher mean and median, the classes are close in these measures, so the results don't seem particularly conclusive. The morning class has more top scorers, but it also includes the lowest scorer. The classes have the same number of students above and below the overall median.

Page T605 Notes, *continued*

- They might try finding an average difference in the *price* values and divide that by 2 (as each price increase is over a two-year period) to get an average increase per year of about $679. The price for Year 0 (1980) would be 6,699 − 679 or 6,020, giving an equation of $y = 679x + 6,020$, which is reasonably close to the regression line.

In **Problem 2,** students are expected to use their equations to find the price in the current year. Those who did not consider the data to be linear, and thus didn't find an equation, should try to extrapolate from the data using the relationship they felt was more appropriate.

4 **Problem Set Wrap-Up** After students complete Problem Set C, you might ask what the average annual increase in price was. Students can calculate it by averaging the biannual increases given in the table and dividing that average by 2. (See the sample strategies for Problem 1.) Or, they can simply look at the coefficient of x (that is, the slope of the line). Ask them whether they think the data support Lydia's argument that her parents should buy a car now. Their opinions might lead nicely into the text on the top of page 606, but don't let the discussion continue for too long.

Page 606 Additional Answers

3.

Month	Miles Driven	Fuel Economy (mpg)
Jun	1,160	27.1
Jul	1,422	38.9
Aug	3,790	27.1
Sep	1,105	26.3
Oct	647	24.4
Nov	813	23.4
Dec	1,020	24.6
Jan	1,113	25.0
Feb	643	23.6
Mar	735	24.8
Apr	1,684	28.1
May	1,021	28.9

Page 607 Additional Answers

Problem Set F

1. A possible table (months are sorted by number of miles driven) is shown. Possible answer: It's hard to tell from the table whether months in which fewer miles were driven have lower fuel economy.

Month	Gas Bought	Miles Driven	Fuel Economy
Feb	27.2	643	23.6
Oct	26.5	647	24.4
Mar	29.6	735	24.8
Nov	34.7	813	23.4
Dec	41.5	1,020	24.6
May	35.3	1,021	28.9
Sep	42.0	1,105	26.3
Jan	44.6	1,113	25.0
Jun	42.8	1,160	27.1
Jul	36.6	1,422	38.9
Apr	60.0	1,684	28.1
Aug	139.7	3,790	27.1

Page T612 Notes, *continued*

2 You can introduce this investigation by going directly to the Think & Discuss.

Think & Discuss

Students' answers to these questions will depend highly on what they have learned in their geography lessons and through maps they may have seen recently in magazines and on television. Students are likely to think of weather maps as the most common nongeographical information displayed on maps today.

Page 612 Additional Answers, continued

Problem Set G

5. Possible answers: For Problem 1a, the first table makes it easier because you see immediately that Mary spent several 10-year intervals in first place. With the second table it's even easier; you just find the greatest number in the first column.
For Problem 1c, the first table is a little easier than the original, but the second table is a lot easier because the number of years are already counted; you just multiply each by its point value and add the products.
For Problem 3, it's a little easier to tell that Mary is first because that name is in first place for several 10-year intervals in a row. Using the second table, it's very easy; you just look at the "Maximum Consecutive Years" columns.
For Problem 4, the original table is easier than this first table, because you can look across a row for a name and see if it is only on the list for a few years; with the first table here, you have to look around for other places the name might be. The second table is easiest, though, because you can look at the results for one name and don't have to count.

6. Possible answer: Jacob, Joshua, and Matthew have clearly become more popular for boys in recent years, and Michael since the mid-century, but otherwise boys' names haven't changed very much. Popular girls' names have changed radically, with a totally different set at the end of the century than at the beginning.

7. Possible answer: The most popular boys' names in recent years have been Jacob, Matthew, and Michael, so these three should be included. The only other listed names popular since 1990 have been Christopher and Joshua, which leaves one name open. The most popular girls' names in recent years have been Ashley, Jessica, Emily, Hannah, Madison, Samantha, Sarah, and Taylor, so those are the most likely names from which to choose.

8. Possible answer: For boys, John, William, and probably James are logical choices; from 1900 to 1917, John had first place, William had second, and James had third, so it seems likely the three would have been popular in 1899 as well. For girls, Mary and maybe Helen and Anna are good choices, because these three were most popular from 1900 to 1902.

Page 614 Additional Answers

5. Possible table (Columns 3 and 4 are added in Problem 9):

Ring	Victims	Area (m²)	Population Density of Victims
1	45	1,963	0.0229
2	100	5,890	0.0170
3	120	9,817	0.0122
4	110	13,744	0.0080
5	110	17,671	0.0062
6	40	21,598	0.0019
7	15	25,525	0.0006
8	5	29,452	0.0002

6. Possible histogram:

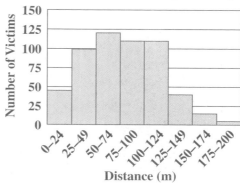

Cholera Victims, Broad Street Pump Vicinity

Page 615 Additional Answers, continued

Share & Summarize

1. Possible answer:
The map supports the conclusion, because it seems obvious that there are more victims living close to the pump.
The table is revealing only when the population density is included; the other information doesn't show the pattern.
The mean, median, and mode don't help you see the overall trend.
The histogram is a little helpful because after a point the bars aren't as tall, but the shorter first couple of bars might hurt the argument for the conclusion.
The population-density plot supports the conclusion, because it makes it clear that there are more victims closer to the pump.

Additional Notes & Answers, *continued*

Page 616 Additional Answers

2a. Possible answer:

Store	Artist	Price
Castle	A K Mango	$12.19
Castle	Screaming Screamers	12.50
Castle	Front Street Girls	13.09
Castle	Out of Sync	14.29
Castle	Aviva	19.00
InstantMusic	A K Mango	13.25
InstantMusic	Front Street Girls	13.25
InstantMusic	Screaming Screamers	13.49
InstantMusic	Out of Sync	13.59
InstantMusic	Aviva	15.00
GLU Sounds	Front Street Girls	13.95
GLU Sounds	A K Mango	14.50
GLU Sounds	Out of Sync	15.49
GLU Sounds	Screaming Screamers	15.50
GLU Sounds	Aviva	16.75
Pineapples	A K Mango	14.99
Pineapples	Screaming Screamers	15.99
Pineapples	Front Street Girls	16.00
Pineapples	Out of Sync	16.25
Pineapples	Aviva	18.89

3a. Possible answer:

Store	Artist	Price
Castle	A K Mango	$12.19
InstantMusic	A K Mango	13.25
GLU Sounds	A K Mango	14.50
Pineapples	A K Mango	14.99
Castle	Screaming Screamers	12.50
InstantMusic	Screaming Screamers	13.49
GLU Sounds	Screaming Screamers	15.50
Pineapples	Screaming Screamers	15.99
Castle	Front Street Girls	13.09
InstantMusic	Front Street Girls	13.25
GLU Sounds	Front Street Girls	13.95
Pineapples	Front Street Girls	16.00
Castle	Out of Sync	14.29
InstantMusic	Out of Sync	13.59
GLU Sounds	Out of Sync	15.49
Pineapples	Out of Sync	16.25
Castle	Aviva	19.00
InstantMusic	Aviva	15.00
GLU Sounds	Aviva	16.75
Pineapples	Aviva	18.89

Page 630 Quick Quiz

Quick Quiz

Note: This quiz is reproduced on Master 59.

Norelle, who attends a large K–8 school, asked the students in a few classrooms how many pets they had. (Some students had more than one.) Here are her results.

Room	Grade	Dogs	Cats	Hamsters	Other
101	3	7	8	3	1
102	5	6	6	2	1
104	6	4	10	0	2
105	3	10	9	4	4
106	5	6	7	0	1
107	5	4	8	1	1
109	3	5	5	9	2
111	4	7	7	1	1
112	5	8	14	2	3
113	4	5	7	2	2
114	6	9	8	1	1

1. Norelle wonders whether students in different grades tend to have different pets. Rearrange the data in a new table to make it easier for her to see whether this is true.

Possible answer:

Room	Grade	Dogs	Cats	Hamsters	Other
101	3	7	8	3	1
105	3	10	9	4	4
109	3	5	5	9	2
111	4	7	7	1	1
113	4	5	7	2	2
102	5	6	6	2	1
106	5	6	7	0	1
107	5	4	8	1	1
112	5	8	14	2	3
104	6	4	10	0	2
114	6	9	8	1	1

2. Assume there are 26 children in each classroom.

a. Make two graphs: one that shows the total number of hamsters in each grade, and one that shows the average number of hamsters per child in each grade.

Graphs can be line graphs or bar graphs. Possible graphs:

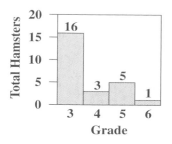

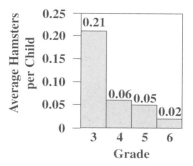

b. What conclusions can you draw from your graphs?

The total number of hamsters is not a useful piece of information because there are different numbers of classrooms at each grade level. The average number per child is clearly dropping as the children get older.

3. Norelle suspects that children who live in the east side of town (where there are more apartments) tend to have more cats than dogs, and that children who live in the west side of town (where there are more houses) tend to have more dogs than cats. What additional data should she collect to add to her table, and what would be the most useful form in which she could present her data? Possible answers: Which part of town each student lives in would help; she could use a pie chart or bar graph. Or, she could get the students' addresses and present the information on a map.

Page 642 Additional Answers

1a.

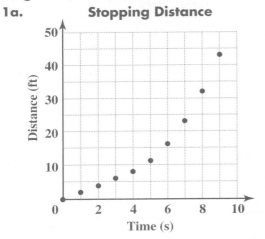

Stopping Distance

2a.

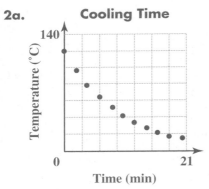

Cooling Time

Page 663 Additional Answers, continued

Share & Summarize

① The reason all the ratios are approximately the same is that all the right triangles are similar. Since the triangles are similar, the ratios of the lengths of their sides will be equivalent. Writing the ratio as a decimal is another way to write a ratio in reduced form. So if all those equivalent ratios are written in reduced form, they should all be the same.

② The ratio of legs is $\frac{a}{b}$. If a is 0, there is no triangle. So $\frac{a}{b}$ can be as small as one wants, but must always be greater than 0. There is no "smallest" ratio, because any thin triangle can be beaten by a still thinner triangle. The same is true of the "largest." There is no largest, because any large ratio can be beaten by a still larger ratio. Students can imagine a very tall skinny triangle with a very tall opposite leg and a tiny adjacent leg. As the opposite leg gets taller and taller, and the adjacent leg gets smaller and smaller, the ratio will get extremely large, but there is always a larger one possible. We say that the ratios "approach" zero and "approach" infinity, but no *triangle* corresponds to either limiting case.

Page 644 Additional Answers

6. Possible answer: They might not be able to sell as many bikes as they thought, because most people would rather buy a new one. The $250 price seems high. Assuming they can sell only 5 the first year and each year after sell 2 more than the previous year, and a price of $150 the first year and an additional 5% each year after that, and $500 advertising costs each year, gives this table:

Year	Costs	Bikes Sold	Price	Gross Income	Cumulative Net Profit
1	$2,100	5	$150.00	$ 750.00	⁻$1,350.00
2	1,500	7	157.50	1,102.50	⁻1,747.50
3	1,700	9	165.38	1,488.42	⁻1,959.08
4	1,900	11	173.64	1,910.04	⁻1,949.04
5	2,100	13	182.33	2,370.29	⁻1,678.75

GLOSSARY/GLOSARIO

English

Español

adjacent leg In a right triangle with acute angle A, the leg next to $\angle A$. [page 662]

cateto adyacente En un triángulo rectángulo con ángulo agudo A, el cateto al lado del $\angle A$.

algebraic expression A combination of numbers, variables, and operation symbols that gives a number when all variables are replaced by numbers. Examples of *algebraic expressions* are $3n + 2$, $x^2 - 2x + 7$, and $p + q$. [page 356]

expresión algebraica Combinación de números, variables y símbolos de operaciones que resulta en un número cuando todas las variables se reemplazan con números. Ejemplos de *expresiones algebraicas* son $3n + 2$, $x^2 - 2x + 7$ y $p + q$.

binomial The sum or difference of two unlike terms. For example, $x + 7$, $x^2 - 3$, and $a + c$ are *binomials*. [page 373]

binomio La suma o diferencia de dos términos no semejantes. Por ejemplo: $x + 7$, $x^2 - 3$ y $a + c$ son *binomios*.

coefficient The numeric multiplier in an algebraic term. For example, in the expression $3x^2 - 2x + 7$, 3 is the coefficient of x^2, and $^-2$ is the coefficient of x. [page 31]

coeficiente El multiplicador numérico en un término algebraico. Por ejemplo: en la expresión $3x^2 - 2x + 7$, 3 es el coeficiente de x^2 y $^-2$ es el coeficiente de x.

congruent Having the same size and shape. [page 294]

congruente Que tiene el mismo tamaño y la misma forma.

conjecture An educated guess or generalization that you haven't yet proved correct. [page 127]

conjetura Suposición o generalización informada que aun no se ha probado como correcta.

cosine In a right triangle with acute angle A, the cosine of $\angle A = \dfrac{\text{leg adjacent } \angle A}{\text{hypotenuse}}$. [page 672]

coseno En un triángulo rectángulo con ángulo agudo A, el coseno del $\angle A = \dfrac{\text{cateto adyacente al } \angle A}{\text{hipotenusa}}$.

cubic equation An equation that can be written in the form $y = ax^3 + bx^2 + cx + d$, where $a \neq 0$. For example, $y = 2x^3$, $y = 0.5x^3 - x^2 + 4$, and $y = x^3 - x$ are *cubic equations*. [page 93]

ecuación cúbica Ecuación que se puede escribir en la forma $y = ax^3 + bx^2 + cx + d$, *donde* $a \neq 0$. Por ejemplo: $y = 2x^3$, $y = 0.5x^3 - x^2 + 4$ y $y = x^3 - x$ son *ecuaciones cúbicas*.

decay factor In a situation in which a quantity decays exponentially, the *decay factor* is the number by which the quantity is repeatedly multiplied. A *decay factor* is always greater than 0 and less than 1. For example, if the value of a computer decreases by 15% per year, then its value each year is 0.85 times its value the previous year. In this case, the *decay factor* is 0.85. [page 176]

factor de desintegración En una situación en que una cantidad se desintegra exponencialmente, el *factor de desintegración* es el número por el cual se multiplica la cantidad repetidas veces. El *factor de descomposición* siempre es mayor que 0 y menor que 1. Por ejemplo: si el costo de una computadora disminuye en un 15% por año, entonces su valor cada año es 0.85 veces el valor del año anterior. En este caso, el *factor de descomposición* es 0.85.

dilation A transformation that creates a figure similar, but not necessarily congruent, to an original figure. [page 329]

dilación Transformación que crea una figura semejante, pero no necesariamente congruente, a una figura original.

English

direct variation A relationship in which two variables are directly proportional. The equation for a *direct variation* can be written in the form $y = mx$, where $m \neq 0$. The graph of a *direct variation* is a line through the origin $(0, 0)$. [page 7]

directly proportional Term used to describe a relationship between two variables in which, if the value of one variable is multiplied by a number, the value of the other variable is multiplied by the same number. For example, if Lara earns $8 per hour, then the variable *hours worked* is *directly proportional* to the variable *dollars earned.* [page 7]

distributive property The *distributive property of multiplication over addition* states that for any numbers n, a, and b, $n(a + b) = na + nb$. The *distributive property of multiplication over subtraction* states that for any numbers n, a, and b, $n(a - b) = na - nb$. [page 358]

domain The set of allowable inputs to a function. For example, the *domain* of $f(x) = \sqrt{x}$ is all non-negative real numbers. The *domain* of $g(t) = \frac{1}{t - 3}$ is all real numbers except 3. [page 495]

elimination A method for solving a system of equations that involves possibly rewriting one or both equations and then adding or subtracting the equations to *eliminate* a variable. For example, you could solve the system $x + 2y = 9$, $3x + y = 7$ by multiplying both sides of the first equation by 3 and then subtracting the second equation from the result. [page 266]

equation A mathematical sentence stating that two quantities are equal. For example, the sentence $3 - 11 = {}^-4 + {}^-4$ and $x^2 - 4 = 0$ are *equations.* [page 226]

expanding Using the distributive property to multiply the factors in an algebraic expression. For example, you can *expand* $x(x + 3)$ to get $x^2 + 3x$. [page 359]

exponent A symbol written above and to the right of a quantity that tells how many times the quantity is multiplied by itself. For example, $t \cdot t \cdot t$ can be written as t^3. [page 146]

exponential decay A decreasing pattern of change in which a quantity is repeatedly multiplied by a number less than 1 and greater than 0. [page 175]

Español

variación directa Relación en que dos variables son directamente proporcionales. La ecuación para una *variación directa* se puede escribir en la forma $y = mx$, donde $m \neq 0$. La gráfica de una *variación directa* es una recta a través del origen $(0, 0)$.

directamente proporcional Término que se usa para describir una relación entre dos variables en el cual, si el valor de una de las variables se multiplica por un número, el valor de la otra variable se multiplica por el mismo número. Por ejemplo: si Lara gana $8 por hora, entonces la variable *horas trabajadas* es *directamente proporcional* a la variable *dólares ganados.*

propiedad distributiva La *propiedad distributiva de la multiplicación sobre la adición* establece que para todo número n, a y b, $n(a + b) = na + nb$. La *propiedad distributiva de la multiplicación sobre la sustracción* establece que para todo número n, a y b, $n(a - b) = na - nb$.

dominio El conjunto de entradas permitidas para una función. Por ejemplo: el *dominio* de $f(x) = \sqrt{x}$ son todos los números reales no negativos. El *dominio* de $g(t) = \frac{1}{t - 3}$ son todos los números reales excepto 3.

eliminación Método para resolver un sistema de ecuaciones que posiblemente involucra reescribir una o ambas ecuaciones y luego sumar o restar las ecuaciones para *eliminar* una de las variables. Por ejemplo: podrías resolver el sistema $x + 2y = 9$, $3x + y = 7$ al multiplicar ambos lados de la primera ecuación por 3 y luego restar la segunda ecuación del resultado.

ecuación Enunciado matemático que establece la igualdad de dos cantidades. Por ejemplo: los enunciados $3 - 11 = {}^-4 + {}^-4$ y $x^2 - 4 = 0$ son *ecuaciones.*

desarrollar Uso de la propiedad distributiva para multiplicar los factores en una expresión algebraica. Por ejemplo: puedes *desarrollar* $x(x + 3)$ para obtener $x^2 + 3x$.

exponente Símbolo que se escribe más arriba y a la derecha de una cantidad y el cual indica el número de veces que la cantidad se multiplica por sí misma. Por ejemplo: $t \cdot t \cdot t$ se puede escribir como t^3.

desintegración exponencial Patrón decreciente de cambio en que una cantidad se multiplica repetidamente por un número menor que 1 y mayor que 0.

English	**Español**

exponential growth An increasing pattern of change in which a quantity is repeatedly multiplied by a number greater than 1. [page 169]

crecimiento exponencial Patrón creciente de cambio en que una cantidad se multiplica repetidamente por un número mayor que 1.

factoring Writing an algebraic expression as a product of factors. For example, $x^2 - x - 6$ can be *factored* to get $(x + 3)(x - 3)$. [page 443]

factorizar Escribir una expresión algebraica como el producto de factores. Por ejemplo: $x^2 - x - 6$ se puede *factorizar* para obtener $(x + 3)(x - 3)$.

function Term used to describe a relationship between an input variable and an output variable in which there is only one output for each input. [page 488]

función Término que se usa para describir la relación entre una variable de entrada y una variable de salida en que sólo hay una salida para cada entrada.

growth factor In a situation in which a quantity grows exponentially, the *growth factor* is the number by which the quantity is repeatedly multiplied. A *growth factor* is always greater than 1. For example, if a population grows by 3% every year, then the population each year is 1.03 times the population the previous year. In this case, the *growth factor* is 1.03. [page 169]

factor de crecimiento En una situación en la cual una cantidad crece exponencialmente, el *factor de crecimiento* es el número por el cual se multiplica la cantidad repetidamente. El *factor de crecimiento* es siempre mayor que 1. Por ejemplo: si una población crece un 3% cada año, entonces cada año la población es 1.03 veces la población del año previo. En este caso, el *factor de crecimiento* es 1.03.

hyperbola The graph of an inverse variation. [page 112]

hipérbola La gráfica de una variación inversa.

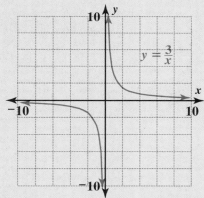

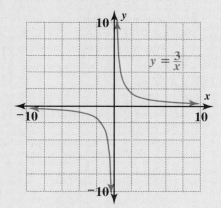

image The figure or point that results from a transformation. [page 292]

imagen Figura o punto que resulta de una transformación.

inequality A mathematical statement that uses one of the symbols $<$, $>$, $\leq$, $\geq$, or $\neq$ to compare quantities. Examples of inequalities are $n - 3 \leq 12$ and $9 - 2 > 1$. [page 226]

desigualdad Enunciado matemático que usa uno de los símbolos $<$, $>$, $\leq$, $\geq$ o $\neq$ para comparar cantidades. Ejemplos de desigualdades son $n - 3 \leq 12$ y $9 - 2 > 1$.

inverse variation A relationship in which two variables are inversely proportional. The equation for an *inverse variation* can be written in the form $xy = c$, or $y = \frac{c}{x}$, where c is a nonzero constant. The graph of an *inverse variation* is a hyperbola. [page 113]

variación inversa Relación en que dos variables son inversamente proporcionales. La ecuación de una *variación inversa* se puede escribir en la forma $xy = c$, o $y = \frac{c}{x}$, donde c es una constante no nula. La gráfica de una *variación inversa* es una hipérbola.

English	**Español**

inversely proportional Term used to describe a relationship in which the product of two variables is a nonzero constant. If two variables are *inversely proportional,* then when the value of one variable is multiplied by a number, the value of the other variable is multiplied by the *reciprocal* of that number. For example, the time it takes to travel 50 miles is *inversely proportional* to the average speed traveled. [page 113]

irrational numbers Numbers that cannot be written as ratios of two integers. In decimal form, *irrational numbers* are non-terminating and non-repeating. Examples of *irrational numbers* include π, $\sqrt{17}$, and $3\sqrt{2}$. [page 200]

like terms In an algebraic expression, terms with the same variables raised to the same powers. For example, in the expression $x + 3 - 7x + 8x^2 - 2x^2 + 1$, $8x^2$ and $-2x^2$ are *like terms,* x and ^-7x are *like terms,* and 3 and 1 are *like terms.* [page 363]

line of reflection A *line* over which a figure is *reflected.* In the figure below, the blue K has been *reflected* over the *line of reflection l* to get the orange K. [page 292]

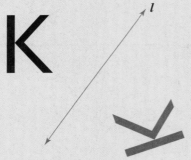

line of symmetry A line that divides a figure into two mirror-image halves. [page 289]

line symmetry See *reflection symmetry.*

inversamente proporcional Término que se usa para describir una relación en la cual el producto de dos variables es una variable no nula. Si dos variables son *inversamente proporcionales,* entonces cuando el valor de una de las variables se multiplica por un número, el valor de la otra variable se multiplica por el *recíproco* de ese número. Por ejemplo: el tiempo que toma viajar 50 millas es *inversamente proporcional* a la rapidez promedio viajada.

números irracionales Números que no se pueden escribir como razones de dos enteros. En forma decimal, los *números irracionales* son decimales no terminales y no periódicos. Ejemplos de *números irracionales* incluyen π, $\sqrt{17}$ y $3\sqrt{2}$.

términos semejantes En una expresión algebraica, los términos con las mismas variables elevadas a las mismas potencias. Por ejemplo: en la expresión $x + 3 - 7x + 8x^2 - 2x^2 + 1$, $8x^2$ y $-2x^2$ son *términos semejantes,* x y ^-7x son *términos semejantes* y 3 y 1 son *términos semejantes.*

eje de reflexión Un *eje* sobre el cual se *refleja* una figura. En la siguiente figura, la K azul ha sido *reflejada* sobre el *eje de reflexión l* para obtener la K anaranjada.

eje de simetría Recta que divide una figura en dos mitades especulares. [pág. 289]

simetría lineal Ver *simetría de reflexión.*

English	**Español**

linear relationship A relationship with a graph that is a straight line. Linear relationships are characterized by a constant rate of change—each time the value of one variable changes by a fixed amount, the value of the other variable changes by a fixed amount. The equation for a *linear relationship* can be written in the form $y = mx + b$, where m is the slope of the graph and b is its y-intercept. [page 4]

relación lineal Relación cuya gráfica es una recta. Las relaciones lineales se caracterizan por una tasa constante de cambio: cada vez que el valor de una de las variables cambia por una cantidad fija, el valor de la otra variable cambia por una cantidad fija. La ecuación de una *relación lineal* se puede escribir en la forma $y = mx + b$, donde m es la pendiente de la gráfica y b es su intersección y.

nth root An *nth root* of a number a is a number b, such that $b^n = a$. For example, -3 and 3 are *fourth roots* of 81 because $(-3)^4 = 81$ and $3^4 = 81$. [page 199]

enésima raíz La *enésima raíz* de un número a es un número b, tal que $b^n = a$. Por ejemplo: -3 y 3 son las *cuartas raíces* de 81 porque $(-3)^4 = 81$ y $3^4 = 81$.

opposite leg In a right triangle with acute angle A, the leg across from $\angle A$. [page 662]

cateto opuesto En un triángulo rectángulo con ángulo agudo A, el cateto al otro lado del $\angle A$.

parabola The graph of a quadratic relationship. [page 71]

parábola La gráfica de una relación cuadrática.

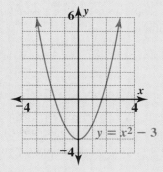

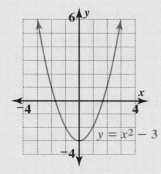

perpendicular bisector A line that intersects a segment at its midpoint and is perpendicular to the segment. [page 294]

mediatriz Recta que interseca un segmento en su punto medio y que es perpendicular al segmento.

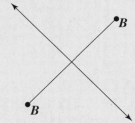

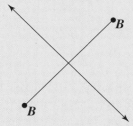

quadratic equation An equation that can be written in the form $y = ax^2 + bx + c$, where $a \neq 0$. For example, $y = x^2$, $y = 3x^2 - x + 4$, and $y = -2x^2 + 1$ are *quadratic equations*. [page 83]

ecuación cuadrática Ecuación que se puede escribir en la forma $y = ax^2 + bx + c$, donde $a \neq 0$. Por ejemplo: $y = x^2$, $y = 3x^2 - x + 4$ y $y = -2x^2 + 1$ son *ecuaciones cuadráticas*.

quadratic expression An expression that can be written in the form $ax^2 + bx + c$, where $a \neq 0$. For example, $x^2 - 4$, $x^2 + 2x + 0.5$, and $-3x^2 + 1$ are *quadratic expressions*. [page 83]

expresión cuadrática Expresión que se puede escribir en la forma $ax^2 + bx + c$, donde $a \neq 0$. Por ejemplo: $x^2 - 4$, $x^2 + 2x + 0.5$ y $-3x^2 + 1$ son *expresiones cuadráticas*.

English	Español

radical sign A symbol $\sqrt{}$ used to indicate a root of a number. The symbol $\sqrt{}$ by itself indicates the positive square root. The symbol $\sqrt[n]{}$ indicates the nth root of a number. For example, $\sqrt{25} = 5$ and $\sqrt[3]{^-64} = $ $^-4$. [page 191]

signo radical Símbolo $\sqrt{}$ que se usa para indicar la raíz de un número. El símbolo $\sqrt{}$ por sí sólo indica la raíz cuadrada positiva. El símbolo $\sqrt[n]{}$ indica la *enésima* raíz de un número. Por ejemplo: $\sqrt{25} = 5$ y $\sqrt[3]{^-64} = ^-4$.

range All the possible output values for a function. For example, the *range* of $h(x) = x^2 + 2$ is all real numbers greater than or equal to 2. The *range* of $f(x) = ^-\sqrt{x}$ is all real numbers less than or equal to 0. [page 518]

rango Todos los posibles valores de salida de una función. Por ejemplo: el *rango* de $h(x) = x^2 + 2$ son todos los números reales mayores que o iguales a 2. El *rango* de $f(x) = ^-\sqrt{x}$ son todos los números reales menores que o iguales a 0.

rational numbers Numbers that can be written as ratios of two integers. In decimal form, *rational numbers* are terminating or repeating. For example, 5, $^-0.274$, and $0.\overline{3}$ are *rational numbers*. [page 200]

números racionales Números que se pueden escribir como razones de dos enteros. En forma decimal, los *números racionales* son números terminales o periódicos. Por ejemplo: 5, $^-0.274$ y $0.\overline{3}$ son *números racionales*.

real numbers The set of rational and irrational numbers. All the numbers that can be located on the number line. [page 200]

números reales El conjunto de números racionales e irracionales. Todos los números que se pueden ubicar en la recta numérica.

reciprocal relationship See *inverse variation*. [page 115]

relación recíproca Ver *variación inversa*.

reflection over a line A transformation that matches each point on a figure to its mirror image over a line. In the figure below the blue curve has been *reflected over the line* to create the orange curve. [page 292]

reflexión sobre una recta Transformación en que cada punto de una figura corresponde con su imagen especular sobre una recta. En la siguiente figura, la curva azul se *reflejó sobre la recta* para crear la curva anaranjada.

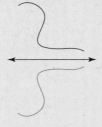

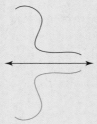

reflection symmetry A figure has *reflection symmetry* (or line symmetry) if you can draw a line that divides the figure into two mirror-image halves. The figures below have reflection symmetry. [page 289]

simetría de reflexión Una figura tiene *simetría de reflexión* (simetría lineal) si puedes dibujar una recta que divida la figura en dos mitades especulares. Las siguientes figuras tienen simetría de reflexión.

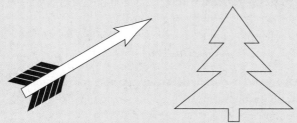

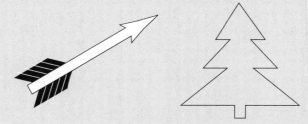

English	**Español**

rotation A transformation in which a figure is turned about a point. A positive angle of rotation indicates a counterclockwise rotation; a negative angle of rotation indicates a clockwise rotation. For example, the orange triangle at the right was created by *rotating* the blue triangle 90° about point *P*. [page 305]

90° rotation about point *P*

rotación Transformación en que se le da vuelta a una figura alrededor de un punto. Un ángulo de rotación positivo indica una rotación en dirección contraria a las manecillas del reloj; un ángulo de rotación negativo indica una rotación en la dirección de las manecillas del reloj. Por ejemplo: el triángulo anaranjado a la derecha se creó al *rotar* el triángulo azul 90° alrededor del punto *P*.

rotación de 90° alrededor del punto *P*

rotation symmetry A figure has *rotation symmetry* if you can rotate it about a centerpoint *without turning it all the way around,* and find a place where it looks exactly as it did in its original position. The figures below have *rotation symmetry*. [page 303]

simetría de rotación Una figura tiene *simetría de rotación* si se puede rotar alrededor de un punto central *sin voltearla completamente a su alrededor* y se puede hallar un lugar en donde se ve exactamente como se veía en su posición original. Las siguientes figuras tienen *simetría de rotación*.

sample space In a probability situation, the set of all possible outcomes. For example, when two coins are tossed, the sample space consists of head/head, head/tail, tail/head, tail/tail. [page 547]

espacio muestral En una situación de probabilidad, el conjunto de todos los resultados posibles. Por ejemplo: al lanzar dos monedas al aire, el espacio muestral consta de cara/cara, cara/escudo, escudo/cara, escudo/escudo.

scale drawing A drawing that is similar to some original figure. [page 330]

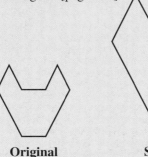 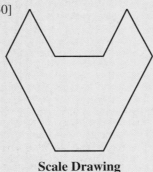

Original   **Scale Drawing**

dibujo a escala Dibujo que es semejante a alguna figura original.

 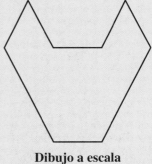

Original   **Dibujo a escala**

scale factor The ratio between corresponding side lengths of similar figures. There are two *scale factors* associated with every pair of non-congruent similar figures. For example, in the figures above, the *scale factor* from the small figure to the large figure is 2, and the *scale factor* from the large figure to the small figure is $\frac{1}{2}$. [page 330]

factor de escala La razón entre las longitudes de lados correspondientes de figuras semejantes. Hay dos *factores de escala* asociados con cada par de figuras semejantes no congruentes. Por ejemplo: en las figuras anteriores, el *factor de escala* de la figura pequeña a la figura grande es 2 y el *factor de escala* de la figura grande a la figura pequeña es $\frac{1}{2}$.

English	Español

scientific notation The method of writing a number in which the number is expressed as the product of a power of 10 and a number greater than or equal to 1 but less than 10. For example, 5,000,000 written in *scientific notation* is 5×10^6. [page 148]

notación científica Método de escribir un número en la cual el número se expresa como el producto de una potencia de 10 y un número mayor que o igual a 1, pero menor que 10. Por ejemplo: 5,000,000 escrito en *notación científica* es 5×10^6.

similar Having the same shape. [page 294]

semejante Que tiene la misma forma.

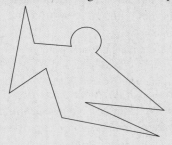 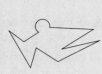

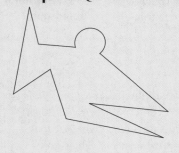 

sine In a right triangle with acute angle A, the sine of $\angle A = \dfrac{\text{leg opposite } \angle A}{\text{hypotenuse}}$. [page 671]

seno En un triángulo rectángulo con ángulo agudo A, el seno del $\angle A = \dfrac{\text{cateto opuesto al } \angle A}{\text{hipotenusa}}$.

slope The ratio $\left(\dfrac{\text{rise}}{\text{run}}\right)$ used to describe the steepness of a non-vertical line. Given the two points on a non-vertical line, you can calculate the *slope* by dividing the difference in the y coordinates by the difference in the x coordinates. (Be sure to subtract the x and y coordinates in the same order.) If a linear equation is written in the form $y = mx + b$, the value m is the *slope* of its graph. For example, the graph of $y = {}^-x - 2$, has *slope* $^-1$. [page 27]

pendiente La razón $\left(\dfrac{\text{altura}}{\text{carrera}}\right)$ que se usa para describir el grado de inclinación de una recta no vertical. Dados los dos puntos de una recta no vertical, puedes calcular la *pendiente* al dividir la diferencia de las coordenadas y entre la diferencia de las coordenadas x. (Asegúrate de restar las coordenadas x y y en el mismo orden.) Si una ecuación lineal se escribe en la forma $y = mx + b$, el valor m es la *pendiente* de su gráfica. Por ejemplo: la *pendiente* de la gráfica de $y = {}^-x - 2$ es $^-1$.

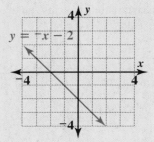 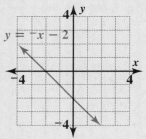

slope-intercept form The form $y = mx + b$ of a linear equation. The graph of an equation of this form has slope m and y-intercept b. For example, the graph of $y = {}^-x - 2$ (shown above) has slope $^-1$ and y-intercept $^-2$. [page 49]

forma pendiente-intersección La forma $y = mx + b$ de una ecuación lineal. La gráfica de una ecuación de esta forma tiene pendiente m e intersección y b. Por ejemplo: la gráfica de $y = {}^-x - 2$ (que se muestra arriba) tiene pendiente $^-1$ e intersección y igual a $^-2$.

square root A *square root* of a number a is a number b, such that $b^2 = a$. For example, $^-9$ and 9 are *square roots* of 81 because $(^-9)^2 = 81$ and $9^2 = 81$. [page 190]

raíz cuadrada La *raíz cuadrada* de un número a es un número b, tal que $b^2 = a$. Por ejemplo: $^-9$ y 9 son *raíces cuadradas* de 81 porque $(^-9)^2 = 81$ y $9^2 = 81$.

English	Español

substitution A method for solving a system of equations that involves using one of the equations to write an expression for one variable in terms of the other variable, and then *substituting* that expression into the other equation. For example, you could solve the system $y = 2x + 1$, $3x + y = 11$ by first *substituting* $2x + 1$ for y in the second equation. [page 264]

sustitución Método para resolver un sistema de ecuaciones y que involucra el uso de las ecuaciones para escribir una expresión para una de las variables en términos de la otra variable y luego *sustituir* esa expresión en la otra ecuación. Por ejemplo: para resolver el sistema $y = 2x + 1$, $3x + y = 11$ podrías primero *sustituir* la y en la segunda ecuación con $2x + 1$.

system of equations A group of two or more equations with the same variables. [page 257]

sistema de ecuaciones Grupo de dos o más ecuaciones con las mismas variables.

term A part of an algebraic expression made up of numbers and/or variables multiplied together. For example, in the expression $5x - 7x^2 + 2$, the terms are $5x$, $^-7x^2$, and 2. [page 363]

término Parte de una expresión algebraica compuesta de números y/o variables que se multiplican entre sí. Por ejemplo: en la expresión $5x - 7x^2 + 2$, los términos son $5x$, $^-7x^2$ y 2.

transformation A way of creating a figure similar or congruent to an original figure. Reflections, rotations, translations, and dilations are four types of *transformations*. [page 288]

transformación Una manera de crear una figura semejante o congruente a una figura original. Las reflexiones, las rotaciones, las traslaciones y las dilataciones son cuatro tipos de *transformaciones*.

translation A transformation within a plane in which a figure is moved a specific distance in a specific direction. For example, the first figure below was *translated* 1 inch to the right to get the second figure. [page 313]

traslación Una transformación dentro de un plano en que la figura se mueve una distancia específica en una dirección dada. Por ejemplo: la primera de las figuras que siguen se *trasladó* 1 pulgada a la derecha para obtener la segunda figura.

trigonometric ratios The ratios of the measures of two sides of a right triangle. [page 671]

rezones trigonométricas Las rezones de las medidas de dos lados de un triángulo rectángulo.

trinomial An expression with three unlike terms. For example, $b^2 + 10b + 25$ is a *trinomial*. [page 443]

trinomio Expresión con tres términos no semejantes. Por ejemplo: $b^2 + 10b + 25$ es un *trinomio*.

variable A quantity that can change or vary, or an unknown quantity. [page 4]

variable Cantidad que cambia o varía o cantidad desconocida.

vector A line segment with an arrowhead used to describe translations. The length of the *vector* tells how far to translate and the arrowhead gives the direction. [page 313]

vector Segmento de recta con punta de flecha que se usa para describir traslaciones. La longitud del *vector* indica la cantidad que hay que trasladar y la punta de flecha indica la dirección.

English	Español

x-intercept The x-coordinate of a point at which a graph crosses the x-axis. The x-intercepts of the graph of $f(x) = x^2 - 4x$ shown below are 0 and 4. [page 522]

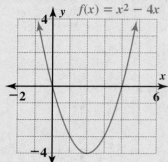

intersección x La coordenada x del punto donde la gráfica atraviesa el eje x. Las *intersecciones* x de la siguiente gráfica de $f(x) = x^2 - 4x$ son 0 y 4.

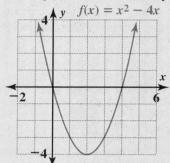

y-intercept The y-coordinate of a point at which a graph crosses the y-axis. The graph of a linear equation of the form $y = mx + b$, has y-intercept b. For example, the graph of $y = {}^-x - 2$, has y-intercept ${}^-2$. [page 31]

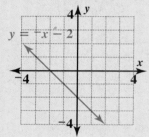

intersección y La coordenada y de un punto en el cual una gráfica atraviesa el eje y. La gráfica de una ecuación lineal de la forma $y = mx + b$, tiene intersección y de b. Por ejemplo: la gráfica de $y = {}^-x - 2$, tiene intersección y de ${}^-2$.

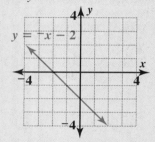

INDEX

PHOTO CREDITS

Cover Image   Mark Wagner/Getty Images

Front Matter   **v,** Ron Rovtar; **xix,** Mark Burnett; **xx,** Getty Images; **xxi,** U.S. Mint; **xxii,** MAK–1; **xxiii,** Getty Images

Chapter 1   **2 (t),** CORBIS; **2 (b),** Laura Sifferlin; **2–3,** CORBIS; **4,** MAK-I; **7,** Life Images; **13,** Daniel Erickson; **16,** George Linyear; **20,** James Westwater; **24,** Getty Images; **28,** Matt Meadows; **33,** Getty Images; **35,** Aaron Haupt; **53,** MAK-I; **57,** J.R. Schnelzer; **59,** Rudi Von Briel; **66,** Matt Meadows

Chapter 2   **68 (t),** Bob Mullenix; **68 (b),** CORBIS; **68–69,** CORBIS; **78,** Getty Images; **80,** Getty Images; **82,** Mark Burnett; **92,** Aaron Haupt; **93,** Doug Martin; **95,** Getty Images; **97,** NRAO/AUI; **101,** Aaron Haupt; **107,** Tom & Therisa Stack; **116,** Tony Goldsmith/Getty Images; **119,** Holiday Film Corp.; **120,** KS Studios; **122,** Getty Images; **124,** CORBIS; **131,** National Archives; **138,** Rod Joslin; **142,** Mark Burnett

Chapter 3   **144 (t),** Aaron Haupt; **144 (b),** Geoff Butler; **144–145,** Aaron Haupt; **151,** Oliver Meckes/Photo Researchers; **157,** NASA; **161,** NASA; **162,** CORBIS; **165,** Doug Martin; **172,** Getty Images; **178,** Getty Images; **180,** Mark Gibson/Index Stock Imagery; **193 (l),** Dominic Oldershaw, **193 (r),** Jeff Smith; **209,** Geoff Butler

Chapter 4   **212,** Getty Images; **212–213,** David R. Frazier Photo Library; **233,** David S. Addison/Visuals Unlimited; **235,** Dominic Oldershaw; **240,** Mark Burnett; **243,** NASA; **251,** Getty Images; **262,** Eric Hoffhines; **265,** Doug Martin; **267,** Courtesy Sperry/New Holland; **272,** Geoff Butler; **282,** Getty Images; **284,** Tim Courlas

Chapter 5   **286 (t),** M.C. Escher, Lizard, © 2003 Cordon Art B.V.; **286 (b),** Cheryl Fenton; **286–287,** CORBIS; **288 (cr),** Tom Palmer; **288 (bl),** Courtesy California Academy of Sciences; **303,** CORBIS; **330,** CORBIS; **344,** Ron Rovtar; **349,** Doug Martin

Chapter 6   **356,** Duomo/CORBIS; **356–357,** Getty Images; **362,** Doug Martin; **369,** Lindsay Gerard; **375,** R.E. Smalley/ Rice University; **396,** Getty Images; **402,** Mark Burnett; **406,** CORBIS; **407,** Howard M. Decruyenaere; **409,** CORBIS; **414,** Courtesy Museum of Fine Arts, Boston. Sears Fund; **421,** Tim Courlas; **425,** United States Mint

Chapter 7   **430 (t),** Getty Images; **430 (b),** CORBIS; **430–431,** CORBIS; **432,** Chris Carroll/CORBIS; **437,** Getty Images; **441,** Getty Images; **444,** Alvin Staffan; **449,** Thomas Veneklasen; **450,** Getty Images; **458,** Matt Meadows; **463,** Ken Frick; **469,** Doug Martin; **484,** courtesy Indianapolis Motor Speedway/Denis Spares

Chapter 8   **486,** Getty Images; **486–487,** Lindsay Gerard; **495,** Getty Images; **496,** Getty Images; **500,** MAK-I; **505,** Getty Images; **507,** CORBIS; **508,** Getty Images; **512,** Joseph Dichello; **518,** CORBIS; **524,** Mark Burnett; **526,** CORBIS; **535,** Mark Burnett

Chapter 9   **542,** Bettmann/CORBIS; **542–543,** Aaron Haupt; **548,** Aaron Haupt; **552,** Mark Burnett; **556,** Life Images; **561,** Getty Images; **562,** Ann Summa; **565,** CORBIS; **567,** Doug Martin; **591,** Bob Mullinex; **594,** Rudi Von Briel; **597,** Jennifer Leigh Sauer

Chapter 10   **600 (t),** Aaron Haupt; **600 (b),** CORBIS; **600–601,** CORBIS; **604,** Getty Images; **606,** Doug Martin; **608,** Getty Images; **618,** Jack Demuth; **627,** Roger Ressmeyer/ CORBIS; **629,** Todd Yarrington; **630,** Otto Greule/Getty Images; **631,** NASA; **634,** Laura Sifferlin; **636,** Fotografia/CORBIS; **639,** Aaron Haupt; **640,** Getty Images; **648–649,** Getty Images; **651,** Aaron Haupt

Unlisted photographs are property of Glencoe/McGraw-Hill